Algebraic Number Theory

Algebraic Number Theory

PROCEEDINGS OF AN INSTRUCTIONAL CONFERENCE
ORGANIZED BY THE LONDON MATHEMATICAL SOCIETY
(A NATO ADVANCED STUDY INSTITUTE)
WITH THE SUPPORT OF THE
INTERNATIONAL MATHEMATICAL UNION

Edited by

J. W. S. CASSELS

Trinity College, University of Cambridge, U.K.

and

A. FRÖHLICH

King's College, University of London, U.K.

1967

THOMPSON BOOK COMPANY INC.
Washington, D.C.

ACADEMIC PRESS INC. (LONDON) LTD.
Berkeley Square House
Berkeley Square
London, W.1.

United States Edition published by
THOMPSON BOOK COMPANY, INC.
National Press Building
Washington, D.C.20004

Library of Congress Catalog Card Number: 67–21945

PRINTED IN GREAT BRITAIN BY THE WHITEFRIARS PRESS LTD.
LONDON AND TONBRIDGE

CONTRIBUTORS

J. V. Armitage, *Department of Mathematics, University of Durham, U.K.*
M. F. Atiyah, *Mathematical Institute, University of Oxford, U.K.*
B. J. Birch, *Mathematical Institute, University of Oxford, U.K.*
D. A. Burgess, *Department of Mathematics, University of Nottingham, U.K.*
J. W. S. Cassels, *Trinity College, University of Cambridge, U.K.*
A. Fröhlich, *Department of Mathematics, King's College, University of London, U.K.*
K. Gruenberg, *Department of Mathematics, Queen Mary College, University of London, U.K.*
H. Halberstam, *Department of Mathematics, University of Nottingham, U.K.*
H. Hasse, *Mathematisches Seminar der Universität, Hamburg, Germany*
H. A. Heilbronn, *Department of Mathematics, University of Toronto, Canada*
K. Hoechsmann, *Mathematisches Institut der Universität, Tübingen, Germany*
M. Kneser, *Mathematisches Institut der Universität, Göttingen, Germany*
R. R. Laxton, *Department of Mathematics, University of Nottingham, U.K.*
A. Lue, *Department of Mathematics, King's College, University of London, U.K.*
I. G. Macdonald, *Mathematical Institute, University of Oxford, U.K.*
J. Neggers, *Department of Mathematics, University of Puerto Rico, Puerto Rico, U.S.A.*
P. Roquette, *Mathematisches Institut der Universität, Tübingen, Germany*
J-P. Serre, *Chaire d'Algèbre et Géométrie, Collège de France, Paris, France*
H. P. F. Swinnerton-Dyer, *Trinity College, University of Cambridge, U.K.*
J. T. Tate, *Department of Mathematics, Harvard University, Cambridge, Mass., U.S.A.*
C. T. C. Wall, *Department of Mathematics, University of Liverpool, U.K.*

PREFACE

This volume is the fruit of an instructional conference on algebraic number theory, held from September 1st to September 17th, 1965, in the University of Sussex, Brighton. It was organized by the London Mathematical Society under the auspices and with the generous financial aid of the International Mathematical Union and of the Advanced Study Programme of NATO. The organizers of the conference owe a great deal to the constant support which they received from the authorities of the host University.

All the lectures held during the conference are recorded here with the exception of a few informal seminars. The drafts for publication were either supplied by the speakers themselves, or were prepared by members of the conference in collaboration with the lecturers. We wish to express our deep gratitude to the lecturers both for ensuring the success of the meeting itself, as well as for enabling us subsequently to publish this volume. We are no less grateful to the "note-takers" for their co-operation. Both they and the lecturers also assisted in the proof correction. The editors must emphasize, however, that neither the lecturers nor the note-takers have any responsibility for any inaccuracies which may remain: they are an act of God.

Apart from accounts of the lectures this volume also contains exercises compiled by Tate with Serre's help, and above all Tate's doctoral thesis, which is for the first time published here after it had over many years had a deep influence on the subject as a piece of clandestine literature.

Finally we wish to express our appreciation for the co-operation which we received from our publishers.

January 1967

J. W. S. Cassels
A. Fröhlich

CONTENTS

CHAPTER III

Cyclotomic Fields and Kummer Extensions

B. J. Birch

CHAPTER IV

Cohomology of Groups

M. F. Atiyah and C. T. C. Wall

(Prepared by I. G. Macdonald on the basis of a manuscript of Atiyah)

CHAPTER V

Profinite Groups

K. GRUENBERG

CHAPTER VI

Local Class Field Theory

J-P. SERRE

(Prepared by J. V. Armitage and J. Neggers)

CHAPTER VII

Global Class Field Theory

J. T. TATE

(Prepared by B. J. Birch and R. R. Laxton)

CHAPTER VIII

Zeta-Functions and L-Functions

H. HEILBRONN

(Prepared by D. A. Burgess and H. Halberstam)

CHAPTER IX

On Class Field Towers

PETER ROQUETTE

CHAPTER X

Semi-Simple Algebraic Groups

M. KNESER

(Prepared by I. G. Macdonald)

CHAPTER XI

History of Class Field Theory

HELMUT HASSE

CHAPTER XII

An Application of Computing to Class Field Theory

CHAPTER XIII

Complex Multiplication

J-P. SERRE

(Prepared by B. J. Birch)

CHAPTER XIV

l-Extensions

K. HOECHSMANN

CHAPTER XV

Fourier Analysis in Number Fields and Hecke's Zeta-Functions

J. T. TATE

(Thesis, 1950)

Exercises

INTRODUCTION

The chapters of this book, with the exception of the final one, are edited texts of lectures and lecture courses, delivered at the Brighton Conference. The topics and the general course programme were chosen with the principal purpose of the Conference in mind. This was to give the non-specialist mathematician (i.e. the mathematician who specializes in some other field) an introduction to algebraic number theory, starting from the more elementary aspects and going on to class field theory, and to acquaint him with some of the recent developments in the subject. The individual contributions thus fit into an overall plan.

The first three chapters provide a broad introduction into algebraic number fields, containing in particular all the more elementary theory needed later on. The subject matters of Chapters I and II are closely interwoven and the respective chapter headings were chosen to indicate—none too accurately—the demarcation line. An alternative choice of titles would have been "Algebraic Theory of Dedekind Domains" for Chapter I and "Topological Arithmetic" for Chapter II.

Chapters IV and V are frankly utilitarian, preparing the tools that are needed for class field theory.

The backbone of the book consists of the two chapters by Serre and by Tate on local and global class field theory, of which the second depends on the first. A feature of special interest in Serre's contribution is that it includes for the first time as an integral part of local class field theory the description of the maximal Abelian extension in terms of formal groups, due to Lubin-Tate. This yields a new approach to the existence theorem and to the refinements of the local reciprocity law dealing with the filtrations of the Galois group and the group of units.

While the first seven chapters were designed as a coherent whole, the rest are more loosely articulated and deal with various aspects and applications of the theory. They presuppose a knowledge of some of the material in the first seven chapters but are substantially independent of one another. The exercises at the end of the book, which were compiled by Serre and Tate after the Conference, are intended to indicate lines of thought for which there was no time at the Conference.

The final chapter does not represent a lecture at the Conference itself. It is the unchanged text of Tate's thesis (1950). There is therefore a certain amount of overlap with the material in earlier chapters.

It was impossible (even if it had been desirable) to impose a completely uniform system of notation on all the contributors. But, in addition to usages which have become too classical for mention, the following more recent conventions are adopted as standard (except in Tate's thesis):

Q, Z, R, C are the rational numbers, the rational integers, the reals and the complex numbers respectively, and **F**, unless otherwise defined, is a finite field.

The special arrow $\mapsto$ denotes the effect of a map on a typical element of a set. Thus the map $\mathbf{R} \to \mathbf{R}$ consisting of squaring can be described by: $r \mapsto r^2 (r \in \mathbf{R})$.

In general, bibliographies are at the ends of chapters and are referred to by the author's name and the date of publication, with a further italic letter to differentiate works by the same author in the same year [e.g. Artin (1927), Hilbert (1900 *b*)]. Titles of periodicals are usually abbreviated as in "The World List of Scientific Periodicals" (Butterworth).

CHAPTER I

Local Fields†

A. FRÖHLICH

1. Discrete Valuation Rings

Preliminaries on Fractional Ideals: Let R be an integral domain (i.e. a commutative ring with $1 \neq 0$ and no zero divisors) and K its quotient field. For R-submodules I_1, I_2 of K we define in the usual way the operations

$$I_1 + I_2 \quad \text{(sum of submodules)}$$

$$I_1 \cap I_2$$

$$I_1 I_2 \quad \text{(submodule generated by products).}$$

In addition we have, for an R-submodule I of K to consider the R-submodules

$$I^{-1} = [x \in K | xI \subset R]$$

$$R(I) = [x \in K | xI \subset I].$$

LEMMA 1. (i) *Addition, multiplication and intersection are commutative and associative.*

(ii) $I(I_1+I_2) = II_1+II_2$.

(iii) $R(I) \supset R \supset II^{-1}$.

(iv) *If* $I \subset R$, *then* $I^{-1} \supset R$.

An R-submodule I of K is a *fractional ideal* of R if it is non-zero and if

† *Back references.* Propositions, Lemmas, etc., within the same section are referred to by their numbers, for other sections this is preceded by the number of the relevant section.

there is a non-zero element a of K so that $aI \subset R$. Here a may always be chosen to lie in R.

LEMMA 2. *If I, I_1, I_2 are fractional ideals, then so are I_1+I_2, $I_1 \cap I_2$, I_1I_2, I^{-1} and $R(I)$.*

Proof. For the first three operations this is obvious. For the last two we prove more generally that if I_1, I_2 are fractional ideals then so is

$$J = [x \in K | xI_2 \subset I_1].$$

Let a, b be non-zero elements with $aI_2 \subset R$, $b \in I_1 \cap R$. Then ab is a non-zero element of J. Let c, d be non-zero elements with $cI_1 \subset R$, $d \in I_2$. Then $cdJ \subset R$.

LEMMA 3. *Suppose R is Noetherian. A non-zero R-submodule I of K is a fractional ideal if and only if it is finitely generated.*

Proof. Necessity: $I \cong aI \subset R$.—Sufficiency: Multiply up by the denominator product of the generators.

Let K^* be the multiplicative group of a field K, and let $\mathbf{Z}$ be the integers under addition. A map

$$v : K \to \mathbf{Z} \cup \infty$$

is a *discrete valuation* of K, if

(i) v defines a surjective homomorphism

$$K^* \to \mathbf{Z}$$

(again denoted by v);

(ii) $v(0) = \infty$;

(iii) $v(x+y) \geq \inf v(x), v(y)$
(usual conventions for the symbol ∞).

We now give the translation into the language of "multiplicative" valuations (see Chap. II): If v is a discrete valuation of K and ρ is real $0 < \rho < 1$, then $|x|_v = \rho^{v(x)}$ is a discrete (non-Archimedean) valuation as defined in the other place. Every discrete (multiplicative) valuation is of this form, and equivalent valuations will correspond to the same v with varying ρ. The results proved in Chap. II can now be translated back. In particular:

(a) If $v(x) \neq v(y)$, then $v(x+y) = \inf v(x), v(y)$.

(b) The set $R_v = [x \in K | v(x) \geq 0]$ is an integral domain with quotient field K, the *valuation ring* of v, and the set $\mathfrak{p}_v = [x \in K | v(x) > 0]$ is a maximal ideal of R_v, the *valuation ideal.*

See the other course for valuation-topology and completion.

PROPOSITION 1. *A discrete valuation v of a field K can uniquely be extended to a discrete valuation on the completion $\overline{K}$ of K with respect to the valuation topology.*

Proof. See Chap. II, §10: A discrete valuation, in the multiplicative sense, extends uniquely to the completion, and with the same set of values.

Example. Let F be a field and let K be the *field of formal series*

$$\sum_{n \geqslant -\infty}^{\infty} a_n t^n, \quad \text{with } a_n \in F \text{ for all } n \in \mathbf{Z}$$

(i.e. $\exists\, m \in \mathbf{Z}$ with $a_n = 0$ for all $n \leq m$). Then we have a "standard" discrete valuation v of K, given by

$$v\left(\sum_{n \geqslant -\infty}^{\infty} a_n t^n\right) = \inf_{a_n \neq 0} n.$$

K is complete in the valuation topology.

We now turn to a ring-theoretic description of the pair K, v where v is a discrete valuation of the field K. The elements u with $v(u) = 0$ form a subgroup $U = U_v$ of K^*, the group of *units* (invertible elements) of R_v. We now choose an element π with $v(\pi) = 1$. Then every $a \in K^*$ has a unique representation

$$a = \pi^n u, \qquad n \in \mathbf{Z}, \qquad u \in U,$$

namely with

$$n = v(a).$$

Turning to the fractional ideals I of R_v we define

$$v(I) = \inf_{x \in I} v(x).$$

A priori $v(I) \in \mathbf{Z} \cup \infty \cup -\infty$. But $I = aJ$, where J is a non-zero ideal of R_v, and $a \in K^*$. Hence $v(I) = v(J) + v(a) \in \mathbf{Z}$. Choose $b \in I$ with $v(b) = v(I)$. Then

$$\pi^{v(b)} R_v = bR_v \subset I.$$

But

$$I \subset [x \in K \mid v(x) \geq v(I)].$$

If $v(x) \geq v(I)$ then $x = \pi^{v(I)} y$, with $y \in R_v$. Thus

$$I \subset \pi^{v(I)} R_v = \pi^{v(b)} R_v,$$

hence

$$I = (\pi R_v)^{v(I)}.$$

In particular

$$\mathfrak{p}_v = \pi R_v$$

and so

$$I = \mathfrak{p}_v^{v(I)}.$$

The last equation shows that R_v has one and only one non-zero prime ideal, namely $\mathfrak{p}_v$, and the preceding one that R_v is a principal ideal domain. We now make the following definition: A *discrete valuation ring* (d.v. ring) R is a principal ideal domain with one and only one non-zero prime ideal. We have then proved one half of

PROPOSITION 2. *The valuation ring R_v of a discrete valuation v is a d.v. ring.*

Conversely a d.v. ring R is the valuation ring R_v for a unique discrete valuation v of its quotient field K.

Proof of converse. Let $\mathfrak{p} = \pi R$ be the non-zero prime ideal of R. R is a unique factorization domain and hence each non-zero element x of R has a unique representation

$$x = \pi^n u, \qquad u \text{ a unit}, \qquad n \geq 0.$$

Allowing n to vary over $\mathbf{Z}$ we get the corresponding statement for $x \in K^*$. But then

$$v(x) = n$$

defines a discrete valuation of K with $R = R_v$. Uniqueness is obvious.

PROPOSITION 3. *An integral domain R is a d.v. ring if and only if it is Noetherian, integrally closed and possesses one and only one non-zero prime ideal.*

(An element x of an extension ring of R is *integral* over R, if it is the root of a monic polynomial with coefficients in R, i.e. if the ring $R[x]$ is a finitely generated R-module. R is *integrally closed* if every element of the quotient field of R, which is integral over R, will already lie in R.)

Proof. (Sufficiency of the conditions.) Let I be a fractional ideal. $R(I)$ is a ring (see the definition preceding Lemma 1). Hence for all $x \in R(I)$, $R[x]$ is a submodule of $R(I)$. By Lemmas 2 and 3, $R(I)$ is a finitely generated R-module, hence so is $R[x]$. Therefore x is integral over R, i.e. $x \in R$. Thus

$$(1) \qquad R(I) = R.$$

Let $\mathfrak{p}$ be the non-zero prime ideal of R. We next show that

$$(2) \qquad \mathfrak{p}^{-1} \neq R.$$

There are non-zero ideals I of R with $I^{-1} \neq R$, e.g. all principal ideals aR with $a \in \mathfrak{p}$, $a \neq 0$. Let then J be a non-zero ideal, maximal with respect to this property. We have to show that J is prime.

Let $x, y \in R$, $x \notin J$, $xy \in J$, $z \notin R$, $z \in J^{-1}$. Then $zy(xR+J) \subset R$, hence $zy \in R$ and thus $z(yR+J) \subset R$. Thus $(yR+J)^{-1} \neq R$, but $yR+J \supset J$. Therefore $y \in J$. We have thus established (2).

By Lemma 1, (iii), (iv)

$$R \supset \mathfrak{p}\mathfrak{p}^{-1} \supset \mathfrak{p}R = \mathfrak{p}.$$

But $\mathfrak{p}\mathfrak{p}^{-1} = \mathfrak{p}$ would imply $\mathfrak{p}^{-1} \subset R(\mathfrak{p})$, which contradicts (1) and (2).

Hence

(3) $$R = \mathfrak{p}\mathfrak{p}^{-1}.$$

Clearly $\mathfrak{p}^{-1} \subset R(\bigcap \mathfrak{p}^n)$. By (1), (2)

(4) $$\bigcap \mathfrak{p}^n = 0.$$

Hence we can choose an element $a \in \mathfrak{p}$, with $aR \not\subset \mathfrak{p}^2$. Then $a\mathfrak{p}^{-1} \subset R$, but by (3) $a\mathfrak{p}^{-1} \not\subset \mathfrak{p}$. Hence $a\mathfrak{p}^{-1}$ is an ideal of R not contained in any maximal ideal, i.e. $a\mathfrak{p}^{-1} = R$, and so

$$\mathfrak{p} = aR.$$

By (4) every non-zero element of R has then a unique representation $a^n u$, $n \geq 0$, u a unit of R. Thus R is a d.v. ring.

We shall finally give a description of some groups associated with a given discrete valuation v of a field K, in terms of the residue class field $k = R/\mathfrak{p}$, where R is the valuation ring of v and $\mathfrak{p}$ the valuation ideal.

The additive group of K is the union of open (and hence closed) subgroups $\mathfrak{p}^n$ ($n \in Z$), whose intersection is zero. The quotient groups $\mathfrak{p}^n/\mathfrak{p}^{n+1}$ have the structure of k-modules and we have

LEMMA 4. *There is an isomorphism*

$$k \cong \mathfrak{p}^n/\mathfrak{p}^{n+1}$$

of k-modules.

Proof. If $\mathfrak{p} = R\pi$, then multiplication by π^n induces such an isomorphism

Turning to the multiplicative group K^* of non-zero elements of K, we first note that the valuation gives rise to an exact sequence

(5) $$0 \to U \to K^* \xrightarrow{v} \mathbf{Z} \to 0,$$

where U is the group of units of R. For each $n \geq 1$ the set

(6) $$U_n = 1 + \mathfrak{p}^n$$

is an open subgroup of U, and $\bigcap_n U_n = 1$. The associated subgroup topology of U coincides with that induced on the subset U of K by the valuation. The quotient groups can again be described in terms of the residue class field.

PROPOSITION 4. (i) *The residue class map $R \to k$ gives rise to an isomorphism*

$$U/U_1 \cong k^* \quad \text{(multiplicative group).}$$

(ii) *For each $n \geq 1$ the map $u \mapsto u-1$ gives rise to an isomorphism*

$$U_n/U_{n+1} \cong \mathfrak{p}^n/\mathfrak{p}^{n+1}.$$

Proof. Straightforward. Observe that for $u_1, u_2 \in U_n$

$$(u_1 u_2 - 1) - (u_1 - 1) - (u_2 - 1) = (u_1 - 1)(u_2 - 1) \in \mathfrak{p}^{2n}.$$

COROLLARY. *For* $n \geq 1$

$$U_n/U_{n+1} \cong k \quad \text{(additive group)}.$$

PROPOSITION 5. (i) *If* k *is of prime characteristic* p, *then for* $n \geq 1$

$$U_n^p \subset U_{n+1}.$$

(ii) *If* K *is complete and if the natural number* m *is not a multiple of the residue class field characteristic, then for each* $n \geq 1$, *the map* $u \mapsto u^m$ *is an automorphism of* U_n.

Proof. (i) follows from the preceding Corollary.

For (ii) we first note that by the same Corollary the endomorphism of U_q/U_{q+1}, induced by the endomorphism $f: u \mapsto u^m$ of U_n, is bijective for each $q \geq n$. Hence in the first place f is injective. In the second place we can find for each element u of U_n elements $v_0 \in U_n$, $w_1 \in U_{n+1}$ so that $u = v_0^m w_1$. Again we can find elements $v_1 \in U_{n+1}$, $w_2 \in U_{n+2}$ so that $w_1 = v_1^m w_2$, i.e. $u = (v_0 v_1)^m w_2$. And so on. The sequence $w_1, w_2, \ldots$ will tend to 1, and as U_n is now complete the infinite product $v_0 v_1 \ldots$ will converge to an element v of U_n. But then $u = v^m \in U_n^m$. We have thus shown that f is surjective, hence bijective.

2. Dedekind Domains

Throughout R is an integral domain, K its quotient field. If $\mathfrak{p}$ is a prime ideal of R, we define the local ring of fractions by

$$R_\mathfrak{p} = [xy^{-1} \in K | x, y \in R, y \notin \mathfrak{p}].$$

$\mathfrak{p}R_\mathfrak{p}$ is the only maximal ideal of $R_\mathfrak{p}$. Clearly $\mathfrak{p} \subset \mathfrak{p}R_\mathfrak{p} \cap R$. If $x \in R$, $x \notin \mathfrak{p}$ then $x^{-1} \in R_\mathfrak{p}$, and so $x \notin \mathfrak{p}R_\mathfrak{p}$. Thus:

LEMMA 1. $\mathfrak{p} = \mathfrak{p}R_\mathfrak{p} \cap R$.

Next we show

LEMMA 2. *If* J *is an ideal of* $R_\mathfrak{p}$ *then*

$$J = (J \cap R)R_\mathfrak{p}.$$

Proof. Let $x, y \in R$, $y \notin \mathfrak{p}$ and $xy^{-1} \in J$. Then $x \in J \cap R$, whence $xy^{-1} \in (J \cap R)R_\mathfrak{p}$. Thus $(J \cap R)R_\mathfrak{p} \supset J$. The opposite relation is even more trivial.

PROPOSITION 1. *Each of the following conditions on an integral domain* R *implies the others:*

(i) R *is Noetherian, integrally closed and its non-zero prime ideals are maximal.*

(ii) *R is Noetherian and, for every non-zero prime ideal* $\mathfrak{p}$, $R_\mathfrak{p}$ *is a d.v. ring.*
(iii) *All fractional ideals of R are invertible.*

(A fractional ideal I is *invertible* if $II^{-1} = R$.)

A domain R satisfying the conditions of the Proposition is a *Dedekind domain.* E.g. a principal ideal domain is a Dedekind domain.

Proof. (a) (i) *implies* (ii).

We shall use 1. Proposition 3. By Lemma 2 every ideal of $R_\mathfrak{p}$ is of form $IR_\mathfrak{p}$, where I is an ideal of R. A finite generating set of I over R is also a finite generating set of $IR_\mathfrak{p}$ over $R_\mathfrak{p}$. Thus $R_\mathfrak{p}$ is Noetherian.

If x is integral over $R_\mathfrak{p}$, i.e. if

$$x^n + b^{-1}a_{n-1}x^{n-1} + \ldots + b^{-1}a_0 = 0,$$

with $b, a_i \in R$, $b \notin \mathfrak{p}$ then bx is integral over R. Hence if x lies in the quotient field K of R then $bx \in R$, whence $x \in R_\mathfrak{p}$.

Let J be a non-zero prime ideal of $R_\mathfrak{p}$. $J \cap R$ is certainly a prime ideal of R, and is non-zero by Lemma 2. But $J \subset \mathfrak{p}R_\mathfrak{p}$, this being the only maximal ideal of $R_\mathfrak{p}$, whence $J \cap R \subset \mathfrak{p}$, by Lemma 1. Hence $J \cap R = \mathfrak{p}$ and so, by Lemma 2, $J = \mathfrak{p}R_\mathfrak{p}$.

(b) (ii) *implies* (iii).

Let I be a fractional ideal of R with generators $a_1, \ldots, a_n$. Then for some i, say $i = 1$, $v_\mathfrak{p}(a_i) = \inf_{x \in I} v_\mathfrak{p}(x)$, $v_\mathfrak{p}$ being the valuation with valuation ring $R_\mathfrak{p}$. But then $IR_\mathfrak{p} = a_1 R_\mathfrak{p}$. Hence

$$a_1^{-1}a_i = x_i y_i^{-1}, \quad \text{with } x_i, y_i \in R, y_i \notin \mathfrak{p} \quad (i = 1, \ldots, n).$$

Let $y = \prod_i y_i$. Then $ya_1{}^{-1}a_i \in R$, hence $ya_1{}^{-1} \in I^{-1}$ and so $y \in II^{-1}$. But $y \notin \mathfrak{p}$. Thus $II^{-1} \not\subset \mathfrak{p}$. This is true for all maximal ideals $\mathfrak{p}$ of R. Hence $II^{-1} = R$.

(c) (iii) *implies* (i).

Let I be a fractional ideal of R. Then $\exists\, a_1, \ldots, a_n \in I$, $b_1, \ldots, b_n \in I^{-1}$ with $\sum a_i b_i = 1$. If $x \in I$ then $x = \sum a_i(b_i x)$, $b_i x \in R$. Hence $a_1, \ldots, a_n$ generate I. Thus R is Noetherian.

Let $x \in K$ be integral over R. By 1. Lemma 3, $S = R[x]$ is a fractional ideal. It is also a ring, i.e. $S^2 = S$. Hence

$$S = SR = SSS^{-1} = SS^{-1} = R.$$

Thus R is integrally closed.

Let I be a non-zero prime ideal, $\mathfrak{p}$ a maximal ideal containing it. Then $I\mathfrak{p}^{-1}$ is an ideal of R and $(I\mathfrak{p}^{-1})\mathfrak{p} = I$. Hence either $I\mathfrak{p}^{-1} \subset I$ or $\mathfrak{p} \subset I$, i.e. $\mathfrak{p} = I$. The first relation however would imply that

$$\mathfrak{p}^{-1} \subset I^{-1}I\mathfrak{p}^{-1} \subset I^{-1}I = R,$$

i.e. $\mathfrak{p}^{-1} = R$ and so $\mathfrak{p} = R$, which is nonsense.

If $\mathfrak{p}$ is a non-zero prime ideal of a Dedekind domain R we shall denote by $v_{\mathfrak{p}}$ the valuation of its quotient field K with valuation ring $R_{\mathfrak{p}}$.

COROLLARY 1. *Let $|x|$ be a non-trivial multiplicative valuation of K, with $|R| \leq 1$. Then $|x| = \rho^{v_{\mathfrak{p}}(x)}$ for some ρ, $0 < \rho < 1$, and some non-zero prime ideal $\mathfrak{p}$ of R.*

Proof. The inequality $|x| < 1$ defines a non-zero prime ideal $\mathfrak{p}$ of R. Hence $R_{\mathfrak{p}}$ is characterized in K by the inequality $|x| \leq 1$. This yields the result.

If I is a non-empty subset of K, define

$$v_{\mathfrak{p}}(I) = \inf_{x \in I} v_{\mathfrak{p}}(x)$$

(possibly $v_{\mathfrak{p}}(I) = -\infty$).

PROPOSITION 2. *The fractional ideals of a Dedekind domain R form an Abelian group $\mathscr{I}(R)$ under multiplication. This group is free on the non-zero prime ideals $\mathfrak{p}$. The representation of a fractional ideal I in terms of these generators is given by*

$$I = \prod_{\mathfrak{p}} \mathfrak{p}^{v_{\mathfrak{p}}(I)}$$

Also then

$$IR_{\mathfrak{p}} = (\mathfrak{p}R_{\mathfrak{p}})^{v_{\mathfrak{p}}(I)}.$$

Proof. The first assertion follows from 1. Lemma 1 and from Proposition 1.

To show that the prime ideals $\mathfrak{p}$ generate $\mathscr{I}(R)$ it suffices to show that every integral ideal I (i.e. $I \subset R$), different from R, is product of prime ideals. Such an ideal I is contained in a maximal ideal $\mathfrak{p}$. Hence $I = \mathfrak{p}(I\mathfrak{p}^{-1})$ with $I \subset I\mathfrak{p}^{-1} \subset R$. The ascending chain condition now yields the required result.

By 1. Lemma 1, $(IR_{\mathfrak{p}})(JR_{\mathfrak{p}}) = (IJ)R_{\mathfrak{p}}$. We thus obtain a surjective homomorphism

$$f_{\mathfrak{p}} : \mathscr{I}(R) \to \mathscr{I}(R_{\mathfrak{p}}) \tag{1}$$

which acts injectively on the subgroup generated by $\mathfrak{p}$. If $\mathfrak{p}_1 \neq \mathfrak{p}$, then $\mathfrak{p}_1 R_{\mathfrak{p}} = R_{\mathfrak{p}}$. For if $a \in \mathfrak{p}_1$, $a \notin \mathfrak{p}$ then already $aR_{\mathfrak{p}} = R_{\mathfrak{p}}$. Thus the $\mathfrak{p}_1$ other than $\mathfrak{p}$ lie in $\operatorname{Ker} f_{\mathfrak{p}}$. As a first consequence we see that the non-zero prime ideals form a free generating set of $\mathscr{I}(R)$. Secondly we see that if

$$I = \prod \mathfrak{p}^{r_{\mathfrak{p}}}$$

then

$$IR_{\mathfrak{p}} = (\mathfrak{p}R_{\mathfrak{p}})^{r_{\mathfrak{p}}}.$$

Hence

$$r_{\mathfrak{p}} = v_{\mathfrak{p}}(IR_{\mathfrak{p}}) = v_{\mathfrak{p}}(I) + v_{\mathfrak{p}}(R_{\mathfrak{p}}) = v_{\mathfrak{p}}(I).$$

COROLLARY 1. *If $a \in K^*$ then $v_{\mathfrak{p}}(a) = 0$ for almost all $\mathfrak{p}$.*

COROLLARY 2.

$$\begin{aligned} v_{\mathfrak{p}}(I_1 I_2) &= v_{\mathfrak{p}}(I_1) + v_{\mathfrak{p}}(I_2), \\ v_{\mathfrak{p}}(I^{-1}) &= -v_{\mathfrak{p}}(I), \\ v_{\mathfrak{p}}(I_1 + I_2) &= \inf v_{\mathfrak{p}}(I_1), v_{\mathfrak{p}}(I_2), \\ v_{\mathfrak{p}}(I_1 \cap I_2) &= \sup v_{\mathfrak{p}}(I_1), v_{\mathfrak{p}}(I_2). \end{aligned}$$

COROLLARY 3. *The maps $f_{\mathfrak{p}}$ induce an isomorphism*

$$\mathscr{I}(R) \cong \coprod_{\mathfrak{p}} \mathscr{I}(R_{\mathfrak{p}}).$$

(The symbol $\coprod$ stands for the restricted direct product (direct sum) of groups.)

Let $\bar{R}_{\mathfrak{p}}$ be the valuation ring of the completion of K at $v_{\mathfrak{p}}$. By 1. Proposition 1,

$$\mathscr{I}(R_{\mathfrak{p}}) \cong \mathscr{I}(\bar{R}_{\mathfrak{p}}) \qquad (\cong \mathbf{Z}!).$$

Hence:

COROLLARY 4.

$$\mathscr{I}(R) \cong \coprod_{\mathfrak{p}} \mathscr{I}(\bar{R}_{\mathfrak{p}}).$$

3. Modules and Bilinear Forms

In this section we introduce some concepts, which will subsequently be used in the discussion of ideal norms, of differents and of discriminants for extensions of Dedekind domains. Throughout this chapter R is a Dedekind domain, K its quotient field, U a finite dimensional vector space over K of dimension $n > 0$. The symbol T always stands for R-submodules of U and the symbols L, M, N for finitely generated R-submodules which span U, i.e. contain a basis of U. If $\mathfrak{p}$ is a non-zero prime ideal of R, then $T_{\mathfrak{p}} = TR_{\mathfrak{p}}$ is the $R_{\mathfrak{p}}$-module generated by T.

LEMMA 1. $\bigcap_{\mathfrak{p}} T_{\mathfrak{p}} = T$.

Proof. This is true for any integral domain R, not necessarily Dedekind, provided only that $\mathfrak{p}$ runs through a set of prime ideals containing the maximal ideals.

Clearly $T \subset \bigcap_{\mathfrak{p}} T_{\mathfrak{p}}$. For the converse we consider an element u of $\bigcap_{\mathfrak{p}} T_{\mathfrak{p}}$, and show that the ideal

$$J_u = [x \in R | xu \in T]$$

is the whole of R, i.e. is not contained in any given maximal ideal $\mathfrak{p}$. In fact $u = x^{-1}w$ with $w \in T$, $x \in R$, but $x \notin \mathfrak{p}$. As $x \in J_u$ we now see that $J_u \not\subset \mathfrak{p}$.

LEMMA 2. *Given M and N, there is a non-zero element a of K with $aM \subset N$.*

Proof. Let $\{u_i\}$ be a basis of U, contained in N. For a given finite generating set $\{w_j\}$ of M, choose the element a as a "common denominator" of the coefficients of the w_j with respect to the basis $\{u_i\}$.

LEMMA 3. *For almost all* $\mathfrak{p}$, $M_\mathfrak{p} = N_\mathfrak{p}$.

Proof. By the previous Lemma we can find non-zero elements a, b of K with $aM \subset N \subset bM$. Thus $M_\mathfrak{p} = N_\mathfrak{p}$ whenever $v_\mathfrak{p}(a) = 0 = v_\mathfrak{p}(b)$. By 2. Proposition 2, Corollary 1, this is the case for almost all $\mathfrak{p}$.

Now suppose for the moment that M and N are free R-modules. They are both of rank n, hence isomorphic. Therefore there is a non-singular linear transformation ℓ of U with $M\ell = N$. The determinant $\det(\ell)$ is non-zero and, apart from a unit in R, solely depends on M and N. Hence the fractional ideal

$$R\det(\ell) = [M : N], \tag{1}$$

solely depends on M and N.

If the restriction on M and N to be free is removed we still get, for each $\mathfrak{p}$, a fractional ideal $[M_\mathfrak{p} : N_\mathfrak{p}]$ of $R_\mathfrak{p}$. Also whenever $M_\mathfrak{p} = N_\mathfrak{p}$ then $[M_\mathfrak{p} : N_\mathfrak{p}] = R_\mathfrak{p}$. By Lemma 3, and by 2. Proposition 2, Corollary 3, there is a unique fractional ideal

$$[M : N] = [M : N]_R$$

of R, the *module index*, such that for all $\mathfrak{p}$

$$[M : N]R_\mathfrak{p} = [M_\mathfrak{p} : N_\mathfrak{p}]. \tag{2}$$

One verifies that definitions (1) and (2) agree when M and N are free. One also sees that when $R = \mathbf{Z}$ and $M \supset N$ then $[M : N]$ is just the ordinary group index, viewed as a $\mathbf{Z}$-ideal.

PROPOSITION 1.

(i) $[M : N][N : L] = [M : L]$
$[M : M] = R$.

(ii) *Suppose that $M \supset N$. Then $[M : N]$ is an integral ideal, and $[M : N] = R$ implies $M = N$.*

Proof. Locally (i.e. for the $R_\mathfrak{p}$) this is obvious. For the global form one applies Lemma 1, and 2. Proposition 2.

PROPOSITION 2. *If t is a non-singular linear transformation of U, then*

$$[Mt : Nt] = [M : N].$$

Proof. Localize and apply definition (1).

One can also show that $M \cong N$, if and only if $[M : N]$ is a principal fractional ideal.

Now let $B(u, v)$ be a non-degenerate, symmetric, K-bilinear form on U. If $\{u_i\}$ is a basis of U, its *dual basis* $\{v_j\}$ is defined by

$$B(u_i, v_j) = \delta_{ij} \quad \text{(Kronecker symbol)}.$$

The *dual module* of T is

$$D(T) = D_R(T) = [u \in U | B(u, T) \subset R]. \tag{3}$$

LEMMA 4. *If M is the free R-module on $\{u_i\}$, then $D(M)$ is the free R-module on the dual basis $\{v_j\}$, and*

$$D(D(M)) = M.$$

Proof. Obvious.

In what follows the symbol D stands for duals with respect to R and in place of $D_{R_\mathfrak{p}}$ we shall write $D_\mathfrak{p}$.

PROPOSITION 3.

(i) $D(M)$ *is a finitely generated R-module, spanning U,*
(ii) $D(M)_\mathfrak{p} = D_\mathfrak{p}(M_\mathfrak{p})$,
(iii) $D(M) = \bigcap_\mathfrak{p} D_\mathfrak{p}(M_\mathfrak{p})$,
(iv) $D(D(M)) = M$,
(v) $[D(M) : D(N)] = [N : M]$.

Proof. (i) M contains a free R-module N, and by Lemma 2 is contained in a free R-module $L = bN$, both L and N spanning U. Hence

$$D(N) \supset D(M) \supset D(L).$$

By Lemma 4, $D(L)$ and $D(N)$ are free and span U. This gives (i).

(ii) Let $\{w_i\}$ be a finite generating set of M. Suppose $v \in D_\mathfrak{p}(M_\mathfrak{p})$. Then for all i, $B(v, w_i) = b^{-1}a_i$, with $a_i, b \in R, b \notin \mathfrak{p}$. Thus $v \in D(M)b^{-1} \subset D(M)_\mathfrak{p}$. We have shown that

$$D_\mathfrak{p}(M)_\mathfrak{p} \subset D_R(M)_\mathfrak{p}.$$

To get the opposite inclusion, observe that

$$B(D_R(M_\mathfrak{p}), M_\mathfrak{p}) \subset B(D_R(M), M)R_\mathfrak{p} \subset R_\mathfrak{p}.$$

(iii) follows from (ii) and Lemma 1, (iv) from (ii) and Lemma 4.

The proof of (v) reduces by (ii) to the case when M and N are free. We then only have to recall that if $\{u_i\}$ and $\{v_i\}$ are dual bases and $\{u_i\ell\}$ and $\{v_i\ell^*\}$ are dual bases then

$$\det(\ell)\det(\ell^*) = 1.$$

We define the *discriminant* of M by

$$\mathfrak{d}(M) = \mathfrak{d}(M/R) = [D_R(M) : M]_R. \tag{4}$$

PROPOSITION 4.

(i) $\mathfrak{d}(N) = \mathfrak{d}(M)[M:N]^2$.

(ii) $\mathfrak{d}(M_{\mathfrak{p}}/R_{\mathfrak{p}}) = \mathfrak{d}(M/R)R_{\mathfrak{p}}$.

(iii) *If M is the free R-module on $\{u_i\}$ then $\mathfrak{d}(M)$ is the fractional ideal generated by*

$$\det B(u_i, u_j).$$

Proof. For (i):

$$\begin{aligned}[D(N):N] &= [D(N):D(M)][D(M):M][M:N] \quad &\text{(Prop. 1(i))}\\ &= [D(M):M][M:N]^2 \quad &\text{(Prop. 3(v)).}\end{aligned}$$

(ii) follows from Proposition 3(ii).

For (iii) let $\{v_i\}$ be the dual basis of $\{u_i\}$ and let $u_i = v_i\ell$. By Lemma 4,

$$[D(M):M] = R\det(\ell).$$

On the other hand

$$\det B(u_i, v_j\ell) = \det(\ell)\det B(u_i, v_j) = \det(\ell).$$

COROLLARY 1. *Suppose $M \supset N$. Then $\mathfrak{d}(M)$ divides $\mathfrak{d}(N)$, and $\mathfrak{d}(M) = \mathfrak{d}(N)$ implies $M = N$.*

The last proposition shows that when $R = \mathbf{Z}$, our discriminant is the same as the classical discriminant over $\mathbf{Z}$ (to within a sign).

Let now $U = U_1 + U_2$ (direct sum of vector spaces). Suppose that M_i and N_i span U_i and write $M = M_1 + M_2$, $N = N_1 + N_2$. For (ii) and (iii) in the following proposition also assume that $B(U_1, U_2) = 0$, so that B gives rise to non-degenerate bilinear forms on U_1 and U_2.

PROPOSITION 5.

(i) $[M:N] = [M_1:N_1][M_2:N_2]$.

(ii) $D(M) = D(M_1) + D(M_2)$.

(iii) $\mathfrak{d}(M) = \mathfrak{d}(M_1)\mathfrak{d}(M_2)$.

Proof. Obvious.

To make life easy, we shall for the next and final proposition consider only free R-modules M and N, although it would remain true generally. Let $\bar{R}$ be a Dedekind domain containing R, with quotient field $\bar{K}$. We shall view U as embedded in the vector space $\bar{U} = U \otimes_K \bar{K}$ over $\bar{K}$. The bilinear form B can uniquely be extended to a $\bar{K}$-bilinear form $\bar{B}$, which is again symmetric and non-degenerate. The $\bar{R}$-module $M\bar{R}$ generated by M is free and spans $\bar{U}$.

PROPOSITION 6.

(i) $[M\bar{R} : N\bar{R}]_{\bar{R}} = [M : N]_R \bar{R}$,

(ii) $D_{\bar{R}}(M\bar{R}) = D_R(M)\bar{R}$,

(iii) $\mathfrak{d}(M\bar{R}/\bar{R}) = \mathfrak{d}(M/R)\bar{R}$.

Proof Obvious.

4. Extensions

Throughout R is a Dedekind domain, K is its quotient field and L is a finite separable algebraic extension field of K. The condition of separability is not needed for part of Proposition 1, and for Proposition 2 (see Z.S., Ch. V, Th. 19 and Serre, Ch. II, Prop. 3).† But we shall not here consider the inseparable case.

The elements of L which are integral over R form a domain S, the *integral closure* of R in L and S is integrally closed (in L) (see Z.S., Ch. V, § 1).

LEMMA 1. *If* $\mathfrak{p}$ *is a prime ideal of* R *then* $SR_{\mathfrak{p}}$ *is the integral closure of* $R_{\mathfrak{p}}$ *in* L.

Proof. The elements of $SR_{\mathfrak{p}}$ are obviously integral over $R_{\mathfrak{p}}$. Conversely, if x is integral over $R_{\mathfrak{p}}$, i.e.

$$x^n + (b^{-1}a_{n-1})x^{n-1} + \ldots + b^{-1}a_0 = 0$$

with $a_i \in R$, $b \in R$, $b \notin \mathfrak{p}$, then $bx \in S$, hence $x \in SR_{\mathfrak{p}}$.

A prime ideal $\mathfrak{P}$ of S is said to lie over the prime ideal $\mathfrak{p}$ of R if

$$\mathfrak{P} \cap R = \mathfrak{p}.$$

We then write $\mathfrak{P}|\mathfrak{p}$.

PROPOSITION 1. *S is a finitely generated R-module which spans L over K and is a Dedekind domain.*

Every non-zero prime ideal $\mathfrak{P}$ *of S lies over a non-zero prime ideal of R, and there is a prime ideal of S lying over every non-zero prime ideal* $\mathfrak{p}$ *of R.*

Proof. Applying Lemma 1 to $\mathfrak{p} = (0)$ we see that S spans L over K.

The trace $t_{L/K} : L \to K$ defines a non-degenerate, symmetric K-bilinear form

$$B(u, v) = t_{L/K}(uv)$$

on L. As $SK = L$, S contains a free R-module N spanning L. But then, in the notation of § 3, $D(N)$ is free and spans L. Also

$$D(N) \supset D(S).$$

The traces of integral elements lie in R, and hence

$$D(S) \supset S,$$

† For the references "Z.S." and "Serre" see the literature list at the end of Chapter I.

i.e.

$$D(N) \supset S.$$

Thus S is a finitely generated R-module. It follows that S is Noetherian, and we have already noted that S is integrally closed.

Let $\mathfrak{P}$ be a non-zero prime ideal of S and let

$$b^n + a_1 b^{n-1} + \ldots + a_0 = 0$$

be the minimal equation of the non-zero element b of $\mathfrak{P}$. Then $a_i \in R$, for all i, hence $a_0 \in \mathfrak{p} = \mathfrak{P} \cap R$. Thus $\mathfrak{p}$ is non-zero. Moreover $\mathfrak{P} \supset \mathfrak{p}S$, i.e. $\mathfrak{P}/\mathfrak{p}S$ is a prime ideal of the commutative algebra $S/\mathfrak{p}S$ over the field $R/\mathfrak{p}$. As S is finitely generated over R, $S/\mathfrak{p}S$ is a finite dimensional algebra, and the same is then true for $(S/\mathfrak{p}S)/(\mathfrak{P}/\mathfrak{p}S) = S/\mathfrak{P}$. Thus $S/\mathfrak{P}$ is a field, i.e. $\mathfrak{P}$ is a maximal ideal. We have now shown that S is a Dedekind domain.

Let $\mathfrak{p}$ be a non-zero prime ideal of R. $\mathfrak{p}S = S$ would imply $\mathfrak{p}^{-1}S = \mathfrak{p}^{-1}(\mathfrak{p}S) = S$, i.e. $\mathfrak{p}^{-1} \subset S \cap K = R$, which is false. If now the prime ideal $\mathfrak{P}$ of S is a factor of $\mathfrak{p}S$ then $\mathfrak{P} \cap R \supset \mathfrak{p}$, i.e. $\mathfrak{P} \cap R = \mathfrak{p}$.

COROLLARY 1. (Used in Chap. II.)

Every discrete (multiplicative) valuation of a field K can be extended to a finite, separable extension field L.

Proof. Take R as the valuation ring in K. A suitably normalized valuation of L of form $\rho^{v_{\mathfrak{P}}(x)}$ will do.

COROLLARY 2. *The map* $I \mapsto IS$ *is an injective homomorphism* $\mathscr{I}(R) \to \mathscr{I}(S)$.

Proof. By the proposition, together with the observation that if I_1 and I_2 are integral ideals of R with $I_1 + I_2 = R$ then also $I_1 S + I_2 S = S$.

Combining Proposition 1 with the theorems proved in Chap. II (see § 10) on the uniqueness and the completeness, for extensions of valuations with complete base fields, we have

PROPOSITION 2. *If R is a d.v. ring and K is complete, then S is a d.v. ring and L is complete.*

In the remainder of the present section and the early part of the next one we shall study a number of concepts, associated with the embedding of R in S. In each instance our aim is to obtain a reduction to the complete local case.

A fractional ideal J of S is finitely generated over S, hence over R. Also if $0 \neq a \in J$ then $J \supset aS$, hence J spans L over K. We can thus define the *ideal norm* by

(1) $$N_{L/K}(J) = [S : J]_R.$$

The connection to element norms is given by

PROPOSITION 3. *If* $a \in L^*$ *then*

$$N_{L/K}(aS) = N_{L/K}(a)R.$$

Proof. $N_{L/K}(a)$ is the determinant of the linear transformation $x \mapsto ax$ of L!

Note that when $R = \mathbf{Z}$, and when J is an ideal of S then $N_{L/K}(J)$ is just the number of residue classes of S mod J, viewed as a $\mathbf{Z}$-ideal. This follows from our remark (cf. § 3) on the interpretation of the module index as a group index in the case $R = \mathbf{Z}$.

The ideal norm commutes—in a sense to be made precise—with the isomorphism exhibited in 2. Proposition 2, Corollary 4. We first recall a theorem, proved in Chap. II (see § 10). Let R be a d.v. ring, $\mathfrak{p}$ its maximal ideal, $\bar{K}$ the completion of K at $v_{\mathfrak{p}}$. Let $\mathfrak{P}_i$ run through the non-zero prime ideals of S and denote by $\bar{L}_i$ the corresponding completions. Then we can identify (as algebras and topological vector spaces over $\bar{K}$)

$$L \otimes_K \bar{K} = \sum \bar{L}_i \quad \text{(direct sum of fields).} \tag{2}$$

View L, $\bar{L}_i$ and $\bar{K}$ as embedded in this algebra. Denote by $\bar{R}$ the valuation ring of $\bar{K}$ and by $\bar{S}_i$ that of $\bar{L}_i$. Then we have

LEMMA 2. $\bar{R}S = \sum \bar{S}_i$.

Proof. $\sum \bar{S}_i$ is the integral closure of $\bar{R}$ in the algebra $\sum \bar{L}_i$. Hence $\bar{R}S \subset \sum \bar{S}_i$. $\bar{R}S$ is complete, hence closed. It will thus suffice to show that S is dense in $\sum \bar{S}_i$. As we have not stated or proved the general approximation theorem which would yield this result, we shall give an *ad hoc* proof. From Chap. II we know that L is dense in $\sum \bar{L}_i$, and so $\sum \bar{S}_i$ is the closure of $(\sum \bar{S}_i) \cap L$. We shall show that the latter module is contained in S. The minimal polynomial of an element x of $(\sum \bar{S}_i) \cap L$ over $\bar{K}$ has coefficients in $\bar{R}$. But it coincides with the minimal polynomial over K, i.e. its coefficients lie in $K \cap \bar{R} = R$. Thus $x \in S$.

Now return to the case of an arbitrary Dedekind domain R. If $\mathfrak{p}$ is a non-zero prime ideal of R write $K_{\mathfrak{p}}$ for the associated completion of K and $\bar{R}_{\mathfrak{p}}$ for its valuation ring. For a non-zero prime ideal $\mathfrak{P}$ of S denote the corresponding objects by $L_{\mathfrak{P}}$ and $\bar{S}_{\mathfrak{P}}$.

PROPOSITION 4. *If J is a fractional ideal of S then*

$$N_{L/K}(J)\bar{R}_{\mathfrak{p}} = \prod_{\mathfrak{P}/\mathfrak{p}} N_{L_{\mathfrak{P}}/K_{\mathfrak{p}}}(J\bar{S}_{\mathfrak{P}})$$

Proof. In view of the definition of the module index and by Lemma 1 we may assume that $R = R_{\mathfrak{p}}$ is a d.v. ring. But then the Proposition follows from Lemma 2 and from 3. Propositions 5 and 6.

COROLLARY 1. *$N_{L/K}$ is a homomorphism $\mathscr{I}(S) \to \mathscr{I}(R)$ of groups.*

Proof. By 2, Proposition 2, Corollary 4 and by the above Proposition 4 the proof reduces to the case when R is a d.v. ring and K is complete. But then every fractional ideal of S is principal, and the Corollary follows from Proposition 3 and the multiplicativity of element norms.

By similar reasoning we get

COROLLARY 2. *For* $I \in \mathscr{I}(R)$

$$N_{L/K}(IS) = I^n,$$

where $n = (L:K)$ *is the degree.*

COROLLARY 3. *If* $L \supset F \supset K$ *then*

$$N_{L/K}(J) = N_{F/K}(N_{L/F}(J)).$$

We can now return to the bilinear form defined by the trace. The dual $D_R(S)$ of S is clearly an S-module. By Proposition 1 and by 3, Proposition 3 it is finitely generated over R, hence over S. As $D_R(S) \supset S$ we have

$$D_R(S) = \mathfrak{D}^{-1} \tag{3}$$

where $\mathfrak{D} = \mathfrak{D}(S/R)$ is an integral ideal of S, *the different.*

We write

$$\mathfrak{d} = \mathfrak{d}(S/R)$$

for the discriminant defined in 3(4). As $D_R(S) \supset S$, $\mathfrak{d}$ is an integral ideal of R. Moreover

$$\mathfrak{d} = N_{L/K}(\mathfrak{D}). \tag{4}$$

In fact

$$\begin{aligned}\mathfrak{d} &= [D_R(S) : S] = [S : D_R(S)]^{-1}\\ &= N_{L/K}(\mathfrak{D}^{-1})^{-1} = N_{L/K}(\mathfrak{D}).\end{aligned}$$

PROPOSITION 5. *In the notation of Proposition* 4*:*

(i) $\mathfrak{D}(S/R)\bar{S}_{\mathfrak{P}} = \mathfrak{D}(\bar{S}_{\mathfrak{P}}/R_{\mathfrak{p}})$.

(ii) $\mathfrak{d}(S/R)\bar{R}_{\mathfrak{p}} = \prod_{\mathfrak{P}/\mathfrak{p}} \mathfrak{d}(\bar{S}_{\mathfrak{P}}/\bar{R}_{\mathfrak{p}})$.

Proof. By Lemma 2 and 3, Proposition 4–6.

The next proposition establishes a connection between the discriminant $\mathfrak{d}(S/R)$ and the discriminants of an integral generator of L. This proposition is usually established via the theory of the "Noether conductor" of a ring, but the concept of a module index will enable us to do without this.

Let x be an element of S so that $L = K[x]$, and let $g(X)$ be the minimal polynomial of x over K. The ring $R[x]$ then spans L and is the free R-module on $1, x, \ldots, x^{n-1}$. In the next Proposition $g'(X)$ is the derivative of $g(X)$.

PROPOSITION 6.

(i) $D(R[x]) = \frac{1}{g'(x)} R[x]$.

(ii) $\mathfrak{d}(R[x]) = (N_{L/K} g'(x))R$.

(iii) $R[x] = S$ *if and only if* $\mathfrak{D}(S/R) = g'(x)S$.

Proof. By Euler's formulae,

$$t_{L/K}(x^i/g'(x)) \in R, \qquad \text{for } i = 0, \ldots, n-1.$$

Hence

$$D(R[x]) \supset \frac{1}{g'(x)} R[x]. \tag{5}$$

By 3, Proposition 4

$$\mathfrak{d}(R[x]) = \det t_{L/K}(x^{i+j})R,$$

but (any old-fashioned textbook on algebra)

$$\det t_{L/K}(x^{i+j}) = \pm N_{L/K}(g'(x)),$$

and so

$$[D(R[x]) : R[x]] = N_{L/K}(g'(x))R = \left[\frac{1}{g'(x)} R[x] : R[x]\right],$$

whence, by (5), in fact

$$D(R[x]) = \frac{1}{g'(x)} R[x].$$

We have now established (i) and (ii), and the necessity of the condition in (iii) is a trivial consequence.

Suppose that $\mathfrak{D}(S/R) = g'(x)S$, then

$$D(R[x]) \supset D(S) = \frac{1}{g'(x)} S \supset \frac{1}{g'(x)} R[x] = D(R[x]).$$

Now take duals again, and apply 3, Proposition 3, to get $S = R[x]$.

Finally we prove the *tower formula:*

PROPOSITION 7. *If* $L \supset F \supset K$ *and if* T *is the integral closure of* R *in* F *then*

(i) $\mathfrak{D}(S/R) = \mathfrak{D}(S/T)\mathfrak{D}(T/R)$,

(ii) $\mathfrak{d}(S/R) = \mathfrak{d}(T/R)^m(N_{F/K}\mathfrak{d}(S/T))$,

where $m = (L : F)$.

Proof. We shall show that

$$\mathfrak{D}(S/R)^{-1} = \mathfrak{D}(S/T)^{-1}\mathfrak{D}(T/R)^{-1}.$$

then (ii) will follow from (4) and the Corollaries to Proposition 4.

By the transivity of the trace we have

$$t_{L/K}(Sx) = t_{F/K}[t_{L/F}(Sx)T].$$

Hence, writing $\mathfrak{D}_0 = \mathfrak{D}(T/R)$,

$$\begin{aligned} t_{L/K}(Sx) \subset R \Leftrightarrow t_{L/F}(Sx) \subset \mathfrak{D}_0^{-1} \\ \Leftrightarrow t_{L/K}(Sx\mathfrak{D}_0) \subset T \Leftrightarrow x\mathfrak{D}_0 \subset \mathfrak{D}(S/T)^{-1} \\ \Leftrightarrow x \in \mathfrak{D}_0^{-1}\mathfrak{D}(S/T)^{-1}. \end{aligned}$$

5. Ramification

We first consider a pair of Dedekind domains R_1 and R_2, with quotient fields K_1 and K_2, and with $R_1 \subset R_2$. Let $\mathfrak{p}_2$ be a non-zero prime ideal of R_2 and suppose that the prime ideal

$$\mathfrak{p}_1 = \mathfrak{p}_2 \cap R_1$$

is also non-zero. Then the residue class field $k = R_1/\mathfrak{p}_1$ is embedded naturally in the residue class field $k_2 = R_2/\mathfrak{p}_2$. The degree

(1) $$(k_2 : k_1) = f(\mathfrak{p}_2/\mathfrak{p}_1)$$

is the *residue class degree* (possibly $f = \infty$). The *ramification index* $e(\mathfrak{p}_2/\mathfrak{p}_1)$ is defined by the equation

(2) $$v_{\mathfrak{p}_2}(\mathfrak{p}_1 R_2) = e(\mathfrak{p}_2/\mathfrak{p}_1),$$

i.e. by

(3) Restriction of $v_{\mathfrak{p}_2}$ to $K_1^* = e(\mathfrak{p}_2/\mathfrak{p}_1)v_{\mathfrak{p}_1}$.

In the obvious notation we have

PROPOSITION 1.

$$\begin{aligned} f(\mathfrak{p}_3/\mathfrak{p}_2)f(\mathfrak{p}_2/\mathfrak{p}_1) = f(\mathfrak{p}_3/\mathfrak{p}_1), \\ e(\mathfrak{p}_3/\mathfrak{p}_2)e(\mathfrak{p}_2/\mathfrak{p}_1) = e(\mathfrak{p}_3/\mathfrak{p}_1). \end{aligned}$$

Proof. Obvious.

PROPOSITION 2. *Let $\bar{\mathfrak{p}}$ be the valuation ideal in the completion of $K = K_i$ with respect to the valuation $v_\mathfrak{p} = v_{\mathfrak{p}_i}$. Then*

$$f(\bar{\mathfrak{p}}/\mathfrak{p}) = 1 = e(\bar{\mathfrak{p}}/\mathfrak{p}).$$

Proof. Let $R_\mathfrak{p}$ be the valuation ring of $v_\mathfrak{p}$ in K. By 2, Proposition 2, $e(\mathfrak{p}R_\mathfrak{p}/\mathfrak{p}) = 1$ and by 1, Proposition 1, $e(\bar{\mathfrak{p}}/\mathfrak{p}R_\mathfrak{p}) = 1$. By Proposition 1, $e(\bar{\mathfrak{p}}/\mathfrak{p}) = 1$.

Every element of $R_\mathfrak{p}/\mathfrak{p}R_\mathfrak{p}$ is of form xy^{-1} with $x, y \in R/\mathfrak{p}$. Hence the two fields coincide, i.e. $f(\mathfrak{p}R_\mathfrak{p}/\bar{\mathfrak{p}}) = 1$. Also $R_\mathfrak{p}$ is dense in the valuation ring $\bar{R}_\mathfrak{p}$ of the completion. Hence the image of $R_\mathfrak{p}/\mathfrak{p}R_\mathfrak{p}$ is dense in the discrete group $\bar{R}_\mathfrak{p}/\bar{\mathfrak{p}}$, i.e. $f(\bar{\mathfrak{p}}/\mathfrak{p}R_\mathfrak{p}) = 1$. Thus $f(\bar{\mathfrak{p}}/\mathfrak{p}) = 1$.

COROLLARY.

$$\begin{aligned} f(\mathfrak{p}_2/\mathfrak{p}_1) = f(\bar{\mathfrak{p}}_2/\bar{\mathfrak{p}}_1) \\ e(\mathfrak{p}_2/\mathfrak{p}_1) = e(\bar{\mathfrak{p}}_2/\bar{\mathfrak{p}}_1). \end{aligned}$$

The results of § 4, together with the last Corollary, show that differents, discriminants, residue class degrees, ramification indices and ideal norms, for extensions L/K, can be described locally in terms of the completions. From now on, and up to § 10, we shall always assume R to be a d.v. ring, and K to be complete in the valuation topology. This situation is inherited by finite separable extensions (4, Proposition 2). The reformulation of our results in global terms will mostly be left to the reader.

We shall now make some changes in the notation, which was introduced in § 4, and shall use for "relative" objects the symbols $\mathfrak{D}(L/K)$, $\mathfrak{d}(L/K)$, $f(L/K)$, $e(L/K)$. v_L is the valuation of L, k_L the residue class field. For k_K we also write k. $\mathfrak{p}$ is the maximal ideal of R, $\mathfrak{P}$ the maximal ideal of the integral closure S of R in L.

Except for § 9, all our results will be established without assuming *a priori* that the residue class field extensions are separable.

PROPOSITION 3.

$$e(L/K)f(L/K) = (L : K).$$

Proof. The vector-space $S/\mathfrak{p}S$ over k has the sequence of quotient spaces

$$S/\mathfrak{P}, \mathfrak{P}/\mathfrak{P}^2, \ldots, \mathfrak{P}^{e-1}/\mathfrak{P}^e \qquad (\mathfrak{P}^e = \mathfrak{p}S),$$

and by 1, Lemma 4 these are isomorphic. The dimension of $S/\mathfrak{P}$ over k is $f = f(L/K)$, hence the dimension of $S/\mathfrak{p}S$ is ef. On the other hand, as S is a free R-module of rank $(L: K)$, the dimension of $S/\mathfrak{p}S$ is $(L: K)$.

Let U_K and U_L be the groups of units of R, and of S respectively. We already know that the embedding $j: K^* \to L^*$ yields a commutative diagram (with exact rows) (cf. 1(5))

$$\begin{array}{ccccccccc} 0 & \longrightarrow & U_K & \longrightarrow & K^* & \xrightarrow{v_K} & Z & \longrightarrow & 0 \\ & & \downarrow & & \downarrow & & \downarrow{\scriptstyle e} & & \\ 0 & \longrightarrow & U_L & \longrightarrow & L^* & \xrightarrow{v_L} & Z & \longrightarrow & 0 \end{array}$$

Now we get in addition

COROLLARY. *The element norm yields a commutative diagram*

$$\begin{array}{ccccccccc} 0 & \longrightarrow & U_L & \longrightarrow & L^* & \longrightarrow & Z & \longrightarrow & 0 \\ & & \downarrow & & \downarrow & & \downarrow{\scriptstyle f} & & \\ 0 & \longrightarrow & U_K & \longrightarrow & K^* & \longrightarrow & Z & \longrightarrow & 0 \end{array}$$

i.e.

$$fv_L(x) = v_K(N_{L/K}x)$$

and

$$N_{L/K}(\mathfrak{P}) = \mathfrak{p}^f.$$

Proof. $N_{L/K}(U_L) \subset U_K$ and $N_{L/K} \circ j = (L: K)$.

Interlude on traces: Let A be a finite dimensional commutative algebra over a field k with the following properties: (i) If N is its radical then $A/N = B$ is a field. (ii) $N^e = 0$, $N^{e-1} \neq 0$ and for $i < e$, $B \cong N^i/N^{i+1}$ (isomorphism of B-modules). Denote by $\bar{a}$ the image in B of an element a of A. Then we have

LEMMA 1. $t_{A/k}(a) = e t_{B/k}(\bar{a})$.

Sketch of proof: $t_{A/k}(a)$ is the trace of the linear transformation $x \mapsto xa$ of the k-space A. Let $B = B_0 = A/N, \ldots, B_i = N^i/N^{i+1}, \ldots$ be the successive quotient modules of the A-module A and let a_i be the linear transformation of B_i induced by a. Then

$$t_{A/k}(a) = \sum_i \operatorname{trace}(a_i).$$

But the B_i are isomorphic A-modules and hence

$$\operatorname{trace}(a_i) = \operatorname{trace}(a_0) = t_{B/k}(\bar{a}).$$

Therefore the Lemma.

Now write $a \mapsto \bar{a}$ for the residue class map $S \to S/\mathfrak{P}$.

LEMMA 2. $\overline{t_{L/K}(a)} = e t_{k_L/k}(\bar{a})$.

Proof. By Lemma 1, with $A = S/\mathfrak{p}S$, $N = \mathfrak{P}/\mathfrak{p}S$.

Remark: Analogously one can show that

$$\overline{N_{L/K}(a)} = N_{k_L/k}(\bar{a})^e. \tag{4}$$

PROPOSITION 4. $v_L(\mathfrak{D}) \geq e-1$.

Proof. Write again $A = S/\mathfrak{p}S$, $N = \mathfrak{P}/\mathfrak{p}S$ and denote by $\tilde{x}$ the image in A of an element x of S. Choose a k-basis $\{a_i\}$ of A, so that for $1 \leq i \leq (e-1)f$ the a_i form a k-basis of N. We can lift $\{a_i\}$ back to an R-basis $\{x_i\}$ of S, so that $\tilde{x}_i = a_i$. For $1 \leq i \leq (e-1)f$ and for all j, $\tilde{x}_i . \tilde{x}_j$ will lie in N, i.e. $\overline{x_i x_j} = 0$, whence by Lemma 2

$$t_{L/K}(x_i x_j) \in \mathfrak{p}.$$

Hence each of the first $(e-1)f$ rows of the matrix

$$(t_{L/K}(x_i x_j))$$

lies in $\mathfrak{p}$, and hence by 3, Proposition 4

$$v_K(\mathfrak{d}) \geqq (e-1)f,$$

i.e.

$$v_L(\mathfrak{D}) = \frac{1}{f} v_K(N_{L/K}\mathfrak{D}) = \frac{1}{f} v_K(\mathfrak{d}) \geqq e-1.$$

L is said to be *non-ramified* over K, if

(i) $e(L/K) = 1$.

(ii) k_L is separable over k.

THEOREM 1. *L is non-ramified over K if and only if* $\mathfrak{d}(L/K) = R$.

Proof. By Proposition 4, $\mathfrak{d} = R$, i.e. $\mathfrak{D} = S$ implies $e = 1$. Now suppose that $e = 1$. Let $\{x_i\}$ be a free generating set of S over R and let

$$d = \det t_{L/K}(x_i x_j).$$

By 3, Proposition 4, $\mathfrak{d} = R$ if and only if the residue class $\bar{d}$ is non-zero, But by Lemma 2,

$$\bar{d} = \det t_{k_L/k}(\bar{x}_i . \bar{x}_j)$$

is the discriminant of the basis $\{\bar{x}_i\}$ of k_L over k, and this does not vanish if and only if k_L is separable over k.

Let in the sequel χ be the characteristic of k. L is said to be *tamely ramified* over K if

(i) $\chi \nmid e(L/K)$.

(ii) k_L is separable over k.

Thus if $\chi = 0$, L is always tamely ramified.

THEOREM 2. *The following conditions are equivalent:*

(i) *L is tamely ramified over K.*

(ii) $t_{L/K}(S) = R$.

(iii) $v_L(\mathfrak{D}) = e-1$.

Note: $t_{L/K}(S)$ is always a non-zero ideal of R.

Proof. The equivalence of (i) and (ii) is immediate from Lemma 2.

For the equivalence of (ii) and (iii) first note that when $a \in K$, then

$$t_{L/K}(Sa) = t_{L/K}(S)a.$$

Hence

$$t_{L/K}(S)^{-1} = \mathfrak{D}^{-1} \cap K,$$

or writing $v = v_L(\mathfrak{D})$, $r = v_K(t_{L/K}(S))$

$$r \leq \frac{v}{e} < r+1.$$

Thus if $v = e-1$ then $r = 0$. If $r = 0$, then $v < e$, and so by Proposition 4. $v = e-1$.

Remark: If L is normal over K one can deduce from condition (ii) in the last theorem a further criterion. For this purpose denote by $R(\Gamma)$ the group ring over R of the Galois group Γ. One then has the

Normal basis theorem: The $R(\Gamma)$-module S is isomorphic with $R(\Gamma)$ if and only if L is tamely ramified over K.†

The proof is left as an exercise. Hints: Interpret the existence of an element of trace 1 in terms of endomorphism rings to deduce that when L is tamely ramified over K then S is projective. Then use Swan's theorem.‡

Global Application

We shall explicitly restate Theorem 1 in terms of arbitrary Dedekind domains. Let then just for the moment R be a Dedekind domain, not necessarily a d.v. ring, K its quotient field, and S the integral closure of R in a finite separable extension field L of K. A non-zero prime ideal $\mathfrak{P}$ of S is non-ramified (over K) if its ramification index over $\mathfrak{P} \cap R$ has value 1 and if $S/\mathfrak{P}$ is separable over $R/\mathfrak{P} \cap R$. A non-zero prime ideal $\mathfrak{p}$ of R is non-ramified (in L) if all prime ideals $\mathfrak{P}$ in S, above $\mathfrak{p}$, are non-ramified over K.

COROLLARY 1 TO THEOREM 1. *$\mathfrak{p}$ is non-ramified in L if and only if $\mathfrak{p}$ does not divide the discriminant $\mathfrak{d}$ of S/R.*

Proof. On the one hand we know (cf. Proposition 2) that both the ramification index and the actual residue class field extension remain unchanged on transition to the completions. Thus $\mathfrak{p}$ is non-ramified in L if and only if the completions $L_{\mathfrak{P}}$, for all $\mathfrak{P}$ above $\mathfrak{p}$, are non-ramified over the completion $K_{\mathfrak{p}}$ of K.

On the other hand it follows from 4, Proposition 5, and 2, Corollary 4 to Proposition 2, that $\mathfrak{p}$ does not divide $\mathfrak{d}$ if and only if the product of the local discriminants is trivial. As each factor is an integral ideal, this is the same as saying that each of the local discriminants is trivial.

Now apply Theorem 1.

(By replacing the discriminant by the different one can obtain a sharper criterion for the individual $\mathfrak{P}$ to be non-ramified.)

COROLLARY 2 TO THEOREM 1. *Almost all non-zero prime ideals of R are non-ramified in S.*

In fact all those which do not divide the discriminant!

6. Totally Ramified Extensions

The notation here, and in § 7 to 9, is that introduced in § 5. R is always a d.v. ring, K is complete and L is a finite, separable extension field of K.

A polynomial $g(X)$ in $K[X]$ is *separable* if $(g(X), g'(X)) = 1$. An *Eisenstein polynomial* in $K[X]$ is a separable polynomial

$$(1) \qquad E(X) = X^m + b_{m-1}X^{m-1} + \dots + b_1 X + b_0,$$

† See E. Noether, Normalbasis bei Körpern ohne höhere Verzweigung, Crelle 1931.

‡ See R. S. Swan, Induced Representations and Projective Modules, Ann. of Math. 1960, Corollary 6.4.

with

(2) $v_K(b_i) \geq 1$ for $i = 1, \ldots, m-1$, and $v_K(b_0) = 1$.

(The condition of separability on either L or $E(X)$ is not really necessary for the following theorem. But as we are only considering separable extension fields, we had to impose the corresponding restriction on $E(X)$).

L is *totally ramified* over K if $e(L/K) = (L\colon K)$, i.e. $f(L/K) = 1$.

THEOREM 1. (i) *An Eisenstein polynomial $E(X)$ is irreducible. If Π is a root of $E(X)$, then $L = K[\Pi]$ is totally ramified and $v_L(\Pi) = 1$.*

(ii) *If L is totally ramified over K and $v_L(\Pi) = 1$, then the minimal polynomial of Π over K is Eisenstein and*

$$S = R(\Pi), \qquad L = K[\Pi].$$

For the proof we shall need a proposition on the representation of elements of a complete field K by convergent series. If, for all $n \in Z$, $v(\Pi_n) = n$, $v(a_n) \geq \rho$ (constant), then the series

$$\sum_{n \gg -\infty}^{\infty} a_n \Pi_n \quad (\text{i.e. } a_n = 0 \text{ for all } n \text{ near } -\infty)$$

converges and thus has a sum in K. Suppose now that we are given maps $\Pi : Z \to K^*$, $r : k \to R$, so that $r(0) = 0$, and that

$$Z \xrightarrow{\Pi} K^* \xrightarrow{v} Z$$

$$k \xrightarrow{r} R \xrightarrow{\text{res. class}} k$$

are the identity maps. Writing Π_n for the image of n under Π, and $\mathfrak{R} = \operatorname{Im} r$, we have

PROPOSITION 1. *Every element of K has a unique representation of form*

$$a = \sum_{n \gg -\infty}^{\infty} a_n \Pi_n, \qquad a_n \in \mathfrak{R}.$$

The value of a is then given by

$$v(a) = \inf_{a_n \neq 0} n.$$

Proof. Standard.

Proof of Theorem 1. First suppose that the polynomial $E(X)$ in (1) is Eisenstein and that $L = K[\Pi]$, where $E(\Pi) = 0$. Write $n = (L\colon K)$, $e = e(L/K)$.

Clearly $v_L(\Pi) \geq 0$. Hence

$$v_L(\Pi^m) = v_L(b_{m-1}\Pi^{m-1} + \ldots + b_0) \geq 1,$$

i.e. $v_L(\Pi) \geq 1$. Let s be the integer with

$$s \geq \frac{e}{v_L(\Pi)} > s-1.$$

Then

$$(3) \qquad m \geq n \geq e \geq s.$$

If $m > s$ then $v_L(\Pi^m) > e$. Also

$$v_L(b_i) = ev_K(b_i) \geq e.$$

and so

$$v_L(b_{m-1}\Pi^{m-1} + \ldots + b_1\Pi) > e.$$

Hence $v_L(b_0) > e$, i.e. $v_K(b_0) > 1$ contrary to (2). We have shown that $m \leq s$, and so by (3)

$$m = n = e = s.$$

Therefore

$$v_L(\Pi) = 1.$$

All the assertions of (i) have now been established.

For (ii) we apply Proposition 1 to L. As $f(L/K) = 1$ we may choose $\mathfrak{R}$ to be in K. Taking c to be an element of K, with $v_K(c) = 1$, we put

$$\Pi_{qe+r} = c^q \Pi^r \qquad (q \in Z, \quad 0 \leq r < e).$$

A rearrangement of the sum $\sum a_n \Pi_n$ now shows that in fact $L = K[\Pi]$ and $S = R[\Pi]$.

Let now the polynomial $E(X)$ in (1) be the minimal polynomial of Π over K. Then it is also the characteristic polynomial. Therefore, in the first place, $b_0 = \pm N_{L/K}(\Pi)$ and so, by 5, Proposition 3, Corollary 1,

$$v_K(b_0) = v_L(\Pi) = 1.$$

In the second place, $E(X)$ reduced mod $\mathfrak{p}$ is the characteristic polynomial of the nilpotent element Π mod $\mathfrak{p}S$ of the algebra $S/\mathfrak{p}S$ over k. Hence $E \equiv X^m (\text{mod } \mathfrak{p})$, i.e. $v_K(b_i) > 0$ for all i.

COROLLARY. *K has a totally ramified extension of prescribed degree e.*

Proof. Let $v_K(c) = 1$ and

$$E(X) = X^e - cX - c.$$

It is worth mentioning some results, which follow on from Proposition 1, but which we shall not be able to give in this course. (See Serre, Ch. II.)

If K is the field of formal series $\sum_{n \gg -\infty} a_n t^n$ over a field F (see example in § 1) then one can clearly take $\Pi_n = t^n$ and $\mathfrak{R} = F$ (i.e. $F \cong k$). Here the characteristics of k and K coincide. Conversely if this is the case then K is (to within value isomorphism) the field of formal power series over k.

There remains the case when $\chi = p \neq 0$ but the characteristic of K is zero. (Typical example the rational p-adic field $\mathbf{Q}_p$.) If one assumes also that k is perfect (e.g. k is finite) then one can at least choose $\mathfrak{R}$ to be multiplicatively closed, and uniquely so. As for the existence problem, one can show that if k is perfect of characteristic $p \neq 0$ then there is one and (essentially) only one discretely valued, complete field K of characteristic zero which has k as its residue class field and for which $v_K(p) = 1$.

7. Non-ramified Extensions

A separable extension L of K determines by transition to the residue class fields an algebraic extension of k. If L is non-ramified over K then the residue class field extension is separable. One of our aims in the present section is to show conversely that each separable extension of k can uniquely be lifted to a non-ramified extension of K (in a proper functorial sense). We first established an analogue to the theorem of the last chapter, which gives a description of non-ramified extensions as root fields of polynomials. Notation: The image in k_L of an element a of S will always be denoted by $\bar{a}$, and analogously the image in the polynomial ring $k_L[X]$ of a polynomial $g(X) \in S[X]$ by $\bar{g}(X)$.

PROPOSITION 1. (i) *Suppose L to be non-ramified over K. Then there exists an element x of S with $k_L = k[\bar{x}]$. If x is such an element and $g(X)$ is its minimal polynomial over K, then $S = R[x]$, $L = K[x]$ and $\bar{g}(X)$ is irreducible in $k[X]$ and separable.*

(ii) *Suppose $g(X)$ is a monic polynomial in $R[X]$, such that $\bar{g}(X)$ is irreducible in $k[X]$ and separable. If x is a root of $g(X)$ then $L = K[x]$ is non-ramified over K and $k_L = k[\bar{x}]$.*

Proof. (i) As k_L is separable over k it is of form $k[\bar{x}]$ with $x \in S$. For every such x the minimal polynomial $G(X)$ of $\bar{x}$ over k is separable. Also

$$(L : K) \geq \text{degree}\, g(X) \geq \text{degree}\, G(X) = (k_L : k) = (L : K).$$

Thus in fact $G(X) = \bar{g}(X)$, i.e. $\bar{g}(X)$ is irreducible, and $L = K[x]$. The equation $S = R[x]$ can now be deduced either from 6, Proposition 1, as applied to L, or from 4, Proposition 6.

(ii) We have

$$(L : K) = \text{degree}\, g(X) = (k[\bar{x}] : k) \leq (k_L : k) \leq (L : K).$$

Hence in the first place $(L: K) = f(L/K)$, i.e. $e(L/K) = 1$ and in the second place $k_L = k[\bar{x}]$, i.e. k_L is separable over k.

Consider now a class of algebraic extension fields $E, E_1, \ldots$ of a given field F. A homomorphism $\sigma : E \to E_1$ over F is a homomorphism of fields, leaving F elementwise fixed. Example: The identity map $E \to E$. If $\sigma : E \to E_1$ and $\tau : E_1 \to E_2$ are homomorphisms over F then so is $\sigma \circ \tau : E \to E_2$. In other words, we have a "category" (for those familiar with the language). We denote by $\text{Hom}^F(E, E_1)$ the set of homomorphisms

$E \to E_1$ over F. If E is normal over F then $\mathrm{Hom}^F(E, E)$ is just the Galois group.

Let E^s be the separable closure of F in E, i.e. the maximal subfield of E which is separable over F. We then obtain maps

$$\text{(1)} \qquad \mathrm{Hom}^F(E, E_1) \to \mathrm{Hom}^F(E^s, E_1^s)$$

which preserve the compositions $\sigma \circ \tau$ and also the identity maps of the fields E, i.e. we have a functor. The maps (1) are moreover injective and if $E = E^s$ also bijective.

Now we apply this formalism to the class of finite, separable, algebraic extensions L of K. As L will vary, we shall now use the symbol R_L for its valuation ring and $\mathfrak{p}_L$ for its valuation ideal.

PROPOSITION 2. *Let $\sigma : L \to L'$ be a homomorphism over K. Then, for all $x \in L$*

$$v_{L'}(x\sigma) = e(L'/L\sigma)v_L(x).$$

Proof. The function v on L defined by

$$e(L'/L\sigma)v(x) = v_{L'}(x\sigma)$$

is a discrete valuation of L, which on K coincides with v_L. By uniqueness (see Chap. II) $v = v_L$.

COROLLARY 1. *Application to normal extensions L of K and their Galois groups.*

COROLLARY 2. *A homomorphism $\sigma : L \to L'$ over K induces, by restriction to the valuation rings and reduction modulo the valuation ideals, a homomorphism $\bar{\sigma} : k_L \to k_{L'}$ over k. The resulting maps*

$$\mathrm{Hom}^K(L, L') \to \mathrm{Hom}^k(k_L, k_{L'})$$

preserve the identity maps of fields and map composition.

Thus the residue class fields k_L define a functor, and so do the separable closures k_L^s of k in k_L. Our next theorem asserts, in the language of category theory, that the functor k_L^s has an adjoint. This will then in particular yield an isomorphism between the category of separable extensions of k and the category of non-ramified extensions of K.

THEOREM 1. *Let $\bar{k}$ be a finite, separable, algebraic extension of k. Then there exists a finite, separable, algebraic extension $L = L(\bar{k})$ of K, such that*

(i) *$\bar{k} \cong k_L$ (over k),*

(ii) *L is non-ramified over K,*

(iii) *the maps*

$$\mathrm{Hom}^K(L, L') \to \mathrm{Hom}^k(k_L, k_{L'})$$

are bijective for all L'.

Properties (i), (ii) *or* (i), (iii) *determine L uniquely, to within isomorphism over K.*

Note: In (iii) one may of course replace k_L and $k_{L'}$ by k_L^s and $k_{L'}^s$.

For the proof we need the

LEMMA 1. *Let $g(X)$ be a monic polynomial in $R[X]$ such that $\bar{g}(X)$ is separable, and suppose that the element α of k is a root of $\bar{g}(X)$. Then there is one and only one element of R, such that*

$$g(x) = 0 \quad \text{and} \quad \bar{x} = \alpha.$$

Proof. See Chap. II, Appendix C.

Proof of Theorem 1. We know that $\bar{k} = k[\alpha]$, where the minimal polynomial $G(X)$ of α over k is separable. Choose any monic polynomial $g(X)$ in $R[X]$ with $\bar{g}(X) = G(X)$ and let $L = K[x]$, where x is a root of $g(X)$. By Proposition 1, L has properties (i) and (ii).

To show that L has property (iii) consider a homomorphism $w: k_L \to k_{L'}$ over k. By the Lemma, L' will contain a unique element y, so that $g(y) = 0$ and $\bar{y} = \bar{x}w$. But then there exists a unique homomorphism $\sigma: L \to L'$ over K with $x\sigma = y$. Clearly $\bar{\sigma} = w$. If also $\bar{\tau} = w$ then $x\tau = y$ and so $\tau = \sigma$.

Now suppose that L' is non-ramified over K and that w is an isomorphism $k_L \cong k_{L'}$ over k. Then $(L': K) = (L: K)$ and therefore the lifted homomorphism $\sigma: L \to L'$ over K must be an isomorphism. We have thus seen that properties (i) and (ii) determine L uniquely, to within isomorphism over K. The corresponding uniqueness result in terms of (i) and (iii) is standard.

COROLLARY. *$L(\bar{k})$ is normal over K if and only if $\bar{k}$ is normal over k, and if so then the Galois groups are isomorphic.*

In the sequel a "subfield" of a finite separable, algebraic extension L of K is always one which contains K.

THEOREM 2. *L has a subfield L_0, such that the subfields L' of L which are non-ramified over K are precisely the subfields of L_0. Also $k_{L_0} = k_L^s$.*

If L is normal over K with Galois group Γ then L_0 is normal over K and is the fixed field of

$$\Gamma_0 = [\gamma \in \Gamma \mid v_L(x\gamma - x) > 0 \textit{ for all } x \in R_L]$$

Γ_0 is called the *inertia group* of L over K.

Proof. The existence of a subfield L_0 which is non-ramified over K, with $k_{L_0} = k_L^s$, follows from Theorem 1. All subfields of L_0 are then also non-ramified over K. In fact, from the definition of the term "non-ramified" we see that, for any tower $E \supset F \supset K$ of fields, E/K is non-ramified if and only if E/F and F/K are non-ramified.

Conversely, let L' be a subfield of L, non-ramified over K. Then $k_{L'} \subset k_L^s = k_{L_0}$. By Theorem 1, as applied to $\bar{k} = k_{L'}$ we obtain a homomorphism $\sigma: L' \to L_0$ over K so that $\bar{\sigma}$ is the inclusion map. Now let

$k_{L'} = k[\bar{x}]$, with $x \in L'$. Then x and $x\sigma$ are elements of L with the same residue class and so, by Lemma 1, $x = x\sigma$. But, by Proposition 1, $L' = K[x]$, and so $L' \subset L_0$.

Now suppose L is normal. The conjugate fields of L_0 in L are all non-ramified over K, hence coincide with L_0, i.e. L_0 is normal. The inertia group Γ_0 by its definition is the kernel of the homomorphism

$$\Gamma \to \mathrm{Hom}^k(k_L, k_L).$$

As the maps (1) are injective, Γ_0 is also the kernel of the homomorphism from Γ into the Galois group $\mathrm{Hom}^k(k_L^s, k_L^s)$ of k_{L_0}. If Ω is the Galois group of L_0/K, it follows from Theorem 1 that

$$\Gamma_0 = \mathrm{Ker}(\Gamma \to \Omega),$$

which is the required result.

COROLLARY 1. *The composite field of non-ramified extensions L and L' in a given separable closure of K is non-ramified.*

The union K_{nr} of all non-ramified extensions L of K in a given separable closure of K is called the *maximal non-ramified extension* of K.

COROLLARY 2. *Every finite extension of K in K_{nr} is non-ramified. The Galois group $\Gamma(K_{nr}/K)$ is isomorphic (as a topological group) with the Galois group $\Gamma(\bar{k}^s/k)$ of the separable closure $\bar{k}^s$ of k.*

Application (see Chapters III and V). We suppose now that k is a finite field of characteristic p with $q = p^m$ elements. Denote by $\bar{\mathbf{Z}}$ the completion of $\mathbf{Z}$ with respect to the topology defined by the subgroups $n\mathbf{Z}$ $(n > 0)$. Then $\Gamma(\bar{k}^s/k)$ is an isomorphic copy of $\bar{\mathbf{Z}}$ under the map

$$\nu \mapsto w_q^{\nu}$$

where

$$\alpha w_q = \alpha^q.$$

Hence:

I. *There is a unique element σ_q in $\Gamma(K_{nr}/K)$ with the following property: If L is a subfield of K_{nr}/K, then for all $a \in R_L$*

$$a\sigma_q \equiv a^q \pmod{\mathfrak{p}_L}.$$

The map $\nu \mapsto \sigma_q^{\nu}$ is an isomorphism $\bar{\mathbf{Z}} \cong \Gamma(K_{nr}/K)$ of topological groups.

(σ_q is the *Frobenius substitution*)

This result implies that for each integer $n > 0$ the field K has one and (to within isomorphism over K) only one non-ramified extension L of degree n. Further L is normal over K with cyclic Galois group.

From the theory of finite fields and by Proposition 1 we also have

II. *K_{nr} is the union of the fields of m-th roots of unity (in a given separable closure of K) for all m prime to p.*

In conclusion we consider the effect of the norm map on the groups of units. (See the Corollary to 5, Proposition 3.) The subgroups defined in § 1(6) for the fields K and L will be denoted by $U_{K,n}$ and $U_{L,n}$.

PROPOSITION 3. *If L is non-ramified over K then for all $n \geq 1$*

$$N_{L/K}(U_{L,n}) = U_{K,n}.$$

Proof. Choose an element Π in K with $v_K(\Pi) = 1$, i.e. $v_L(\Pi) = 1$. Then $U_{L,n}$ consists of the elements

$$u = 1 - \Pi^n x, \qquad x \in R_L.$$

If $m = (L:K)$, the characteristic polynomial $h(X)$ of $\Pi^n x$ over K is of form

$$h(X) = X^m - \Pi^n t_{L/K}(x) X^{m-1} + \Pi^{n+1} h_1(X), \qquad h_1(X) \in R[X].$$

Therefore

$$N_{L/K}(u) = h(1) \equiv 1 + \Pi^n t_{L/K}(x) \pmod{\mathfrak{p}^{n+1}}.$$

This implies in the first place that

$$N_{L/K}(U_{L,n}) \subset U_{K,n}.$$

By 5, Theorem 2, $t_{L/K}(R_L) = R$ and hence also

$$N_{L/K}(U_{L,n}) U_{K,n+1} = U_{K,n}.$$

Now one uses completeness, proceeding as for 1, Proposition 5, to finish the proof.

COROLLARY. *Suppose that L is non-ramified over K. Then a unit in U_K is norm of U_L if and only if its residue class mod $\mathfrak{p}$ is norm of k_L. In particular if k is finite then*

$$N_{L/K}(U_L) = U_K.$$

Proof. By 5, (4).

8. Tamely Ramified Extensions

The notation is the same as in § 7. χ is the characteristic of k. The term "subfield" is used as in 7, Theorem 2. Γ_0 is always the inertia group defined there.

THEOREM 1. (i) *L has a subfield L_1 such that the subfields L' of L which are tamely ramified over K are precisely the subfields of L_1. If $\chi = p \neq 0$ then $(L:L_1)$ is a power of p.*

(ii) *Suppose that L is normal over K with Galois group Γ. Then L_1 is normal over K and is the fixed field of*

$$\Gamma_1 = [\gamma \in \Gamma \mid v_L(x\gamma - x) \geq v_L(x) + 1 \textit{ for all } x \in R_L].$$

If $v_L(\Pi) = 1$, then the map

$$\gamma \mapsto \overline{\Pi\gamma/\Pi}$$

defines a homomorphism θ_0 of Γ_0 into $k^*_{L_0}$, which is independent of the choice of Π and whose kernel is Γ_1. Γ_0/Γ_1 is a cyclic group. If $\chi = p \neq 0$ then Γ_1 is the (*unique*) *p-Sylow group of Γ_0.*

Note: If $\chi = 0$ then L is tamely ramified anyway. In this case, the theorem just asserts the existence of the homomorphism θ_0 and the resulting fact that Γ_0 is cyclic.

Proof. We first consider the normal case, and begin by establishing the properties of the homomorphism θ_0. Γ_1 is clearly a subgroup of Γ_0 and a normal subgroup of Γ.

If $\gamma \in \Gamma_0$ and if u is a unit of R_L then $u\gamma/u \equiv 1 \pmod{\mathfrak{p}_L}$. Hence the residue class $\theta_0(\gamma) = \overline{\Pi\gamma/\Pi}$ in k^*_L is independent of the particular choice of Π (within the condition $v_L(\Pi) = 1$). As Γ_0 acts trivially on k^*_L one sees that $\theta_0(\gamma_1\gamma_2) = \theta_0(\gamma_1)\theta_0(\gamma_2)$. As Γ_0 is a finite group, the $\theta_0(\gamma)$ are roots of unity, and so lie in $(k^s_L)^* = k^*_{L_0}$. Moreover, it follows that $\Gamma_0/\text{Ker}\,\theta_0 \cong \text{Im}\,\theta_0$ is cyclic, and that its order is not divisible by χ. Finally, as $\overline{u\gamma/u} = 1$ for all units u, we have, for $a \in L^*$, the equation $\overline{a\gamma/a} = \theta_0(\gamma)^{v_L(a)}$. Hence in fact $\Gamma_1 = \text{Ker}\,\theta_0$.

Let now L_1 be the fixed field of Γ_1. We have seen that if $\chi = p \neq 0$ then the degree $(L_1 : L_0)$ is prime to p. As $k_L \supset k_{L_1} \supset k_{L_0}$ and as $(k_L : k_{L_0})$ is a power of p it follows that $f(L_1/L_0) = 1$. Also $e(L_1/L_0)$ is prime to p. Thus L_1 is tamely ramified over L_0.

In the sequel we shall use repeatedly the fact that, for any tower $E \supset F \supset K$ of fields, E/K is tamely ramified if and only if E/F and F/K are tamely ramified. This follows from the definition of tame ramification. As a first consequence we conclude the L_1 and its subfields are tamely ramified over K.

Let L' be a subfield of L, tamely ramified over K. We shall now show that $L' \subset L_1$. Let $L'L_0 = E$, $L' \cap L_0 = F$. Then L'/F is tamely ramified and hence, by 5, Theorem 2, there exists an element $a \in R_{L'}$ with $t_{L'/F}(a) = 1$. As Γ_0 is normal, we then also have $t_{E/L_0}(a) = 1$, and so, again by 5, Theorem 2, E is tamely ramified over L_0, i.e. over K. Hence $k_E \subset k^s_L$, i.e. $k_E = k_{L_0}$ and so E is also totally ramified over L_0.

Let $v_E(c) = 1$ and let $g(X)$ be the minimal polynomial of c over L_0. By 6, Theorem 1 and 4, Proposition 6, we have

$$\mathfrak{D}(E/L_0) = R_E g'(c),$$

and hence by 5, Theorem 2,

$$v_E(g'(c)) = e-1, \qquad e = e(E/L_0),$$

i.e.

$$v_L(g'(c)) = (e-1)v_L(c). \tag{1}$$

Now let E be the fixed field of the subgroup Δ of Γ_0. Choose in each right coset of Γ_0 mod Δ, other than Δ itself, an element γ. Then

$$g'(c) = \prod_{\gamma} (c - c\gamma).$$

For each of the $e-1$ factors of the product we have

$$v_L(c - c\gamma) \geq v_L(c),$$

and so by (1)

$$v_L(c - c\gamma) = v_L(c).$$

Hence $\gamma \notin \Gamma_1$. This however implies that $\Delta \supset \Gamma_1$, i.e. that $E \subset L_1$, and so $L' \subset L_1$.

Now suppose that $\chi = p \neq 0$ and that L'' is a proper extension of L_1 in L. Then L'' is not tamely ramified over L_1, i.e. either $p|e(L''/L_1)$ or $p|f(L''/L_1)$ and so certainly $p|(L'' : L_1)$. It follows that Γ_1 coincides with its p-Sylow group.

The results for non-normal L now follow by embedding L in a normal extension of K. The details are left to the reader.

COROLLARY 1. *The inertia group* Γ_0 *is always soluble. More precisely, if* $\chi = 0$, *then* Γ_0 *is cyclic, and if* $\chi = p \neq 0$, *then* Γ_0 *is the extension of a p-group by a cyclic group.*

If k is finite then the Galois group of a normal extension is soluble.

COROLLARY 2. *The composite field of tamely ramified extensions L and L′ in a separable closure of K is again tamely ramified.*

The *maximal tamely ramified extension* K_{tr} of K is the union of all tamely ramified extensions in a separable closure of K.

COROLLARY 3. *All finite extensions of K in* K_{tr} *are tamely ramified.* K_{tr} *contains* K_{nr}. *If* $\chi = 0$ *then* $\Gamma(K_{tr}/K_{nr}) \cong \bar{\mathbf{Z}}$, *if* $\chi = p \neq 0$ then $\Gamma(K_{tr}/K_{nr}) \cong \prod_{q \neq p} \mathbf{Z}_q$.

Remark: The group Γ_1 has an interesting module theoretic characterization. R_L has the structure of a module over the group ring $R(\Gamma)$. For a subgroup Δ of the Galois group Γ one can show that R_L will be relative projective with respect $R(\Delta)$ if and only if $\Delta \supset \Gamma_1$.

From Theorem 1, one sees that in order to "catch" the tamely ramified extensions one has to proceed in two steps. First construct a non-ramified extension (dealt with in § 7) and then a totally and tamely ramified normal extension. This last step can also be described explicitly.

We first recall a bit of Kummer theory (see Chap. III). Suppose that K contains the primitive e-th roots of unity and that the element c of K^* has true order e modulo K^{*e}. Then the field $K(\Pi)$, $\Pi^e = c$, is normal over K of degree e and the equations

$$\psi_c(\gamma) = \Pi\gamma/\Pi$$

define an injective homomorphism ψ_c of the Galois group into K^*. We shall then write

$$\overline{\psi}_c(\gamma) = \overline{\psi_c(\gamma)}.$$

PROPOSITION 1. (i) *Let L be a normal totally and tamely ramified extension of degree e. Then K contains the primitive e-th roots of unity and there is an element* $c \in K^*$ *with* $v_K(c) = 1$ *and* $L = K(c^{1/e})$.

Moreover $\overline{\psi}_c$ *coincides with the homomorphism* θ_0 *of Theorem* 1.

Also $L = K(b^{1/e})$ *with* $v_K(b) = 1$ *if and only if*

$$\overline{bc^{-1}} \in k^{*e}.$$

(ii) *If* $\chi \nmid e$ *and if K contains the primitive e-th roots of unity, and if* $v_K(c) = 1$, *then the field* $L = K(c^{1/e})$ *is normal, totally and tamely ramified over K, of degree e.*

Proof. (i) By Theorem 1, Im θ_0 is precisely the group of primitive e-th roots of unity of k^*. As the polynomial $X^e - 1$ is separable over k it follows from 7, Lemma 1, that K contains the primitive e-th roots of unity and that these are mapped injectively into k^*. The Galois group Γ of L/K being cyclic of order e it follows from Kummer theory that $L = K(c^{1/e})$, where e is the order of $c \bmod K^{*e}$. Moreover, both $\overline{\psi}_c$ and θ_0 are now injective homomorphisms $\Gamma \to k^*$, with the same image. Therefore

$$\overline{\psi}_c = \theta_0^r, \qquad (r, e) = 1. \tag{2}$$

But as seen in the proof of Theorem 1,

$$r = v_L(c^{1/e}) = v_K(c). \tag{3}$$

Thus $(v_K(c), e) = 1$. We may now replace c by $c^s a^e$ with $(s, e) = 1$ and $a \in K^*$, and we can thus ensure that $v_K(c) = 1$, and then by (2) (3) $\overline{\psi}_c = \theta_0$.

If now also $L = K(b^{1/e})$ then, by Kummer theory, $b = c^r a^e$ with $a \in K^*$, $(r, e) = 1$ and $0 < r < e$. If $v_K(b) = 1$ then we must have $r = 1$, and so the element a is a unit. The final form of our criterion will now follow from 1, Proposition 5.

(ii) follows from Kummer theory and by 6, Theorem 1.

COROLLARY 1. *Let* $v_K(c) = 1$. *Then* K_{tr} *is the union of fields* $K_{nr}(c^{1/e})$, *for all e not divisible by* χ.

We finally turn again to unit norms. Using the notation of 7, Proposition 3, we have

PROPOSITION 2. *If L is tamely ramified over K then*

$$N_{L/K}(U_{L,1}) = U_{K,1}.$$

Proof. By 5(4) we know that always $N_{L/K}(U_{L,1}) \subset U_{K,1}$. In view of 7, Proposition 3 and the transitivity of the norm, we may also assume that

L is totally ramified over K, say of degree e. But then we have by 1, Proposition 5,

$$U_{K,1} = U_{K,1}^{e} \subset N_{L/K}(U_{L,1}).$$

9. The Ramification Groups

Throughout this chapter L is normal over K with Galois group $\Gamma = \Gamma(L/K)$. The series of subgroups beginning with Γ_0, Γ_1 (cf. § 7, 8) can be continued. Apart from a brief indication of the general case, we shall from now on always assume that k_L is separable over k, i.e. that $k_L = k_{L_0}$. This is certainly the case whenever k is a finite field. Under this hypothesis we have (irrespective of whether L is normal or not)

PROPOSITION 1. $R_L = R[a]$.

Proof. In the notation of 7, Theorem 2, and by 7, Proposition 1, there exists an element b of L_0, so that $k_L = k[\bar{b}]$ and so that the residue class polynomial $\bar{g}(X)$ of the minimal polynomial $g(X)$ of b over K is separable. Thus $\bar{g}'(\bar{b}) \neq 0$.

Let now $a = b+h$, with $v_L(h) = 1$. Then we get from the Taylor expansion of $g(X)$ the equation

$$g(a) = hg'(b)+0(h^2).$$

Hence

$$v_L(g(a)) = 1.$$

Now we apply 6, Proposition 1 to L. As $k_L = k[\bar{a}]$ we can choose an $\mathfrak{R}$ consisting of "polynomials" in a with coefficients in R. If $n = me+r$, $e = e(L/K)$, $0 \leq r < e$, $m \in Z$ we take $\Pi_n = g(a)^r c^m$, where $c \in K$, $v_K(c) = 1$. Re-arranging the series expansion for an element of R_L one sees that $R_L = R[a]$.

With a as in the proposition we now define a function $i = i_{L/K} : \Gamma \to Z \cup \infty$ by

(1) $$i_{L/K}(\gamma) = i(\gamma) = v_L(a\gamma - a).$$

We furthermore define (for $i \geq -1$)

(2) $$\Gamma_i = [\gamma \in \Gamma \,|\, v_L(x\gamma - x) \geq i+1, \textit{for all } x \in R_L].$$

Thus $\Gamma_{-1} = \Gamma$. For $i = 0$ this was precisely the definition of the inertia group in § 7. For $i = 1$ we shall subsequently see that this definition agrees with that in § 8.

The following proposition connects the Γ_i with the function $i_{L/K}$, and shows incidentally that this function is independent of the choice of the generator a.

PROPOSITION 2.

(i) $\gamma \in \Gamma_i \Leftrightarrow i(\gamma) \geq i+1$.

(ii) $i(\gamma\delta) \geqq \inf(i(\gamma), i(\delta))$.

(iii) $i(\delta\gamma\delta^{-1}) = i(\gamma)$.

Proof. Obvious.

COROLLARY 1. *The* Γ_i *are normal subgroups of* Γ *with* $\Gamma_{i+1} \subset \Gamma_i$, *and* $\Gamma_m = 1$ *for large m.*

In fact

$$m = \sup_{\gamma \neq 1} i(\gamma)$$

will do.

COROLLARY 2. *If* $i(\gamma) \neq i(\delta)$ *then*

$$i(\gamma\delta) = \inf(i(\gamma), i(\delta)).$$

The Γ_i are the *ramification groups* (Hilbert).

If Δ is a subgroup of Γ, then it is the Galois group of L over the fixed field of Δ. We have clearly:

PROPOSITION 3. $\Delta_i = \Gamma_i \cap \Delta$.

In the sequel U is the group of units of R_L and the U_i are the subgroups defined in § 1(6) (with K replaced by L).

THEOREM 1. *Let* $i \geq 1$. *Then* $\gamma \in \Gamma_i$ *if and only if for all* $x \in L^*$, $x\gamma/x$ *lies in* U_i.

Choose an element Π *of* L *with* $v_L(\Pi) = 1$. *Then the map*

$$\gamma \mapsto \Pi\gamma/\Pi \bmod U_{i+1}$$

is a homomorphism

$$\theta_i : \Gamma_i \to U_i/U_{i+1},$$

which is independent of the particular choice of Π, *and whose kernel is* Γ_{i+1}.

Note: We now know that $\Gamma_1(\S\, 8) = \Gamma_1(\S\, 10)$.

Proof. If $x\gamma/x \in U_i$ for all $x \in L^*$, then γ acts trivially on k_L, hence $\gamma \in \Gamma_0$. As $k_L = k_{L_0}$ the elements of R_L are of form $y+z$, $y \in \mathfrak{p}_L$, $z \in R_{L_0}$. But then

$$v_L((y+z)\gamma-(y+z)) = v_L(y\gamma-y) = v_L\left(\frac{y\gamma}{y}-1\right)+v_L(y) \geqq i+1.$$

Thus $\gamma \in \Gamma_i$.

Suppose conversely that $\gamma \in \Gamma_i$. If $y \in U$ then

$$v_L(y\gamma/y-1) = v_L(y\gamma-y) \geq i+1,$$

hence

$$y\gamma/y \in U_{i+1}. \tag{3}$$

Now let $v_L(\Pi) = 1$. Then

$$v_L(\Pi\gamma/\Pi - 1) = v_L(\Pi\gamma - \Pi) - 1 \geqq i,$$

i.e. $\Pi\gamma/\Pi \in U_i$. Write

$$\theta_i(\gamma) = \Pi\gamma/\Pi \bmod U_{i+1}.$$

By (3) we see firstly that $\theta_i(\gamma)$ is independent of the choice of Π, and secondly that if $x \in L^*$ then

$$\theta_i(\gamma)^{v_L(x)} = x\gamma/x \bmod U_{i+1}.$$

Hence in the first place

$$x\gamma/x \in U_i,$$

and in the second place—applying what we have proved already—

$$\theta_i(\gamma) = 1 \text{ if and only if } \gamma \in \Gamma_{i+1}.$$

Finally for $\gamma, \delta \in \Gamma_i$ we have

$$\Pi\gamma\delta/\Pi = (\Pi\gamma/\Pi)\delta(\Pi\delta/\Pi).$$

As $\Pi\gamma/\Pi \in U$, we know from (3) that

$$(\Pi\gamma/\Pi)\delta = \Pi\gamma/\Pi \pmod{U_{i+1}}$$

and thus we have

$$\theta_i(\gamma\delta) = \theta_i(\gamma)\theta_i(\delta).$$

We know that if $\chi = 0$, then already $\Gamma_1 = 1$. On the other hand, if $\chi = p \neq 0$, then by 1, Proposition 5, $U_i^p \subset U_{i+1}$. Hence:

COROLLARY. *If $\chi = p \neq 0$ then, for $i \geq 1$, Γ_i/Γ_{i+1} is an elementary Abelian p-group.*

For the commutator properties of the ramification groups see Serre, Ch. IV.

Note: If k_L is not assumed to be separable over k, one has to define two sequences of subgroups. One is given by (2) (for $i \geq 0$), and we shall denote these groups for the moment by Γ_{i*}. On the other hand, the criterion of Theorem 1: "$x\gamma/x \in U_i$ for all $x \in L^*$" defines a second sequence of subgroups Γ_i^* $(i \geq 1)$. Corollary 1 to Proposition 2 and Proposition 3 remain valid for each of the two sequences, and so does the Corollary to Theorem 1. In other words, for $i \geq 1$ the quotients $\Gamma_{i*}/\Gamma_{i+1*}$ and $\Gamma_i^*/\Gamma_{i+1}^*$ are elementary Abelian p-groups.

The two sequences are interwoven, i.e. for $i \geq 0$, $\Gamma_{i*} \supset \Gamma_{i+1}^* \supset \Gamma_{i+1*}$. If k_L is separable over k then, by Theorem 1, $\Gamma_{i+1}^* = \Gamma_{i+1*}$. On the other hand if $e(L/L_1) = 1$ then $\Gamma_{i*} = \Gamma_{i+1}^*$ (for $i \geq 1$).

From now on k_L is again assumed to be separable over k. The ramification groups yield an explicit determination of the different, which generalizes the formula (cf. 5, Theorem 2) holding in the tamely ramified case. We shall write

$$g_i = \text{order}\,\Gamma_i. \tag{4}$$

Note that L/L_0 is now totally ramified, i.e.

$$g_0 = e(L/L_0) = e(L/K).$$

PROPOSITION 4.

$$v_L(\mathfrak{D}) = \sum_{\gamma \neq 1} i(\gamma) = \sum_{i=0}^{\infty} (g_i - 1).$$

Proof. Let $R_L = R[a]$ and let $g(X)$ be the minimal polynomial of a over K. By 4, Proposition 6,

$$\mathfrak{D} = g'(a)R_L,$$

and hence

$$\begin{aligned} v_L(\mathfrak{D}) = v_L(g'(a)) &= v_L\Big(\prod_{\gamma \neq 1} (a - a\gamma)\Big) \\ &= \sum_{\gamma \neq 1} i(\gamma) = \sum_{i=0}^{\infty} i((g_{i-1}-1)-(g_i-1)) \\ &= \sum_{i=0}^{\infty} (g_i - 1). \end{aligned}$$

COROLLARY. *Let Δ be a subgroup of Γ, F its fixed field. Then*

$$e(L/F)v_F(\mathfrak{D}(F/K)) = \sum_{\gamma \notin \Delta} i_{L/K}(\gamma).$$

Proof. By the tower formula (cf. 4, Proposition 7) we have

$$e(L/F)v_F(\mathfrak{D}(F/K)) = v_L(\mathfrak{D}(L/K)) - v_L(\mathfrak{D}(L/F)).$$

Now apply the last proposition to evaluate the right-hand side, noting that for $\delta \in \Delta$, $i_{L/K}(\delta) = i_{L/F}(\delta)$ (by Proposition 3).

From now on we shall be concerned with the following situation: Δ is a normal subgroup of Γ with fixed field F. F is then normal over K with Galois group Γ/Δ. Our first aim is to determine the function $i_{F/K}$.

PROPOSITION 5. *For $\omega \in \Gamma/\Delta$*

$$e(L/F)i_{F/K}(\omega) = \sum_{\gamma \to \omega} i_{L/K}(\gamma).$$

Proof. For $\omega = 1$ both sides are infinite. Assume now that $\omega \neq 1$. Let $R_L = R[a]$ and let $g(X)$ be the minimal polynomial of a over F. Acting with ω on $g(X)$ coefficientwise, we obtain a polynomial $(g\omega)(X)$. Then

$$\mathfrak{p}_F^{i_{F/K}(\omega)} = \mathfrak{p}_L^{e(L/F)i_{F/K}(\omega)}$$

divides the coefficients of $(g\omega)(X)-g(X)$, and so divides

$$(g\omega)(a)-g(a) = (g\omega)(a) = \prod_{\gamma\to\omega}(a-a\gamma).$$

In other words

$$e(L/F)i_{F/K}(\omega) \leqq \sum_{\gamma\to\omega} i_{L/K}(\gamma). \tag{5}$$

Now evaluate $e(L/F)v_F(\mathfrak{D}(F/K))$ first via Proposition 4 (with F in place of L) and then via the corollary to that proposition. Comparing the results we obtain the equation

$$\sum_{\omega\neq 1} e(L/F)i_{F/K}(\omega) = \sum_{\omega\neq 1}\sum_{\gamma\to\omega} i_{L/K}(\gamma).$$

But this implies that we must have equality in (5).

We now turn to the ramification groups of Γ/Δ. Our results in § 7 and § 8 imply that $(\Gamma/\Delta)_i = \Gamma_i\Delta/\Delta$ for $i = 0, 1$. But the same is no longer generally true for $i > 1$. To obtain an analogue to Proposition 3 for quotient groups one has, following Herbrand, to introduce a new enumeration of the ramification groups.

In the sequel x is a real variable ≥ -1. We write

$$\Gamma_x = \Gamma_i, \text{ where } i \text{ is the least integer} \geq x. \tag{6}$$

We then define a function $\phi = \phi_{L/K}$ by

$$\phi(x) = \begin{cases} x, \text{ if } -1 \leq x \leq 0, \\ \dfrac{1}{g_0}[g_1+\ldots+g_m+(x-m)g_{m+1}] \\ \text{if } x \geq 0 \text{ and } m \text{ is the integral part of } x \end{cases} \tag{7}$$

(i.e. m the integer with $m \leq x < m+1$).

$\phi(x)$ is a continuous, strictly increasing function and thus possesses a continuous, strictly increasing inverse function $\psi(y)$ $(-1 \leq y)$. The new, "upper" enumeration of the ramification groups is then given by

$$\Gamma^y = \Gamma_x \text{ if } x = \psi(y), \text{ i.e. } y = \phi(x). \tag{8}$$

We shall need some formal properties of the function ϕ.

LEMMA 1. *The function ϕ is characterized by the following properties:*

(i) $\phi(0) = 0$.

(ii) *$\phi(x)$ is continuous.*

(iii) *If m is an integer ≥ -1, then $\phi(x)$ is linear in the closed interval $[m, m+1]$ and has derivative*

$$\phi'(x) = \text{order}\,\Gamma_x/e(L/K)$$

in the open interval $(m, m+1)$.

Proof. Obvious.

LEMMA 2. *If $\phi(x)$ is integral, then so is x.*

Proof. For $x \in [-1, 0]$ this is obvious. If $x \in [m, m+1]$ $(m \geqq 0)$ and $y = \phi(x)$, then

$$x = \frac{1}{g_{m+1}}[g_0 y + m g_{m+1} - (g_1 + \ldots + g_m)].$$

The lemma now follows by observing that g_{m+1} divides $g_0, \ldots, g_m$.

LEMMA 3.

$$\phi(x)+1 = \frac{1}{g_0}\sum_{\gamma\in\Gamma} \inf(i(\gamma), x+1).$$

Proof. We shall give the proof for $x > 0$ only. Let m be the integer with $m < x \leq m+1$. Then

$$x+1 = \inf(i(\gamma), x+1) \Leftrightarrow \gamma \in \Gamma_{m+1}.$$

Therefore

$$\begin{aligned}\frac{1}{g_0}\sum_{\gamma\in\Gamma}\inf(i(\gamma), x+1) &= \frac{1}{g_0}\Big(\sum_{\gamma\notin\Gamma_{m+1}} i(\gamma) + g_{m+1}(x+1)\Big)\\ &= \frac{1}{g_0}\Big(\sum_{i=0}^{m+1}(g_{i-1}-g_i)i + g_{m+1}(x+1)\Big)\\ &= \frac{1}{g_0}\Big(\sum_{i=0}^{m} g_i - g_{m+1}(m+1) + g_{m+1}(x+1)\Big)\\ &= \phi(x)+1.\end{aligned}$$

The theorem we wish to prove is:

THEOREM 2.

(i) $\phi_{L/K}(x) = \phi_{F/K}(\phi_{L/F}(x))$.

(ii) *For all* $y \geq -1$

$$(\Gamma/\Delta)^y = \Gamma^y\Delta/\Delta.$$

Proof. For $\omega \in \Gamma/\Delta$ define

$$j(\omega) = \sup_{\gamma\to\omega} i_{L/K}(\gamma). \tag{9}$$

Our first step is to prove that

$$i_{F/K}(\omega) - 1 = \phi_{L/F}(j(\omega)-1). \tag{10}$$

Choose $\gamma_0 \in \Gamma$ so that $\gamma_0 \to \omega$ and that $i_{L/K}(\gamma_0) = j(\omega)$. Then the equation in Proposition 5 can be written in the form

$$e(L/F) i_{F/K}(\omega) = \sum_{\delta\in\Delta} i_{L/K}(\gamma_0\delta). \tag{11}$$

If $i_{L/K}(\delta) < j(\omega)$, then by Proposition 2, Corollary 2, $i_{L/K}(\gamma_0\delta) = i_{L/K}(\delta)$. If $i_{L/K}(\delta) \geqq j(\omega)$, then by Proposition 2,

$$j(\omega) \geqq i_{L/K}(\gamma_0\delta) \geqq \inf(i_{L/K}(\delta), j(\omega)) = j(\omega),$$

i.e.

$$i_{L/K}(\gamma_0\delta) = j(\omega).$$

Thus in all cases

$$(12) \qquad i_{L/K}(\gamma_0\delta) = \inf(i_{L/F}(\delta), j(\omega)),$$

(recalling that $i_{L/F}(\delta) = i_{L/K}(\delta)$ by Proposition 3). Now substitute (12) into (11) and apply Lemma 3 (for L/F), to obtain (10).

Using (10) we now have:

$$\omega \in \Gamma_x\Delta/\Delta \Leftrightarrow x \leqq j(\omega)-1 \Leftrightarrow \phi_{L/F}(x) \leqq \phi_{L/F}(j(\omega)-1)$$
$$\Leftrightarrow \phi_{L/F}(x) \leqq i_{F/K}(\omega)-1 \Leftrightarrow \omega \in (\Gamma/\Delta)_y$$

with $y = \phi_{L/F}(x)$. In other words we have shown that

$$(13) \qquad \Gamma_x\Delta/\Delta = (\Gamma/\Delta)_y, \quad \text{for } y = \phi_{L/F}(x).$$

We now establish Theorem 2(i). Write $\theta(x) = \phi_{F/K}(\phi_{L/F}(x))$. We shall use the characterization of $\phi_{L/K}$ given in Lemma 1. $\theta(x)$ clearly has properties (i) and (ii). Moreover, if x varies over an open interval $(m, m+1)$ then, by Lemma 2, the interval $(\phi_{L/F}(m), \phi_{L/F}(m+1))$ does not contain integral values. Hence $\phi_{F/K}(y)$ is linear in the closed interval $[\phi_{L/F}(m), \phi_{L/F}(m+1)]$ and so $\theta(x)$ is linear in $[m, m+1]$.

It remains to compare the derivatives for non-integral x. We have

$$(14) \qquad \theta'(x) = \phi'_{F/K}(y).\phi'_{L/F}(x), \quad \text{with } y = \phi_{L/F}(x).$$

By Lemma 1 (for F/K)

$$\phi'_{F/K}(y) = \text{order}\,(\Gamma/\Delta)_y/e(F/K)$$

and so by (13)

$$(15) \qquad \phi'_{F/K}(y) = (\Gamma_x\Delta : \Delta)/e(F/K).$$

By Lemma 1 (for L/F) and by Proposition 3

$$\phi'_{L/F}(x) = \text{order}\,(\Gamma_x \cap \Delta)/e(L/F).$$

Hence by (14), (15) and by Lemma 1 (for L/K)

$$\theta'(x) = \phi'_{L/K}(x),$$

and so finally

$$\phi_{L/K}(x) = \phi_{F/K}(\phi_{L/F}(x)).$$

But this equation, in conjunction with (13) now implies that

$$\Gamma^z\Delta/\Delta = (\Gamma/\Delta)^z$$

($z = \phi_{F/K}(y) = \phi_{L/K}(x)$). We have thus established the theorem.

For further properties of the Herbrand function see Serre, Ch. IV and V.

10. Decomposition

We now return to the global case. R is an arbitrary Dedekind domain, K its quotient field, and S the integral closure of R in a finite separable extension L of K. $\mathfrak{p}$ is a non-zero prime ideal of R and $\mathfrak{P}$ a non-zero prime ideal of S. The associated completions will be denoted by $K_\mathfrak{p}$, and by $L_\mathfrak{P}$. For the ramification index of $\mathfrak{P}$ over $\mathfrak{P} \cap R$ we write $e_{\mathfrak{P}}$ and for the residue class degree $f_{\mathfrak{P}}$. Thus

(1) $$\mathfrak{p}S = \prod_{\mathfrak{P}|\mathfrak{p}} \mathfrak{P}^{e_{\mathfrak{P}}}.$$

(2) $$N_{L/K}(\mathfrak{P}) = \mathfrak{p}^{f_{\mathfrak{P}}} \qquad (\mathfrak{p} = \mathfrak{P} \cap R).$$

PROPOSITION 1.

$$(L:K) = \sum_{\mathfrak{P}|\mathfrak{p}} e_{\mathfrak{P}} f_{\mathfrak{P}}.$$

Proof. By 4(2)

$$(L:K) = \sum_{\mathfrak{P}|\mathfrak{p}} (L_{\mathfrak{P}} : K_{\mathfrak{p}})$$

and by 5, Proposition 3,

$$(L_{\mathfrak{P}} : K_{\mathfrak{p}}) = e_{\mathfrak{P}} f_{\mathfrak{P}}.$$

From now on suppose that L is normal over K with Galois group Γ. As $S\gamma = S$, the conjugate $\mathfrak{P}\gamma$ ($\gamma \in \Gamma$) of the prime ideal $\mathfrak{P}$ will again be a prime ideal of S, and if $\mathfrak{P}|\mathfrak{p}$ then clearly also $\mathfrak{P}\gamma|\mathfrak{p}$. Conversely one has

PROPOSITION 2. *All prime ideals in S lying above $\mathfrak{p} = \mathfrak{P} \cap R$ are conjugates $\mathfrak{P}\gamma$ of $\mathfrak{P}$.*

Proof. The proof involves a special case of the Chinese remainder theorem, which we have not even stated earlier on. Let I be the product of the prime ideals of S, above $\mathfrak{p}$ and different from $\mathfrak{P}$. Then $\mathfrak{P}+I = S$. Thus there exist elements $a \in \mathfrak{P}$, $b \in I$ with $a+b = 1$. But then

$$a \in \mathfrak{P},\ a \notin \mathfrak{P}_1 \text{ if } \mathfrak{P}_1|\mathfrak{p} \text{ and } \mathfrak{P}_1 \neq \mathfrak{P}.$$

More generally

$$a\gamma \in \mathfrak{P}\gamma,\ a\gamma \notin \mathfrak{P}_1 \text{ of } \mathfrak{P}_1|\mathfrak{p} \text{ and } \mathfrak{P}_1 \neq \mathfrak{P}\gamma.$$

Taking the product over $\gamma \in \Gamma$ we see that

$$\prod (a\gamma) \notin \mathfrak{P}_1 \text{ if } \mathfrak{P}_1|\mathfrak{p} \text{ and } \mathfrak{P}_1 \neq \mathfrak{P}\gamma \text{ for all } \gamma.$$

But

$$\prod (a\gamma) = N_{L/K}(a) \in \mathfrak{P} \cap R = \mathfrak{p}.$$

Thus $\mathfrak{P}_1|\mathfrak{p}$ does in fact imply $\mathfrak{P}_1 = \mathfrak{P}\gamma$.

COROLLARY. *$e_{\mathfrak{P}} = e$ and $f_{\mathfrak{P}} = f$ solely depend on $\mathfrak{p} = \mathfrak{P} \cap R$. If g is the number of prime ideals of S, lying above $\mathfrak{p}$, then*

(3) $$efg = (L:K).$$

The elements γ of Γ with $\mathfrak{P}\gamma = \mathfrak{P}$ form a subgroup $\Gamma_{\mathfrak{P}}$, the *decomposition group*. They are characterized by the equation

$$v_{\mathfrak{P}}(x\gamma) = v_{\mathfrak{P}}(x)$$

for all $x \in L$ (or for all $x \in S$)). If $\gamma \in \Gamma$ then clearly

(4) $$\Gamma_{\mathfrak{P}\gamma} = \gamma^{-1}\Gamma_{\mathfrak{P}}\gamma.$$

PROPOSITION 3. *Suppose $\mathfrak{P}$ lies above $\mathfrak{p}$. Then $L_{\mathfrak{P}}$ is normal over $K_{\mathfrak{p}}$. Denote the Galois group by $\Sigma_{\mathfrak{P}}$. The restriction to L of the automorphisms $\sigma \in \Sigma_{\mathfrak{P}}$ then gives rise to an isomorphism*

$$\Sigma_{\mathfrak{P}} \cong \Gamma_{\mathfrak{P}}.$$

Proof. Define in the first place $\Sigma_{\mathfrak{P}}$ as the group of automorphisms of $L_{\mathfrak{P}}$ leaving $K_{\mathfrak{p}}$ elementwise fixed. An element σ of $\Sigma_{\mathfrak{P}}$ maps L into the extension field $L_{\mathfrak{P}}$ of K and leaves the elements of K fixed. As L is normal it follows that $L\sigma = L$. In other words, there is a unique element $\hat{\sigma}$ of Γ whose action on L coincides with that of σ. Moreover, by 7, Proposition 2, $v_{\mathfrak{P}}(x\hat{\sigma}) = v_{\mathfrak{P}}(x)$ for all $x \in L$, i.e. $\hat{\sigma} \in \Gamma_{\mathfrak{P}}$. We thus obtain a homomorphism

$$h : \Sigma_{\mathfrak{P}} \to \Gamma_{\mathfrak{P}}, \qquad h(\sigma) = \hat{\sigma}. \tag{5}$$

Let $\gamma \in \Gamma_{\mathfrak{P}}$. γ acts continuously on L with respect to the $v_{\mathfrak{P}}$-topology. It then follows from the universal embedding property of completions that there is an element $\gamma' = t(\gamma)$ of $\Sigma_{\mathfrak{P}}$, making the diagram

$$\begin{array}{ccc} L & \xrightarrow{\gamma} & L \\ \downarrow & \gamma' & \downarrow \\ L_{\mathfrak{P}} & \longrightarrow & L_{\mathfrak{P}} \end{array}$$

commutative. We obtain a homomorphism

$$t : \Gamma_{\mathfrak{P}} \to \Sigma_{\mathfrak{P}}, \qquad t(\gamma) = \gamma',$$

so that both $h \circ t$ and $t \circ h$ are identity maps, and thus h is in fact an isomorphism.

We now only have to show that the order of $\Sigma_{\mathfrak{P}}$, i.e. of $\Gamma_{\mathfrak{P}}$ coincides with the degree $(L_{\mathfrak{P}} : K_{\mathfrak{p}}) = e_{\mathfrak{P}} f_{\mathfrak{P}} = ef = (L:K)/g$ (cf. Corollary to Proposition 2), i.e. that the group index $(\Gamma : \Gamma_{\mathfrak{P}})$ is g. This, however, is immediate from the definition of $\Gamma_{\mathfrak{P}}$ and by Proposition 2.

Now we can get a definition for the *ramification groups* of L/K. Identify $\Gamma_{\mathfrak{P}}$ with the Galois group of $L_{\mathfrak{P}}/K_{\mathfrak{p}}$ and define the $\Gamma_{\mathfrak{P},i}$ in the first place locally as in § 9. As S is dense in each of its completions it follows then that in fact

$$\Gamma_{\mathfrak{P},i} = [\gamma \in \Gamma_{\mathfrak{P}} | v_{\mathfrak{P}}(x\gamma - x) \geq i+1, \quad \text{for all } x \in S].$$

For $i \geq 0$, one can moreover show that

$$\Gamma_{\mathfrak{P},i} = [\gamma \in \Gamma | v_{\mathfrak{P}}(x\gamma - x) \geq i+1, \quad \text{for all } x \in S].$$

BIBLIOGRAPHY

J-P. Serre, "Corps locaux", Hermann, Paris 1962. (Quoted as "Serre".)
O. Zariski and P. Samuel, "Commutative Algebra", Vol. 1, Van Nostrand 1958. (Quoted as "Z.S.".)

Chapter II

Global Fields

J. W. S. Cassels

1. Valuations

We shall be concerned only with rank 1 valuations, so for brevity, valuation will mean "rank 1 valuation".

Definition. *A valuation* $| \ |$ *on a field* k *is a function defined on* k *with values in the non-negative real numbers satisfying the following axioms.*

(1) $|\alpha| = 0$ *if and only if* $\alpha = 0$.

(2) $|\alpha\beta| = |\alpha|\,|\beta|$.

(3) *There is a constant* C *such that* $|1+\alpha| \leq C$ *whenever* $|\alpha| \leq 1$.

Definition. *The trivial valuation of* k *is that for which* $|\alpha| = 1$ *for all* $\alpha \neq 0$.

Note: This will often be tacitly excluded from consideration.

From (2) we have

$$|1| = |1| . |1|,$$

so $|1| = 1$ by (1). If now some power of $\omega \in k$ is 1, say $\omega^n = 1$ we have $|\omega| = 1$ by (2). In particular the only valuation of the finite fields is the trivial one.

The same argument shows that $|-1| = 1$ and so

$$|-\alpha| = |\alpha| \quad \text{all } \alpha \in k.$$

DEFINITION. *Two valuations* $|\ |_1$, $|\ |_2$ *on the same field* k *are equivalent if there is a* $c > 0$ *such that*

$$|\alpha|_2 = |\alpha|_1^c. \tag{1.1}$$

Note: If $|\alpha|_1$ is a valuation then $|\alpha|_2$ defined by (1.1) is one also. Equivalence is clearly an equivalence relation.

Trivially every valuation is equivalent to one with $C = 2$. For such a valuation it can be shown† that

(3′) $$|\beta+\gamma| \le |\beta|+|\gamma|$$

(The "triangle inequality".) Conversely (1), (2) and (3′) trivially imply (3) with $C = 2$. We shall at first be almost entirely concerned with properties of valuations unaffected by equivalence and so will often use (3′) instead of (3).

† We shall actually be concerned only with valuations with $C = 1$, for which (3′) is trivial (see next section), or with valuations equivalent to the ordinary absolute value of the real or complex numbers, for which (3′) is well known to hold: and we use (3) instead of (3′) (following Artin) only for the technical reason that we will want to call the square of the absolute value of the complex numbers a valuation. For completeness, however, we give the deduction of (3′) from (3) with $C = 2$. First, $|\alpha_1 + \alpha_2| \le 2 \max |\alpha_1|, |\alpha_2|$, on putting $\alpha_2 = \alpha\alpha_1$ if, say, $|\alpha_1| \ge |\alpha_2|$. Then, by induction,

$$\left|\sum_{j=1}^{2^r} \alpha_j\right| \le 2^r \max |\alpha_j|,$$

and so for any $n > 0$, we have

$$\left|\sum_{j=1}^{n} \alpha_j\right| \le 2^r \max |\alpha_j| \le 2n \max |\alpha_j|,$$

where $2^{r-1} < n \le 2^r$, on inserting $2^r - n$ zero summands. In particular

$$|n| \le 2n|1| = 2n \qquad (n > 0).$$

But now

$$\begin{aligned} |\beta + \gamma|^n &= \left|\sum_j \binom{n}{j} \beta^j \gamma^{n-j}\right| \\ &\le 2(n+1) \max \left|\binom{n}{j}\right| |\beta|^j |\gamma|^{n-} \\ &< 4(n+1) \max \binom{n}{j} |\beta|^j |\gamma|^{n-j} \\ &\le 4(n+1)(|\beta| + |\gamma|)^n; \end{aligned}$$

and (3′) follows on extracting nth roots and making $n \to \infty$.

For later use we note the formal consequence

$$\big||\beta|-|\gamma|\big| \le |\beta-\gamma|$$

of (3′) where the outside $|\ |$ are the ordinary absolute value. For one need only apply the triangle inequality to the identity

$$\beta = \gamma+\beta-\gamma, \qquad \gamma = \beta+(\gamma-\beta).$$

2. Types of Valuation

We define two important properties of a valuation, both of which apply to whole equivalence classes of valuation.

DEFINITION. *The valuation* $|\ |$ *is discrete if there is a* $\delta > 0$ *such that*

$$1-\delta < |\alpha| < 1+\delta$$

implies $|\alpha| = 1$.

This is the same as saying that the set of $\log|\alpha|$, $\alpha \in k$, $\alpha \ne 0$ form a discrete subgroup of the reals under addition. Such a group is necessarily free on one generator, i.e. there is a $c < 1$ such that $|\alpha|$, $\alpha \ne 0$ runs through precisely the set of c^m, $m \in \mathbf{Z}$. If $|\alpha| = c^m$ we call $m = m(\alpha)$ the *order* of α. Axiom 2 implies

$$\operatorname{ord}(\alpha\beta) = \operatorname{ord}\alpha + \operatorname{ord}\beta.$$

DEFINITION. *The valuation* $|\ |$ *is non-archimedean if one can take* $C = 1$ *in Axiom* 3, *i.e. if*

$$|\beta+\gamma| \le \max\{|\beta|, |\gamma|\}. \tag{2.1}$$

If it is not non-archimedean, then it is archimedean.

We note at once the consequence

$$|\beta+\gamma| = |\beta| \quad \text{if } |\gamma| < |\beta|$$

of (2.1). For

$$|\beta| = |(\beta+\gamma)-\gamma| \le \max\{|\beta+\gamma|, |\gamma|\}.$$

For non-arch. $|\ |$ the α with $|\alpha| \le 1$ clearly form a ring, the *ring* $\mathfrak{o}$ *of integers*. Two non-archimedean valuations are equivalent if and only if they give the same $\mathfrak{o}$: for $|\beta| < |\gamma|$ if and only if $\beta\gamma^{-1} \in \mathfrak{o}$, $\beta^{-1}\gamma \notin \mathfrak{o}$ (cf. § 4).

The set of α with $|\alpha| < 1$ form an ideal $\mathfrak{p}$ in $\mathfrak{o}$, clearly maximal. It consists precisely of the $\alpha \in \mathfrak{o}$ with $\alpha^{-1} \notin \mathfrak{o}$.

The notation $\mathfrak{o}$ and $\mathfrak{p}$ will be standard. The reader will easily prove the

LEMMA. *Let* $|\ |$ *be non-archimedean. A necessary and sufficient condition for it to be discrete is that* $\mathfrak{p}$ *is a principal ideal.*

We need later the

LEMMA. *A necessary and sufficient condition that* $|\ |$ *be non-archimedean is that* $|n| \le 1$ *for all* n *in the ring generated by* 1 *in* k.

Note: We cannot identify this ring with $\mathbf{Z}$ if k has a characteristic.

Proof. Necessity is obvious. For sufficiency let $|\alpha| \leq 1$, and then by the triangle inequality

$$\begin{aligned} |1+\alpha|^n &= |(1+\alpha)^n| \\ &\leq \sum_{j=0}^{n} \left|\binom{n}{j}\right| |\alpha| \\ &\leq 1+1+\ldots+1 = n, \end{aligned}$$

so $(n \to \infty)$, $|1+\alpha| \leq 1$.

COROLLARY. *If* Char $k = p \neq 0$ *then any valuation of* k *is non-archimedean.*

For the ring generated by 1 in k is the field $\mathbf{F}$ of p elements. If $b \in \mathbf{F}$, then $b^{p-1} = 1$ and so $|b| = 1$.

3. Examples of Valuations

The archetypal example of an arch. valuation is the absolute value on the field $\mathbf{C}$ of complex numbers. It is essentially the only one:

THEOREM (Gelfand-Tornheim). *Any field* k *with an arch. valuation is isomorphic to a subfield of* $\mathbf{C}$, *the valuation being equivalent to that induced by the absolute valuation on* $\mathbf{C}$.

We do not prove this as we do not need it. See e.g. E. Artin, "Theory of Algebraic Numbers" (Striker, Göttingen), pp. 45 and 67.

The non-arch. valuations are legion. On the rationals $\mathbf{Q}$ there is one for every prime $p > 0$, the *p-adic valuation* defined by

$$|p^a u/v|_p = p^{-a}$$

for $a, u, v \in \mathbf{Z}$, $p \nmid u$, $p \nmid v$.

THEOREM (Ostrowski). *The only non-trivial valuations on* $\mathbf{Q}$ *are those equivalent to the* $|\ |_p$ *or the ordinary absolute value* $|\ |_\infty$.

Proof. Let $|\ |$ be a non-trivial valuation on $\mathbf{Q}$ which (without loss of generality) satisfies the triangle inequality.

Let $a \in \mathbf{Z}$ be greater than 1. Every $b \in \mathbf{Z}$ can be put in the shape

$$b = b_m a^m + b_{m-1} a^{m-1} + \ldots + b_0$$

where

$$0 \leq b_j < a \qquad (0 \leq j \leq m)$$

and

$$m \leq \frac{\log b}{\log a}.$$

By the triangle inequality

$$|b| \leq \mathcal{M}\left(\frac{\log b}{\log a} + 1\right) \max\left\{1, |a|^{\frac{\log b}{\log a}}\right\}$$

where

$$\mathscr{M} = \max_{1 \le d < a} |d|.$$

On putting $b = c^n$ and letting $n \to \infty$, we have

$$|c| \le \max\left\{1, |a|^{\frac{\log c}{\log a}}\right\}. \tag{3.1}$$

First Case. $\exists\, c > 1$ in $\mathbf{Z}$ with $|c| > 1$. Then $|a| > 1$ for every $a > 1$ in $\mathbf{Z}$ and (3.1) gives

$$|c|^{\frac{1}{\log c}} = |a|^{\frac{1}{\log a}}.$$

Hence $|\;|$ is equivalent to the ordinary absolute value.

Second Case. $|c| \le 1$ for all $c \in \mathbf{Z}$ so by a previous lemma $|\;|$ is non-arch. Since $|\;|$ is non-trivial the set $\mathfrak{a}$ of $a \in \mathbf{Z}$ with $|a| < 1$ is non-empty and is clearly a $\mathbf{Z}$-ideal. Since $|bc| = |b|\,|c|$ the ideal $\mathfrak{a}$ is prime, say belonging to $p > 0$ and then clearly $|\;|$ is equivalent to $|\;|_p$.

Now let k_0 be any field and let $k = k_0(t)$, where t is transcendental. If $p = p(t)$ is an irreducible polynomial in the ring $k_0[t]$ we define a valuation by

$$|(p(t))^a u(t)/v(t)|_p = c^{-a} \tag{3.2}$$

where $c < 1$ is fixed, $a \in \mathbf{Z}$ and $u(t), v(t) \in k_0[t]$, $p(t) \nmid u(t)$, $p(t) \nmid v(t)$.

In addition there is the *non-arch.* valuation $|\;|_\infty$ defined by

$$\left|\frac{u(t)}{v(t)}\right|_\infty = c^{\deg v - \deg u}. \tag{3.3}$$

Note the analogy between $k_0(t)$ and $\mathbf{Q}$, which is however not perfect. If $s = t^{-1}$, so $k_0(t) = k_0(s)$, the valuation $|\;|_\infty$ is seen to be of the type (3.2) belonging to the irreducible polynomial $p(s) = s$.

The reader will easily prove the

Lemma. *The only non-trivial valuations on $k_0(t)$ which are trivial on k_0 are equivalent to the valuation* (3.2) *or* (3.3).

Corollary. *If $\mathbf{F}$ is a finite field the only non-trivial valuations on $\mathbf{F}(t)$ are equivalent to* (3.2) *or* (3.3).

4. Topology

A valuation $|\;|$ on a field k induces a topology in which a basis for the neighbourhoods of α are the "open spheres"

$$S_d(\alpha) = \{\xi \mid \; |\xi - \alpha| < d\}$$

for $d > 0$. Equivalent valuations induce the same topology. A valuation satisfying the triangle inequality gives a metric for the topology on defining the distance from α to β to be $|\alpha - \beta|$.

LEMMA. *A field with the topology induced by a valuation is a topological field, i.e. the operations sum, product, reciprocal are continuous.*

Proof. For example (product) the triangle inequality implies that

$$|(\alpha+\theta)(\beta+\phi)-\alpha\beta| \leq |\theta||\phi|+|\alpha||\phi|+|\beta||\theta|$$

is small when $|\theta|$, $|\phi|$ are small (α, β fixed).

LEMMA. *If two valuations $| \, |_1$, $| \, |_2$ on the same field induce the same topology then they are equivalent in the sense defined above.*

Proof. $|\alpha|_1 < 1$ if and only if $\alpha^n \to 0$ ($n \to +\infty$) in the topology and so $|\alpha|_1 < 1$ if and only if $|\alpha|_2 < 1$. On taking reciprocals we see that $|\alpha|_1 > 1$ if and only if $|\alpha|_2 > 1$ so finally $|\alpha|_1 = 1$ if and only if $|\alpha|_2 = 1$.

Let now $\beta, \gamma \in k$ and not 0. On applying the foregoing to

$$\alpha = \beta^m \gamma^n \qquad (m, n \in \mathbf{Z})$$

we see that

$$m \log |\beta|_1 + n \log |\gamma|_1 \gtreqless 0$$

according as

$$m \log |\beta|_2 + n \log |\gamma|_2 \gtreqless 0$$

and so

$$\frac{\log |\beta|_1}{\log |\beta|_2} = \frac{\log |\gamma|_1}{\log |\gamma|_2}.$$

5. Completeness

A field k is *complete* with respect to a valuation $| \, |$ if it is complete as a metric space with respect to the metric $|\alpha-\beta|$ ($\alpha, \beta \in k$) i.e. if given any sequence α_n ($n = 1, 2, \ldots$) with

$$|\alpha_m - \alpha_n| \to 0 \qquad (m, n \to \infty, \infty)$$

(a fundamental sequence), there is an $\alpha^* \in k$ such that

$$\alpha_n \to \alpha^* \qquad \text{w.r.t.} \; | \, |$$

(i.e. $|\alpha_n - \alpha^*| \to 0$).

THEOREM. *Every field k with valuation $| \, |$ can be embedded in a complete field $\bar{k}$ with a valuation $| \, |$ extending the original one in such a way that $\bar{k}$ is the closure of k with respect to $| \, |$. Further, $\bar{k}$ is unique (up to isomorphism).*

Proof (sketch). We define $\bar{k}$ as a metric space to be the completion of k as a metric space with respect to $| \, |$. Since the field operations $+$, $\times$ and inverse are continuous on k they are well-defined on $\bar{k}$. Q.E.D.

COROLLARY 1. *$| \, |$ is non-arch. on $\bar{k}$ if and only if it is so on k. If that is so, the set of values taken by $| \, |$ on k and $\bar{k}$ are the same.*

Proof. Use second lemma of § 2. Alternatively, if k is non-arch., the functional inequality

$$|\beta+\gamma| \leq \max(|\beta|, |\gamma|)$$

holds also in $\bar{k}$ by continuity. If now $\beta \in \bar{k}$, $\beta \neq 0$ there is a $\gamma \in k$ such that $|\beta - \gamma| < |\beta|$ and then $|\beta| = |\gamma|$. Converse trivial.

COROLLARY 2. *Any valuation-preserving embedding of k in a complete field K can be uniquely continued to an embedding of $\bar{k}$.*

6. Independence

The following theorem asserts that inequivalent valuations are in fact almost totally independent. For our purposes it will be superseded by the result of § 15.

LEMMA ("weak approximation theorem"). *Let $|\ |_n$ $(1 \leq n \leq N)$ be inequivalent non-trivial valuations of a field k. For each n let k_n be the topological space consisting of the set of elements of k with the topology induced by $|\ |_n$. Let Δ be the image of k in the topological product $\prod = \prod_{1 \leq n \leq N} k_n$ (with the product topology). Then Δ is everywhere dense in $\prod$.*

The conclusion of the lemma may be expressed in a less topological manner: given any $\alpha_n \in k$ $(1 \leq n \leq N)$ and real $\varepsilon > 0$ there is a $\xi \in k$ such that simultaneously:

$$|\alpha_n - \xi|_n < \varepsilon \qquad (1 \leq n \leq N).$$

Note. If $k = \mathbf{Q}$ and the $|\ |$ are p-adic valuations this is related to the "Chinese Remainder Theorem", but the strong approximation theorem is the real generalization.

Proof. We note first that it will be enough to find $\theta_n \in k$ such that

$$|\theta_n|_n > 1, \quad |\theta_n|_m < 1 \qquad (n \neq m) \tag{6.1}$$

where $1 \leq n \leq N$, $1 \leq m \leq N$. For then as $r \to +\infty$ we have

$$\frac{\theta_n^r}{1+\theta_n^r} = \frac{1}{1+\theta_n^{-r}} \to \begin{cases} 1 \text{ w.r.t. } |\ |_n \\ 0 \text{ w.r.t. } |\ |_m, \quad m \neq n \end{cases}$$

and it is enough to take

$$\xi = \sum_{n=1}^{N} \frac{\theta_n^r}{1+\theta_n^r} \alpha_n$$

with sufficiently large r.

By symmetry it is enough to show the existence of $\theta = \theta_1$ with

$$|\theta|_1 > 1 \qquad |\theta|_n < 1 \qquad (2 \leq n \leq N)$$

and we use induction on N.

$N = 2$. Since $|\ |_1$ and $|\ |_2$ are unequivalent there is an α such that

$$|\alpha|_1 < 1, \qquad |\alpha|_2 \geq 1$$

and similarly a β such that

$$|\beta|_1 \geq 1, \qquad |\beta|_2 < 1$$

and then $\theta = \beta\alpha^{-1}$ will do.

$N \geq 3$. By the case $N-1$ there is a $\phi \in k$ such that

$$|\phi|_1 > 1, \quad |\phi|_n < 1 \quad (2 \leq n \leq N-1)$$

and by the case $N = 2$ there is a $\psi \in k$ such that

$$|\psi|_1 > 1, \quad |\psi|_N < 1.$$

Then put

$$\theta = \begin{cases} \phi & \text{if } |\phi|_N < 1 \\ \phi^r \psi & \text{if } |\phi|_N = 1 \\ \dfrac{\phi^r}{1+\phi^r}\psi & \text{if } |\phi|_N > 1 \end{cases}$$

where $r \in \mathbf{Z}$ is sufficiently large.

7. Finite Residue Field Case

Let k be a field with non-archimedean valuation $| \, |$. Then the set of $\alpha \in k$ with $|\alpha| \leq 1$ form a ring $\mathfrak{o}$, the ring of integers for $| \, |$. The $\varepsilon \in k$ with $|\varepsilon| = 1$ are a group under multiplication, the group of units. Finally, the set of α with $|\alpha| < 1$ is a maximal ideal $\mathfrak{p}$, so the quotient ring $\mathfrak{o}/\mathfrak{p}$ is a field. We consider the case when $\mathfrak{o}/\mathfrak{p}$ has a finite number P of elements.

Suppose further, that $| \, |$ is discrete. Then $\mathfrak{p}$ is a principal ideal (π), say, and every α is of the form $\alpha = \pi^v \varepsilon$, where ε is a unit. We call v the *order* of α. If also $\mathfrak{p} = (\pi')$ then π/π' is a unit and conversely, so the order of α is independent of the choice of α.

Let $\bar{\mathfrak{o}}, \bar{\mathfrak{p}}$ be defined with respect to the completion $\bar{k}$ of k. Then clearly $\bar{\mathfrak{o}}/\bar{\mathfrak{p}} = \mathfrak{o}/\mathfrak{p}$ and $\bar{\mathfrak{p}} = (\pi)$ as an $\bar{\mathfrak{o}}$-ideal.

LEMMA. *Suppose, further, that k is complete with respect to $| \, |$ then $\mathfrak{o}$ is precisely the set of*

$$\alpha = \sum_{j=0}^{\infty} a_j \pi^j \tag{7.1}$$

where the a_j run independently through some set $\sum$ of representatives in $\mathfrak{o}$ of $\mathfrak{o}/\mathfrak{p}$.

By (7.1) is meant of course the limit of the fundamental sequence $\sum^{J} a_j \pi^j$ as $J \to \infty$.

For there is a uniquely defined $a_0 \in \sum$ such that $|\alpha - a_0| < 1$. Then $\alpha_1 = \pi^{-1}(\alpha - a_0) \in \mathfrak{o}$. Now define $a_1 \in \sum$ by $|\alpha_1 - a_1| < 1$. And so on.

THEOREM. *Under the conditions of the preceding lemma $\mathfrak{o}$ is compact with respect to the $| \, |$-topology.*

Proof. Let O_λ $(\lambda \in \Lambda)$ be some family of open sets covering $\mathfrak{o}$. We must show there is a finite subcover. We suppose not.

Let $\sum$ be a set of representatives of $\mathfrak{o}/\mathfrak{p}$. Then $\mathfrak{o}$ is the union of the finite number of sets $a+\pi\mathfrak{o}$ ($a \in \sum$). Hence for at least one $a_0 \in \sum$ the set $a_0+\pi\mathfrak{o}$ is not covered by finitely many of the O_λ. Then similarly there is an $a_1 \in \sum$ such that $a_0+a_1\pi+\pi^2\mathfrak{o}$ is not finitely covered. And so on. Let $\alpha = a_0+a_1\pi+\ldots$. Then $\alpha \in O_{\lambda_0}$ for some $\lambda_0 \in \Lambda$. Since O_{λ_0} is open, $\alpha+\pi^J\mathfrak{o} \subset O_{\lambda_0}$ for some J. Contradiction.

COROLLARY. *k is locally compact.*

[The converse is also true. If k is locally compact with respect to a non-arch. valuation $| \, |$ then

(1) k is complete;
(2) the residue field is finite;
(3) the valuation is discrete.

For there is a compact neighbourhood c of 0. Then $\pi^v\mathfrak{o} \subset c$ for sufficiently large v so $\pi^v\mathfrak{o}$ is compact, being closed. Hence $\mathfrak{o}$ is compact. Since $| \, |$ is a metric, $\mathfrak{o}$ is sequentially compact, i.e. every fundamental sequence in $\mathfrak{o}$ has a limit, which implies (1). Let a_λ ($\lambda \in \Lambda$) be a set of representatives in $\mathfrak{o}$ of $\mathfrak{o}/\mathfrak{p}$. Then $O_\lambda : |\xi - a_\lambda| < 1$ is an open covering of $\mathfrak{o}$. Thus (2) holds since $\mathfrak{o}$ is compact. Finally, $\mathfrak{p}$ is compact being a closed subset of $\mathfrak{o}$. Let S_n be the set of $\alpha \in k$ with $|\alpha| < 1 - 1/n$. Then S_n ($1 \le n < \infty$) is an open cover of $\mathfrak{p}$, so $\mathfrak{p} = S_n$ for some n, i.e. (3) is true.

If we allow $| \, |$ to be archimedean the only further possibilities are $k = \mathbf{R}$ and $k = \mathbf{C}$ with $| \, |$ equivalent to the absolute value.]

We denote by k^+ the commutative topological group whose points are the elements of k, whose law is addition and whose topology is that induced by $| \, |$. General theory tells us that there is an invariant measure (Haar measure) defined on k^+ and that this measure is unique up to a multiplicative constant. We can easily deduce what that measure μ is.

Since μ is invariant

$$\mu(\alpha+\pi^v\mathfrak{o}) = \mu_v$$

is independent of α. Further

$$\alpha+\pi^v\mathfrak{o} = \bigcup_{1 \le j \le P} (\alpha+\pi^v a_j+\pi^{v+1}\mathfrak{o}$$

where a_j ($1 \le j \le P$) is a set of representatives of $\mathfrak{o}/\mathfrak{p}$. Hence

$$\mu_v = P\mu_{v+1}.$$

If we normalize μ by putting

$$\mu(\mathfrak{o}) = 1, \tag{7.2}$$

we have

$$\mu_v = P^{-v}.$$

Conversely, without the theory of Haar measure, it is easy to see that there is a unique invariant measure on k^+ subject to (7.2).

Everything so far in this section has depended not on the valuation $| \, |$ but only on its equivalence class. The above considerations now single out one valuation as particularly important.

DEFINITION. *Let k be a field with discrete valuation $|\ |$ and residue class field with $P < \infty$ elements. We say that $|\ |$ is normalized if*

$$|\pi| = P^{-1},$$

where $\mathfrak{p} = (\pi)$.

THEOREM. *Suppose, further, that k is complete with respect to the normalized valuation $|\ |$. Then*

$$\mu(\alpha+\beta\mathfrak{o}) = |\beta|$$

where μ is the Haar measure on k^+ normalized by $\mu(\mathfrak{o}) = 1$.

We can express the result of the theorem in a more suggestive way. Let $\beta \in k$, $\beta \neq 0$ and let μ be a Haar measure on k^+ (not necessarily normalized as in the theorem). Then we can define a new Haar measure μ_β on k^+ by putting $\mu_\beta(E) = \mu(\beta E)$ $(E \subset k^+)$. But Haar measure is unique up to a multiplicative constant and so $\mu_\beta(E) = \mu(\beta E) = f\mu(E)$ for all measurable sets E, where the factor f depends only on β. The theorem states that f is just $|\beta|$ in the normalized valuation.

[The theory of locally compact topological groups leads to the consideration of the dual (character) group of k^+. It turns out that it is isomorphic to k^+. We do not need this fact for class field theory so do not prove it here. For a proof and applications see Tate's thesis (Chapter XV of this book) or Lang: "Algebraic Numbers" (Addison Wesley), and, for generalizations; Weil: "Adeles and Algebraic Groups" (Princeton lecture notes) and Godement: Bourbaki seminars 171 and 176. The determination of the character group of $k^\times$ is local class-field theory.]

The set of non-zero elements of k form a group $k^\times$ under multiplication. Clearly multiplication and taking the reciprocal are continuous with respect to the topology induced in $k^\times$ as a subset of k, so $k^\times$ is a topological group with this topology.† We have

$$k^\times \supset E \supset E_1$$

where E is the group of units of k and where E_1 is the group of einseinheiten, i.e. the $\varepsilon \in k$ with $|\varepsilon - 1| < 1$. Clearly E and E_1 are both open and closed in $k^\times$.

Obviously $k^\times/E$ is isomorphic to the additive group $\mathbf{Z}^+$ of integers with the discrete topology, the map being

$$\pi^v E \to v \qquad (v \in \mathbf{Z}).$$

Further, E/E_1 is isomorphic to the multiplicative group $\kappa^\times$ of the non-zero elements of the residue class field, where the finite group $\kappa^\times$ has the discrete topology.‡ Further, E is compact, so $k^\times$ is locally compact, Clearly the

† We shall later have to consider the situation for topological rings R, where $R^\times$ in general is given a different topology from the subset topology.

‡ $\kappa^\times$ is cyclic of order $P-1$. It can be shown that k always contains a primitive $P-1$-th root of unity ρ and so the elements of $k^\times$ are just the $\pi^v\rho^u\varepsilon$, $\varepsilon \in E_1$, i.e. $k^\times$ is the direct product of $\mathbf{Z}$, $\mathbf{Z}/(P-1)\mathbf{Z}$ and E_1.

In fact let $f(X) = X^{P-1} - 1$ and let $\alpha \in \mathfrak{o}$ be such that $\alpha \bmod \mathfrak{p}$ generates $\kappa^\times$. Then $|f(\alpha)| < 1$, $|f'(\alpha)| = 1$. Then by Hensel's Lemma (App. C) there is $\rho \in k$ such that $f(\rho) = 0$, $\rho \equiv \alpha \pmod{\mathfrak{p}}$.

additive Haar measure on E_1 is also invariant under multiplication so gives a Haar measure on E_1: and this gives the Haar measure on $k^\times$ in an obvious way.

Finally we note the

LEMMA. *k^+ and $k^\times$ are totally disconnected (the only connected sets are points).*

Beweis. Klar.

[It is perhaps worth mentioning that $k^\times$ and k^+ are locally isomorphic if k has characteristic 0. We have the exponential map

$$\alpha \to \exp \alpha = \Sigma \frac{\alpha^n}{n!}$$

valid for all sufficiently small α with its inverse

$$\log \alpha = \Sigma \frac{(-)^{n-1}(\alpha - 1)^n}{n}$$

valid for all α sufficiently near to 1.]

8. Normed Spaces

DEFINITION. *Let k be a field with valuation $|\;|$ and let V be a vector space over k. A real-valued function $\|\;\|$ on V is called a norm if*

(1) $\|\mathfrak{a}\| > 0$ *for* $\mathfrak{a} \in V$, $\mathfrak{a} \neq 0$.

(2) $\|\mathfrak{a}+\mathfrak{b}\| \leq \|\mathfrak{a}\| + \|\mathfrak{b}\|$.

(3) $\|\alpha\mathfrak{a}\| = |\alpha|\,\|\mathfrak{a}\|$ $(\alpha \in k,\ \mathfrak{a} \in K)$.

DEFINITION. *Two norms $\|\;\|_1$, $\|\;\|_2$ on the same space are equivalent if there exist constants c_1, c_2 such that*

$$\|\mathfrak{a}\|_1 \leq c_1\|\mathfrak{a}\|_2 \qquad \|\mathfrak{a}_2\| \leq c_2\|\mathfrak{a}_1\|.$$

This is clearly an equivalence relation.

LEMMA. *Suppose that k is complete with respect to $|\;|$ and that V is finite-dimensional. Then any two norms on V are equivalent.*

Note. As we shall see, completeness is essential.

Proof. Let $\mathfrak{a}_1, \ldots, \mathfrak{a}_N$ be any basis for V. We define a norm $\|\;\|_0$ by

$$\left\|\sum \xi_n \mathfrak{a}_n\right\|_0 = \max_n |\xi_n|.$$

It is enough to show that any norm $\|\;\|$ is equivalent to $\|\;\|_0$. Clearly

$$\begin{aligned}\left\|\sum \xi_n \mathfrak{a}_n\right\| &\leq \sum |\xi_n|\,\|\mathfrak{a}_n\| \\ &\leq c_1\left\|\sum \xi_n \mathfrak{a}_n\right\|_0\end{aligned}$$

with

$$c_1 = \sum {}_{\|}\mathfrak{a}_{n\|}.$$

Suppose that there is no c_2 such that†

$$\|\mathfrak{a}\|_0 \le c_2\|\mathfrak{a}\|.$$

Then for any $\varepsilon > 0$ there exist $\xi_1,\ldots, \xi_n$ such that

$$0 < \|\sum \xi_n \mathfrak{a}_n\| \le \varepsilon \max|\xi_n|.$$

By symmetry we may suppose that

$$\max|\xi_n| = |\xi_N|$$

and then by homogeneity that

$$\xi_N = 1.$$

For $m = 1, 2,\ldots,$ we thus have $\xi_{n,m}$ $(1 \le n \le N-1)$ with

$$\|\sum_{n=1}^{N-1} \xi_{n,m}\mathfrak{a}_n + \mathfrak{a}_N\| \to 0 \qquad (m \to \infty);$$

so

$$\|\sum_{n=1}^{N-1} (\xi_{n,\ell} - \xi_{n,m})\mathfrak{a}_n\| \to 0 \qquad (\ell, m \to \infty, \infty).$$

The lemma being trivial for $N = 1$, we may suppose by induction that it is true for the $(N-1)$-dimensional space spanned by $\mathfrak{a}_1,\ldots, \mathfrak{a}_{N-1}$ and hence

$$|\xi_{n,\ell} - \xi_{n,m}| \to 0 \qquad (\ell, m \to \infty, \infty)$$

for $1 \le n \le N-1$. Since k is complete there are $\xi_n^* \in k$ with

$$|\xi_{n,m} - \xi_n^*| \to 0 \qquad (m \to \infty).$$

Then

$$\|\sum^{N-1} \xi_n^*\mathfrak{a}_n + \mathfrak{a}_N\| \le \|\sum^{N-1} \xi_{n,m}\mathfrak{a}_n + \mathfrak{a}_n\| + \sum^{N-1} |\xi_n^* - \xi_{n,m}|\,\|\mathfrak{a}_n\| \to 0 \qquad (m \to \infty)$$

in contradiction to (1).

9. Tensor Product

We need only a special case. Let A, B be commutative rings containing a field k and suppose that B is of finite dimension N over k, say with basis

$$1 = \omega_1, \omega_2, \ldots, \omega_N.$$

Then B is determined up to isomorphism by the multiplication table

$$\omega_\ell\omega_m = \sum c_{\ell mn}\omega_n \qquad c_{\ell mn} \in k.$$

We can define a new ring C containing k whose elements are expressions of

† When k is not merely complete with respect to $|\ |$ but locally compact, which will be the case of primary interest, one can argue more simply as follows. By what has been shown already, the function $\|\mathfrak{a}\|$ is continuous in the $\|\ \|_0$-topology, and so attains its lower bound δ on $\|\mathfrak{a}\|_0 = 1$. Then $\delta > 0$ by condition (i), and then $\|\mathfrak{a}\|_0 \le \delta^{-1}\|\mathfrak{a}\|$ by homogeneity for all $\mathfrak{a}$.

the type

$$\sum a_m \varpi_m \qquad a_m \in A$$

where the ϖ_m have the same multiplication rule

$$\varpi_\ell \varpi_m = \sum c_{\ell mn} \varpi_n$$

as the ω_m. There are ring isomorphisms

$$i : a \to a\varpi_1$$

and

$$j : \sum \lambda_m \omega_m \to \sum \lambda_m \varpi_m$$

of A and B respectively into C. It is clear that C is defined up to isomorphism by A and B and is independent of the particular choice of basis ω_m. We write

$$C = A \otimes_k B$$

since it is, in fact, a special case of the ring tensor-product.

[The reader will have no difficulty in checking that C together with the maps i, j possesses the defining Universal Mapping Property.]

Let us now suppose, further, that A is a topological ring, i.e. has a topology with respect to which addition and multiplication are continuous. The map

$$\sum a_m \varpi_m \to (a_1, \ldots, a_N)$$

is a $1-1$ correspondence between C and N copies of A (considered as sets). We give C the product topology. It is readily verified (i) that this topology is independent of the choice of basis $\omega_1, \ldots \omega_N$ and (ii) that multiplication and addition in C are continuous with respect to it; i.e. C is now a topological ring.

We shall speak of this topology on C as the tensor product topology.

Now let us drop our supposition that A has a topology but suppose that A, B are not merely rings but fields.

Lemma. *Let A, B be fields containing the field k and suppose that B is a separable extension of degree $[B:k] = N < \infty$. Then $C = A \otimes_k B$ is the direct sum of a finite number of fields K_j, each containing an isomorphic image of A and an isomorphic image of B.*

Proof. By a well-known theorem (appendix B) we have $B = k(\beta)$ where $f(\beta) = 0$, for some separable $f(X) \in k[X]$ of degree N irreducible in $k[X]$.

Then $1, \beta, \ldots, \beta^{N-1}$ is a basis for B/k and so $A \otimes_k B = A[\bar{\beta}]$ where $1, \bar{\beta}, \ldots, \bar{\beta}^{N-1}$ are linearly independent over A and $f(\bar{\beta}) = 0$.

Although $f(X)$ is irreducible in $k[X]$ it need not be in $A[X]$, say

$$f(X) = \prod_{1 \le j \le J} g_j(X)$$

where $g_j(X) \in A[X]$ is irreducible. The $g_j(X)$ are distinct because $f(X)$ is separable. Let $K_j = A(\beta_j)$ where $g_j(\beta_j) = 0$. Clearly the map

$$A \otimes_k B \overset{\mu_j}{\to} K_j$$

given by

$$h(\bar{\beta}) \overset{\mu_j}{\to} h(\beta) \qquad h(X) \in AX$$

is a ring homomorphism.

We thus have a ring homomorphism

$$A \otimes_k B \xrightarrow{\mu_1 \oplus \ldots \oplus \mu_J} \bigoplus_{1 \le j \le J} K_j. \tag{9.1}$$

Let $h(\bar{\beta})$, $h(X) \in A[X]$ be in the kernel. Then $h(X)$ is divisible by every $g_j(X)$, so also by $f(X)$, i.e. $h(\bar{\beta}) = 0$. Thus (9.1) is an injection. Since both sides of (9.1) have the same dimension as vector spaces over A it must be an isomorphism, as required.

It remains to show that the ring homomorphisms

$$\lambda_j : B \to A \otimes_k B \overset{\mu_j}{\to} K_j$$

are injections. If $\lambda_j(\beta) \neq 0$ for any $\beta \in B$ then $\lambda_j(\beta_1) \neq 0$ for all $\beta_1 \neq 0$ because $\lambda_j(\beta) = \lambda_j(\beta_1)\lambda_j(\beta\beta^{-1})$. Hence all we have to show is that λ_j does not map the whole of B onto 0: and this is trivial.

COROLLARY. *Let $\alpha \in B$ and let $F(X) \in k[X]$, $G_j(X) \in A[X]$ $(1 \le j \le J)$ be the characteristic polynomial of α over k and of the image of α under*

$$B \to A \otimes_k B \to K_j$$

over A respectively. Then

$$F(X) = \prod_{1 \le j \le J} G_j(X). \tag{9.2}$$

Proof. We show that both sides of (9.2) are the characteristic polynomial $T(X)$ of the image of α in $A \otimes_k B$ over A. That $F(X) = T(X)$ follows at once by computing the characteristic polynomial in terms of a basis $\varpi_1, \ldots \varpi_N$, where $\omega_1, \ldots, \omega_n$ is a basis for B/k. That $T(X) = \Pi G_j(X)$ follows similarly by using a base of

$$A \otimes_k B = \bigoplus K_j$$

composed of bases of the individual K_j/A.

COROLLARY. For $\alpha \in B$ we have

$$\mathrm{Norm}_{B/k}\, \alpha = \prod_{1 \le j \le J} \mathrm{Norm}_{K_j/A}\, \alpha$$

$$\mathrm{Trace}_{B/k}\, \alpha = \sum_{1 \le j \le J} \mathrm{Trace}_{K_j/A}\, \alpha.$$

Proof. For the norm and trace are just the second and the last coefficient in the characteristic equation.

10. Extension of Valuations

Let $k \subset K$ be fields and $|\ |$, $\|\ \|$ be valuations on k, K respectively. We say that $\|\ \|$ extends $|\ |$ if $|b| = \|b\|$ for all $b \in k$.

THEOREM. *Let k be complete with respect to the valuation k and let K be an extension of k with $[K:k] = N < \infty$. Then there is precisely one extension of $|\ |$ to K namely*

$$\|\alpha\| = |\mathrm{Norm}_{K/k}\,\alpha|^{1/N}. \tag{10.1}$$

Proof. Uniqueness. K may be regarded as a vector space over k and then $\|\ \|$ is a norm in the sense defined earlier. Hence any two extensions $\|\ \|_1$ and $\|\ \|_2$ of $|\ |$ are equivalent as norms and so induce the same topology in K. But as we have seen two valuations which induce the same topology are equivalent valuations, i.e. $\|\ \|_1 = \|\ \|_2^c$ for some c. Finally $c = 1$ because $\|b\|_1 = \|b\|_2$ for all $b \in k$.

Existence. For a proof of existence in the general case see e.g. E. Artin: "Theory of Algebraic Numbers" (Striker, Göttingen) and for a proof valid for separable non-arch. discrete valuations see Chapter I, § 4, Prop. 1, Corollary. Here we give a proof (suggested by Dr. Geyer at the conference) valid when k is locally compact, the only case which will be used. In any case it is easy to see that the definition (10.1) satisfies the conditions (i) that $\|\alpha\| \geq 0$ with equality only for $\alpha = 0$ and (ii) $\|\alpha\beta\| = \|\alpha\|\,\|\beta\|$: the difficulty is to show that there is a constant C such that $\|\alpha\| \leq 1$ implies $\|1+\alpha\| \leq C$. Let $\|\ \|_0$ be any norm on K considered as a vector space over k. Then $\|\alpha\|$ defined by (10.1) is a continuous non-zero function on the compact set $\|\alpha\|_0 = 1$, so $\Delta \geq \|\alpha\| \geq \delta > 0$ for some constants Δ, δ. Hence by homogeneity

$$\Delta \geq \frac{\|\alpha\|}{\|\alpha\|_0} \geq \delta > 0. \quad (\text{all } \alpha \neq 0).$$

Suppose, now, that $\|\alpha\| \leq 1$. Then $\|\alpha\|_0 \leq \delta^{-1}$ and so

$$\begin{aligned}\|1+\alpha\| &\leq \Delta\|1+\alpha\|_0 \\ &\leq \Delta(\|1\|_0+\|\alpha\|_0) \\ &\leq \Delta(\|1\|_0+\delta^{-1}) \\ &= C \quad (\text{say}),\end{aligned}$$

as required.

Formula. Geyer's existence proof also gives (10.1). But it is perhaps worth noting that in any case (10.1) is a consequence of unique existence, as follows. Let $L \supset K$ be a finite normal extension of k. Then by the above there is a unique extension of $|\ |$ to L which we shall denote also by $\|\ \|$. If σ is an automorphism of L/K then

$$\|\alpha\|_\sigma = \|\sigma\alpha\|$$

is also an extension of $| \; |$ to L, so $\| \; \|_\sigma = \| \; \|$, i.e.

$$\|\sigma\alpha\| = \|\alpha\| \quad (\text{all } \alpha \in L).$$

But now

$$\text{Norm}_{K/k}\,\alpha = \sigma_1\alpha\,\sigma_2\alpha \ldots \sigma_N\alpha$$

for $\alpha \in K$, where $\sigma_1, \ldots, \sigma_N$ are automorphisms of L/k. Hence

$$\begin{aligned} |\text{Norm}_{K/k}\,\alpha| &= \|\text{Norm}_{K/k}\,\alpha\| \\ &= \prod_{1 \le n \le N} \|\sigma_n\alpha\| \\ &= \|\alpha\|^N, \end{aligned}$$

as required.

COROLLARY. *Let $\omega_1, \ldots, \omega_N$ be a basis for K/k. Then there are constants c_1, c_2 such that*

$$c_1 \le \frac{|\sum b_n\omega_n|}{\max |b_n|} \le c_2$$

for $b_1, \ldots, b_N \in k$ (not all 0).

Proof. For $|\sum b_n\omega_n|$ and $\max |b_n|$ are two norms on K considered as a vector space over k.

COROLLARY 2. *A finite extension of a completely valued field k is complete with respect to the extended valuation.*

For by the preceding corollary it has the topology of a finite-dimension vector space over k.

When k is no longer complete under $| \; |$ the position is more complicated:

THEOREM. *Let K be a separable extension of k of degree $[K\colon k] = N < \infty$. Then there are at most N extensions of a valuation $| \; |$ of k to K, say $\| \; \|_j$ $(1 \le j \le J)$. Let $\bar{k}$, K_j be the completion of k resp. K with respect to $| \; |$, resp. $\| \; \|_j$. Then*

$$\bar{k} \otimes_k K = \bigoplus_{1 \le j \le J} K_j \tag{10.2}$$

algebraically and topologically, where the R.H.S. is given the product topology.

Proof. We know already that $\bar{k} \otimes K$ is of the shape (10.2) where the K_j are finite extensions of $\bar{k}$. Hence there is a unique extension $| \; |_j^*$ of $| \; |$ to the K_j and the K_j are complete with respect to the extended valuation. Further, by a previous proof, the ring homomorphisms

$$\lambda_j : K \to \bar{k} \otimes_k K \to K_j$$

are injections. Hence we get an extension $\| \; \|_j$ of $| \; |$ to K by putting

$$\|\beta\|_j = |\lambda_j(\beta)|_j^*.$$

Further, $K \cong \lambda_j(K)$ is dense in K_j with respect to $\| \; \|_j$ because $K = k \otimes_k K$ is dense in $\bar{k} \otimes_k K$. Hence K_j is exactly the completion of K.

It remains to show that the $\| \|_j$ are distinct and that they are the only extensions of $| |$ to K.

Let $\| \|$ be any valuation of K extending $| |$. Then $\| \|$ extends by continuity to a real-valued function of $\bar{k} \otimes_k K$, a function also to be denoted by $\| \|$. By continuity we have

$$\left.\begin{aligned} \|\alpha+\beta\| &\leq \max \|\alpha\|, \|\beta\| \\ \|\alpha\beta\| &= \|\alpha\| \, \|\beta\| \end{aligned}\right\} \quad \alpha, \beta \in \bar{k} \otimes K.$$

We consider the restriction of $\| \|$ to one of the K_j. If $\|\alpha\| \neq 0$ for some $\alpha \in K_j$ the $\|\alpha\| = \|\beta\| \, \|\alpha\beta^{-1}\|$ for every $\beta \neq 0$ in K_j so $\|\beta\| \neq 0$. Hence either $\| \|$ is identically 0 on K_j or it induces a valuation on K_j.

Further, $\| \|$ cannot induce a valuation on *two* of the K_j. For

$$(\alpha_1 \oplus 0 \oplus \ldots \oplus 0) . (0 \oplus \alpha_2 \oplus 0 \ldots \oplus 0) = (0 \oplus 0 \ldots \oplus 0)$$

and so

$$\|\alpha_1\| \, \|\alpha_2\| = 0 \qquad \alpha_1 \in K_1, \quad \alpha_2 \in K_2.$$

Hence $\| \|$ induces a valuation in precisely one of the K_j and it clearly extends the given valuation $| |$ of $\bar{k}$. Hence $\| \| = \| \|_j$ for precisely one j.

It remains only to show that (10.2) is also a topological homomorphism. For $(\beta_1, \ldots, \beta_J) \in K_1 \oplus \ldots \oplus K_J$ put

$$\|(\beta_1, \ldots, \beta_J)\|_0 = \max_{1 \leq j \leq J} \|\beta_j\|_j.$$

Clearly, $\| \|_0$ is a norm on the R.H.S. of (10.2), considered as a vector space over $\bar{k}$ and it induces the product topology. On the other hand, any two norms are equivalent, since $\bar{k}$ is complete, and so $\| \|_0$ induces the tensor product topology on the left-hand side of (10.2).

COROLLARY. *Let $K = k(\beta)$ and let $f(x) \in k[X]$ be the irreducible equation for β. Suppose that*

$$f(X) = \prod_{1 \leq j \leq J} g_j(X)$$

in $\bar{k}[X]$, where the g_j are irreducible. Then $K_j = \bar{k}(\beta_j)$ where $g_j(\beta_j) = 0$.

11. Extensions of Normalized Valuations

Let k be a field with valuation $| |$. We consider the three cases:

(1) $| |$ is discrete non-arch. and the residue class field is finite.
(2(i)) The completion of k with respect to $| |$ is **R**.
(2(ii)) The completion of k with respect to $| |$ is **C**.

[In virtue of the remarks in § 7, these cases can be subsumed in one: the completion $\bar{k}$ is locally compact.]

In case (1) we have already defined a normalized valuation (§ 7). In case (2(i)) we say $| |$ is normalized if it is the ordinary absolute value and in case (2(ii)) if it is the *square* of the absolute value. Thus in every case the map

$$\alpha : \xi \to \alpha\xi \qquad \xi \in \bar{k}^+ \quad (\alpha \in \bar{k})$$

of the additive group $\bar{k}^+$ of the completion of k multiplies the Haar measure on $\bar{k}^+$ by $|\alpha|$: and this characterizes the normalized valuation among equivalent ones.

LEMMA. *Let k be complete with respect to the normalized valuation $|\,|$ and let K be an extension of k of degree $[K:k] = N < \infty$. Then the normalized valuation $\|\,\|$ of K which is equivalent to the unique extension of $|\,|$ to K is given by the formula*

$$\|\alpha\| = |\text{Norm}_{K/k}\,\alpha| \qquad (\alpha \in K).$$

Proof. By the preceding section we have

$$\|\alpha\| = |\text{Norm}_{K/k}\,\alpha|^c \qquad (\alpha \in K) \tag{11.1}$$

for some real $c > 0$ and all we have to do is to prove that $c = 1$. This is trivial in case 2 and follows from the structure theorems of Chapter I in case 1. Alternatively one can argue in a unified way as follows. Let $\omega_1, \ldots, \omega_N$ be a basis for K/k. Then the map

$$\Xi = \sum \xi_n \omega_n \leftrightarrow (\xi_1, \ldots, \xi_N) \qquad (\xi_1, \ldots, \xi_n \in k)$$

gives an isomorphism between the additive group K^+ and the direct sum $\oplus^N k^+$ of N copies of k^+, and this is a homomorphism if the R.H.S. is given the product topology. In particular, the Haar measures on K^+ and $\oplus^N k^+$ are the same up to a multiplicative constant. Let $b \in k$. Then the map

$$b : \Xi \to b\Xi$$

of K^+ is the same as the map

$$(\xi_1, \ldots, \xi_N) \to (b\xi_1, \ldots, b\xi_N)$$

of $\oplus^N k^+$ and so multiplies the Haar measure by $|b|^N$, since $|\,|$ is normalized. Hence

$$\|b\| = |b|^N.$$

But $\text{Norm}_{K/L}\, b = b^N$ and so $c = 1$ in (11.1).

In the incomplete case we have

THEOREM. *Let $|\,|$ be a normalized valuation of a field k and let K be a finite extension of k. Then*

$$\prod_{1 \le j \le J} \|\alpha\|_j = |\text{Norm}_{K/k}\,\alpha|,$$

where the $\|\,\|_j$ are the normalized valuations equivalent to the extensions of $|\,|$ to K.

Proof. Let

$$\bar{k} \otimes_k K = \bigoplus_{1 \le j \le J} K_j,$$

where $\bar{k}$ is the completion of K. Then (§ 9)

$$\text{Norm}_{K/k} \alpha = \prod_{1 \le j \le J} (\text{Norm}_{K_j/\bar{k}} \alpha).$$

The theorem now follows from the preceding lemma and the results of § 10.

12. Global Fields

By a global field k we shall mean either a finite extension of the rational field **Q** or a finite separable† extension of **F**(t), where **F** is a finite field and t is transcendental over **F**. We shall focus attention in the exposition on the extensions of **Q** (algebraic number case) leaving the extension of **F**(t) (function field case) to the reader.

LEMMA. *Let $\alpha \neq 0$ be in the global field k. Then there are only finitely many unequivalent valuations $|\ |$ of k for which*

$$|\alpha| > 1.$$

Proof. We know this already for **Q** and **F**(t). Let k be a finite extension of **Q**, so

$$\alpha^n + a_1\alpha^{n-1} + \ldots + a_n = 0$$

for some n and $a_1, \ldots, a_n$. If $|\ |$ is a non-arch. valuation of k we have

$$\begin{aligned} |\alpha|^n &= |-a_1\alpha^{n-1} - \ldots - a_n| \\ &\le \max(1, |\alpha|^{n-1}) \max(|a_1|, \ldots, |a_n|) \end{aligned}$$

and so

$$|\alpha| \le \max(1, |a_1|, \ldots, |a_n|).$$

Since every valuation of **Q** has finitely many extensions to k and since there are only finitely many arch. valuations altogether, the theorem for k follows from that for **Q**.

All the valuations of a global field k are of the type described in § 11, since this is true of **Q** and **F**(t). Hence it makes sense to talk of normalized valuations.

THEOREM. *Let $\alpha \in k$, where k is a global field and $\alpha \neq 0$. Let $|\ |_v$ run through all the normalized valuations of k. Then $|\alpha|_v = 1$ for all except finitely many v and*

$$\prod_v |\alpha|_v = 1.$$

Note. We shall later give a less computational proof of this.

† This condition is not really necessary. If k is any finite extension of **F**(t) there is a "separating element" s, i.e. an $s \in k$ such that k is a finite separable extension of **F**(s).

Proof. By the lemma $|\alpha|_v \leq 1$ for almost all v (i.e. all except finitely many). Similarly $|\alpha^{-1}|_v \leq 1$ for almost all v, so $|\alpha|_v = 1$ for almost all v.

Let V run through all the normalized valuations of $\mathbf{Q}$ [or $\mathbf{F}(t)$] and write $v|V$ to mean that the restriction of v to $\mathbf{Q}$ is equivalent to V. Then

$$\prod_v |\alpha|_v = \prod_V \Big(\prod_{v|V} |\alpha|_v\Big) = \prod_V |\mathrm{Norm}_{k/\mathbf{Q}}\,\alpha|_V,$$

by the preceding section. This reduces the theorem to the case $k = \mathbf{Q}$. But if now

$$b = \pm \prod_p p^{\beta_p} \in \mathbf{Q},$$

where p runs through all the primes and $\beta_p \in \mathbf{Z}$, we have

$$|b|_p = p^{-\beta_p}$$

for the p-adic valuation $|\;|_p$ and

$$|b|_\infty = \prod_p p^{\beta_p}$$

for the absolute value $|\;|_\infty$. Q.E.D.

Let K be a finite separable extension of the global field k. Then for every valuation v of k we have an isomorphism

$$k_v \otimes_k K = K_1 \oplus \ldots \oplus K_J$$

where k_v is the completion of k with respect to v and $K_1, \ldots, K_J$, are the completions of K with respect to the extensions $V_1, \ldots, V_J$ of v to K (§ 10), the number $J = J(v)$ depending on v. We shall later need the

LEMMA. *Let $\omega_1, \ldots, \omega_N$ be a basis for K/k. Then for almost all normalized v we have*

$$\omega_1\mathfrak{o} \oplus \omega_2\mathfrak{o} \oplus \ldots \oplus \omega_N\mathfrak{o} = \mathfrak{O}_1 \oplus \ldots \oplus \mathfrak{O}_J \tag{12.1}$$

where $N = [K:k]$, $\mathfrak{o} = \mathfrak{o}_v$ is the ring of integers of k for $|\;|_v$ and $\mathfrak{O}_j \subset K_j$ is the ring of integers for $|\;|_{V_j}$ $(1 \leq j \leq J)$. Here we have identified $\alpha \in K$ with its canonical image in $k_v \otimes K$.

Proof. The L.H.S. of (12.1) is included in the R.H.S. provided that $|\omega_n|_{V_j} \leq 1$ $(1 \leq n \leq N,\ 1 \leq j \leq J)$. Since $|\alpha|_V \leq 1$ for almost all V it follows that L.H.S. $\subset$ R.H.S. for almost all v.

To get an inclusion the other way we use the discriminant

$$D(\gamma_1, \ldots, \gamma_N) = \det_{m,n}(\mathrm{trace}_{K/k}\,\gamma_m\gamma_n),$$

where $\gamma_1, \ldots, \gamma_N \in k_v \otimes_k K$. If $\gamma_n \in$ R.H.S. $(1 \leq n \leq N)$ we have (§ 9)

$$\mathrm{trace}_{K/k}\,\gamma_m\gamma_n = \sum_{1 \leq j \leq J} \mathrm{trace}_{K_j/\bar{k}}\,\gamma_m\gamma_n \in \mathfrak{o} = \mathfrak{o}_v$$

and so

$$D(\gamma_1, \ldots, \gamma_N) \in \mathfrak{o}_v.$$

Now suppose that $\alpha \in$ R.H.S. and that

$$\beta = \sum_1^N b_n \omega_n \in \text{R.H.S.} \quad (b_n \in k_v). \tag{12.2}$$

Then for any m, $1 \le m \le N$ we have

$$D(\omega_1, \ldots, \omega_{m-1}, \beta, \omega_{m+1}, \ldots, \omega_N) = b_m^2 D(\omega_1, \ldots, \omega_N),$$

and so

$$db_m^2 \in \mathfrak{o}_v \quad (1 \le m \le N)$$

where

$$d = D(\omega_1, \ldots, \omega_N) \in k.$$

But (Appendix B) we have $d \neq 0$, and so $|d|_v = 1$ for almost all v. For almost all v the condition (12.2) thus implies

$$b_m \in \mathfrak{o}_v \quad (1 \le m \le N),$$

i.e.

$$\text{R.H.S.} \subset \text{L.H.S.}$$

This proves the lemma.

[COROLLARY. *Almost all v are unramified in the extension K/k.*

For by the results of Chapter I a necessary and sufficient condition for v to be unramified is that there are $\gamma_1, \ldots, \gamma_N \in$ R.H.S. with $|D(\gamma_1, \ldots, \gamma_N)|_v = 1$. And for almost all v we can put $\gamma_n = \alpha^{n-1}$.]

13. Restricted Topological Product

We describe here a topological tool which will be needed later:

DEFINITION. *Let Ω_λ ($\lambda \in \Lambda$) be a family of topological spaces and for almost all† λ let $\Theta_\lambda \subset \Omega_\lambda$ be an open subset of Ω_λ. Consider the space Ω whose points are sets $\boldsymbol{\alpha} = \{\alpha_\lambda\}_{\lambda \in \Lambda}$, where $\alpha_\lambda \in \Omega_\lambda$ for every λ and $\alpha_\lambda \in \Theta_\lambda$ for almost all λ. We give Ω a topology by taking as a basis of open sets the sets*

$$\prod \Gamma_\lambda$$

where $\Gamma_\lambda \subset \Omega_\lambda$ is open for all λ and $\Gamma_\lambda = \Theta_\lambda$ for almost all λ. With this topology Ω is the restricted topological product of the Ω_λ with respect to the Θ_λ.

COROLLARY. *Let S be a finite subset of Λ and let Ω_S be the set of $\boldsymbol{\alpha} \in \Omega$ with $\alpha_\lambda \in \Theta_\lambda$ ($\lambda \notin S$), i.e.*

$$\Omega_S = \prod_{\lambda \in S} \Omega_\lambda \prod_{\lambda \notin S} \Theta_\lambda. \tag{13.1}$$

Then Ω_S is open in Ω and the topology induced in Ω_S as a subset of Ω is the same as the product topology.

Beweis. Klar.

The restricted topological product depends on the totality of the Θ_λ but not on the individual Θ_λ:

† i.e. all except possibly finitely many.

LEMMA. *Let $\Theta'_\lambda \subset \Omega_\lambda$ be open sets defined for almost all λ and suppose that $\Theta_\lambda = \Theta'_\lambda$ for almost all λ. Then the restricted product of the Ω_λ with respect to the Θ'_λ is the same as*† *the restricted product with respect to the Θ_λ.*

Beweis. Klar.

LEMMA. *Suppose that the Ω_λ are locally compact and that the Θ_λ are compact. Then Ω is locally compact.*

Proof. The Ω_S are locally compact by (13.1) since S is finite. Since $\Omega = \cup \Omega_S$ and the Ω_S are open in Ω, the result follows.

DEFINITION. *Suppose that measures μ_λ are defined on the Ω_λ with $\mu_\lambda(\Theta_\lambda) = 1$ when Θ_λ is defined. We define the product measure μ on Ω to be that for which a basis of measurable sets is the*

$$\prod_\lambda M_\lambda$$

where $M_\lambda \subset \Omega_\lambda$ has finite μ_λ-measure and $M_\lambda = \Theta_\lambda$ for almost all λ and where

$$\mu\left(\prod_\lambda M_\lambda\right) = \prod_\lambda \mu_\lambda(M_\lambda).$$

COROLLARY. *The restriction of μ to Ω_S is just the ordinary product measure.*

14. Adele Ring (or Ring of Valuation Vectors)

Let k be a global field. For each normalized valuation $|\ |_v$ of k denote by k_v the completion of k. If $|\ |_v$ is non-archimedean denote by $\mathfrak{o}_v$ the ring of integers of k_v. The adele ring V_k of k is the topological ring whose underlying topological space is the restricted product of the k_v with respect to the $\mathfrak{o}_v$ and where addition and multiplication are defined componentwise:

$$(\alpha\beta)_v = \alpha_v \beta_v \qquad (\alpha+\beta)_v = \alpha_v + \beta_v \qquad \alpha, \beta \in V_k. \tag{14.1}$$

It is readily verified (i) that this definition makes sense, i.e. if $\boldsymbol{\alpha}, \boldsymbol{\beta} \in V_k$ then $\boldsymbol{\alpha\beta}$, $\boldsymbol{\alpha}+\boldsymbol{\beta}$ whose components are given by (14.1) are also in V_k and (ii) that addition and multiplication are continuous in the V_k-topology, so V_k is a topological ring, as asserted.

V_k is locally compact because the k_v are locally compact and the $\mathfrak{o}_v$ are compact (§ 7).

There is a natural mapping of k into V_k which maps $\alpha \in k$ into the adele every one of whose components is α: this *is* an adele because $\alpha \in \mathfrak{o}_v$ for almost all v. The map is an injection, because the map of k into any k_v is an injection. The image of k under this injection is the ring of *principal adeles*. It will cause no trouble to identify k with the principal adeles, so we shall speak of k as a subring of V_k.

LEMMA. *Let K be a finite (separable) extension of the global field k. Then*

$$V_k \otimes_k K = V_K \tag{14.2}$$

† A purist would say "canonically isomorphic to".

algebraically and topologically. In this correspondence $k \otimes_k K = K \subset V_k \otimes_k K$, *where* $k \subset V_k$, *is mapped identically on to* $K \subset V_K$.

Proof. We first established an isomorphism of the two sides of (14.2) as topological spaces. Let $\omega_1, \ldots, \omega_N$ be a basis for K/k and let v run through the normalized valuations of k. It is easy to see that the L.H.S. of (14.2), with the tensor product topology, is just the restricted product of the

$$k_v \otimes_k K = k_v\omega_1 \oplus \ldots \oplus k_v\omega_N \tag{14.3}$$

with respect to the

$$\mathfrak{o}_v\omega_1 \oplus \ldots \oplus \mathfrak{o}_v\omega_N. \tag{14.4}$$

But now (cf. §10), (14.3) is just

$$K_{V_1} \oplus \ldots \oplus K_{V_J}, \quad (V_1|v, \ldots, V_J|v) \tag{14.5}$$

where $V_1, \ldots, V_J$, $J = J(v)$ are the normalized extensions of v to K. Further (§ 12) the identification of (14.3) with (14.5) identifies (14.4) with

$$\mathfrak{O}_{V_1} \oplus \ldots \oplus \mathfrak{O}_{V_J} \tag{14.6}$$

for almost all† v. Hence the L.H.S. of (14.2) is the restricted product of (14.3) with respect to (14.4), which is clearly the same thing as the restricted product of the K_V with respect to the $\mathfrak{O}_V$, where V runs through all the normalized valuations of K. This is just the R.H.S. of (14.2). This establishes an isomorphism between the two sides of (14.2) as topological spaces. A moment's consideration shows that it is also an algebraic isomorphism.

Q.E.D.

COROLLARY. *Let* V_k^+ *denote the topological group obtained from* V_k *by forgetting the multiplicative structure. Then*

$$V_K^+ = \underbrace{V_k^+ \oplus \ldots \oplus V_k^+}_{N \text{ summands}} \quad (N = [K:k]).$$

In this isomorphism the additive group $K^+ \subset V_K^+$ *of the principal adeles is mapped into* $k^+ \oplus \ldots \oplus k^+$, *in an obvious notation.*

Proof. $\omega V_k^+ \subset V_K^+$, for any non-zero $\omega \in K$, is clearly isomorphic to V_k^+ as a topological group. Hence we have the isomorphisms

$$V_K^+ = V_k^+ \otimes_k K = \omega_1 V_k^+ \oplus \ldots \oplus \omega_N V_k^+ = V_k^+ \oplus \ldots \oplus V_k^+.$$

THEOREM. *k is discrete‡ in V_k and V_k^+/k^+ is compact in the quotient topology.*

Proof. The preceding corollary (with k for K and $\mathbf{Q}$ or $\mathbf{F}(t)$ for k) shows that it is enough to verify the theorem for $\mathbf{Q}$ or $\mathbf{F}(t)$ and we shall do it for $\mathbf{Q}$.

To show that $\mathbf{Q}^+$ is discrete in $V_{\mathbf{Q}}^+$ it is enough because of the group

† This was proved there only when $\omega_n = \alpha^{n-1}$, where $K = k(\alpha)$. We should therefore take this choice of ω_n.

‡ It is impossible to conceive of any other uniquely defined topology in k. This metamathematical reason is more persuasive than the argument that follows!

structure to find a neighbourhood U of 0 which contains no other elements of k^+. We take for U the set of $\boldsymbol{\alpha} = \{\alpha_v\} \in V_{\mathbf{Q}}^+$ with

$$|\alpha_\infty|_\infty < 1$$
$$|\alpha_p|_p \le 1 \quad \text{(all } p\text{)},$$

where $|\ |_p$, $|\ |_\infty$ are respectively the p-adic and the absolute values on $\mathbf{Q}$.

If $b \in \mathbf{Q} \cap U$ then in the first place $b \in \mathbf{Z}$ (because $|b|_p \le 1$ for all p) and then $b = 0$ because $|b|_\infty < 1$.

Now let $W \subset V_{\mathbf{Q}}^+$ consists of the $\boldsymbol{\alpha} = \{\alpha_v\}$ with

$$|\alpha_\infty|_\infty \le \tfrac{1}{2}, \quad |\alpha_p|_p \le 1 \qquad \text{(all } p\text{)}.$$

We show that every adele β is of the shape

$$\boldsymbol{\beta} = b + \boldsymbol{\alpha}, \qquad b \in \mathbf{Q}, \quad \boldsymbol{\alpha} \in W. \tag{14.7}$$

For each p we can find an

$$r_p = z_p/p^{x_p} \qquad (z_p \in \mathbf{Z}, \quad x_p \in \mathbf{Z}, \quad x_p \ge 0)$$

such that

$$|\beta_p - r_p|_p \le 1$$

and since $\boldsymbol{\alpha}$ is an adele we may take

$$r_p = 0 \quad \text{(almost all } p\text{)}.$$

Hence $r = \sum_p r_p$ is well defined and

$$|\beta_p - r| \le 1 \quad \text{(all } p\text{)}.$$

Now choose $s \in \mathbf{Z}$ such that

$$|\beta_\infty - r - s| \le \tfrac{1}{2}.$$

Then $b = r+s$, $\boldsymbol{\beta} = \boldsymbol{\alpha} - b$ do what is required.

Hence the continuous map $W \to V_{\mathbf{Q}}^+/\mathbf{Q}^+$ induced by the quotient map $V_{\mathbf{Q}}^+ \to V_{\mathbf{Q}}^+/\mathbf{Q}^+$ is surjective. But W is compact (topological product of $|\alpha_\infty|_\infty \le \frac{1}{2}$ and the $\mathfrak{o}_p$) and hence so is $V_{\mathbf{Q}}^+/\mathbf{Q}^+$.

As already remarked, V_k^+ is a locally compact group and so it has an invariant (Haar) measure. It is easy to see that in fact this Haar measure is the product of the Haar measures on the k_v in the sense described in the previous section.

COROLLARY 1. *There is a subset W of V_k defined by inequalities of the type $|\xi_v|_v \le \delta_v$, where $\delta_v = 1$ for almost all v, such that every $\varphi \in V_k$ can be put in the form*

$$\varphi = \theta + \gamma, \qquad \theta \in W, \quad \gamma \in k$$

Proof. For the W constructed in the proof is clearly contained in some W of the type described above.

COROLLARY 2. *V_k^+/k^+ has finite measure in the quotient measure induced by the Haar measure on V_k^+.*

Note. This statement is, of course, independent of the particular choice of the multiplicative constant in the Haar measure on V_k^+. We do not here go into the question of finding the measure of V_k^+/k^+ in terms of our explicitly given Haar measure. (See Tate's thesis, Chapter XV of this book.)

Proof. This can be reduced similarly to the case of **Q** or **F**(t), which is almost immediate: thus W defined above has measure 1 for our Haar measure.

Alternatively finite measure follows from compactness. For cover V_k^+/k^+ with the translates of F, where F is an open set of finite measure. The existence of a finite subcover implies finite measure.

[We give an alternative proof of the product formula $\Pi\,|\xi|_v = 1$ for $\xi \in k$, $\xi \neq 0$. We have seen that if $\beta_v \in k_v$ then multiplication by β_v magnifies the Haar measure in k_v^+ by the factor $|\beta_v|_v$. Hence if $\boldsymbol{\beta} = \{\beta_v\} \in V_k$, multiplication by $\boldsymbol{\beta}$ magnifies Haar measure in V_k^+ by $\Pi\,|\beta_v|_v$. In particular multiplication by the principal adele ξ magnifies Haar measure by $\Pi\,|\xi|_v$. But now multiplication by ξ takes $k^+ \subset V_k^+$ into k^+ and so gives a well-defined $1-1$ map of V_k^+/k^+ onto V_k^+/k^+ which magnifies the measure by the factor $\Pi\,|\xi|_v$. Hence $\Pi\,|\xi|_v = 1$ by the Corollary.]

In the next section we shall need the

LEMMA. *There is a constant $C > 0$ depending only on the global field k with the following property:*

Let $\boldsymbol{\alpha} = \{\alpha_v\} \subset V_k$ be such that

$$\prod_v |\alpha_v|_v > C. \tag{14.8}$$

Then there is a principal adele $\beta \in k \subset V_k$, $\beta \neq 0$ such that

$$|\beta|_v \leq |\alpha_v|_v \quad \text{(all } v\text{)}.$$

Proof. This is modelled on Blichfeldt's proof of Minkowski's Theorem in the Geometry of Numbers and works in quite general circumstances.

Note that (14.8) implies $|\alpha_v|_v = 1$ for almost all v because $|\alpha_v|_v \leq 1$ for almost all v.

Let c_0 be the Haar measure of V_k^+/k^+ and let c_1 be that of the set of $\boldsymbol{\gamma} = \{\gamma_v\} \subset V_k^+$ with

$$|\gamma_v|_v \leq \tfrac{1}{10} \quad \text{if } v \text{ is arch.}$$
$$|\gamma_v|_v \leq 1 \quad \text{if } v \text{ is if } v \text{ is non-arch.}$$

Then $0 < c_0 < \infty$ and $0 < c_1 < \infty$ because the number of arch. v's is finite. We show that

$$C = c_0/c_1$$

will do.

The set T of $\boldsymbol{\tau} = \{\tau_v\} \subset V_k^+$ with

$$|\tau_v|_v \leq \tfrac{1}{10}|\alpha_v|_v \quad \text{if } v \text{ is arch.}$$
$$|\tau_v|_v \leq |\alpha_v|_v \quad \text{if } v \text{ is non-arch.}$$

has measure

$$c_1 \prod_v |\alpha_v|_v > c_1 C = c_0.$$

Hence in the quotient map $V_k^+ \to V_k^+/k^+$ there must be a pair of distinct points of T which have the same image in V_k^+/k^+, say

$$\boldsymbol{\tau}' = \{\tau_v'\} \in T, \qquad \boldsymbol{\tau}'' = \{\tau_v''\} \in T$$

and

$$\boldsymbol{\tau}' - \boldsymbol{\tau}'' = \beta \text{ (say)} \in k^+.$$

Then

$$|\beta|_v = |\tau_v' - \tau_v''|_v \leq |\alpha_v|_v$$

for all v, as required.

COROLLARY. *Let v_0 be a normalized valuation and let $\delta_v > 0$ be given for all $v \neq v_0$ with $\delta_v = 1$ for almost all v. Then there is a $\beta \in k$, $\beta \neq 0$ with*

$$|\beta|_v \leq \delta_v \quad (\text{all } v \neq v_0).$$

Proof. This is just a degenerate case. Choose $\alpha_v \in k_v$ with $0 < |\alpha_v|_v \leq \delta_v$ and $|\alpha_v|_v = 1$ if $\delta_v = 1$. We can then choose $\alpha_{v_0} \in k_{v_0}$ so that $\prod_{\text{all } v \text{ inc. } v_0} |\alpha_v|_v > C$.

Then the lemma does what is required.

[The character group of the locally compact group V_k^+ is isomorphic to V_k^+ and k^+ plays a special role. See Chapter XV (Tate's thesis), Lang: "Algebraic Numbers" (Addison-Wesley), Weil: "Adeles and Algebraic Groups" (Princeton lecture notes) and Godement: Bourbaki seminars 171 and 176. This duality lies behind the functional equation of ζ and L-functions. Iwasawa has shown (*Annals of Math.*, **57** (1953), 331–356) that the rings of adeles are characterized by certain general topologico-algebraic properties.]

15. Strong Approximation Theorem

The results of the previous section, in particular the discreteness of k in V_k depend critically on the fact that *all* normalized valuations are used in the definition of V_k:

THEOREM. (Strong approximation theorem.) *Let v_0 be any valuation of the global field k. Define $\mathscr{V}$ to be the restricted topological product of the k_v with respect to the $\mathfrak{o}_v$, where v runs through all normalized $v \neq v_0$. Then k is everywhere dense in $\mathscr{V}$.*

Proof.† It is easy to see that the theorem is equivalent to the following statement. Suppose we are given (i) a finite set S of valuations $v \neq v_0$, (ii) elements $\alpha_v \in k_v$ for all $v \in S$ and (iii) $\varepsilon > 0$. Then there is a $\beta \in k$ such that $|\beta - \alpha_v|_v < \varepsilon$ for all $v \in S$ and $|\beta|_v \leq 1$ for all $v \notin S$, $v \neq v_0$.

By Corollary 1 to the Theorem of § 14 there is a $W \subset V_k$ defined by inequalities of the type $|\xi_v|_v \leq \delta_v$ ($\delta_v = 1$ for almost all v) such that every

† Suggested by Prof. Kneser at the Conference.

$\varphi \in V_k$ is of the form

$$\varphi = \theta + \gamma, \qquad \theta \in W, \ \gamma \in k. \tag{15.1}$$

By the corollary to the last lemma of §14, there is a $\lambda \in k$, $\lambda \neq 0$ such that

$$\begin{aligned} |\lambda|_v &< \delta_v^{-1}\varepsilon \quad (v \in S), \\ |\lambda|_v &\leq \delta_v^{-1} \quad (v \notin S, v \neq v_0). \end{aligned} \tag{15.2}$$

Hence, on putting $\varphi = \lambda^{-1}\alpha$ in (15.1) and multiplying by λ we see that every $\alpha \in V_k$ is of the shape

$$\alpha = \psi + \beta, \qquad \psi \in \lambda W, \ \beta \in k, \tag{15.3}$$

where λW is the set of $\lambda\xi$, $\xi \in W$. If now we let α have components the given α_v at $v \in S$ and (say) 0 elsewhere, it is easy to see that β has the properties required.

[The proof clearly gives a quantitative form of the theorem (i.e. with a bound for $|\beta|_{v_0}$). For an alternative approach, see K. Mahler: Inequalities for ideal bases, *J. Australian Math. Soc.* **4** (1964), 425–448.]

16. Idele Group

The set of invertible elements of any commutative topological ring R form a group $R^\times$ under multiplication. In general, $R^\times$ is not a topological group if it is endowed with the subset topology because inversion need not be continuous. It is usual therefore to give $R^\times$ the following topology. There is an injection

$$x \to (x, x^{-1}) \tag{16.0}$$

of $R^\times$ into the topological product $R \times R$. We give to $R^\times$ the corresponding subset topology. Clearly $R^\times$ with this topology is a topological group and the inclusion map $R^\times \to R$ is continuous.

DEFINITION. *The idele group J_k of k is the group $V_k^\times$ of invertible elements of the adele ring V_k with the topology just defined.*

We shall usually speak of J_k as a subset of V_k and will have to distinguish between the J_k- and V_k-topologies.†

We have seen that k is naturally embedded in V_k and so $k^\times$ is naturally embedded in J_k. We shall call $k^\times$ considered as a subgroup of J_k the *principal* ideles.

LEMMA. *$k^\times$ is a discrete subgroup of J_k.*

Proof. For k is discrete in V_k and so $k^\times$ is injected into $V_k \times V_k$ by (16.0) as a discrete subset.

LEMMA. *J_k is just the restricted topological product of the $k_v^\times$ with respect to the units $U_v \subset k_v$ (with the restricted product topology).*

Beweis. Klar.

† Let $\alpha^{(q)}$ for a rational prime q be the element of $J_{\mathbb{Q}}$ with components $\alpha_q^{(q)} = q$, $\alpha_v^{(q)} = 1$ $(v \neq q)$. Then $\alpha^{(q)} \to 1$ $(q \to \infty)$ in the $V_{\mathbb{Q}}$-topology, but not in the $J_{\mathbb{Q}}$-topology.

DEFINITION. *For* $\boldsymbol{\alpha} = \{\alpha_v\} \subset J_k$ we define $c(\boldsymbol{\alpha}) = \prod_{\text{all } v} |\alpha_v|_v$ *to be the content of* α.

LEMMA. *The map* $\boldsymbol{\alpha} \rightarrow c(\boldsymbol{\alpha})$ *is a continuous homomorphism of the topological group* J_k *into the multiplicative group of the (strictly) positive real numbers.*

Beweis. Klar.

[*Lemma.* Let $\boldsymbol{\alpha} \in J_k$. Then the map $\xi \rightarrow \boldsymbol{\alpha}\xi$ of V_k^+ onto itself multiplies Haar measure on V_k^+ by a factor $c(\boldsymbol{\alpha})$.

Beweis. Klar.

Note also that the J_k-topology is that appropriate to a group of operators on V_k^+: a basis of open sets is the $S(C, O)$ where $C, O \subset V_k^+$ are respectively V_k-compact and V_k-open and S consists of the $\boldsymbol{\alpha} \in J_k$ such that $(1 - \boldsymbol{\alpha})C \subset O$, $(1 - \boldsymbol{\alpha}^{-1})C \subset O$.]

Let J_k^1 be the kernel of the map $\boldsymbol{\alpha} \rightarrow c(\boldsymbol{\alpha})$ with the topology as a subset of J_k. We shall need the

LEMMA. J_k^1 *considered as a subset of* V_k *is closed and the* V_k*-subset topology on* J_k^1 *coincides with the* J_k*-topology.*

Proof. Let $\boldsymbol{\alpha} \in V_k$, $\boldsymbol{\alpha} \notin J_k^1$. We must find a V_k-neighbourhood W of $\boldsymbol{\alpha}$ which does not meet J_k^1.

1st Case. $\prod |\alpha_v|_v < 1$ (possibly $= 0$). Then there is a finite set S of v such that

(i) S contains all the v with $|\alpha_v|_v > 1$ and

(ii) $\prod_{v \in S} |\alpha_v|_v < 1$. Then the set W can be defined by

$$|\xi_v - \alpha_v|_v < \varepsilon \quad v \in S$$
$$|\xi_v|_v \leq 1 \quad v \notin S$$

for sufficiently small ε.

2nd Case. $\prod_v |\alpha_v|_v = C$ (say) > 1. Then there is a finite set S of v such that (i) S contains all the v with $|\alpha_v|_v > 1$ and (ii) if $v \notin S$ an inequality $|\xi_v|_v < 1$ implies† $|\xi_v|_v < \frac{1}{2}C$. We can choose ε so small that $|\xi_v - \alpha_v|_v < \varepsilon$ $(v \in S)$ implies $1 < \prod_{v \in S} |\xi_v| < 2C$. Then W may be defined by

$$|\xi_v - \alpha_v|_v < \varepsilon \quad (v \in S)$$
$$|\xi_v| \leq 1 \quad (v \notin S).$$

We must now show that the J_k- and V_k-topologies on J_k^1 are the same. If $\boldsymbol{\alpha} \in J_k^1$ we must show that every J_k-neighbourhood of $\boldsymbol{\alpha}$ contains a V_k-neighbourhood and vice-versa.

Let‡ $W \subset J_k^1$ be a V_k-neighbourhood of $\boldsymbol{\alpha}$. Then it contains a V_k-neigh-

† If $k \supset \mathbf{Q}$ and v is a normalized extension of the p-adic valuation then the value group of v consists of (some of the) powers of p. Hence it is enough for (ii) to include in S all the arch. v and all the extensions of p-adic valuations with $p \leq 2C$. Similarly if $k \supset \mathbf{F}(t)$.

‡ This half of the proof of the equality of the topologies makes no use of the special properties of ideles. It is only an expression of the fact noted above that the inclusion $R^\times \rightarrow R$ is continuous for any topological ring R.

bourhood of the type

$$\left.\begin{aligned}|\xi_v-\alpha_v|_v &< \varepsilon \quad (v\in S)\\ |\xi_v|_v &\le 1 \quad (v\notin S)\end{aligned}\right\} \tag{16.1}$$

where S is a finite set of v. This contains the J_k-neighbourhood in which $\le$ in (16.1) is replaced by $=$.

Now let $H \subset J_k^1$ be a J_k-neighbourhood. Then it contains a J_k-neighbourhood of the type

$$\left.\begin{aligned}|\xi_v-\alpha_v|_v &< \varepsilon \quad (v\in S)\\ |\xi_v|_v &= 1 \quad (v\notin S)\end{aligned}\right\} \tag{16.2}$$

where the finite set S contains at least all arch. v and all v with $|\alpha_v|_v \neq 1$. Since $\prod |\alpha_v|_v = 1$ we may also suppose that ε is so small that (16.2) implies

$$\prod_v |\xi_v|_v < 2.$$

Then the intersection of (16.2) with J_k^1 is the same† as that of (16.1) with J_k^1, i.e. (16.2) defines a V_k-neighbourhood.

By the product formula we have $k^\times \subset J_k^1$. The following result is of vital importance in class-field theory.

THEOREM. *$J_k^1/k^\times$ with the quotient topology is compact.*

Proof. After the preceding lemma it is enough to find a V_k-compact set $W \subset V_k$ such that the map

$$W \cap J_k^1 \to J_k^1/k^\times$$

is surjective.

We take for W the set of $\boldsymbol{\xi} = \{\xi_v\}$ with

$$|\xi_v|_v \le |\alpha_v|_v$$

where $\boldsymbol{\alpha} = \{\alpha_v\}$ is any idele of content greater than the C of the last lemma of § 14.

Let $\boldsymbol{\beta} = \{\beta_v\} \in J_k^1$. Then by the lemma just quoted there is a $\eta \in k^\times$ such that

$$|\eta|_v \le |\beta_v^{-1}\alpha_v|_v \quad (\text{all } v).$$

Then $\eta\boldsymbol{\beta} \in W$, as required.

[$J_k/k^\times$ is totally disconnected in the function field case. For the structure of its connected component in the number theory case see papers of Artin and Weil in the "Proceedings of the Tokyo Symposium on Algebraic Number Theory, 1955" (Science Council of Japan) or Artin-Tate: "Class Field Theory", 1951/2 (Harvard, 1960(?)). The determination of the character group of $J_k/k^\times$ is global class field theory.]

17. Ideals and Divisors

Suppose that k is a finite extension of $\mathbf{Q}$. We define the ideal group I_k of k to be the free abelian group on a set of symbols in $1-1$ correspondence

† See previous footnote.

with the *non-arch.* valuations v of k, i.e. formal sums

$$\sum_{v \text{ non-arch.}} n_v . v \tag{17.1}$$

where $n_v \in \mathbf{Z}$ and $n_v = 0$ for almost all v, addition being defined componentwise. We call (17.1) an ideal and call it integral if $n_v \geq 0$ for all v. This language is justified by the existence of a $1-1$ correspondence between integral ideals and the ideals (in the ordinary sense) in the Dedekind ring

$$\mathfrak{o} = \bigcap_{\text{non-arch.}} \mathfrak{o}_v:$$

cf. Chapter I, §2, Prop. 2.

There is a natural continuous map

$$J_k \to I_k$$

of the idele group on to the ideal group† given by

$$\boldsymbol{\alpha} = \{\alpha_v\} \to \sum (\operatorname{ord}_v \alpha) . v.$$

The image of $k^\times \subset J_k$ is the group of principal ideals.

THEOREM. *The group of ideal classes, i.e. I_k modulo principal ideals, is finite.*

Proof. For the map $J_k^1 \to I_k$ is surjective and so the group of ideal classes is the continuous image of the compact group $J_k^1/k^\times$ and hence compact. But a compact discrete group is finite.

When k is a finite separable extension of $\mathbf{F}(t)$ we define the divisor group D_k of k to be the free group on all the v. For each v the number of elements in the residue class field of v is a power, say q^{d_v} of the number q of elements in $\mathbf{F}$. We call d_v the degree of v and similarly define $\sum n_v d_v$ to be the degree of $\sum n_v . v$. The divisors of degree 0 form a group D_k^0. One defines the principal divisors similarly to principal ideals and then one has the

THEOREM. *D_k^0 modulo principal divisors is a finite group.*

For the quotient group is the continuous image of the compact group $J_k^1/k^\times$.

18. Units

In this section we deduce the structure theorem for units from our results about idele classes.

Let S be any finite non-empty set of normalized valuations and suppose that S contains all the archimedean valuations. The set of $\eta \in k$ with

$$|\eta|_v = 1 \quad (v \notin S) \tag{18.1}$$

are a group under multiplication, the group H_S of S-units. When $k \supset \mathbf{Q}$ and S is just the archimedean valuations, then H_S is the group of units *tout court*.

† I_k being given the discrete topology.

LEMMA 1. *Let* $0 < c < C < \infty$. Then the set of S-units η with

$$c \le |\eta|_v \le C \quad (v \in S) \tag{18.2}$$

is finite.

Proof. The set W of ideles $\boldsymbol{\alpha} = \{\alpha_v\}$ with

$$|\alpha_v|_v = 1 \quad (v \notin S), \qquad c \le |\alpha_v|_v \le C \quad (v \in S) \tag{18.3}$$

is compact (product of compact sets with the product topology). The required set of units is just the intersection of W with the discrete subset k of J_k and so is both discrete and compact, hence finite.

LEMMA 2. *There are only finitely many* $\varepsilon \in k$ *such that* $|\varepsilon|_v = 1$ *for every* v. *They are precisely the roots of unity in* k.

Proof. If ε is a root of unity it is clear that $|\varepsilon|_v = 1$ for every v. Conversely, by the previous lemma (with any S and $c = C = 1$) there are only finitely many $\varepsilon \in k$ with $|\varepsilon|_v = 1$ for all v. They form a group under multiplication and so are all roots of 1.

THEOREM. (Unit theorem.) H_S *is the direct sum of a finite cyclic group and a free abelian group of rank* $s-1$.

Proof. To avoid petty notational troubles we treat only the case when $\mathbf{Q} \subset k$ and S is the set of arch. valuations.

Let J_S consist of the ideals $\boldsymbol{\alpha} = \{\alpha_v\}$ with $|\alpha_v|_v = 1$ $(v \notin S)$ and put

$$J_S^1 = J_S \cap J_k^1.$$

Clearly J_S^1 is open in J_k^1 and so

$$J_S^1/H_S = J_S^1/(J_S^1 \cap k^\times) \tag{18.4}$$

is open in $J_k^1/k^\times$. Since it is a subgroup, it is also closed, and so compact (§ 16).

Consider the map

$$\lambda : J_S \to \underbrace{\mathbf{R}^+ \oplus \mathbf{R}^+ \oplus \ldots \oplus \mathbf{R}^+}_{s \text{ times}},$$

where $\mathbf{R}^+$ is the additive group of reals, given by

$$\boldsymbol{\alpha} \to (\log|\alpha_1|_1, \log|\alpha_2|_2, \ldots, \log|\alpha_s|_s),$$

where $1, 2, \ldots, s$ are the valuations in S. Clearly λ is both continuous and surjective.

The kernel of λ restricted to H_S consists just of the ε with $|\varepsilon|_v = 1$ for every v, so is a finite cyclic group by Lemma 2. By Lemma 1 there are only finitely many $\eta \in H_S$ with

$$\tfrac{1}{2} \le |\eta|_v \le 2 \quad v \in S. \tag{18.5}$$

Hence the group Λ (say) $= \lambda(H_S)$ is discrete.

Further, $T = \lambda(J_S^1)$ is just the set of $(x_1, \ldots, x_s)$ with

$$x_1 + x_2 + \ldots + x_s = 0,$$

i.e. an $s-1$ dimensional real vector space. Finally, T/Λ is compact, being the continuous image of the compact set (18.4). Hence Λ is free on $s-1$ generators, as asserted.

Of course this structure-theorem (Dirichlet) and the finiteness of the class-number (Minkowski) are older than ideles. It is more usual to deduce the compactness of $J_k^1/k^\times$ from these theorems instead of vica versa.

19. Inclusion and Norm Maps for Adeles, Ideles and Ideals

Let K be a finite extension of the global field k. We have already seen (§ 14, Lemma) that there is a natural isomorphism

$$V_k \otimes_k K = V_K \tag{19.1}$$

algebraically and topologically. Hence $V_k = V_k \otimes_k k$ can naturally be regarded as a subring of V_K which is closed in the topology of V_K. This injection of V_k into V_K is called the injection map or the conorm map and is written

$$\text{con}: \quad \boldsymbol{\alpha} \to \text{con}\, \boldsymbol{\alpha} = \text{con}_{K/k}\, \boldsymbol{\alpha} \in V_K \quad (\boldsymbol{\alpha} \in V_k).$$

Explicitly if $\mathbf{A} = \text{con}\, \boldsymbol{\alpha}$, then the components satisfy

$$A_V = \alpha_v \in k_v \subset K_V \tag{19.2}$$

where V runs through the normalized valuations of K and v is the normalized valuation of k which extends to V. If $k \subset L \subset K$ it follows that

$$\text{con}_{K/k}\, \boldsymbol{\alpha} = \text{con}_{L/k}(\text{con}_{K/L}\, \boldsymbol{\alpha}). \tag{19.3}$$

Finally, for principal adeles the conorm map is just the usual injection of k into K.

It is customary, and usually leads to no confusion, to identify $\text{con}_{K/k}\, \boldsymbol{\alpha}$ with $\boldsymbol{\alpha}$.

One can also define norm and trace maps from V_K to V_k by imitating the usual procedure (cf. Appendix A). Let $\omega_1, \ldots, \omega_n$ be a basis for K/k. Then by (19.1) every $\mathbf{A} \in V_K$ is uniquely of the shape

$$\mathbf{A} = \sum \boldsymbol{\alpha}_j \omega_j \quad \boldsymbol{\alpha}_j \in V_k \tag{19.4}$$

and the map $\mathbf{A} \to \boldsymbol{\alpha}_j$ of V_K into V_k is continuous by the very definition of the tensor product topology (§ 9). Hence if we define

$$\boldsymbol{\alpha}_{ij} = \boldsymbol{\alpha}_{ij}(\mathbf{A}) \in V_k$$

by

$$\mathbf{A}\omega_i = \sum_j \boldsymbol{\alpha}_{ij} \omega_j \tag{19.5}$$

the $n \times n$ matrices (α_{ij}) give a a continuous representation of the ring V_K over V_k. In particular, the

$$S_{K/k}\mathbf{A} = \sum \boldsymbol{\alpha}_{ii} \tag{19.6}$$

$$N_{K/k}\mathbf{A} = \det(\boldsymbol{\alpha}_{ij}) \tag{19.7}$$

are *continuous* functions of A and have the usual formal properties

$$S_{K/k}(\mathbf{A}_1+\mathbf{A}_2) = S_{K/k}\mathbf{A}_1+S_{K/k}\mathbf{A}_2 \tag{19.8}$$

$$S_{K/k}\,\mathrm{con}_{K/k}\,\alpha = n\alpha \tag{19.9}$$

$$N_{K/k}(\mathbf{A}_1\mathbf{A}_2) = N_{K/k}\mathbf{A}_1\,N_{K/k}\mathbf{A}_2 \tag{19.10}$$

$$N_{K/k}\,\mathrm{con}_{K/k}\,\alpha = \alpha^n. \tag{19.11}$$

Further, the norm and trace operations are compatible with the embedding of k, V in V_k, V_K respectively, i.e. if $A \in K \subset V_K$ we get the same answer whether we compute $N_{K/k}A$, $S_{K/k}A$ in K or in V_K, so there is no ambiguity in the notation.

Finally if $K \supset L \supset k$ we have $V_k \subset V_L \subset V_K$ (on regarding conorm as an identification), and so the usual relations (cf. Appendix A)

$$S_{L/k}(S_{K/L}\mathbf{A}) = S_{K/k}\mathbf{A} \tag{19.12}$$

and

$$N_{L/k}N_{K/L}\mathbf{A} = \ = N_{K/k}\mathbf{A}. \tag{19.13}$$

We can express the maps (19.6), (19.7) componentwise if we like. Let $V_1,\ldots, V_J$ be the extensions of any given valuation v of k to K. Then (§ 9)

$$K_v\ (\text{say}) = \bigoplus_{1\le j\le J} K_j = k_v \otimes_k K = \bigoplus_{1\le i\le n} k_v\omega_i \tag{19.14}$$

where k_v, K_j are the completions of k, K with respect to v, V_j respectively. Any $\mathbf{A} \in V_K$ can be regarded as having components

$$A_{V_1}\oplus\ldots\oplus A_{V_J} = A_v \tag{19.15}$$

in the K_v and then the components in the matrix representation (19.5) of $\mathbf{A}$ are just the representations of the A_v. In particular

$$S_{K/k}(\mathbf{A}) = \{S_{K_v/k_v}A_v\} \tag{19.16}$$

and

$$N_{K/k}\mathbf{A} = \{N_{K_v/k_v}A_v\}. \tag{19.17}$$

Finally, making use of the final remarks of § 9, we deduce that

$$S_{K/k}\mathbf{A} = \Big\{\sum_{V|v} S_{K_V/k_v}(A_V)\Big\}_v \tag{19.18}$$

and

$$N_{K/k}\mathbf{A} = \Big\{\prod_{V|v} N_{K_v/k_v}A_V\Big\}_v, \tag{19.19}$$

where $V|v$ means "V is a continuation of v".

We now consider the consequences for ideles. If α is an idele, it is clear from the definition (19.2) that $\mathrm{con}_{K/k}\,\alpha$ is an idele, so we have an injection

$$\mathrm{con}_{K/k} : J_k \to J_K$$

which is clearly a homomorphism of J_k with a closed subset of V_K. Further, if $\mathbf{A} \in J_K \subset V_K$, so $\mathbf{A}$ is invertible, it follows from (19.9) that $N_{K/k}\mathbf{A}$ is invertible, i.e. is an element of J_k. Hence we have a map

$$N_{K/k} : J_K \to J_k$$

which is continuous by the definition of the idele topology (§16) and which clearly satisfies (19.10), (19.11), (19.13) and (19.19). On the other hand, the definition of trace does not go over to ideles.

Finally, we consider the conorm and norm maps for ideals, where k is a finite extension of $\mathbf{Q}$. The kernel of the map (§17)

$$J_k \to I_k$$

of the idele group into the ideal group is just the group U_k (say) of ideles $\boldsymbol{\alpha} = \alpha_v$ which have $|\alpha_v|_v = 1$ for every non-archimedean v. If K is a finite extension of k, it is clear that

$$\mathrm{con}_{K/k} U_k \subset U_K$$

and from the Lemma of §11 and (19.17) we have

$$N_{K/k} U_K \subset U_k.$$

Hence on passing to the quotient from J_k we have the induced maps

$$\mathrm{con}_{K/k} : I_k \to I_K$$

$$N_{K/k} : I_K \to I_k$$

with the usual properties (19.10), (19.11) and (19.13); and these maps are compatible with the norm and conorm maps for elements of K and k on taking principal ideals. By definition (19.2) we have

$$\mathrm{con}_{K/k} v = \sum_{V|v} e_V \; V \tag{19.20}$$

where the positive integers e_V are defined by

$$|\pi_v|_V = |\Pi_V|_V^{e_V}, \tag{19.21}$$

π_v and Π_V being prime elements of k_v, K_V respectively. Similarly, it follows from (19.19) that

$$N_{K/k} V = f_V \, v, \tag{19.22}$$

where f_V is the degree of the residue class field of V over that of v. We note in passing that (19.11), (19.20) and (19.22) imply that

$$\sum_{V|v} e_V f_V = n,$$

as it should since

$$e_V f_V = [K_V : k_V].$$

Similarly, when k is a finite extension of $\mathbf{F}(t)$ one defines conorm and norm of divisors, with the appropriate properties.

APPENDIX A

Norms and Traces

Let R be a commutative ring with 1. By a vector space V over R of dimension n we shall mean a free R-module on n generators, say $\omega_1, \ldots, \omega_n$ (a *basis*). If $\omega'_1, \ldots, \omega'_n$ is another basis, there are $u_{ij}, v_{ij} \in R$ such that

$$\omega_i = \sum_j u_{ij}\omega'_j, \omega'_j = \sum v_{ij}\omega_j \tag{A.1}$$

and

$$\sum_j u_{ij}v_{jl} = \sum v_{ij}u_{jl} = \delta_{il} \tag{A.2}$$

(Kronecker δ).

The set of all R-linear endomorphisms of V is a ring, which we denote by $\mathrm{End}_R V$. The ring R is injected into $\mathrm{End}_R V$ if we identify $b \in R$ with the module action of b on V, and we shall do this. The ring $\mathrm{End}_R V$ is isomorphic but not canonically, to the ring of all $n \times n$ matrices with elements in R. The isomorphism becomes canonical if V is endowed with a fixed choice of basis. In fact if $\beta \in \mathrm{End}_R (V)$ and

$$\beta\omega_i = \sum_j b_{ij}\omega_j, \quad (b_{ij} \in R) \tag{A.3}$$

the $1-1$ correspondence between β and the transposed matrix (b_{ji}) is a ring isomorphism.

For $\beta \in \mathrm{End}_V$ we denote by

$$F_\beta(x) = \det(x\delta_{ij} - b_{ij}) \tag{A.4}$$

the characteristic polynomial of R. On using (A.2) it is easy to see that $F_\beta(x)$ is independent of the choice of bases of V. The Cayley-Hamilton theorem† states that

$$F_\beta(\beta) = 0. \tag{A.5}$$

We define further the *trace*

$$\begin{aligned} S_{V/R}(\beta) = S(\beta) &= \sum_j b_{jj} \\ &= -\text{coefficient of } x^{n-1} \text{ in } F_\beta(x) \end{aligned} \tag{A.6}$$

and the *norm*

$$\begin{aligned} N_{V/R}(\beta) = N(\beta) &= \det(b_{ij}) \\ &= (-)^n \text{ constant term in } F_\beta(x), \end{aligned} \tag{A.7}$$

† *Proof.* Write (A.3) in the form

$$\sum_j (\delta_{ij}\beta - b_{ij})\omega_j = 0.$$

Working in the commutative ring $R[\beta]$ multiply the equations (*) by the cofactors of the "coefficients" of ω_1, and add. Then $\omega_2, \ldots, \omega_n$ are "eliminated" and one obtains $F_\beta(\beta)\omega_1 = 0$. Similarly $F_\beta(\beta)\omega_j = 0$ $(2 \le j \le n)$ and so $F_\beta(\beta) = 0$.

which are independent of the choice of basis because $F_\beta(x)$ is. Clearly

$$S(\beta_1+\beta_2) = S(\beta_1)+S(\beta_2) \tag{A.8}$$

$$S(b) = nb \quad (b \in R) \tag{A.9}$$

$$N(\beta_1\beta_2) = N(\beta_1)N(\beta_2) \tag{A.10}$$

$$N(b) = b^n \quad (b \in R), \tag{A.11}$$

because the correspondence (A.3) between $\beta \in \mathrm{End}_R(V)$ and the matrix b_{ji} is a ring isomorphism.

LEMMA A.1. *Let t be transcendental over R. Then*

$$N(t-\beta) = F_\beta(t). \tag{A.12}$$

Pedantically, what is meant is, of course, that we consider a vector space V with basis $\omega_1,\ldots,\omega_n$ defined over $R[t]$ and a β given by (A.3).

Proof. We have

$$(t-\beta)\omega_i = \sum_j (t\delta_{ij}-b_{ij})\omega_j$$

and so

$$N(t-\beta) = \det(t\delta_{ij}-b_{ij})$$
$$= F_\beta(t)$$

by (A.4) and (A.7).

COROLLARY. (A.12) *holds for any $t \in R$.*

LEMMA A.2. *Let $\beta_1,\ldots,\beta_l \in \mathrm{End}_R V$ and let t be transcendental over R. Then*

$$N(t^l+\beta_1 t^{l-1}+\ldots+\beta_l) = t^{nl}+g_1 t^{nl-1}+\ldots+g_{nl} \tag{A.13}$$

where $g_1,\ldots,g_{nl} \in R$ and in particular

$$g_1 = S(\beta_1); \qquad g_{nl} = N(\beta_l). \tag{A.14}$$

Proof. Similar to that of Lemma A.1 and left to the reader.

Now let R and $P \subset R$ be commutative rings with 1 and suppose that R regarded as a P-module is free on a finite-number, say, m of generators $\Omega_1,\ldots,\Omega_m$ (i.e. an m-dimensional P-vector space). Let V be an n-dimensional R-vector space with basis $\omega_1,\ldots,\omega_n$. Then V can also be regarded as an mn-dimensional P-vector space with basis

$$\Omega_i\omega_j \qquad (1 \le i \le m, \quad 1 \le j \le n)$$

and there is an obvious natural injection of $\mathrm{End}_R(V)$ into $\mathrm{End}_P(V)$. We have now the key

THEOREM A.1. *Let*

$$\beta \in \mathrm{End}_R(V) \subset \mathrm{End}_P(V). \tag{A.15}$$

Then

$$S_{V/P}\beta = S_{R/P}(S_{V/R}\beta), \tag{A.16}$$

$$N_{V/P}\beta = N_{R/P}(N_{V/R}\beta). \tag{A.17}$$

Further

$$\Phi(x) = N_{R/P}F(x), \tag{A.18}$$

where $\Phi(x) \in P[x]$, $F(x) \in R[x]$ *are the characteristic polynomials of* β *in* $End_P(V)$ *and* $End_R(V)$ *respectively.*

Proof. If β is given by (A.3) let $\gamma \in \mathrm{End}_R(V)$ be given by

$$\begin{aligned} \gamma\omega_1 &= \omega_1 - \sum_{j>1} b_{ij}\omega_j \\ \gamma\omega_i &= b_{11}\omega_i \quad (i > 1). \end{aligned} \tag{A.19}$$

Then for $\alpha = \gamma\beta$ we have

$$\begin{aligned} \alpha\omega_1 &= b_{11}\omega_1 \\ \alpha\omega_i &= b_{i1}\omega_1 + \sum_{j>1}(b_{11}b_{ij} - b_{i1}b_{1j})\omega_j \\ &= b_{i1}\omega_1 + \sum_{j>1} a_{ij}\omega_j \quad \text{(say)}. \end{aligned} \tag{A.20}$$

Hence

$$N_{V/R}\alpha = b_{11}N_{W/R}\alpha^* \tag{A.21}$$

where W is the $n-1$ dimensional R-vector space spanned by $\omega_2, \ldots, \omega_n$ and α^* is the R-linear map

$$\omega_i \to \sum_{j>1} a_{ij}\omega_j \quad (i > 1).$$

Consequently

$$N_{R/P}(N_{V/R}\alpha) = N_{R/P}b_{11} . N_{R/P}(N_{W/R}\alpha^*). \tag{A.22}$$

We now use induction on the dimension n, since the Theorem is trivial for $n = 1$. Since W has dimension $n-1$ we have by the induction hypothesis

$$N_{R/P}(N_{W/R}\alpha^*) = N_{W/P}\alpha^*. \tag{A.23}$$

On the other hand, it follows directly from (A.20) that

$$N_{V/P}\alpha = N_{R/P}b_{11}N_{W/P}\alpha^*$$

and so

$$N_{V/P}\alpha = N_{R/P}N_{V/P}\alpha. \tag{A.24}$$

Further, clearly

$$N_{V/P}\gamma = N_{R/P}N_{V/P}\gamma = (N_{R/P}b_{11})^{n-1}.$$

Since $\alpha = \beta\gamma$ and both $N_{V/P}$ and $N_{R/P}N_{V/R}$ are multiplicative (by (A.10)), it follows from (A.24) that

$$(N_{R/P}b_{11})^{n-1}N_{V/P}\beta = (N_{R/P}b_{11})^{n-1}N_{R/P}(N_{V/R}\beta). \tag{A.25}$$

If $N_{R/P}b_{11}$ were invertible, this would give (A.17) at once. In general, however, this is not the case and we must use a common trick.

Let t be a transcendental over R and let β_t be the transformation obtained from β by replacing b_{11} by $b_{11}+t$ but leaving the remaining b_{ij} unchanged. Then (A.25) applied to β_t gives

$$(N_{R/P}(b_{11}+t))^{n-1}N_{V/P}\beta_t = N_{R/V}(b_{11}+t)^{n-1}N_{R/P}(N_{V/R}\beta_t). \quad \text{(A.26)}$$

All the norms occurring in (A.26) are polynomials in t. On comparing coefficients of powers of t in (A.26), starting at the top, we deduce that

$$N_{V/P}\beta_t = N_{R/P}(N_{V/R}\beta_t) \quad \text{(A.27)}$$

because the coefficient of the highest power of t in $N_{R/P}(b_{11}+t)$ is 1. Then (A.17) follows on putting $t = 0$.

We now prove (A.18). By Lemma 1 we have

$$\Phi(x) = N_{V/P}(x-\beta), \qquad F(x) = N_{V/R}(x-\beta)$$

and so (A.18) is just (A.17) with $x-\beta$ for β.

Finally, (A.16) follows from (A.18) on using (A.6) and the first half of (A.14).

When $R = k$ is a field there is some simplification, since every finitely-generated module V over k is free, i.e. is a vector space. Further each $\beta \in \mathrm{End}_k(V)$ has a minimum polynomial, i.e. a non-zero polynomial $f(x)$ of lowest degree, with highest coefficient 1, such that $f(\beta) = 0$. Then $g(\beta) = 0$ for $g(x) \in k[x]$ if and only if $f(x)$ divides $g(x)$ in $k[x]$. In particular the Cayley-Hamilton theorem (A.5) now states that $f(x)$ divides the characteristic polynomial $F_\beta(x)$.

Finally we have

THEOREM A.2. *Let K be a field of finite degree n over the field k and let $\beta \in K$. Then the degree m (say) of the minimum polynomial $f(x)$ of β over k divides n and*

$$F(x) = (f(x))^{n/m},$$

where $F(x)$ is the characteristic polynomial of β. In particular

$$S_{K/k}(\beta) = \frac{n}{m}(\beta_1 + \ldots + \beta_m),$$

$$N_{K/k}(\beta) = (\beta_1, \beta_2, \ldots, \beta_m)^{n/m},$$

where $\beta_1, \ldots, \beta_m$ are the roots of $f(x)$ in any splitting field.

Proof. Suppose first that $K = k(\beta)$. Then the minimum polynomial $f(x)$ and the characteristic polynomial $F(x)$ of β have the same degree and highest coefficient, so $F(x) = f(x)$ by the remarks preceding the enunciation of the Lemma.

The general case now follows from Theorem A.1, with $V = K$, $R = k(\beta)$, $P = k$ on using (A.11).

APPENDIX B

Separability

In this book we are primarily interested in separable algebraic field extensions. Here we recall their most important elementary properties.

LEMMA B.1. *Let K, M be extensions of finite degree of the field k. Then there are at most* $[K:k]$ *injections of K into M which leave k elementwise fixed.*

Proof. Trivial when $K = k(\alpha)$ for some α on considering the minimal polynomial for α. For general K we have a chain

$$k = K_0 \subset K_1 \subset K_2 \ldots \subset K_J = K \tag{B.1}$$

where $K_j = K_{j-1}(\alpha_{j-1})$ and use induction on J.

DEFINITION. *The finite field extension* K/k *is separable if there is some finite extension* M/k *such that there are* $[K:k]$ *distinct injections of K into k which leave k elementwise fixed. If* K/k *is not separable then it is said to be inseparable.*

COROLLARY 1. *Let* $K \supset L \supset k$. *If* K/k *is separable then so are* K/L *and* L/k.

Proof. By Lemma 1 there are at most $[L:k]$ distinct injections of L into M and by Lemma 1 again each of these can be extended in at most $[K:L]$ ways into injections of K into M. By definition, there are

$$[K:k] = [K:L][L:k]$$

injections of K into M, and so there must be equality both times.

COROLLARY 2. *Let* $\alpha \in K$ *where* K/k *is separable and let* $\alpha_1, \ldots, \alpha_m$ *be the roots in M of the irreducible polynomial* $f(x)$ *for* α *over k. Then the* $\sigma_i\alpha$ $(1 \le i \le n = [K:k])$ *are just the* $\alpha_1, \ldots, \alpha_m$ *each taken* n/m *times, where* $\sigma_1, \ldots, \sigma_m$ are the injections of K into some M.

Proof. For put $L = k(\alpha)$ in the preceding argument.

COROLLARY 3.

$$S_{K/k}(\alpha) = \sum_i \sigma_i \alpha.$$

Proof. Follows from Theorem A.2 and the preceding Corollary.

LEMMA B.2. *Let* K/k *be a finite field extension and let* σ *be an injection of k into some field M. Then there is a finite extension* M_1 *of M and an injection* σ_1 *of K into* M_1 *which reduces to* σ *on k.*

Proof. Trivial if $K = k(\alpha)$, and then follows for general K on using a chain (B.1).

THEOREM B.1. *Let* K/L *and* L/k *be separable extensions. Then* K/k *is a separable extension.*

Proof. Let U/L be a finite extension and

$$\tau_i : K \to U \quad (1 \le i \le [K:L])$$

be injections extending the identity on L and similarly let V/k be a finite extension and

$$\sigma_j : L \to V \quad (1 \le j \le [L:k])$$

extend the identity on k. By repeated application of Lemma 2 there is a finite field extension M/V and $[L:k]$ injections

$$\sigma'_j : U \to M \quad (1 \le j \le [L:k])$$

which extend the σ_j. Then the $\sigma'_j\tau_i$ give

$$[K:L][L:k] = [K:k]$$

distinct injections of K into M extending the identity on k.

COROLLARY. *In characteristic zero every finite field extension is separable.*

Proof. For a simple extension $k(\alpha)/k$ clearly is, and then apply the theorem to a tower of simple extensions.

THEOREM B.2. *Let K/k be a separable extension. Then it is simple, i.e. $K = k(\gamma)$ for some γ.*

Note. The converse is, of course, false.

Proof. If k is a finite field then so is K and so indeed $K = \Pi(\alpha)$ for some $\alpha \in K$, where Π is the prime field, by the structure theory of finite fields. Hence we need consider only the case when k has infinitely many elements. Suppose first that $K = k(\alpha, \beta)$ and let $\sigma_1, \ldots, \sigma_n$ where $n = [K:k]$ be the distinct injections of K into M (say). If $i \ne j$, distinctness implies that

$$\text{either} \quad \sigma_i\alpha \ne \sigma_j\alpha \quad \text{or} \quad \sigma_i\beta \ne \sigma_j\beta$$

(or both). Hence we may find $a, b \in k$ to satisfy the finitely many inequalities

$$a(\sigma_i\alpha - \sigma_j\alpha) + b(\sigma_i\beta - \sigma_j\beta) \ne 0 \; (i \ne j).$$

Put

$$\gamma = a\alpha + b\beta,$$

so

$$\sigma_i\gamma \ne \sigma_j\gamma \quad (i \ne j).$$

The $\sigma_i\gamma$ are all roots of the irreducible equation for γ over k and so

$$[k(\gamma):k] \ge n.$$

But $k(\gamma) \subset K$, so $K = k(\gamma)$.

For the general case when $K = k(\alpha_1, \alpha_2, \ldots, \alpha_J)$ with $J > 2$ one uses induction on J. We have $k(\alpha_2, \ldots, \alpha_J) = k(\beta)$ for some β and then $k(\alpha_1, \beta) = k(\gamma)$.

THEOREM B.3. *Let K/k be a separable extension. Then*

$$S(\alpha, \beta) = S_{K/k}(\alpha\beta)$$

is a non-degenerate symmetric bilinear form on K considered as a vector space over k.

Proof. Only the non-degeneracy needs proof. Let $\omega_1, \ldots, \omega_n$ be a base of K/k. The statement of the Theorem is equivalent to

$$D\,(\text{say}) = \det\{S_{K/k}(\omega_i\omega_j)\}_{\substack{1 \le i \le n \\ 1 \le j \le n}} \neq 0.$$

Let $\sigma_1, \ldots, \sigma_n$ be distinct injections of K into some M. By Lemma B.1, Corollary 3 we have

$$D = \Delta^2$$

where

$$\Delta = \det(\sigma_i\omega_j)_{\substack{1 \le i \le n \\ 1 \le j \le n}}.$$

By Theorem B.2 we have $K = k(\gamma)$ and so can take $\omega_j = \gamma^{j-1}$. Then

$$\Delta = \prod_{i<j} (\sigma_j\gamma - \sigma_i\gamma)$$
$$\neq 0,$$

as required.†

We now consider when a simple extension $k(\alpha)/k$ is separable. Let $f(x)$ be an irreducible polynomial in $k[x]$ and let $f'(x)$ be its derivative. If $f'(x) \neq 0$ it must be coprime to $f(x)$, since it is of lower degree, and so there are $a(x)$, $b(x) \in k[x]$ such that

$$a(x)f(x) + b(x)f'(x) = 1.$$

Hence $f(\beta) = 0$ for β in any extension of k, implies that $f'(\beta) \neq 0$, and so β is a simple root. Hence the number of roots of $f(x)$ in a splitting field is equal to the degree. On the other hand, if $f'(x) = 0$, every root of $f(x)$ is multiple, and so the total number of roots is less than the degree. In the first case we say that $f(x)$ is separable, in the second inseparable. The second case occurs if and only if $f(x) = g(x^p)$ for some $g(x) \in k[x]$, where p is the characteristic.

LEMMA B.3. *A necessary and sufficient condition for $k(\alpha)/k$ to be separable is that the irreducible polynomial $f(x) \in k[x]$ for α be separable.*

Proof. Clear.

COROLLARY 1. *Let $K \supset k$, and suppose that $k(\alpha)/k$ is separable. Then $K(\alpha)/K$ is separable.*

Proof. For the irreducible polynomial $F(x) \in K[x]$ over K divides $f(x)$.

COROLLARY 2. *A necessary and sufficient condition that K/k be separable is that every element of K be separable $/k$.*

Proof. Suppose that every element of K is separable and that K is given by a chain

$$k = K_0 \subset K_1 \subset \ldots \subset K_J = K$$

† Instead of using the fact that $K = k(\gamma)$ we could have used Artin's theorem that any set of injections of one field into another is linearly independent. See Artin: "Galois Theory" (Notre Dame) or Adamson: "Introduction to Field Theory" (Oliver and Boyd).

where $K_j = K_{j-1}(\alpha_{j-1})$. Then K_j/K_{j-1} is separable by the previous corollary and so K/k is separable by Theorem 1.

The converse follows from Lemma 1 Corollary.

In striking contrast to Theorem B.3 we have

THEOREM B.4. *Let K/k be inseparable. Then the trace $S_{K/k}(\beta)$ vanishes for all $\beta \in K$.*

Proof. Suppose, first, that $K = k(\alpha)$ where $\alpha^p \in k$, $\alpha \notin k$ and p is the characteristic. Then

$$\omega_1 = 1, \omega_2 = \alpha, \ldots, \omega_p = \alpha^{p-1}$$

is a basis for K/k. If $\beta = b_1 + b_2\alpha + \ldots + b_p\alpha^{p-1}$ with $b_j \in k$, then

$$\beta\omega_i = \sum b_{ij}\omega_j \quad b_{ij} \in k$$

where clearly

$$b_{ii} = b_1 \quad (1 \le i \le p).$$

Hence

$$S_{K/k}\beta = \sum_i b_{ii} = pb_1 = 0.$$

Now let K/k be any inseparable extension. By the latest Corollary there is an inseparable $\alpha \in K$. Put $L = k(\alpha)$, $M = k(\alpha^p)$, so L/M is an extension of the kind just discussed. The general result now follows because of the transitivity of the trace:

$$S_{K/k}\beta = S_{M/k}\{S_{L/M}(S_{K/L}\beta)\}.$$

APPENDIX C

Hensel's Lemma

In the literature a variety of results go under this name. Their common feature is that the existence of an approximate solution of an equation or system of equations in a complete valued field implies the existence of an exact solution to which it is an approximation, subject to conditions to the general effect that the approximate solution is "good enough". These results are essentially just examples of the process of solution by successive approximation, which goes back to Newton (at least). In this appendix we give a typical specimen.

LEMMA. *Let k be a field complete with respect to the non-archimedean valuation $|\ |$ and let*

$$f(X) \in \mathfrak{o}[X], \tag{C.1}$$

where $\mathfrak{o} \subset k$ is the ring of integers for $|\ |$. Let $\alpha_0 \in \mathfrak{o}$ be such that

$$|f(\alpha_0)| < |f'(\alpha_0)|^2, \tag{C.2}$$

where $f'(X)$ is the (formal) derivative of $f(X)$. Then there is a solution of

$$f(\alpha) = 0, \qquad |\alpha - \alpha_0| \le |f(\alpha)|/|f'(\alpha)|. \tag{C.3}$$

Proof. (Sketch.) Let $f_j(X) \in \mathfrak{o}[X]$ be defined by the identity

$$f(X+Y) = f(X)+f_1(X)Y+\ldots+f_j(X)Y^j+\ldots, \tag{C.4}$$

where X, Y are independent variables, so $f_1(X) = f'(X)$. Define β_0 by

$$f(\alpha_0)+\beta_0 f_1(\alpha_0) = 0. \tag{C.5}$$

Then by (C.4) and since $f_j(\alpha_0) \in \mathfrak{o}$ we have

$$\begin{aligned} |f(\alpha_0+\beta_0)| &\leq \max_{j\geq 2} |f_j(\alpha_0)\beta_0^j| \\ &\leq \max_{j\geq 2} |\beta_0|^j \\ &\leq |f(\alpha_0)|^2/|f_1(\alpha_0)|^2 \\ &< |f(\alpha_0)|. \end{aligned} \tag{C.6}$$

On using the analogue of (C.4) for $f_1(X)$, it is easy to verify that

$$|f_1(\alpha_0+\beta_0)-f_1(\alpha_0)| < |f_1(\alpha_0)|.$$

Thus on putting $\alpha_1 = \alpha_0+\beta_0$, we have

$$|f(\alpha_1)| \leq |f(\alpha_0)|^2/|f_1(\alpha_0)|^2,$$
$$|f_1(\alpha_1)| = |f_1(\alpha_0)|$$

and

$$|\alpha_1-\alpha_0| \leq |f(\alpha_0)|/|f_1(\alpha_0)|.$$

On repeating the process with α_1, etc., we get a sequence $\alpha_0, \alpha_1, \alpha_2, \ldots$, which is easily seen to be a fundamental sequence. By the completeness of k there is an $\alpha = \lim_{n\to\infty} \alpha_n \in k$, which clearly does what is required.

In fact, the solution of (C.3) not merely exists, but is unique. For if $\alpha+\beta$, $\beta \neq 0$ is another solution one readily gets a contradiction by putting $X = \alpha$ $Y = \beta$ in (C.4).

Chapter III

Cyclotomic Fields and Kummer Extensions

B. J. Birch

1. Cyclotomic Fields

Let K be any field of characteristic zero, and $m > 1$ be an integer. Then there is a minimal extension L/K such that $x^m - 1$ splits completely in L. The zeros of $x^m - 1$ form a subgroup of the multiplicative group of L; this subgroup is cyclic (since every finite subgroup of the multiplicative group of a field is). The generators of this subgroup are called the primitive mth roots of unity. If ζ is a primitive mth root of unity then every zero of $(x^m - 1)$ is a power of ζ, and $L = K(\zeta)$. Clearly, L is a normal extension of K; we write $L = K(\sqrt[m]{1})$.

If σ is an element of the Galois group $G(L/K)$, then $\sigma\zeta$ must be another primitive mth root of unity, so $\sigma\zeta = \zeta^k$ for some integer k, $(k, m) = 1$. If ζ^a is another primitive root of unity then $\sigma\zeta^a = \zeta^{ak}$; accordingly, $\sigma \mapsto k$ is a canonical map of $G(L/K)$ into the multiplicative group $G(m)$ of residues modulo m prime to m. In particular, $[L : K] \leq \phi(m)$.

If $m = rs$ where $(r, s) = 1$ then there exist integers a, b with $ar + bs = 1$, $\zeta = (\zeta^r)^a(\zeta^s)^b$, so $K(\zeta) = K(\zeta^r, \zeta^s)$; one obtains the extension $K(\zeta)$ by composing $K(\zeta^r)$ and $K(\zeta^s)$. So to some extent it is enough to consider $K(\sqrt[m]{1})$ when m is a prime power. If p is odd then the group $G(p^n)$ is cyclic, so if $m = p^n$, $L = K(\sqrt[m]{1})$, then $G(L/K)$ is cyclic; on the other hand $G(2^n)$ is generated by -1 and 5, so if we write $\eta = \zeta + \zeta^{-1}$ where $\zeta^{2^n} = 1$ then $K(\zeta) = K(i, \eta)$ and $G[K(\eta)/K]$ is cyclic.

We are particularly interested in the extensions $\mathbf{Q}(\sqrt[m]{1})$ and $\mathbf{Q}_p(\sqrt[m]{1})$; by Chapter I (Section 4 and start of Section 5) the study of the factorization of the prime p in the extension $\mathbf{Q}(\sqrt[m]{1})/\mathbf{Q}$ is essentially the same as the study of the extension $\mathbf{Q}_p(\sqrt[m]{1})/Q_p$. As one of my jobs is to supply explicit examples for abstract theorems, I will prove things several times over by different routes. Good accounts of cyclotomic extensions are given by Weyl: "Algebraic Theory of Numbers" (Princeton U.P., Annals of Math. Studies

No. 1), pp. 129–140, and by Weiss: "Algebraic Number Theory" (McGraw Hill), Chapter 7.

LEMMA 1. *$\mathbf{Q}(\sqrt[m]{1})$ is a normal extension of $\mathbf{Q}$ of degree $\phi(m)$; its Galois group is naturally isomorphic to $G(m)$.*

Proof (after van der Waerden). Let ζ be a primitive mth root of unity; after what has been said already, it is enough to show that an equation of minimal degree for ζ over Q has degree $\phi(m)$ so we need to show that if $f(x) \in \mathbf{Z}[x]$ and $f(\zeta) = 0$ then $f(\zeta^a) = 0$ whenever $(a, m) = 1$. For this, it is enough to show that $f(\zeta^p) = 0$ whenever p is a prime not dividing m.

Consider the field k_p with p elements; if $f(x) \in \mathbf{Z}[x]$, denote its natural image in $k_p[x]$ by $f^*(x)$. Let L^*, a finite extension of k_p, be a splitting field for $(x^m - 1)$; $(x^m - 1)$ is prime to its derivative mx^{m-1}, so has distinct roots.

Suppose that the factorization in $\mathbf{Z}[x]$ of $(x^m - 1)$ is $f_1(x).f_2(x)\ldots.f_r(x)$, so that the $f_i(x)$ are irreducible. Then in $k_p[x]$, $(x^m - 1) = \prod f_i^*(x)$, and all the zeros in L^* of all the f^*, being roots of $x^m = 1$, are distinct. Choose the numbfering so that ζ is a root of $f_1(x)$, and suppose that ζ^p is a root of $f_J(x)$. Then $_1(x)$ divides $f_J(x^p)$, so $f_1^*(x)$ divides $f_J^*(x^p)$. Let ζ^* be a zero of $f_1^*(x)$; then $f_J^*(\zeta^{*p}) = 0$, and on the other hand $f_1^*(\zeta^{*p}) = [f_1^*(\zeta^*)]^p = 0$. So f_J is the same as f_1.

COROLLARY 2. *If $p \nmid m$ there is a unique element σ_p of the Galois group $G[\mathbf{Q}(\sqrt[m]{1})/\mathbf{Q}]$ such that $\sigma_p \alpha \equiv \alpha^p(p)$ for all integers $\alpha \in Q(\sqrt[m]{1})$. In fact, if ζ is a primitive mth root of unity then σ_p is given by $\sigma_p(\sum a_i \zeta^i) = \sum a_i \zeta^{ip}$ for $a_i \in \mathbf{Q}$. (σ_p is the Frobenius automorphism.)*

Proof. The field basis $1, \zeta, \ldots, \zeta^{\phi(m)-1}$ has discriminant prime to p, so by Chapter I, Section 3, certainly every integer can be expressed as $\sum a_i \zeta^i / b$ with $a_1, \ldots, a_{p-2}, b \in \mathbf{Z}$ and $(b, p) = 1$; so σ_p defined above does what is wanted. We need to show that it is unique. The effect of an element σ of the Galois group is clearly determined by its effect on ζ; and clearly every σ takes ζ to another primitive root, ζ^a say, with $(a, m) = 1$. We need to show that $\zeta^a \equiv \zeta^b(p)$ only if $\zeta^a = \zeta^b$; that is, $1 - \zeta^b \equiv 0(p)$ only if $\zeta^b = 1$.

First method. Suppose $\zeta^b \neq 1$. We know

$$x^m - 1 = \prod_{i=1}^{m} (x - \zeta^i),$$

so

$$mx^{m-1} = \sum_j \prod_{i \neq j} (x - \zeta^i),$$

and

$$m = \prod_{i=1}^{m-1} (1 - \zeta^i).$$

So $(1 - \zeta^b)$ divides m, so p does not divide $(1 - \zeta^b)$.

Second method. Take the completion $\mathbf{Q}_p$ of $\mathbf{Q}$, and form the extension $\mathbf{Q}_p(\sqrt[m]{1})$. Let L^* be the residue class field of $\mathbf{Q}_p(\sqrt[m]{1})$. Then L^* is a finite extension of k_p and is a splitting field for x^m-1. $\mathbf{Q}(\sqrt[m]{1}) \subseteq \mathbf{Q}_p(\sqrt[m]{1})$, so the residue class map makes a root of x^m-1 in L^* correspond to each root of x^m-1 in $Q(\sqrt[m]{1})$. Conversely, the roots of $x^m = 1$ in L^* are distinct, and each of them is the residue class of an element of $\mathbf{Q}_p(\sqrt[m]{1})$, by Hensel's Lemma (Chapter I, Section 7, Lemma 1, or Chapter II, Appendix C). So we have a one–one correspondence between the mth roots of unity in L^* and in $\mathbf{Q}(\sqrt[m]{1})$, and everything follows.

LEMMA 3. *If $q = p^f$ is a prime power and ζ is a primitive qth root of unity, then the prime p is totally ramified and in fact $(p) = (1-\zeta)^{\phi(q)}$.*

First Proof. Write $\lambda = 1-\zeta$. Then $\zeta^q = 1$ but $\zeta^{q/p} \neq 1$, so λ is a root of the polynomial $F(x) = [(1+x)^q - 1]/[(1+x)^{q/p} - 1]$. F has leading coefficient 1 and constant term p, and it is readily verified that all the other coefficients are divisible by p. So F is an Eisenstein equation, and by Chapter I, Section 6, Theorem 1, $\mathbf{Q}_p(\sqrt[q]{1})$ is a totally ramified extension of $\mathbf{Q}_p$ of degree $\phi(q)$ and $(p) = (\lambda)^{\phi(q)}$. Going back to $\mathbf{Q}(\sqrt[q]{1})$, we see that $\mathbf{Q}(\sqrt[q]{1})$ is an extension of $\mathbf{Q}$ of degree $\phi(q)$ (so we get another proof of Lemma 1 in this case) and p is totally ramified in this extension.

Second Proof. We can see all this more explicitly. If $(a,p) = (b,p) = 1$, then we can solve $a \equiv bs(q)$, so

$$(1-\zeta^a)/(1-\zeta^b) = (1-\zeta^{bs})/(1-\zeta^b) = 1+\zeta^b+\ldots+\zeta^{b(s-1)}$$

is an integer, and similarly so is $(1-\zeta^b)/1-\zeta^a)$; so $(1-\zeta^a)/(1-\zeta^b)$ is a unit whenever $(a,p) = (b,p) = 1$. Also,

$$p = \lim_{x\to 1} \frac{x^q-1}{x^{q/p}-1} = \lim_{x\to 1} \prod_{\substack{(a,p)=1 \\ 0<a<q}} (x-\zeta^a) = (1-\zeta)^{\phi(q)} \prod \frac{1-\zeta^a}{1-\zeta},$$

so (p) is simply the $\phi(q)$th power of $(\lambda) = (1-\zeta)$.

LEMMA 4. *Let ζ be a primitive mth root of* 1. *If p is a prime not dividing m then it is unramified in* $\mathbf{Q}(\sqrt[m]{1})$ *and its residue class degree f_p* (see Chapter I, Section 5) *is the least integer $f \geq 1$ such that $p^f \equiv 1(m)$.*

Proof [after Serre: "Corps Locaux" (Hermann, Paris)]. Consider the extension $Q_p(\zeta)$ of Q_p; the residue class field k_p has p elements. The polynomial x^m-1 splits in k_{p^f} if and only if $m|(p^f-1)$. Take the least f with $p^f \equiv 1(m)$, and construct the unramified extension L of Q_p with residue class field k_{p^f} (see Chapter I, Section 7, Theorem 1). There is a multiplicative map $k_{p^f}^\times \to L^\times$ as in the second proof of Corollary 2, so x^m-1 splits in L, and clearly L is minimal with this property. So $L = Q_p(\zeta)$.

Going back to $\mathbf{Q}(\zeta)$, we see that p is unramified in $\mathbf{Q}(\zeta)$ and has residue class degree f_p as described.

(In fact, the lemma is an immediate consequence of the properties of the Frobenius automorphism obtained in Corollary 2.)

COROLLARY. *If $p \not| m$, then p splits completely if and only if $p \equiv 1(m)$.*

LEMMA 5. *If $q = p^t$ is a prime power and ζ is a primitive qth root of unity, the discriminant of the extension $\mathbf{Q}(\zeta)$ of $\mathbf{Q}$ is $q^{\phi(q)}/p^{q/p}$; a basis for the $\mathbf{Z}$-module of integers of $\mathbf{Q}(\zeta)$ is $1, \zeta, \zeta^2, \ldots, \zeta^{\phi(q)-1}$.*

Proof. Consider first the case $t = 1$. By Lemmas 3 and 4, the only prime ramified in $\mathbf{Q}(\zeta)$ is p, and the ramification of p is tame with $e = p-1$. Hence by Chapter I, Section 5, Theorem 2, the discriminant is p^{p-2}. Hence by Chapter I, Section 4, Prop. 6, $1, \zeta, \zeta^2, \ldots, \zeta^{p-2}$ is a basis as asserted.

In case $t \geq 2$, the ramification is wild, so all that is obvious from Chapter I (until the final section) is that the discriminant is a power of p, at least $p^{\phi(q)}$. We give a direct proof that the powers of ζ form a basis for the integers, which works for all t. Consider the $\mathbf{Z}$-module $\mathbf{Z}[\zeta]$. By Chapter I, Section 4, Prop. 6, $Z[\zeta]$ has discriminant $N_{\mathbf{Q}(\zeta)/\mathbf{Q}}[g'(\zeta)]$, where

$$g(x) = \prod_{(k,p)=1} (x - \zeta^k);$$

after dull computation this turns out to be $q^{\phi(q)}/p^{q/p}$.

We want to show that $\mathbf{Z}[\zeta]$ is the whole ring of integers of $\mathbf{Q}(\zeta)$; after Chapter I, Section 3, Prop. 4 it remains to check that

$$\sum_{0 \leq i \leq \phi(q)-1} a_i \zeta^i$$

with $a_i \in \mathbf{Z}$ is divisible by p if and only if all the a_i are divisible by p; that is, that

$$\sum_{0 \leq i \leq \phi(q)-1} b_i (1-\zeta)^i$$

is divisible by p if and only if all the b_i are. To check this, suppose that $p | \sum b_i (1-\zeta^i)$; recollect that $(p) = (1-\zeta)^{\phi(q)}$, and suppose that $p | b_i$ for $i = 1, \ldots, s-1$. Then

$$(1-\zeta)^{\phi(q)} | b_s (1-\zeta)^s + b_{s+1}(1-\zeta)^{s+1} + \ldots, \quad \text{so } (1-\zeta) | b_s, \quad \text{so } p | b_s;$$

so by induction we get what we want. The conclusions of the Lemma follow.

LEMMA 6. *If ζ is a primitive mth root of unity, then $\mathbf{Q}(\zeta)$ is an extension of $\mathbf{Q}$ of degree $\phi(m)$; the discriminant of $\mathbf{Q}(\zeta)$ over $\mathbf{Q}$ is*

$$m^{\phi(m)} \Big/ \prod_{p/m} p^{\phi(m)/(p-1)};$$

a basis for the $\mathbf{Z}$-module of integers of $\mathbf{Q}(\zeta)$ is $1, \zeta, \zeta^2, \ldots, \zeta^{\phi(m)-1}$; p is ramified if and only if $p | m$.

Most of this has been proved already (Lemmas 1, 3 and 4); the extra assertions about the discriminant and the basis for integers are equivalent to each other, and may in fact be proved directly (see Weiss, Section 7.5). One may also pick up the assertions about $\mathbf{Q}(\sqrt[m]{1})$ by fitting together the extensions $\mathbf{Q}(\sqrt[q]{1})$ where q runs through the prime power factors of m.

First, remark that if q, q' are powers of different primes,

$$\mathbf{Q}(\sqrt[q]{1}) \cap \mathbf{Q}(\sqrt[q']{1}) = \mathbf{Q}.$$

Now work out the discriminant. Suppose $p^h \| m$. By Lemma 5 the discriminant of $\mathbf{Q}_p(\sqrt[p^h]{1})$ over $\mathbf{Q}_p$ is $p^{hp^h-(h+1)p^{h-1}}$. There is no further ramification of p in $\mathbf{Q}_p(\sqrt[m]{1})$, so by Chapter I, Section 4, Prop. 7, the discriminant of $\mathbf{Q}_p(\sqrt[m]{1})$ over $\mathbf{Q}_p$ is $p^{h\phi(m)-\phi(m)/(p-1)}$. By Chapter I, Section 4, Prop 6, the discriminant of $\mathbf{Q}(\zeta)$ over $\mathbf{Q}$ is

$$m^{\phi(m)} \Big/ \prod_{p/m} p^{\phi(m)/(p-1)}.$$

By computation this is the discriminant of $\mathbf{Z}[\zeta]$, so by Chapter I, Section 3, Prop. 4, $1, \zeta, \zeta^2, \ldots, \zeta^{\phi(m)-1}$ really is a basis for the Z-module of integers.

Remark. All assertions about factorization of primes in $\mathbf{Q}(\sqrt[m]{1})$ may be regained from Lemma 6, by using Kummer's theorem (see for instance Weiss, Section 4.9; or the Appendix). "If $\mathbf{Z}[\zeta]$ is the complete ring of integers of $\mathbf{Q}(\zeta)$, and $g(x) = 0$ is the characteristic equation of ζ over $\mathbf{Q}$, then a prime p factorizes in $\mathbf{Q}(\zeta)$ in the same way as $g(x)$ factorizes modulo p, and in fact if $g(x) \equiv \prod g_i(x) \pmod p$ then $(p) = \prod [p, g_i(\zeta)]$."

It is, of course, perfectly possible to work out the ramification groups explicitly in this case—for this we refer to Serre: "Corps Locaux" (Hermann, Paris), pp. 84–87.

To conclude. We have shown that every cyclotomic extension, and so every subfield of a cyclotomic extension of $\mathbf{Q}$ has abelian Galois group. The converse is true—every abelian extension of $\mathbf{Q}$ is a subfield of a cyclotomic extension (Kronecker's Theorem); but that is Class Field Theory (Chapter VII, § 5.7.)

2. Kummer Extensions

Throughout this lecture, K is a field of characteristic prime to n in which $x^n - 1$ splits; and ζ will be a primitive nth root of unity. It will be shown that the cyclic extensions of K of exponent dividing n are the same as the so-called "Kummer" extensions $K(\sqrt[n]{a})$.

Let a be a non-zero element of K. If L is an extension of K such that $x^n = a$ has a root α in L, then all the roots $\alpha, \zeta\alpha, \zeta^2\alpha, \ldots, \zeta^{n-1}\alpha$ of $x^n = a$ are in L, and any automorph of L over K permutes them. We denote the minimal splitting field for $x^n - a$ by $K(\sqrt[n]{a})$. If σ is an element of the Galois group $G[K(\sqrt[n]{a})/K]$, then, once we have chosen a root of $x^n = a$, σ is determined completely by the image $\sigma\alpha = \zeta^b \alpha$. In particular, if a is of order n in the multiplicative group $K^\times/(K^\times)^n$, then a^r is a nth power only if $n|r$, so

$x^n - a$ is irreducible; in this case, the map $\sigma \mapsto \zeta^b$ gives an isomorphism of the Galois group on to a cyclic group of order n. Let us state all this as a lemma.

LEMMA 1. *If a is a non-zero element of K, there is a well-defined normal extension $K(\sqrt[n]{a})$, the splitting field of $x^n - a$. If α is a root of $x^n = a$, there is a map of $G[K(\sqrt[n]{a})/K]$ into $K^\times$ given by $\sigma \mapsto \sigma\alpha/\alpha$; in particular, if a is of order n in $K^\times/(K^\times)^n$, the Galois group is cyclic and can be generated by σ with $\sigma\alpha = \zeta\alpha$.*

LEMMA 2. *If L is a cyclic extension of K (i.e. $G(L/K)$ is cyclic) then $L = K(\sqrt[n]{b})$ for some $b \in K$. (b must generate $K^\times/(K^\times)^n$.)*

The proof is by direct construction, which is providentially possible. Let σ be a generator of $G(L/K)$; then $L = K(\gamma)$ for some γ, since all separable extensions are simple, and we can choose γ so that $\gamma, \sigma\gamma, \ldots, \sigma^{n-1}\gamma$ is a basis for L over K. Form the sum

$$\beta = \sum_{s=0}^{n-1} \zeta^s \sigma^s \gamma.$$

Then $\sigma\beta = \zeta^{-1}\beta$, and $\beta \neq 0$ since $\gamma, \ldots, \sigma^{n-1}\gamma$ are linearly independent over K; so $\beta^n \in K$ and $\beta^r \notin K$ for $0 < r < n$. Thus $\beta^n = b$ is of order n in $K^\times/(K^\times)^n$; by Lemma 1, $K(\sqrt[n]{b})$ is a cyclic extension of degree n contained in L, so $L = K(\sqrt[n]{b})$.

LEMMA 3. *Two cyclic extensions $K(\sqrt[n]{a})$, $K(\sqrt[n]{b})$ of K of the same degree are the same if and only if $a = b^r c^n$ for some $c \in K$ and $r \in Z$ with $(r, n) = 1$.*

In fact, "if" is obvious; we have to prove the "only if" part. This is easy by elementary Galois theory. Suppose that $K(\alpha) = K(\beta)$ with $\alpha^n = a$, $\beta^n = b$. Let σ be a generator of the Galois group with $\sigma\alpha = \zeta\alpha$, then $\sigma\beta = \zeta^i\beta$ for some i. Suppose

$$\beta = \sum_{0}^{n-1} c_j \alpha^j,$$

then

$$\sigma\beta = \sum c_j \zeta^j \alpha^j,$$

so we can only have

$$\beta = c_i \alpha^i.$$

COROLLARY. *Let L be a finite extension of K with abelian Galois group G of exponent dividing n. Then G is the direct product of cyclic subgroups $G_1, \ldots, G_r$. For each i, let L_i be the fixed field of $G_1 \times \ldots \times G_{i+1} \times \ldots \times G_r$; then $G(L_i/K) = G_i$, $L_i = K(\alpha_i)$ with $\alpha_i^n = a_i \in K$, and $L = K(\alpha_1, \ldots, \alpha_r)$.*

We may approach the last couple of lemmas via Galois cohomology (see Serre, p. 163). We quote a generalization of Lemma 2.

LEMMA 4. *If L is a normal algebraic extension of K with Galois group G then*

$$H^1(G, L^\times) = 0.$$

[A 1-cocycle is a "continuous" map $G \to L^\times$ in which $\sigma \to \alpha_\sigma$ with $\sigma(\alpha_\tau) = \alpha_\sigma^{-1}\alpha_{\sigma\tau}$; "continuous" means that the map may be factored through a finite quotient G' of G. Form the sum $\beta = \sum_{\sigma \in G'} \alpha_\sigma \sigma(\gamma)$; by the linear independence of automorphisms [Artin: "Galois Theory", (Notre Dame), Theorem 12 and Corollary and Theorem 21], we may choose γ so that $\beta \neq 0$; and then $\alpha_\sigma = \beta/\sigma\beta$.]

Apply Lemma 4 taking L as the (separable) algebraic closure of K. There is an exact sequence $0 \to E_n \xrightarrow{v} L^\times \to L^\times \to 0$ where v is the map $x \mapsto x^n$ and E_n is the nth roots of unity. Taking homology, we get

$$H^0(G, E_n) \to H^0(G, L^\times) \xrightarrow{v} H^0(G, L^\times) \to H^1(G, E_n) \to H^1(G, L^\times) \to \ldots$$

Since G acts trivially on E_n, $H^1(G, E_n)$ is $\mathrm{Hom}(G, E_n)$, and of course $H^0(G, L^\times)$ is the part of $L^\times$ fixed under G, so this is

$$E_n \to K^\times \xrightarrow{v} K^\times \to \mathrm{Hom}(G, E_n) \to 0,$$

i.e.

$$K^\times/(K^\times)^n \cong \mathrm{Hom}(G, E_n).$$

One can make the isomorphism explicit. Recollect that if $0 \to A \to B \to C \to 0$ then an element $c \in C^G$ gives a map $G \to A$ by taking b with $b \to c$, and then $\sigma \mapsto b/\sigma b$ is a map $G \to A$. In our case, we start with $c \in K^\times$; take γ so that $\gamma^n = c$; and then $\sigma \mapsto \gamma/\sigma\gamma$ is a map $G \to E_n$. Conversely, if $\phi \in \mathrm{Hom}(G, E_n)$, let G' be the kernel of ϕ. Then G/G' is the Galois group of a cyclic extension K' of K of exponent dividing n, and if $\sigma \in G$ is such that $\phi(\sigma) = \zeta$, there is an element $\gamma \in K'$ such that $\sigma\gamma = \zeta\gamma$; then $\gamma^n \in K^\times$, so determines a class of $K^\times/K^{\times n}$.

The elements of G whose exponent divides n are preserved in $\mathrm{Hom}(G, E_n)$. Let K_n be the union of the abelian extensions of K whose Galois groups have exponent dividing n; then $\mathrm{Hom}[G(K_n/K), E_n] \cong K^\times/(K^\times)^n$. In particular the finite abelian extensions of G whose exponents divide n correspond to finite subgroups of $K^\times/(K^\times)^n$.

Finally we want to look at the factorization of primes $\mathfrak{p}$ of K in the extension $K(\sqrt[n]{a})$; by Chapter I, as before, this is the same as the study of the extensions $K_\mathfrak{p}(\sqrt[n]{a})$ of the local field $K_\mathfrak{p}$.

LEMMA 5. *The discriminant of $K(\sqrt[n]{a})$ over K divides $n^n a^{n-1}$; $\mathfrak{p}$ is unramified if $\mathfrak{p} \nmid na$. If a^f is the least power of a such that $a^f \equiv x^n(\mathfrak{p})$ is soluble, then f is the residue class degree.*

Suppose $\alpha^n = a$; then, if $\mathfrak{o}$ is the ring of integers of K, $\mathfrak{o}[\alpha]$ is a submodule of the ring of integers of $K(\alpha)$, and by Chapter I, Section 4, Prop 6, its discriminant is $(n\alpha^{n-1})^n = n^n a^{n-1}$; so the discriminant of $K(\alpha)$ over K divides $n^n a^{n-1}$. In particular, by Chapter I, Section 5, $\mathfrak{p}$ is unramified if $\mathfrak{p} \nmid na$, and indeed by Kummer's theorem (or by Chapter, II Section 16 and Hensel's Lemma) the factorization of $\mathfrak{p}$ then mimics that of $x^n - a$ modulo $\mathfrak{p}$. Hence, if a^f is the least power of a such that $x^n \equiv a^f(\mathfrak{p})$ is soluble, then $\mathfrak{p}$ factors as the product of n/f prime ideals in $K(\alpha)$, and the residue class degree is f. Alternatively, this last bit can be proved like Lemma 4 of the cyclotomic lecture, by forming the unramified extension of $K_{\mathfrak{p}}$ in which $x^n - a$ splits.

LEMMA 6. *If $\mathfrak{p}|a$, $\mathfrak{p} \nmid n$ and $\mathfrak{p}^n \nmid a$ then $\mathfrak{p}$ is tamely ramified in $K(\sqrt[n]{a})$; if $\mathfrak{p}|a$ and $\mathfrak{p}^2 \nmid a$ then $\mathfrak{p}$ is totally ramified in $K(\sqrt[n]{a})$.*

Let α be a root of $x^n = a$. The second part of the lemma is easy; if $\mathfrak{p}|a$ but $\mathfrak{p}^2 \nmid a$ then, quite explicitly, $\mathfrak{p} = (\mathfrak{p}, \alpha)^n$. The result can also be obtained from Chapter I, Section 6, Theorem 1, since in this case $x^n - a$ is an Eisenstein polynomial.

If $\mathfrak{p} \nmid n$, so that $\mathfrak{p}$ does not divide the degree of the extension then any ramification must certainly be tame (see Chapter I, Section 5). On the other hand, if $\mathfrak{p}|a$ but $\mathfrak{p}^n \nmid a$ then $\mathfrak{p}$ is certainly ramified, since $(\mathfrak{p}, \alpha)|\mathfrak{p}|(\mathfrak{p}, \alpha)^n$, but $\alpha \notin \mathfrak{p}$.

There remains the case where $\mathfrak{p}^r|a$, $\mathfrak{p}^{r+1} \nmid a$, $\mathfrak{p} \nmid n$ with $2 \leq r \leq n-1$. If $(r, n) = 1$, we have k, m so that $rk + nm = 1$, and choose $q \in K$ with $\mathfrak{p}|q$, $\mathfrak{p}^2 \nmid q$. Then $K[\sqrt[n]{(a^k q^{-nm})}] = K(\sqrt[n]{a})$, and we have got back to the case $r = 1$. If $(r, n) = s > 1$, the ramification is no longer total, and there may or may not be splitting as well. The ramification index is n/s : $\mathfrak{p}$ is unramified in the extension $K(\sqrt[s]{a})$ of K, and then the factors of $\mathfrak{p}$ are totally ramified in the extension $K(\sqrt[n]{a})$ of $K(\sqrt[s]{a})$.

APPENDIX

Kummer's Theorem

Throughout this appendix, K is an algebraic number field with ring of integers $\mathfrak{o}$, and $L = K(\theta)$ is an extension of degree n; we suppose that θ is an integer and that $f(x) \in \mathfrak{o}[x]$ is the characteristic polynomial of θ. $\mathfrak{p}$ is a prime ideal of $\mathfrak{o}$, v is the associated valuation, $K_{\mathfrak{p}}$ is the completion of K at $\mathfrak{p}$, $\mathfrak{o}_{\mathfrak{p}}$ is the ring of integers of $K_{\mathfrak{p}}$, and $K_{\mathfrak{p}}^*$ is the residue class field. The prime ideal factorization of $\mathfrak{p}$ in L is $\mathfrak{p} = \prod \mathfrak{q}_j^{e_j}$; the associated valuations, completions, rings of integers, and residue class fields are V_j, L_j, $\mathfrak{o}_j$, L_j^*. If f, g are polynomials in $\mathfrak{o}[x]$, $\mathfrak{o}_{\mathfrak{p}}[x]$ their images under the residue class map are denoted by f^*, g^*.

In Chapter II, Section 10, it was shown that, if the irreducible factorization of $f(x)$ in $\mathfrak{o}[x]$ is

$$f(x) = \prod_{1 \leq j \leq J} g_j(x)$$

then $L_j = K_{\mathfrak{p}}(\theta_j)$ where $g_j(\theta_j) = 0$. There is an injection map $\mu_j : L \to L_j$, with $\mu_j \theta = \theta_j$; and a residue class map $\psi_j : \mathfrak{o}_j \to L_j^*$.

We wish to relate the factorization of $\mathfrak{p}$ in L to the factorization of $f_j^*(x)$ in $K_{\mathfrak{p}}^*[x]$. First we need a lemma.

LEMMA. *With the above notations,* $g_j^*(x)$ *is a power of an irreducible polynomial of* $K_\mathfrak{p}^*[x]$, *say* $g_j^*(x) = [G_j^*(x)]^{e_j}$, *and* $\psi_j\theta_j$ *is a zero of* $G_j^*(x)$.

This will be clear enough if we show that the modulo $\mathfrak{p}$ reduction of every irreducible polynomial of $\mathfrak{o}_\mathfrak{p}[x]$ is a power of an irreducible polynomial of $K_\mathfrak{p}^*[x]$. Put another way, we wish to show that if $h(x) \in \mathfrak{o}_\mathfrak{p}[x]$ and

$$h^*(x) = h_1^*(x).h_2^*(x) \quad \text{with} \quad (h_1^*(x), h_2^*(x)) = 1,$$

then we can find $h_1(x), h_2(x)$ from $\mathfrak{o}_\mathfrak{p}[x]$ such that $h(x) = h_1(x).h_2(x)$. This is just a version of Hensel's Lemma (see Chapter II, Appendix C; Weiss 2.2.1.).

KUMMER'S THEOREM. *Suppose that* $\mathfrak{p}, \theta$ *have the property that*

$$\sum_0^{n-1} a_i\theta^i \in K[\theta]$$

is an integer only if $v(a_i) \geq 0$ *for* $i = 0,\ldots,n-1$. *Suppose that the irreducible factorization of* $f^*(x)$ *in* $K_\mathfrak{p}^*[x]$ *is* $f^*(x) = \prod [G_j^*(x)]^{e_j}$, *and for each* j *let* $G_j(x) \in \mathfrak{o}[x]$ *be a monic polynomial whose image by the residue class map is* $G_j^*(x)$. *Then the prime ideal factorization of* $\mathfrak{p}$ is $\mathfrak{p} = \prod \mathfrak{q}_j^{e_j}$, with $\mathfrak{q}_j = (\mathfrak{p}, G_j(\theta))$.

[cf. Chapter II, 19.20; $\mathfrak{p} = \Pi\ \mathfrak{q}_j^{e_j}$ is equivalent to saying that the valuations of L extending v are V_j for $j = 1, \ldots, J$, the corresponding ramification indices are the e_j, and the set of integers α of L with $V_j(\alpha) > 0$ is $\mathfrak{q}_j$. In our notation, $V_j(\alpha) > 0$ if $\psi_j\alpha = 0$.]

We have to check that the ramification indices are correct and that $\mathfrak{q}_j = (\mathfrak{p}, G_j(\theta))$; also, that different polynomials G_j^* come from different polynomials g_j.

We know already that $L_j \cong K_\mathfrak{p}[x]/(g_j(x))$. By the hypothesis of the theorem, every integer of L is of form $\sum a_i\theta^i$ with $v(a_i) \geq 0$, so every element of L_j^* is of form $\sum a_i^*(\psi_j\theta)^i$; so $L_j^* \cong K_\mathfrak{p}^*[x]/(G_j^*(x))$, and $e_j = [L_j : K_\mathfrak{p}]/[L_j^*; K_\mathfrak{p}^*]$ is the correct ramification index.

If $\alpha \in (\mathfrak{p}, G_j(\theta))$ then clearly $\psi_j\alpha = 0$, so $\alpha \in \mathfrak{q}_j$. Conversely, suppose $\alpha \in \mathfrak{q}_j$; then

$$\alpha = \sum_0^{n-1} a_i\theta^i,$$

and by the hypothesis of the theorem $v(a_i) \geq 0$ for $i = 0,\ldots,n-1$. Write $h(x) = \sum a_i x^i$ so that $h(x) \in \mathfrak{o}_\mathfrak{p}[x]$. Since $\alpha \in \mathfrak{q}_j$, $\psi_j\alpha = 0$ so $h^*(\psi_j\theta) = 0$. We can express $h(x) = G_j(x)q_j(x) + r_j(x)$, with q_j, $r_j \in \mathfrak{o}_\mathfrak{p}[x]$ and

$$\deg(r_j) < \deg(G_j);$$

and then $r_j^*(\psi_j\theta) = 0$, so $r_j^*(x)$ is identically zero, and $h(\theta) \in (\mathfrak{p}, G_j(\theta))$. Hence $\mathfrak{q}_j = (\mathfrak{p}, G_j(\theta))$, as required.

Finally, if $G_i^* = G_j^*$ with $i \neq j$, then $\mathfrak{q}_i = \mathfrak{q}_j$, so $g_i(x)$ would be the same as $g_j(x)$, a contradiction.

CHAPTER IV

Cohomology of Groups

M. F. ATIYAH and C. T. C. WALL

1. Definition of Cohomology

Let G be a group, $\Lambda = \mathbf{Z}[G]$ its integral group ring. A (left) G-module is the same thing as a (left) Λ-module. By G-module we shall always mean *left* G-module. Note that if A is a left G-module we can define a right G-module structure on A by putting $a.g = g^{-1}.a$.

If A, B are G-modules, the group of all abelian group homomorphisms $A \to B$ is denoted by $\mathrm{Hom}(A, B)$, and the group of all G-module homomorphisms by $\mathrm{Hom}_G(A, B)$. $\mathrm{Hom}(A, B)$ has a G-module structure defined as follows: if $\varphi \in \mathrm{Hom}(A, B)$, $g.\varphi$ is the mapping $a \mapsto g.\varphi(g^{-1}a)$ $(a \in A)$.

For any G-module A, the subset of elements of A invariant under the action of G is denoted by A^G. A^G is an abelian group which depends functorially on A. It is the largest submodule of A on which G acts trivially. If A, B are G-modules then

$$\mathrm{Hom}_G(A, B) = (\mathrm{Hom}(A, B))^G; \tag{1.1}$$

in particular,

$$\mathrm{Hom}_G(\mathbf{Z}, A) = (\mathrm{Hom}(\mathbf{Z}, A))^G \cong A^G,$$

regarding $\mathbf{Z}$ as a G-module on which G acts trivially. Since the functor Hom is left-exact, it follows that A^G is a left-exact covariant functor of A, i.e. if

$$0 \to A \to B \to C \to 0 \tag{1.2}$$

is an exact sequence of G-modules, then

$$0 \to A^G \to B^G \to C^G$$

is an exact sequence of abelian groups.

If X is any abelian group we can form the G-module $\mathrm{Hom}(\Lambda, X)$. A G-module of this type is said to be *co-induced.*

By a *cohomological extension* of the functor A^G we mean a sequence of functors $H^q(G, A)$ $(q = 0, 1, \ldots)$, with $H^0(G, A) = A^G$, together with *connecting* (or *boundary*) homomorphisms

$$\delta : H^q(G, C) \to H^{q+1}(G, A)$$

defined functorially for exact sequences (1.2), such that

(i) the sequence

$$\ldots \to H^q(G, A) \to H^q(G, B) \to H^q(G, C) \xrightarrow{\delta} H^{q+1}(G, A) \to \ldots \tag{1.3}$$

is exact; and

(ii) $\qquad H^q(G, A) = 0$ for all $q \geq 1$ if A is co-induced.

THEOREM 1. *There exists one and, up to canonical equivalence, only one cohomological extension of the functor A^G.*

The groups $H^q(G, A)$, uniquely determined by Theorem 1, are called the *cohomology groups* of the G-module A.

The existence part of Theorem 1 is established by the following construction. Choose a resolution P of the G-module $\mathbf{Z}$ (G acting trivially on $\mathbf{Z}$) by free G-modules:

$$\ldots \to P_1 \to P_0 \to \mathbf{Z} \to 0$$

and form the complex $K = \mathrm{Hom}_G(P, A)$, i.e.

$$0 \to \mathrm{Hom}_G(P_0, A) \to \mathrm{Hom}_G(P_1, A) \to \ldots.$$

Let $H^q(K)$ $(q \geqslant 0)$ denote the qth cohomology group of this complex. Then $H^q(G, A) = H^q(K)$ satisfies the conditions for a cohomological extension of the functor A^G. For by a basic theorem of homological algebra, the $H^q(G, A)$ so defined satisfy the exactness property (1.3); also $H^0(G, A) = H^0(K) = \mathrm{Hom}_G(\mathbf{Z}, A) = A^G$; finally, if A is co-induced, say $A = \mathrm{Hom}(\Lambda, X)$ where X is an abelian group, then for any G-module B we have

$$\mathrm{Hom}_G(B, A) \cong \mathrm{Hom}(B, X)$$

(the isomorphism being as follows: if $\varphi : B \to A$ is a G-homomorphism, then φ corresponds to the map $B \to X$ defined by $b \mapsto \varphi(b)(1)$, where 1 is the identity element of G). Hence the complex K is now

$$0 \to \mathrm{Hom}(P_0, X) \to \mathrm{Hom}(P_1, X) \to \ldots$$

which is exact at every place after the first, because the P_i are free as abelian groups; and therefore $H^q(G, A) = 0$ for all $q \geqslant 1$.

To prove the uniqueness of the cohomology groups we consider, for each G-module A, the G-module $A^* = \mathrm{Hom}(\Lambda, A)$. There is a natural injection

$A \to A^*$ which maps $a \in A$ to φ_a, where φ_a is defined by $\varphi_a(g) = ga$. Hence we have an exact sequence of G-modules

$$0 \to A \to A^* \to A' \to 0 \tag{1.4}$$

where $A' = A^*/A$; since A^* is co-induced, it follows from (1.3) that

$$\delta : H^q(G, A') \to H^{q+1}(G, A) \tag{1.5}$$

is an isomorphism for all $q \geqslant 1$, and that

$$H^1(G, A) \simeq \text{Coker}\,(H^0(G, A^*) \to H^0(G, A')). \tag{1.6}$$

The $H^q(G, A)$ can therefore be constructed inductively from H^0, and so are unique up to canonical equivalence. This procedure could also be used as an inductive definition of the H^q.

Remark. It follows from the uniqueness that the $H^q(G, A)$ are independent of the resolution P of $\mathbf{Z}$ used to construct them. So we may take any convenient choice of P.

2. The Standard Complex

As a particular choice for the resolution P we can take $P_i = \mathbf{Z}[G^{i+1}]$, i.e. P_i is the free $\mathbf{Z}$-module with basis $G \times \ldots \times G$ ($(i+1)$ factors), G acting on each basis element as follows:

$$s(g_0, g_1, \ldots, g_i) = (sg_0, sg_1, \ldots, sg_i).$$

The homomorphism $d: P_i \to P_{i-1}$ is given by the well-known formula

$$d(g_0, \ldots, g_i) = \sum_{j=0}^{i} (-1)^j (g_0, \ldots, g_{j-1}, g_{j+1}, \ldots, g_i), \tag{2.1}$$

and the mapping $\varepsilon: P_0 \to \mathbf{Z}$ is that which sends each generator (g_0) to $1 \in \mathbf{Z}$. (To show that the resulting sequence

$$\ldots \xrightarrow{d} P_1 \xrightarrow{d} P_0 \xrightarrow{\varepsilon} \mathbf{Z} \to 0 \tag{2.2}$$

is exact, choose an element $s \in G$ and define $h: P_i \to P_{i+1}$ by the formula

$$h(g_0, \ldots, g_i) = (s, g_0, g_1, \ldots, g_i).$$

It is immediately checked that $dh + hd = 1$ and that $dd = 0$, from which exactness follows.)

An element of $K^i = \text{Hom}_G(P_i, A)$ is then a function $f: G^{i+1} \to A$ such that

$$f(sg_0, sg_1, \ldots, sg_i) = s.f(g_0, g_1, \ldots, g_i).$$

Such a function is determined by its values at elements of G^{i+1} of the form $(1, g_1, g_1g_2, \ldots, g_1g_2 \ldots g_i)$: if we put

$$\varphi(g_1, \ldots, g_i) = f(1, g_1, g_1g_2, \ldots, g_1 \ldots g_i)$$

the boundary is given by the formula

$$(d\varphi)(g_1,\ldots,g_{i+1})$$
$$= g_1.\varphi(g_2,\ldots,g_{i+1}) + \sum_{j=1}^{i}(-1)^j\varphi(g_1,\ldots,g_jg_{j+1},\ldots,g_{i+1}) + $$
$$+(-1)^{i+1}\varphi(g_1,\ldots,g_i). \quad (2.3)$$

This shows that a 1-cocycle is a *crossed homomorphism*, i.e. a map $G \to A$ satisfying

$$\varphi(gg') = g.\varphi(g') + \varphi(g)$$

and φ is a coboundary if there exists $a \in A$ such that $\varphi(g) = ga - a$. In particular, if G acts trivially on A then

$$H^1(G, A) = \mathrm{Hom}\,(G, A). \quad (2.4)$$

From (2.3) we see also that a 2-cocycle is a function $\varphi : G \times G \to A$ such that

$$g_1\varphi(g_2, g_3) - \varphi(g_1g_2, g_3) + \varphi(g_1, g_2g_3) - \varphi(g_1, g_2) = 0.$$

Such functions (called *factor systems*) arise in the problem of group extensions, and $H^2(G, A)$ describes the possible extensions E of G by A, i.e. exact sequences $1 \to A \to E \to G \to 1$, where A is an abelian normal subgroup of E, and G operates on A by inner automorphisms. If E is such an extension, choose a section $\sigma : G \to E$ (a system of coset representatives). Then we have

$$\sigma(g_1).\sigma(g_2) = \varphi(g_1, g_2)\sigma(g_1g_2)$$

for some $\varphi(g_1, g_2) \in A$. The function φ is a 2-cocycle of G with values in A; if we change the section σ, we alter φ by a coboundary, so that the class of φ in $H^2(G, A)$ depends only on the extension. Conversely, every element of $H^2(G, A)$ arises from an extension of G by A in this way.

For later use, we give an explicit description of the connecting homomorphism $\delta : H^0(G, C) \to H^1(G, A)$ in the exact sequence (1.3). Let $c \in H^0(G, C) = C^G$, and lift c up to $b \in B$. Then db is the function $s \mapsto sb - b$; the image of $sb - b$ in C is zero, hence $sb - b \in A$ and therefore db is a 1-cocycle of G with values in A. If we change b by the addition of an element of A, we change db by a coboundary, hence the class of db in $H^1(G, A)$ depends only on c, and is the image of c under δ.

3. Homology

If A, B are G-modules, $A \otimes B$ denotes their tensor product over $\mathbf{Z}$, and $A \otimes_G B$ their tensor product over Λ. $A \otimes B$ has a natural G-module structure, defined by $g(a \otimes b) = (ga) \otimes (gb)$.

Let I_G be the kernel of the homomorphism $\Lambda \to \mathbf{Z}$ which maps each $s \in G$ to $1 \in \mathbf{Z}$. I_G is an ideal of Λ, generated by all $s - 1$ ($s \in G$). From the exact sequence

$$0 \to I_G \to \Lambda \to \mathbf{Z} \to 0 \quad (3.1)$$

and the right-exactness of $\otimes$ it follows that, for any G-module A,

$$\mathbf{Z} \otimes_G A \cong A/I_G A.$$

The G-module $A/I_G A$ is denoted by A_G. It is the largest quotient module of A on which G acts trivially. Clearly A_G is a right-exact functor of A. For any two G-modules A, B we have

$$A \otimes_G B \cong (A \otimes B)_G. \tag{3.2}$$

A G-module of the form $\Lambda \otimes X$, where X is any abelian group, is said to be *induced*. By interchanging right and left, induced and co-induced, we define a *homological extension* of the functor A_G.

THEOREM 2. *There exists a unique homological extension of the functor* A_G

The homology group $H_q(G, A)$ given by Theorem 2 may be constructed from the standard complex P of § 2 by taking

$$H_q(G, A) = H_q(P \otimes_G A).$$

Uniqueness follows by using the exact sequence

$$0 \to A' \to A_* \to A \to 0 \tag{3.3}$$

where $A_* = \Lambda \otimes A$. The details are exactly similar to those of the proof of Theorem 1.

The connecting homomorphism $\delta : H_1(G, C) \to H_0(G, A)$ may be described explicitly as follows. A 1-cycle of G with values in C is a function $f: G \to C$ such that $f(s) = 0$ for almost all $s \in G$ and such that $df = \sum_{s \in G} (s^{-1} - 1) f(s) = 0$. For each $s \in G$ lift $f(s)$ to $\bar{f}(s) \in B$ (if $f(s) = 0$, choose $\bar{f}(s) = 0$). Then $d\bar{f}$ has zero image in C, hence is an element of A. The class of $d\bar{f}$ in $H_0(G, A)$ is then the image under δ of the class of f.

PROPOSITION 1. $H_1(G, \mathbf{Z}) \cong G/G'$, *where* G' *is the commutator subgroup of* G.

Proof. From the exact sequence (3.1) and the fact that Λ is an induced G-module, the connecting homomorphism

$$\delta : H_1(G, \mathbf{Z}) \to H_0(G, I_G) = I_G/I_G^2$$

is an isomorphism. On the other hand, the map $s \mapsto s-1$ induces an isomorphism of G/G' onto I_G/I_G^2.

4. Change of Groups

Let G' be a subgroup of G. If A' is a G'-module, we can form the G-module $A = \operatorname{Hom}_{G'}(\Lambda, A')$: A is really a right G-module, but we turn it into a left G-module as described in § 1 (if $\varphi \in A$, then $g.\varphi$ is the homomorphism $g' \mapsto \varphi(g'g^{-1})$). Then we have

PROPOSITION 2 (Shapiro's Lemma).

$$H^q(G, A) = H^q(G', A') \quad \text{for all } q \geqslant 0.$$

Proof. If P is a free Λ-resolution of $\mathbf{Z}$ it is also a free Λ'-resolution, and $\text{Hom}_G(P, A) \cong \text{Hom}_{G'}(P, A')$.

The analogous result holds for homology, with Hom replaced by $\otimes$. Note that Prop. 2 may be regarded as a generalization of property (ii) of the cohomology groups (§ 1): if $G' = (1)$, then $\Lambda' = \mathbf{Z}$ and A is a co-induced module, and the $H^q(G', A')$ are zero for $q \geqslant 1$.

If $f: G' \to G$ is a homomorphism of groups, it induces a homomorphism $P' \to P$ of the standard complexes, hence a homomorphism

$$f^* : H^q(G, A) \to H^q(G', A)$$

for any G-module A. (We regard A as a G'-module via f.) In particular, taking $G' = H$ to be a subgroup of G, and f to be the embedding $H \to G$, we have *restriction* homomorphisms

$$\text{Res} : H^q(G, A) \to H^q(H, A).$$

If H is a normal subgroup of G we consider $f: G \to G/H$. For any G-module A we have the G/H-module A^H and hence a homomorphism $H^q(G/H, A^H) \to H^q(G, A^H)$. Composing this with the homomorphism induced by $A^H \to A$ we obtain the *inflation* homomorphisms

$$\text{Inf} : H^q(G/H, A) \to H^q(G, A).$$

Similarly, for homology, a homomorphism $f: G' \to G$ gives rise to a homomorphism

$$f_* : H_q(G', A) \to H_q(G, A);$$

in particular, taking $G' = H$ to be a subgroup of G, and $f: H \to G$ the embedding, we have the *corestriction* homomorphisms

$$\text{Cor} : H_q(H, A) \to H_q(G, A).$$

Consider the inner automorphism $s \mapsto tst^{-1}$ of G. This turns A into a new G-module, denoted by A^t, and gives a homomorphism

$$H^q(G, A) \to H^q(G, A^t). \tag{4.1}$$

Now $a \mapsto t^{-1}a$ defines an isomorphism $A^t \to A$ and hence induces

$$H^q(G, A) \to H^q(G, A). \tag{4.2}$$

PROPOSITION 3. *The composition of* (4.1) *and* (4.2) *is the identity map of* $H^q(G, A)$.

The proof employs a standard technique, that of dimension-shifting: we verify the result for $q = 0$ and then proceed by induction on q, using (1.5) to shift the dimension downwards.

For $q = 0$, we have $H^0(G, A^t) = (A^t)^G = t.A^G$, and (4.1) is just multiplication by t. Since (4.2) is multiplication by t^{-1}, the composition is the identity.

Now assume that $q > 0$ and that the result is true for $q - 1$. Corresponding to the exact sequence (1.4) we have an exact sequence

$$0 \to A^t \to (A^*)^t \to (A')^t \to 0.$$

Since $(A^*)^t$ is G-isomorphic to A^*, it is a co-induced module, hence we have functorial isomorphisms

$$H^q(G, A^t) \cong H^{q-1}(G, (A')^t) \quad (q \geqslant 2)$$

and

$$H^1(G, A^t) \cong \operatorname{Coker}(H^0(G, (A^*)^t) \to H^0(G, (A')^t)).$$

Now apply the inductive hypothesis.

5. The Restriction–Inflation Sequence

PROPOSITION 4. *Let H be a normal subgroup of G, and let A be a G-module. Then the sequence*

$$0 \to H^1(G/H, A^H) \xrightarrow{\text{Inf}} H^1(G, A) \xrightarrow{\text{Res}} H^1(H, A)$$

is exact.

The proof is by direct verification on cocycles.

(1) *Exactness at $H^1(G/H, A^H)$.* Let $f: G/H \to A^H$ be a 1-cocycle, then f induces $\bar{f}: G \to G/H \to A^H \to A$, which is a 1-cocycle, and the class of $\bar{f}$ is the inflation of the class of f. Hence if $\bar{f}$ is a coboundary, there exists $a \in A$ such that $\bar{f}(s) = sa - a$ $(s \in G)$. But $\bar{f}$ is constant on the cosets of H in G, hence $sa - a = sta - a$ for all $t \in H$, i.e. $ta = a$ for all $t \in H$. Hence $a \in A^H$ and therefore f is a coboundary.

(2) $\text{Res} \circ \text{Inf} = 0$. If $\varphi : G \to A$ is a 1-cocycle, then the class of $\varphi | H : H \to A$ is the restriction of the class of φ. But if $\varphi = \bar{f}$, it is clear that $\bar{f} | H$ is constant and equal to $f(1) = 0$.

(3) *Exactness at $H^1(G, A)$.* Let $\varphi : G \to A$ be a 1-cocycle whose restriction to H is a coboundary; then there exists $a \in A$ such that $\varphi(t) = ta - a$ for all $t \in H$. Subtracting from φ the coboundary $s \mapsto sa - a$, we are reduced to the case where $\varphi | H = 0$. The formula

$$\varphi(st) = \varphi(s) + s.\varphi(t)$$

then shows (taking $t \in H$) that φ is constant on the cosets of H in G, and then (taking $s \in H$, $t \in G$) that the image of φ is contained in A^H. Hence φ is the inflation of a 1-cocycle $G/H \to A^H$, and the proof is complete.

PROPOSITION 5. *Let $q \geqslant 1$, and suppose that $H^i(H, A) = 0$ for $1 \leqslant i \leqslant q-1$. Then the sequence*

$$0 \to H^q(G/H, A^H) \xrightarrow{\text{Inf}} H^q(G, A) \xrightarrow{\text{Res}} H^q(H, A)$$

is exact.

This is another example of dimension-shifting: we reduce to the case $q = 1$, which is Proposition 4. Suppose then that $q > 1$ and that the result is true for $q-1$. In the exact sequence (1.4), the G-module A^* is co-induced *as an H-module* (since $\Lambda = \mathbf{Z}[G]$ is a free $\mathbf{Z}[H]$-module), hence

$$H^i(H, A') \cong H^{i+1}(H, A) = 0 \quad \text{for } 1 \leqslant i \leqslant q-2.$$

Also, since $H^1(H, A) = 0$, the sequence

$$0 \to A^H \to (A^*)^H \to (A')^H \to 0$$

is exact, and $(A^*)^H$ is co-induced as a G/H-module (because $(A^*)^H \cong \operatorname{Hom}(\mathbf{Z}[G/H], A)$). Hence in the diagram

$$\begin{array}{ccccccc} 0 \to & H^{q-1}(G/H, (A')^H) & \to & H^{q-1}(G, A') & \to & H^{q-1}(H, A') \\ & \downarrow \delta & & \downarrow \delta & & \downarrow \delta \\ 0 \to & H^q(G/H, A^H) & \to & H^q(G, A) & \to & H^q(H, A) \end{array}$$

the three vertical arrows are isomorphisms, the diagram is commutative, and by the inductive assumption applied to A', the top line is exact. Hence so is the bottom line.

COROLLARY. *Under the hypotheses of Prop.* 5,

$$H^i(G/H, A^H) \cong H^i(G, A), \quad 1 \leqslant i \leqslant q-1.$$

6. The Tate Groups

From now on we assume that G is finite, and we denote by N the element $\sum_{s \in G} s$ of Λ. For any G-module A, multiplication by N defines an endomorphism $N: A \to A$, and clearly

$$I_G A \subseteq \operatorname{Ker}(N), \qquad \operatorname{Im}(N) \subseteq A^G.$$

Hence N induces a homomorphism

$$N^*: H_0(G, A) \to H^0(G, A)$$

and we define

$$\hat{H}_0(G, A) = \operatorname{Ker}(N^*), \qquad \hat{H}^0(G, A) = \operatorname{Coker}(N^*) = A^G/N(A).$$

Since G is finite, we can define a mapping $\operatorname{Hom}(\Lambda, X) \to \Lambda \otimes X$ (where X is any abelian group) by the rule

$$\varphi \mapsto \sum_{s \in G} s \otimes \varphi(s),$$

and it is immediately verified that this is a G-module isomorphism. Hence for a finite group the notions of induced and co-induced modules coincide.

PROPOSITION 6. *If A is an induced G-module, then $\hat{H}_0(G, A) = \hat{H}^0(G, A) = 0$.*

Proof. Let $A = \Lambda \otimes X$, X an abelian group. Since Λ is $\mathbf{Z}$-free, every element of A is uniquely of the form $\sum_{s \in G} s \otimes x_s$. If this element is G-invariant, then $\sum_s gs \otimes x_s = \sum_s s \otimes x_s$ for all $g \in G$, from which it follows that all the x_s are equal. Hence such an element is of the form $N.(1 \otimes x)$ and therefore lies in $N(A)$. Hence $\hat{H}^0(G, A) = 0$.

Similarly, if $N.\sum_s s \otimes x_s = 0$, we find that $\sum x_s = 0$, and therefore $\sum s \otimes x_s = \sum (s-1)(1 \otimes x_s) \in I_G A$. Hence $\hat{H}_0(G, A) = 0$.

Now we define the Tate cohomology groups $\hat{H}^q(G, A)$ for *all* integers q by

$$\begin{aligned} \hat{H}^q(G, A) &= H^q(G, A) \qquad \text{for } q \geqslant 1 \\ \hat{H}^{-1}(G, A) &= \hat{H}_0(G, A) \\ \hat{H}^{-q}(G, A) &= H_{q-1}(G, A) \quad \text{for } q \geqslant 2. \end{aligned}$$

THEOREM 3. *For every exact sequence of G-modules*

$$0 \to A \to B \to C \to 0$$

we have an exact sequence

$$\ldots \to \hat{H}^q(G, A) \to \hat{H}^q(G, B) \to \hat{H}^q(G, C) \xrightarrow{\delta} \hat{H}^{q+1}(G, A) \to \ldots$$

Proof. We have to splice together the homology and cohomology sequences. Consider the diagram

$$\begin{array}{ccccccccc} \ldots \to H_1(G, C) & \xrightarrow{\delta} & H_0(G, A) & \to & H_0(G, B) & \to & H_0(G, C) & \to & 0 \\ \downarrow & & \downarrow N_A^* & & \downarrow N_B^* & & \downarrow N_C^* & & \downarrow \\ 0 & \to & H^0(G, A) & \to & H^0(G, B) & \to & H^0(G, C) & \xrightarrow{\delta} & H^1(G, A) \to \ldots \end{array}$$

where N_A^* is the homomorphism N^* relative to A, and so on. It is clear that the inner two squares are commutative, and for the outer two squares commutativity follows immediately from the explicit descriptions of the connecting homomorphism δ given in §§ 2 and 3.

We define $\hat{\delta} : \hat{H}_0(G, C) \to \hat{H}^0(G, A)$ as follows. If $c \in \hat{H}_0(G, C) = \operatorname{Ker}(N_C^*)$, lift c to $b \in H_0(G, B)$, then $N_B^*(b) \in H^0(G, B)$ has zero image in $H^0(G, C)$ and therefore comes from an element $a \in H^0(G, A)$, whose image in $\hat{H}^0(G, A)$ is independent of the choice of b; this element of $\hat{H}^0(G, A)$ we define to be (c). The definitions of the other maps in the sequence

$$H_1(G, C) \to \hat{H}_0(G, A) \to \hat{H}_0(G, B) \to \hat{H}_0(G, C)$$
$$\xrightarrow{\delta} \hat{H}^0(G, A) \to \hat{H}^0(G, B) \to \hat{H}^0(G, C) \to H^1(G, A)$$

are the obvious ones, and the verification that the whole sequence is exact is a straightforward piece of diagram-chasing.

The Tate groups can be considered as the cohomology groups of a complex constructed out of a *complete resolution* of G. Let P denote a G-resolution of $\mathbf{Z}$ by finitely-generated free G-modules (for example, the standard resolution of § 2), and let $P^* = \operatorname{Hom}(P, \mathbf{Z})$ be its dual, so that we have exact sequences

$$\ldots \to P_1 \to P_0 \xrightarrow{\varepsilon} \mathbf{Z} \to 0$$

$$0 \to \mathbf{Z} \xrightarrow{\varepsilon^*} P_0^* \to P_1^* \to \ldots$$

(the dual sequence is exact because each P_i is $\mathbf{Z}$-free). Putting $P_{-n} = P_{n-1}^*$ and splicing the two sequences together we get a doubly-infinite exact sequence

$$L: \qquad \ldots \to P_1 \to P_0 \to P_{-1} \to P_{-2} \to \ldots.$$

The Tate groups are then the cohomology groups $H^q(\operatorname{Hom}_G(L, A))$ for any G-module A. This assertion is clear if $q \geqslant 1$. If $q \leqslant -2$ we use the following fact: if C is a finitely generated free G-module, let $C^* = \operatorname{Hom}(C, \mathbf{Z})$ be its dual; then the mapping $\sigma : C \otimes A \to \operatorname{Hom}(C^*, A)$ defined as follows:

$$\sigma(c \otimes a) \text{ maps } f \in C^* \text{ to } f(c).a$$

is a G-module isomorphism. Hence the composition

$$\tau : C \otimes_G A = (C \otimes A)_G \xrightarrow{N^*} (C \otimes A)^G \xrightarrow{\sigma} (\operatorname{Hom}(C^*, A))^G = \operatorname{Hom}_G(C^*, A)$$

is an isomorphism (N^* is an isomorphism because $C \otimes A$ is an induced G-module). From this it follows that $\operatorname{Hom}_G(P_{-n}, A) \cong P_{n-1} \otimes_G A$, and hence that $H^{-q}(\operatorname{Hom}_G(L, A)) = H_{q-1}(G, A)$ for $q \geqslant 2$.

Finally, we have to consider the cases $q = 0, 1$. The mapping

$$\operatorname{Hom}_G(P_{-1}, A) \to \operatorname{Hom}_G(P_0, A) \tag{6.1}$$

is induced by the composition $P_0 \xrightarrow{\varepsilon} \mathbf{Z} \xrightarrow{\varepsilon^*} P_{-1}$. If we identify $\operatorname{Hom}_G(P_{-1}, A)$ with $P_0 \otimes_G A$ by means of the isomorphism τ, the mapping (6.1) becomes a mapping from $P_0 \otimes_G A$ to $\operatorname{Hom}_G(P_0, A)$, and from the definition of τ it is not difficult to see that this mapping factorizes into

$$P_0 \otimes_G A \to A_G \xrightarrow{N^*} A^G \to \operatorname{Hom}_G(P_0, A) \tag{6.2}$$

where the extreme arrows are the mappings induced by ε. From this it follows that $H^q(\operatorname{Hom}_G(L, A)) = \hat{H}^q(G, A)$ for $q = 0, 1$.

Remark. Since any G-module can be expressed either as a sub-module or as a quotient module of an induced module, it follows from Prop. 6 and Theorem 3 that the Tate groups $\hat{H}^q$ can be "shifted" both up and down.

If H is a subgroup of G, the restriction homomorphism

$$\operatorname{Res} : H^q(G, A) \to H^q(H, A)$$

has been defined for all $q \geqslant 0$. It is therefore defined for the Tate groups $\hat{H}^q$, $q \geqslant 1$, and commutes with the connecting homomorphism δ. By dimension-shifting it then gets extended to all $\hat{H}^q$ (use the exact sequence (3.3) and the fact that A_* is induced as an H-module). Similarly, the corestriction, which was defined in the first place for H_q (i.e. $\hat{H}^{-q-1}$, $q \geqslant 1$) gets extended by dimension-shifting to all $\hat{H}^q$ (use (1.4) likewise).

PROPOSITION 7. *Let H be a subgroup of G, and let A be a G-module. Then*

(i) $\mathrm{Res}: \hat{H}_0(G, A) \to \hat{H}_0(H, A)$ *is induced by* $N'_{G/H}: A_G \to A_H$, *where*

$$N'_{G/H}(a) = \sum_i s_i^{-1} a$$

and (s_i) *is a system of coset representatives of* G/H;

(ii) $\mathrm{Cor}: \hat{H}^0(H, A) \to \hat{H}^0(G, A)$ *is induced by* $N_{G/H}: A^H \to A^G$, *where*

$$N_{G/H}(a) = \sum_i s_i a.$$

We shall prove (i), and leave (ii) to the reader. First of all, since $\hat{\delta}: \hat{H}^0(G, A) \to H^1(G, A')$ is induced by $\delta: H^0(G, A) \to H^1(G, A)$, and since $\mathrm{Res}: H^0(G, A) \to H^0(H, A)$ is the embedding $A^G \to A^H$ and is compatible with δ, it follows that $\mathrm{Res}: \hat{H}^0(G, A) \to \hat{H}^0(H, A)$ is induced by $A^G \to A^H$. Now let $v: \hat{H}_0(G, A) \to \hat{H}_0(H, A)$ be the map induced by $N'_{G/H}$. We have to check that the diagram

$$\begin{array}{ccc} \hat{H}_0(G, A) & \xrightarrow{\delta} & \hat{H}^0(G, A') \\ {\scriptstyle v}\downarrow & & \downarrow{\scriptstyle \mathrm{Res}} \\ \hat{H}_0(H, A) & \xrightarrow{\delta} & \hat{H}^0(H, A') \end{array}$$

is commutative. Let $a \in A$ be a representative of $\bar{a} \in \hat{H}_0(G, A)$, so that $N_G(a) = 0$. Lift a to $b \in A_*$, then $N_G(b)$ has zero image in A and is G-invariant, hence belongs to $(A')^G \subseteq (A')^H$. The class of $N_G(b)$ mod. $N_H(A')$ is $\mathrm{Res} \circ \hat{\delta}(\bar{a})$. On the other hand, $v(\bar{a})$ is the class mod. $I_H A$ of $N'_{G/H}(a)$, which lifts to $N'_{G/H}(b)$, and $\hat{\delta} \circ v(\bar{a})$ is represented by $N_H \circ N'_{G/H}(b) = N_G(b)$.

Note: For $q = -2$ and $A = \mathbf{Z}$ we have $\hat{H}^{-2}(G, \mathbf{Z}) = H_1(G, \mathbf{Z}) \cong G/G'$; $\mathrm{Res}: G/G' \to H/H'$ is classically called the *transfer* and can be defined as follows. G/G' is dual to $\mathrm{Hom}(G, \mathbf{C}^*)$, hence the transfer will be dual to a homomorphism

$$\mathrm{Hom}(H, \mathbf{C}^*) \to \mathrm{Hom}(G, \mathbf{C}^*).$$

This homomorphism is given by

$$\rho \mapsto \det(i_* \rho)/\det(i_* 1),$$

where $i_* \rho$ is the representation of G *induced* by ρ, and det denotes the corresponding one-dimensional representation obtained by taking determinants ($\mathrm{Hom}(G, \mathbf{C}^*)$ is here written multiplicatively).

PROPOSITION 8. *If* $(G:H) = n$, *then*

$$\mathrm{Cor} \circ \mathrm{Res} = n.$$

Proof. For $\hat{H}^0$ this follows from Prop. 7(ii): Res is induced by the embedding $A^G \to A^H$, and Cor by $N_{G/H}: A^H \to A^G$; and $N_{G/H}(a) = na$ for all $a \in A^G$. The general case then follows by dimension-shifting.

COROLLARY 1. *If G has order n, all the groups* $\hat{H}^q(G, A)$ *are annihilated by n.*

Proof. Take $H = (1)$ in Prop. 8, and use the fact that $\hat{H}^q(H, A) = 0$ for all q.

COROLLARY 2. *If A is a finitely-generated G-module, all the groups* $\hat{H}^q(G, A)$ *are finite.*

Proof. The calculation of the $\hat{H}^q(G, A)$ from the standard complete resolution L shows that they are finitely generated abelian groups; since by Cor. 1 they are killed by $n = \mathrm{Card}\,(G)$, they are therefore finite.

COROLLARY 3. *Let S be a Sylow p-subgroup of G. Then*

$$\mathrm{Res}: \hat{H}^q(G, A) \to \hat{H}^q(S, A)$$

is a monomorphism on the p-primary component of $\hat{H}^q(G, A)$.

Proof. Let $\mathrm{Card}\,(G) = p^a.m$ where m is prime to p. Let x belong to the p-primary component of $\hat{H}^q(G, A)$, and suppose that $\mathrm{Res}\,(x) = 0$. Then

$$mx = \mathrm{Cor} \circ \mathrm{Res}(x) = 0$$

by Prop. 8, since $m = (G:S)$. On the other hand, we have $p^a x = 0$ by Cor. 1; since $(p^a, m) = 1$, it follows that $x = 0$.

COROLLARY 4. *If an element x of* $\hat{H}^q(G, A)$ *restricts to zero in* $\hat{H}^q(S, A)$ *for all Sylow subgroups S of G, then* $x = 0$.

7. Cup-products

THEOREM 4. *Let G be a finite group. Then there exists one and only one family of homomorphisms*

$$\hat{H}^p(G, A) \otimes \hat{H}^q(G, B) \to \hat{H}^{p+q}(G, A \otimes B)$$

(denoted by $(a \otimes b) \to a.b$*), defined for all integers p, q and all G-modules A, B, such that:*

(i) *These homomorphisms are functorial in A and B;*

(ii) *For* $p = q = 0$ *they are induced by the natural product*

$$A^G \otimes B^G \to (A \otimes B)^G;$$

(iii) *If* $0 \to A \to A' \to A'' \to 0$ *is an exact sequence of G-modules, and if* $0 \to A \otimes B \to A' \otimes B \to A'' \otimes B \to 0$ *is exact, then for* $a'' \in \hat{H}^p(G, A'')$ *and* $b \in \hat{H}^q(G, B)$ *we have*

$$(\delta a'').b = \delta(a''.b) \quad (\in \hat{H}^{p+q+1}(G, A \otimes B));$$

(iv) *If* $0 \to B \to B' \to B'' \to 0$ *is an exact sequence of G-modules, and if* $0 \to A \otimes B \to A \otimes B' \to A \otimes B'' \to 0$ *is exact, then for* $a \in \hat{H}^p(G, A)$ *and* $b'' \in \hat{H}^q(G, B'')$ *we have*

$$a.(\delta b'') = (-1)^p \delta(a.b'') \quad (\in \hat{H}^{p+q+1}(G, A \otimes B)).$$

Let $(P_n)_{n \in \mathbf{Z}}$ be a complete resolution for G, as in § 6. The proof of existence depends on constructing G-module homomorphisms

$$\varphi_{p,q} : P_{p+q} \to P_p \otimes P_q$$

for all pairs of integers p, q, satisfying the following two conditions:

$$\varphi_{p,q} \circ d = (d \otimes 1) \circ \varphi_{p+1,q} + (-1)^p (1 \otimes d) \circ \varphi_{p,q+1}; \tag{7.1}$$

$$(\varepsilon \otimes \varepsilon) \circ \varphi_{0,0} = \varepsilon, \tag{7.2}$$

where $\varepsilon : P_0 \to \mathbf{Z}$ is defined by $\varepsilon(g) = 1$ for all $g \in G$.

Once the $\varphi_{p,q}$ have been defined, we proceed as follows. Let $f \in \operatorname{Hom}_G(P_p, A)$, $g \in \operatorname{Hom}_G(P_q, B)$ be cochains, and define the product cochain $f \circ g \in \operatorname{Hom}_G(P_{p+q}, A \otimes B)$ by

$$f.g = (f \otimes g) \circ \varphi_{p,q}.$$

Then it follows immediately from (7.1) that

$$(f.g) = (df).g + (-1)^p f.(dg). \tag{7.3}$$

Hence if f, g are cocycles, so is $f.g$, and the cohomology class of $f.g$ depends only on the classes of f and g: in other words, we have a homomorphism

$$\hat{H}^p(G, A) \otimes \hat{H}^q(G, B) \to \hat{H}^{p+q}(G, A \otimes B).$$

Clearly condition (i) is satisfied, and (ii) is a consequence of (7.2). Consider (iii). We have an exact sequence

$$0 \to \operatorname{Hom}_G(P_p, A) \to \operatorname{Hom}_G(P_p, A') \to \operatorname{Hom}_G(P_p, A'') \to 0.$$

Let $\alpha'' \in \operatorname{Hom}_G(P_p, A'')$ be a representative cocycle of the class a'', and lift α'' back to $\alpha' \in \operatorname{Hom}_G(P_p, A')$; $d\alpha'$ has zero image in $\operatorname{Hom}_G(P_{p+1}, A'')$ and therefore lies in $\operatorname{Hom}_G(P_{p+1}, A)$. The class of $d\alpha'$ in $\hat{H}^{p+1}(G, A)$ is $\delta(\alpha'')$. Hence if $\beta \in \operatorname{Hom}_G(P_q, B)$ is a cocycle in the class b, then $\alpha''.\beta$ represents the class $a''.b$; $d(\alpha'.\beta)$ represents $\delta(a''.b)$; and $(d\alpha').\beta$ represents $(\delta a'').b$. But (since $d\beta = 0$) we have $d(\alpha'.\beta) = (d\alpha').\beta$ from (7.3); hence $\delta(a''.b) = (\delta a'').b$. The proof of (iv) is similar.

Thus it remains to define the $\varphi_{p,q}$, which we shall do for the standard complete resolution ($P_q = \mathbf{Z}[G^{q+1}]$ if $q \geq 0$; $P_{-q} =$ dual of P_{q-1} if $q \geq 1$). If $q \geq 1$, $P_{-q} = P_{q-1}^*$ has a basis (as $\mathbf{Z}$-module) consisting of all $(g_1^*, \ldots, g_q^*)$, where $(g_1^*, \ldots, g_q^*)$ maps $(g_1, \ldots, g_q) \in P_{q-1}$ to $1 \in \mathbf{Z}$, and every other basis element of P_{q-1} to 0. In terms of this basis of P_{-q}, $d : P_{-q} \to P_{-q-1}$ is given by

$$d(g_1^*, \ldots, g_q^*) = \sum_{s \in G} \sum_{i=0}^{q} (-1)^i (g_1^*, \ldots, g_i^*, s^*, g_{i+1}^*, \ldots, g_q^*)$$

and $d: P_0 \to P_{-1}$ by $d(g_0) = \sum_{s \in G} (s^*)$.

We define $\varphi_{p,q}: P_{p+q} \to P_p \otimes P_q$ as follows:

(1) if $p \geqslant 0$ and $q \geqslant 0$,

$$\varphi_{p,q}(g_0, \ldots, g_{p+q}) = (g_0, \ldots, g_p) \otimes (g_p, \ldots, g_{p+q});$$

(2) if $p \geqslant 1$ and $q \geqslant 1$,

$$\varphi_{-p,-q}(g_1^*, \ldots, g_{p+q}^*) = (g_1^*, \ldots, g_p^*) \otimes (g_{p+1}^*, \ldots, g_{p+q}^*);$$

(3) if $p \geqslant 0$ and $q \geqslant 1$,

$$\varphi_{p,-p-q}(g_1^*, \ldots, g_q^*) = \sum (g_1, s_1, \ldots, s_p) \otimes (s_p^*, \ldots, s_1^*, g_1^*, \ldots, g_q^*);$$

$$\varphi_{-p-q,p}(g_1^*, \ldots, g_q^*) = \sum (g_1^*, \ldots, g_q^*, s_1^*, \ldots, s_p^*) \otimes (s_p, \ldots, s_1, g_q);$$

$$\varphi_{p+q,-q}(g_0, \ldots, g_p) = \sum (g_0, \ldots, g_p, s_1, \ldots, s_q) \otimes (s_q^*, \ldots, s_1^*);$$

$$\varphi_{-q,p+q}(g_0, \ldots, g_p) = \sum (s_1^*, \ldots, s_q^*) \otimes (s_q, \ldots, s_1, g_0, \ldots, g_p).$$

(In the sums on the right-hand side, the s_i run independently through G.) The verification that the $\varphi_{p,q}$ satisfy (7.1) is tedious, but entirely straightforward.

This completes the existence part of the proof of Theorem 4. The uniqueness is proved by starting with (ii) and shifting dimensions by (iii) and (iv): the point is that the exact sequence (3.3), namely

$$0 \to A' \to A_* \to A \to 0,$$

splits over $\mathbf{Z}$, as the $\mathbf{Z}$-homomorphism $A \to A_* = \Lambda \otimes A$ defined by $a \mapsto 1 \otimes a$ shows; hence the result of tensoring it with any G-module B is still exact, and $A_* \otimes B = \Lambda \otimes A \otimes B = (A \otimes B)_*$. Similarly for the exact sequence (1.4).

Note the following properties of the cup-product, which are easily proved by dimension-shifting:

PROPOSITION 9.

(i) $(a.b).c = a.(b.c)$ (*identifying* $(A \otimes B) \otimes C$ *with* $A \otimes (B \otimes C)$).

(ii) $a.b = (-1)^{\dim a . \dim b} b.a$ (*identifying* $A \otimes B$ *with* $B \otimes A$).

(iii) $\operatorname{Res}(a.b) = \operatorname{Res}(a).\operatorname{Res}(b)$.

(iv) $\operatorname{Cor}(a.\operatorname{Res}(b)) = \operatorname{Cor}(a).b$.

As an example, let us prove (iv). Here H is a subgroup of G, $a \in \hat{H}^p(H, A)$, $b \in \hat{H}^q(G, B)$, so that both sides of (iv) are elements of $\hat{H}^{p+q}(G, A \otimes B)$. If $p = q = 0$, a is represented by say $\alpha \in A^H$, and by Prop. 7(ii) $\operatorname{Cor}(a)$ is represented by $N_{G/H}(\alpha) = \sum_i s_i \alpha \in A^G$; b is represented by $\beta \in B^G$, hence $\operatorname{Cor}(a).b$ is represented by

$$N_{G/H}(\alpha) \otimes \beta = (\sum s_i \alpha) \otimes \beta = \sum s_i(\alpha \otimes \beta) = N_{G/H}(\alpha \otimes \beta).$$

On the other hand, $a.\operatorname{Res}(b)$ is represented by $\alpha \otimes \beta \in (A \otimes B)^H$, hence

Cor $(a.\text{Res}(b))$ by $N_{G/H}(\alpha \otimes \beta)$. This establishes (iv) for $p = q = 0$. Now use dimension-shifting as in the proof of the uniqueness of the cup-products and the fact that both Cor and Res commute with the connecting homomorphisms relative to exact sequences of the types (3.3) and (1.4).

We shall later have to consider cup-products of a slightly more general type. Let A, B, C be G-modules, $\varphi: A \otimes B \to C$ a G-homomorphism. If we compose the cup-product with the cohomology homomorphism φ^* induced by φ, we have mappings

$$\hat{H}^p(G, A) \otimes \hat{H}^q(G, B) \to \hat{H}^{p+q}(G, C);$$

explicitly, $a \otimes b \mapsto \varphi^*(a.b)$. $\varphi^*(a.b)$ is the *cup-product of a, b relative to φ.*

8. Cyclic Groups; Herbrand Quotient

If G is a cyclic group of order n, and s is a generator of G, we can define a particularly simple complete resolution K for G. Each K_i is isomorphic to Λ, and $d: K_{i+1} \to K_i$ is multiplication by $T = s-1$ if i is even (resp. by N if i is odd). The kernel of T is $\Lambda^G = N.\Lambda =$ image of N, and the image of T is $I_G =$ kernel of N. Hence for any G-module A the complex $\text{Hom}_G(K, A)$ is

$$\ldots \leftarrow A \overset{N}{\leftarrow} A \overset{T}{\leftarrow} A \overset{N}{\leftarrow} A \overset{T}{\leftarrow} \ldots$$

and therefore

$$\hat{H}^{2q}(G, A) = \hat{H}^0(G, A) = A^G/NA,$$
$$\hat{H}^{2q+1}(G, A) = \hat{H}_0(G, A) = {}_NA/I_GA,$$

where ${}_NA$ is the kernel of $N: A \to A$.

In particular, $H^2(G, \mathbf{Z}) = \mathbf{Z}^G/N\mathbf{Z} = \mathbf{Z}/n\mathbf{Z}$ is cyclic of order n.

THEOREM 5. *Cup-product by a generator of $H^2(G, \mathbf{Z})$ induces an isomorphism*

$$\hat{H}^q(G, A) \to \hat{H}^{q+2}(G, A)$$

for all integers q and all G-modules A.

Proof. The exact sequences

$$0 \to I_G \to \Lambda \to \mathbf{Z} \to 0, \tag{8.1}$$

$$0 \to \mathbf{Z} \overset{N}{\to} \Lambda \overset{T}{\to} I_G \to 0, \tag{8.2}$$

give rise to isomorphisms

$$\hat{H}^0(G, \mathbf{Z}) \overset{\delta}{\to} H^1(G, I_G) \overset{\delta}{\to} H^2(G, \mathbf{Z}).$$

Since both (8.1), (8.2) split over $\mathbf{Z}$, they remain exact when tensored with A, and we are therefore reduced to showing that cup-product by a generator of $\hat{H}^0(G, \mathbf{Z})$ induces an automorphism of $\hat{H}^q(G, A)$. By dimension-shifting again, we reduce to the case $q = 0$. Since $\hat{H}^0(G, \mathbf{Z}) = \mathbf{Z}/n\mathbf{Z}$, a generator b of $\hat{H}^0(G, \mathbf{Z})$ is represented by an integer β prime to n, and cup-product with b is multiplication by β. Now β is prime to n, hence there is an integer γ such that $\beta\gamma \equiv 1$ (mod. n); $\hat{H}^0(G, A)$ is killed by n, hence multiplication by β is an automorphism of $\hat{H}^0(G, A)$.

Let $h_q(A)$ denote the order of $\hat{H}^q(G, A)$ ($q = 0, 1$) whenever this is finite. If both are finite we define the *Herbrand quotient*

$$h(A) = h_0(A)/h_1(A).$$

PROPOSITION 10. *Let $0 \to A \to B \to C \to 0$ be an exact sequence of G-modules (G a cyclic group). Then if two of the three Herbrand quotients $h(A)$, $h(B)$, $h(C)$ are defined, so is the third and we have*

$$h(B) = h(A) . h(C).$$

Proof. In view of the periodicity of the $\hat{H}^q$, the cohomology exact sequence is an exact hexagon:

$$\begin{array}{ccccc} & H^0(A) & \rightarrow & H^0(B) & \\ \nearrow & & & & \searrow \\ H^1(C) & & & & H^0(C) \\ \nwarrow & & & & \swarrow \\ & H^1(B) & \leftarrow & H^1(A) & \end{array}$$

where $H^0(A)$ means $\hat{H}^0(G, A)$, and so on. Suppose for example that $H^0(A)$, $H^1(A)$, $H^0(B)$, $H^1(B)$ are finite. Let M_1 be the image of $H^0(A)$ in $H^0(B)$, and so on in clockwise order round the hexagon. Then the sequence $0 \to M_2 \to H^0(C) \to M_3 \to 0$ is exact, and M_2, M_3 are finite groups (M_2 because it is a homomorphic image of $H^0(B)$, M_3 because it is a subgroup of $H^1(A)$). Hence $H^0(C)$ is finite, and similarly $H^1(C)$ is finite. The orders of the groups $H^0(A), \ldots, H^1(C)$ are respectively $m_6 m_1, m_1 m_2, \ldots, m_5 m_6$ (m_i = order of M_i), hence $h(B) = h(A) . h(C)$.

PROPOSITION 11. *If A is a finite G-module, then $h(A) = 1$.*

Proof. Consider the exact sequences

$$0 \to A^G \to A \xrightarrow{T} A \to A_G \to 0,$$

$$0 \to H^1(A) \to A_G \xrightarrow{N^*} A^G \to H^0(A) \to 0.$$

The first one shows that A^G and A_G have the same order, and then the second one shows that $H^0(A)$ and $H^1(A)$ have the same order.

COROLLARY. *Let A, B be G-modules, $f\colon A \to B$ a G-homomorphism with finite kernel and cokernel. Then if either of $h(A)$, $h(B)$ is defined, so is the other, and they are equal.*

Proof. Suppose for example that $h(A)$ is defined. From the exact sequences

$$0 \to \mathrm{Ker}(f) \to A \to f(A) \to 0$$
$$0 \to f(A) \to B \to \mathrm{Coker}(f) \to 0$$

it follows from Prop. 10 and 11 that $h(f(A))$ is defined and equal to $h(A)$, then that $h(B)$ is defined and equal to $h(f(A))$.

PROPOSITION 12. *Let E be a finite-dimensional real representation space of G, and let L, L' be two lattices of E which span E and are invariant under G. Then if either of $h(L)$, $h(L')$ is defined, so is the other, and they are equal.*

For the proof of Prop. 12 we need the following lemma:

LEMMA. *Let G be a finite group and let M, M' be two finite-dimensional $\mathbf{Q}[G]$-modules such that $M_{\mathbf{R}} = M \otimes_{\mathbf{Q}} \mathbf{R}$ and $M'_{\mathbf{R}} = M' \otimes_{\mathbf{Q}} \mathbf{R}$ are isomorphic as $\mathbf{R}[G]$-modules. Then M, M' are isomorphic as $\mathbf{Q}[G]$-modules.*

Proof. Let K be any field, L any extension field of K, A a K-algebra. If V is any K-vector space let V_L denote the L-vector space $V \otimes_K L$. Let M, M' be A-modules which are finite-dimensional as K-vector spaces. An A-homomorphism $\varphi: M \to M'$ induces an A_L-homomorphism $\varphi \otimes 1: M_L \to M'_L$, and $\varphi \mapsto \varphi \otimes 1$ gives rise to an isomorphism (of vector spaces over L)

$$(\mathrm{Hom}_A(M, M'))_L \cong \mathrm{Hom}_{A_L}(M_L, M'_L). \tag{8.3}$$

In the case in point, take $K = \mathbf{Q}$, $L = \mathbf{R}$, $A = \mathbf{Q}[G]$, so that $A_L = \mathbf{R}[G]$. The hypotheses of the lemma imply that M and M' have the same dimension over $\mathbf{Q}$, hence by choosing bases of M and M' we can speak of the *determinant* of an element of $\mathrm{Hom}_{\mathbf{Q}[G]}(M, M')$, or of $\mathrm{Hom}_{\mathbf{R}[G]}(M_{\mathbf{R}}, M'_{\mathbf{R}})$. (It will of course depend on the bases chosen.)

From (8.3) it follows that if ξ_i are a $\mathbf{Q}$-basis of $\mathrm{Hom}_{\mathbf{Q}[G]}(M, M')$, they are also an $\mathbf{R}$-basis of $\mathrm{Hom}_{\mathbf{R}[G]}(M_{\mathbf{R}}, M'_{\mathbf{R}})$. Since $M_{\mathbf{R}}$, $M'_{\mathbf{R}}$ are $\mathbf{R}[G]$-isomorphic, there exist $a_i \in \mathbf{R}$ such that $\det(\sum a_i \xi_i) \neq 0$. Hence the polynomial

$$F(t) = \det(\textstyle\sum t_i \xi_i) \in \mathbf{Q}[t_1, \ldots, t_m],$$

where t_i are independent indeterminates over $\mathbf{Q}$, is not identically zero, since $F(a) \neq 0$. Since $\mathbf{Q}$ is infinite, there exist $b_i \in \mathbf{Q}$ such that $F(b) \neq 0$, and then $\sum b_i \xi_i$ is a $\mathbf{Q}[G]$-isomorphism of M onto M'.

For the proof of Prop. 12, let $M = L \otimes \mathbf{Q}$, $M' = L' \otimes \mathbf{Q}$. Then $M_{\mathbf{R}}$ and $M'_{\mathbf{R}}$ are both $\mathbf{R}[G]$-isomorphic to E. Hence by the lemma there is a $\mathbf{Q}[G]$-isomorphism $\varphi: L \otimes \mathbf{Q} \to L' \otimes \mathbf{Q}$. L is mapped injectively by φ to a lattice contained in $(1/N)L'$ for some positive integer N. Hence $f = N.\varphi$ maps L injectively into L'; since L, L' are both free abelian groups of the same (finite) rank, $\mathrm{Coker}(f)$ is finite. The result now follows from the Corollary to Prop. 11.

9. Cohomological Triviality

A G-module A is *cohomologically trivial* if, for every subgroup H of G, $\hat{H}^q(H, A) = 0$ for all integers q. For example, an induced module is cohomologically trivial.

LEMMA 1. *Let p be a prime number, G a p-group and A a G-module such that $pA = 0$. Then the following three conditions are equivalent:*

(i) $A = 0$;
(ii) $H^0(G, A) = 0$;
(iii) $H_0(G, A) = 0$.

Proof. Clearly (i) implies (ii) and (iii).

(ii) ⇒ (i): Suppose $A \neq 0$, let x be a non-zero element of A. Then the submodule B generated by x is finite, of order a power of p. Consider the G-orbits of the elements of B; they are all of p-power order (since the order of G is a power of p), and there is at least one fixed point, namely 0. Hence there are at least p fixed points, so that $H^0(G, A) = A^G \neq 0$.

(iii) ⇒ (i). Let $A' = \text{Hom}\,(A, \mathbf{F}_p)$ be the dual of A, considered as a vector-space over the field $\mathbf{F}_p$ of p elements. Then

$$H^0(G, A') = (A')^G = \text{Hom}_G\,(A, \mathbf{F}_p)$$

is the dual of $H_0(G, A)$. Hence $H^0(G, A') = 0$, so that $A' = 0$ and therefore $A = 0$.

LEMMA 2. *With the same hypotheses as in Lemma 1, suppose that $H_1(G, A) = 0$. Then A is a free module over $\mathbf{F}_p[G] = \Lambda/p\Lambda$.*

Proof. Since $pA = 0$, we have $p.H_0(G, A) = 0$ and therefore $H_0(G, A)$ is a vector space over $\mathbf{F}_p$. Take a basis e_λ of this space and lift each e_λ to $a_\lambda \in A$. Let A' be the submodule of A generated by the a_λ, and let $A'' = A/A'$. Then we have an exact sequence

$$H_0\,(G, A') \xrightarrow{\alpha} H_0\,(G, A) \rightarrow H_0\,(G, A'') \rightarrow 0$$

in which by construction α is an isomorphism. Hence $H_0(G, A'') = 0$ and therefore $A'' = 0$ by Lemma 1, so that the a_λ generate A as a G-module. Hence they define a G-epimorphism $\varphi : L \rightarrow A$, where L is a free $\mathbf{F}_p[G]$-module. By construction, φ induces an isomorphism

$$\beta : H_0(G, L) \rightarrow H_0(G, A).$$

Let $R = \text{Ker}\,(\varphi)$. Then since $H_1(G, A) = 0$, the sequence

$$0 \rightarrow H_0(G, R) \rightarrow H_0(G, L) \xrightarrow{\beta} H_0(G, A) \rightarrow 0$$

is exact; since β is an isomorphism, $H_0(G, R) = 0$ and therefore $R = 0$ by Lemma 1. Hence φ is an isomorphism.

THEOREM 6. *Let G be a p-group and let A be a G-module such that $pA = 0$. Then the following conditions are equivalent:*

(i) *A is a free $\mathbf{F}_p[G]$-module;*
(ii) *A is an induced module;*
(iii) *A is cohomologically trivial;*
(iv) *$\hat{H}^q(G, A) = 0$ for some integer q.*

Proof. Clearly (i) ⇒ (ii) ⇒ (iii) ⇒ (iv).

(iv) ⇒ (i). By dimension-shifting we construct a module B such that $pB = 0$ and $\hat{H}^{q+r}(G, A) = \hat{H}^{r-2}(G, B)$ for all r. Hence $H_1(G, B) = 0$ and therefore (Lemma 2) B is free over $\mathbf{F}_p[G]$; hence

$$\hat{H}^{-2}(G, A) = \hat{H}^{-q-4}(G, B) = 0$$

and therefore (Lemma 2 again) A is free over $\mathbf{F}_p[G]$.

THEOREM 7. *Let G be a p-group and A a G-module without p-torsion. Then the following conditions are equivalent:*

(i) *A is cohomologically trivial;*
(ii) *$\hat{H}^q(G, A) = \hat{H}^{q+1}(G, A) = 0$ for some integer q;*
(iii) *A/pA is a free $\mathbf{F}_p[G]$-module.*

Proof. (i) ⇒ (ii) is clear.

(ii) ⇒ (iii): From the exact sequence

$$0 \to A \xrightarrow{p} A \to A/pA \to 0$$

we have an exact sequence $\hat{H}^q(G, A) \to \hat{H}^q(G, A/pA) \to \hat{H}^{q+1}(G, A)$, hence $\hat{H}^q(G, A/pA) = 0$. Hence, by Theorem 6, A/pA is free over $\mathbf{F}_p[G]$.

(iii) ⇒ (i): From the same exact sequence it follows that

$$\hat{H}^q(H, A) \xrightarrow{p} \hat{H}^q(H, A)$$

is an isomorphism for all integers q and all subgroups H of G. But $\hat{H}^q(H, A)$ is a p-group (Prop. 8, Cor. 1), hence $\hat{H}^q(H, A) = 0$.

COROLLARY. *Let A be a G-module which is $\mathbf{Z}$-free and satisfies the equivalent conditions of Theorem 7. Then, for any torsion-free G-module B, the G-module $N = \mathrm{Hom}(A, B)$ is cohomologically trivial.*

Proof. Since A is $\mathbf{Z}$-free, the exact sequence

$$0 \to B \xrightarrow{p} B \to B/pB \to 0$$

gives an exact sequence

$$0 \to N \xrightarrow{p} N \to \mathrm{Hom}(A, B/pB) \to 0,$$

so that N has no p-torsion and $N/pN \simeq \mathrm{Hom}(A/pA, B/pB)$. Since A/pA is a free $\mathbf{F}_p[G]$-module, it is induced, hence is the direct sum of the

$s.A'$ ($s \in G$), where A' is a subgroup of A/pA. Hence N/pN is the direct sum of the subgroup $s.\text{Hom}(A', B/pB)$ and is therefore induced. Therefore N is cohomologically trivial by Theorems 6 and 7.

A G-module A is *projective* if $\text{Hom}_G(A, \quad)$ is an exact functor, or equivalently if A is a direct summand of a free G-module. A projective G-module is cohomologically trivial.

THEOREM 8. *Let G be a finite group, A a G-module which is $\mathbf{Z}$-free, G_p a Sylow p-subgroup of G. Then the following are equivalent:*

(i) *For each prime p, the G_p-module A satisfies the equivalent conditions of Theorem 7;*

(ii) *A is a projective G-module.*

Proof. (ii) $\Rightarrow$ (i) is clear.

(i) $\Rightarrow$ (ii): Choose an exact sequence $0 \to Q \to F \to A \to 0$, where F is a free G-module. Since A is $\mathbf{Z}$-free, this gives an exact sequence

$$0 \to \text{Hom}(A, Q) \to \text{Hom}(A, F) \to \text{Hom}(A, A) \to 0$$

By the Corollary to Theorem 7, $\text{Hom}(A, Q)$ is cohomologically trivial as a G_p-module for each p, hence $H^1(G, \text{Hom}(A, Q)) = 0$ by Prop. 8, Cor. 4. Bearing in mind that $H^0(G, \text{Hom}(A, Q)) = (\text{Hom}(A, Q))^G = \text{Hom}_G(A, Q)$, and so on, it follows that $\text{Hom}_G(A, F) \to \text{Hom}_G(A, A)$ is surjective, hence the identity map of A extends to a G-homomorphism $A \to F$. Consequently A is a direct summand of F and is therefore projective.

THEOREM 9. *Let A be any G-module. Then the following are equivalent:*

(i) *For each prime p, $\hat{H}^q(G_p, A) = 0$ for two consecutive values of q (which may depend on p);*

(ii) *A is cohomologically trivial;*

(iii) *There is an exact sequence $0 \to B_1 \to B_0 \to A \to 0$ in which B_0 and B_1 are projective G-modules.*

Proof. (ii) $\Rightarrow$ (i) is clear; so is (iii) $\Rightarrow$ (ii), since a projective G-module is cohomologically trivial.

(i) $\Rightarrow$ (iii): Choose an exact sequence of G-modules

$$0 \to B_1 \to B_0 \to A \to 0,$$

with B_0 a free G-module. Then $\hat{H}^q(G_p, B_1) \cong \hat{H}^{q-1}(G_p, A)$ for all q and all p, hence $\hat{H}^q(G_p, B_1) = 0$ for two consecutive values of q. Also B_1 is $\mathbf{Z}$-free (because B_0 is); hence, by Theorem 8, B_1 is projective.

10. Tate's Theorem

THEOREM 10. *Let G be a finite group, B and C two G-modules and $f: B \to C$ a G-homomorphism. For each prime p, let G_p be a Sylow p-subgroup of G,* *and suppose that there exists an integer n_p such that*

$$f_q^* : \hat{H}^q(G_p, B) \to \hat{H}^q(G_p, C)$$

is surjective for $q = n_p$, bijective for $q = n_p+1$ and injective for $q = n_p+2$. Then for any subgroup H of G and any integer q,

$$f_q^* : \hat{H}^q(H, B) \to \hat{H}^q(H, C)$$

is an isomorphism.

Proof. Let $B^* = \operatorname{Hom}(\Lambda, B)$ and let $i : B \to B^*$ be the injection (defined by $i(b)(g) = g.b$). Then $(f, i) : B \to C \oplus B^*$ is injective, so that we have an exact sequence

$$0 \to B \to C \oplus B^* \to D \to 0.$$

Since B^* is cohomologically trivial, the cohomology of $C \oplus B^*$ is the same as that of C. Hence the cohomology exact sequence and the hypotheses of the theorem imply that $\hat{H}^q(G_p, D) = 0$ for $q = n_p$ and $q = n_p+1$. It follows from Theorem 9 that D is cohomologically trivial, whence the result.

THEOREM 11. *Let A, B, C be three G-modules and $\varphi : A \otimes B \to C$ a G-homomorphism. Let q be a fixed integer and a a given element of $\hat{H}^q(G, A)$. Assume that for each prime p there exists an integer n_p such that the map $\hat{H}^n(G_p, B) \to \hat{H}^{n+q}(G_p, C)$ induced by cup-product with* $\operatorname{Res}_{G/Gp}(a)$ *(relative to φ) is surjective for $n = n_p$, bijective for $n = n_p+1$ and injective for $n = n_p+2$. Then, for all subgroups H of G and all integers n, the cup-product with* $\operatorname{Res}_{G/H}(a)$ *induces an isomorphism*

$$\hat{H}^n(H, B) \to \hat{H}^{n+q}(H, C).$$

(Explicitly, this mapping is $b \mapsto \varphi^*_{n+q}(\operatorname{Res}_{G/H}(a).b)$.)

Proof. The case $q = 0$ is essentially Theorem 10. We have $a \in \hat{H}^0(G, A)$: choose $\alpha \in A^G$ representing a (then α also represents $\operatorname{Res}_{G/H}(a)$ for every subgroup H of G). Define $f: B \to C$ by $f(\beta) = \varphi(\alpha \otimes \beta)$; f is a G-homomorphism, since α is G-invariant. We claim that, for every $b \in \hat{H}^n(H, B)$,

$$\varphi^*(\operatorname{Res}_{G/H}(a).b) = f^*(b). \tag{10.1}$$

Indeed, this is clear for $n = 0$ (from the definition of f), and the general case then follows by dimension-shifting. To shift downwards, for example, assume (10.1) true for $n+1$, and consider the commutative diagram

$$\begin{array}{ccccccccc} 0 & \to & B' & \to & B_* & \to & B & \to & 0 \\ & & {\scriptstyle f'}\downarrow & & {\scriptstyle 1\otimes f}\downarrow & & \downarrow{\scriptstyle f} & & \\ 0 & \to & C' & \to & C_* & \to & C & \to & 0 \end{array} \tag{10.2}$$

where $B_* = \Lambda \otimes B$, $C_* = \Lambda \otimes C$, and the rows are exact. B_*, C_* are induced modules and therefore cohomologically trivial, hence the connecting homomorphisms $\hat{\delta}$ are isomorphisms, and the diagram

$$\begin{array}{ccc} \hat{H}^n(H,B) & \xrightarrow{\delta} & \hat{H}^{n+1}(H,B') \\ \downarrow f^* & & \downarrow f'^* \\ \hat{H}^n(H,C) & \xrightarrow{\delta} & \hat{H}^{n+1}(H,C') \end{array}$$

is commutative. Moreover, the rows of (10.2) split over $\mathbf{Z}$, hence (10.2) remains exact (and commutative) when tensored with A (over $\mathbf{Z}$). Let $\varphi'' : A \otimes B' \to C'$ be the homomorphism induced by $\varphi : A \otimes B \to C$. Then using the inductive hypothesis and the compatibility of cup-products with connecting homomorphisms, we have

$$\begin{aligned} \hat{\delta} \circ f^*(b) = f'^* \circ \hat{\delta}(b) &= \varphi''^*(\mathrm{Res}_{G/H}(a).\hat{\delta}(b)) \\ &= \varphi''^* \circ \hat{\delta}(\mathrm{Res}_{G/H}(a).b) = \hat{\delta} \circ \varphi^*(\mathrm{Res}_{G/H}(a).b). \end{aligned}$$

Since $\hat{\delta}$ is an isomorphism, (10.1) is proved.

Now f satisfies the hypotheses of Theorem 10, hence f_n^* is an isomorphism. This establishes Theorem 11 for the case $q = 0$.

The general case now follows by another piece of dimension-shifting. To shift downwards from $q+1$ to q, for example, consider the exact sequence

$$0 \to A' \to A_* \to A \to 0$$

where $A_* = \Lambda \otimes A$; this gives rise to isomorphisms $\hat{\delta} : \hat{H}^q(H,A) \to \hat{H}^{q+1}(H,A')$. Let $u = \mathrm{Res}_{G/H}(a) \in \hat{H}^q(H, A)$; then $u' = \hat{\delta}(u) = \mathrm{Res}_{G/H}(\hat{\delta}(a))$. Also $\varphi : A \otimes B \to C$ induces $\varphi' : A' \otimes B \to C'$. Consider the diagram

$$\begin{array}{ccccc} \hat{H}^n(H,B) & \xrightarrow{u.} & \hat{H}^{n+q}(H, A \otimes B) & \xrightarrow{\varphi^*} & \hat{H}^{n+q}(H,C) \\ \| & & & & \downarrow \hat{\delta} \\ \hat{H}^n(H,B) & \xrightarrow{u'.} & \hat{H}^{n+q+1}(H, A' \otimes B) & \xrightarrow{\varphi'^*} & \hat{H}^{n+q+1}(H,C'); \end{array}$$

it is commutative, because

$$\hat{\delta} \circ \varphi^*(u.b) = \varphi'^* \circ \hat{\delta}(u.b) = \varphi'^*(\hat{\delta}(u).b) = \varphi'^*(u'.b);$$

by the inductive hypothesis, the bottom line is an isomorphism, and $\hat{\delta}$ is an isomorphism; hence the top line is an isomorphism.

THEOREM 12 (Tate). *Let A be a G-module, $a \in H^2(G, A)$. For each prime p let G_p be a Sylow p-subgroup of G, and assume that*

(i) $H^1(G_p, A) = 0$;

(ii) $H^2(G_p, A)$ *is generated by* $\mathrm{Res}_{G/G_p}(a)$ *and has order equal to that of* G_p.

Then for all subgroups H of G and all integers n, cup-product with $\mathrm{Res}_{G/H}(a)$ *induces an isomorphism*

$$\hat{H}^n(H,\mathbf{Z}) \to \hat{H}^{n+2}(H,A).$$

Proof. Take $B = \mathbf{Z}$, $C = A$, $q = 2$, $n_p = -1$ in Theorem 11. For $n = -1$ the surjectivity follows from (i). For $n = 0$, $\hat{H}^0(G_p, \mathbf{Z})$ is cyclic of order equal to the order of G_p, so the bijectivity follows from (iii). For $n = 1$, the injectivity follows from the fact that $H^1(G_p \mathbf{Z}) = \mathrm{Hom}(G_p, \mathbf{Z}) = 0$. Thus all the hypotheses of Theorem 11 are satisfied.

CHAPTER V

Profinite Groups

K. GRUENBERG

1. The Groups

1.1. *Introduction*

A profinite group is an inverse limit of finite groups. We begin by explaining this definition in some detail. [For all basic facts concerning inverse limits (and direct limits—these will be needed later) we refer to Chapter VIII in Eilenberg-Steenrod: *Foundations of Algebraic Topology* (E–S).]

All our topological groups are assumed to have the Hausdorff separation axiom. We recall that a morphism of topological groups means a continuous homomorphism.

1.2. *Inverse Systems*

Let I be a directed set with respect to a relation $\leq$. This means that $\leq$ is reflexive, transitive and to every i_1, i_2 in I, there exists i in I such that $i \geq i_1$ and $i \geq i_2$.

An inverse system of topological groups over I is an object $(I;\ G^i;\ \pi_i^j)$, where, for each i in I, G_i is a topological group and, for each $i \leq j$ in I,

π_i^j is a morphism: $G_j \to G_i$. Moreover, π_i^i is the identity on G_i; and if $i \leq j \leq k$, then $\pi_i^j\ \pi_j^k = \pi_i^k$ (read mappings from right to left). We shall often simply write our inverse system as (G_i).

Suppose $(G'_{i'})$ (over I') is a second inverse system. Let ϕ: $I' \to I$ be an order preserving mapping and assume that to each i' in I' we are given a morphism $\phi_{i'}$: $G_{\phi(i')} \to G'_{i'}$ such that, whenever $i' \leq j'$ in I',

$$\begin{array}{ccc} G_{\phi(i')} & \xrightarrow{\quad\phi_{i'}\quad} & G'_{i'} \\ \pi_{\phi(i')}^{\phi(j')}\Big\uparrow & & \Big\uparrow \pi'^{j'}_{i'} \\ G_{\phi(j')} & \xrightarrow{\quad\phi_{j'}\quad} & G'_{j'} \end{array}$$

commutes. Then we call $(\phi; \phi_{i'}, i' \in I') = \Phi$ a morphism of (G_i) to $(G'_{i'})$.

1.3. *Inverse Limits*

We shall view finite groups as topological groups with the discrete topology. Let (G_i) be an inverse system of *finite* groups and form ΠG_i, the cartesian product, made into a topological group in the usual way by letting the kernels of the projections $\Pi G_i \to G_i$ form a sub-basis of 1. Let L be the subset of all (x_i) in ΠG_i with the property that whenever $i \leq j$, $\pi_i^j(x_j) = x_i$. Then L is a subgroup of ΠG_i and we give it the induced topology. We say L is the *inverse* (*or projective*) *limit* of the system (G_i) (or, more loosely, of the groups G_i, $i \in I$). If all the groups G_i are finite p-groups we call L a *pro-p-group*. The notation will be $L = \varprojlim G_i$.

Clearly, L is closed in ΠG_i: for if $x \notin L$, there exists $i \leq j$ so that $\pi_i^j x_j \neq x_i$ and the set of all elements in ΠG_i with i-term x_i and j-term x_j is open and contains x but contains no element of L.

If Φ: $(G_i) \to (G'_{i'})$ is a morphism of inverse systems, we may define a mapping ψ of ΠG_i into $\Pi G'_{i'}$ as follows: given x in ΠG_i and any i' in I', $\psi(x)$ is to be the element in $\Pi G'_{i'}$ whose i'-term is $\phi_{i'}(x_{\phi(i')})$. Obviously, ψ is a group homomorphism and is continuous because, for each i', the kernel of $\Pi G_i \to G'_{i'}$ is open. By restriction, we obtain a continuous homomorphism of $\varprojlim G_i$ into $\varprojlim G'_{i'}$.

1.4. *Topological Characterization of Profinite Groups*

The main result of this section will not be needed later in these two lectures (but the corollaries will be: the reader may take them on trust). Nevertheless, we give the proof in some detail because it is not too easy to extract from the existing literature.

THEOREM 1. *A topological group is profinite if, and only if, it is compact and totally disconnected.*

We recall two facts for which we refer to Montgomery-Zippin: *Topological Transformation Groups* (M–Z).

(i) To say that a compact group is totally disconnected is equivalent to saying that 1 is the meet of all compact open neighbourhoods of 1: M–Z, p. 38.

(ii) In a compact, totally disconnected group every neighbourhood of 1 contains an open normal subgroup (and hence 1 is the meet of all open normal subgroups): M–Z, p. 56.

Proof. Let (G_i) be an inverse system of finite groups and write $L = \varprojlim G_i$, $C = \Pi G_i$. Then C is compact (Tychonoff's theorem) and hence L is also compact because L is closed in C.

We must show next that L is totally disconnected. Consider first C. If $x \neq 1$ in C, then $x_i \neq 1$ for some i. Put $U_i = 1_i$, $U_j = G_j$ for $j \neq i$ and $U = \Pi U_k$. Then U is compact and open and contains 1 but not x. Hence C is totally disconnected (by (i), above). Now in a compact group, a subset is compact if, and only if, it is closed. Thus in C, 1 is the meet of all open and closed subsets containing 1. It follows that the same is true in L (induced topology) and hence L is totally disconnected.

Next assume, conversely, that G is a compact, totally disconnected group. Let (H_i) be the family of all open, normal subgroups of G. Then (G/H_i) forms an inverse system (we put $i \leq j$ whenever $H_i \supseteq H_j$ and use the natural epimorphism $G/H_j \to G/H_i$). Let $L = \varprojlim G/H_i$. Since each G/H_i is finite, L is profinite. The mapping θ: $g \to (gH_i)$ is clearly a continuous homomorphism of G into L. Since $1 = \bigcap H_i$ (by (ii), above), θ is one–one. On the other hand, if $a = (a_i H_i) \in L$ and $S = \bigcap a_i H_i$, then S is not empty (by compactness) and so, if $g \in S$, $\theta(g) = a$: thus θ is surjective. Hence θ^{-1} is also a mapping; and it is continuous. We conclude that θ is an isomorphism and thus G is profinite.

The last part of our argument also yields

COROLLARY 1. *For any profinite group G,*

$$G \simeq \varprojlim G/U,$$

where U runs through all open, normal subgroups of G.

COROLLARY 2. *If H is a closed subgroup of G,*

$$H \cong \varprojlim H/H \cap U.$$

Proof. If V is an open normal subgroup of H, $V = O \cap H$ for some neighbourhood O of 1 in G. Hence O contains some open normal subgroup U of G ((ii) above) and so $U \cap H \subseteq V$. Thus the family $(U \cap H)$, for varying U, is cofinal in the family of all open normal subgroups of H. The result follows now by Corollary 1 and E–S, p. 220, Corollary 3.16.

COROLLARY 3. *If H is a closed normal subgroup of G,*

$$G/H \cong \varprojlim G/UH.$$

Proof. We have only to show that G/H is profinite. Clearly, G/H is compact. It remains to check that G/H is totally disconnected. Take any $x \notin H$. For each h in H we may choose an open and compact neighbourhood O_h of h not containing x (because G is totally disconnected). Then $H \subseteq \bigcup O_h$ and so, by the compactness of H, $H \subseteq O_{h_1} \cup \ldots \cup O_{h_r} = S$, say. Then S is open and compact and contains H but not x.

1.5. *Construction of Profinite Groups from Abstract Groups*

Let G be an abstract group and suppose $(H_i;\, i \in I)$ is a family of normal subgroups such that given any H_{i_1}, H_{i_2}, there exists $H_i \subseteq H_{i_1} \cap H_{i_2}$. If we partially order I by defining $i \leq j$ whenever $H_i \supseteq H_j$, then I becomes a directed set and (G/H_i) is an inverse system of groups (π_i^j being the natural homomorphism $G/H_j \to G/H_i$). The mapping $\theta\colon g \to (gH_i)$ is a homomorphism of G into $L = \varprojlim G/H_i$.

If $G_0 = \bigcap H_i$, then G/G_0 becomes a topological group if we use as basis for open sets at 1 the groups H_i/G_0 (*M–Z*, p. 25). The homomorphism θ induces a continuous homomorphism: $G/G_0 \to L$ and L is the *completion* of G/G_0 with respect to (H_i/G_0).

There are two important cases.

(i) (H_i) is the family of all normal subgroups of finite index in G. We denote the profinite group $\varprojlim G/H_i$ by $\hat{G}$. For example, $\hat{\mathbf{Z}}$ is the inverse limit of all finite cyclic groups.

(ii) (H_i) is the family of all normal subgroups of index a power of p, where p is a given prime number. Here $\varprojlim G/H_i = \hat{G}_p$ is a pro-p-group.

For example, $\hat{\mathbf{Z}}_p$ (usually written $\mathbf{Z}_p$) is the inverse limit of all finite cyclic p-groups. This is the group of p-adic integers.

Exercise: $\hat{\mathbf{Z}} = \prod\limits_p \mathbf{Z}_p$.

1.6. *Profinite Groups in Field Theory*

Let E/F be a Galois extension of fields. This means that E is algebraic over F and the group $G = G(E/F)$ of all F-automorphisms of E has no fixed points outside F. [For simple facts about field theory (including finite Galois theory) we refer to Bourbaki: *Algèbre*, Chapter V (B).]

Let $(K_i, i \in I)$ be the family of all finite Galois extensions of F contained in E. Then $E = \bigcup K_i$ (B, Section 10.1).

Now (i) if $K_i \subseteq K_j$, then we have a natural homomorphism π_i^j: $G(K_j/F) \to G(K_i/F)$ (B, Section 10.2); and (ii) the F-composite of K_{i_1} and K_{i_2} is some K_j. Hence the finite Galois groups $(G(K_i/F))$ form an inverse system and we may construct its inverse limit, call it L.

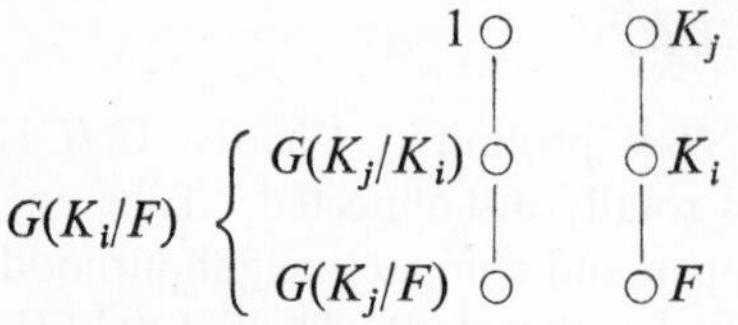

PROPOSITION 1. $G(E/F) \cong L$.

Proof. For each i in I, we have a homomorphism $G(E/F) \to G(K_i/F)$. These together yield a homomorphism θ: $G(E/F) \to \Pi G(K_i/F)$. The image of θ is obviously contained in L. We assert θ is an isomorphism onto L.

If $g \neq 1$ in G, there exists x in E such that $g(x) \neq x$; and then there exists K_i containing x. Now the image of g in $G(K_i/F)$ maps x to $g(x)$ and thus is not the identity. Hence θ is one–one.

Take (g_i) in L. If $x \in E$ and we set $g(x) = g_i(x)$, where $x \in K_i$, then this is an unambiguous definition of a mapping g of E into E. It is easy to check that g is, in fact, an F-automorphism of E. Since $\theta(g) = (g_i)$, L is the image of θ.

We use the isomorphism θ to transfer the topology on L to G. *Thus* $G = G(E/F)$ *is now a profinite group* and if $U_i = G(E/K_i)$, (U_i) is a defining system of neighbourhoods of 1 (M–Z, pp. 25–26).

Example. If E is an algebraic closure of the field $\mathbf{F}_p$ of p elements, then $G(E/\mathbf{F}_p) \cong \hat{\mathbf{Z}}$ (cf. Section 1.5).

THEOREM 2 (Fundamental theorem of Galois theory).

Let E/F be a Galois extension with group G, $\mathcal{S}$ the set of all closed subgroups of G and $\mathcal{F}$ the set of all fields between E and F. Then $K \to G(E/K)$ is a one–one mapping of $\mathcal{F}$ onto $\mathcal{S}$. The inverse of this is the mapping $S \to E^S$, where E^S denotes the field of fixed points for the closed subgroup S.

Proof: *First Step.* We show that if $K \in \mathcal{F}$, then $G(E/K) \in \mathcal{S}$.

Let $(L_j; j \in J)$ be the family of all finite extensions of F contained in K. Then $K = \bigcup L_j$ and thus $G(E/K) = \bigcap G(E/L_j)$.

Each L_j is contained in some finite Galois extension K_i and hence $G(E/L_j) \supseteq G(E/K_i)$. By Proposition 1, $G(E/K_i)$ is open and therefore $G(E/L_j)$ is also open in $G(E/F)$. Hence $G(E/L_j)$ is closed and thus $\bigcap G(E/L_j) = G(E/K)$ is closed.

Second step. If $K \in \mathcal{F}$ then $K = E^{G(E/K)}$ (B, Section 10.2).

Third step. Let S be a closed subgroup of G, $K = E^S$ and $T = G(E/K)$. Clearly $S \subseteq T$. But by the second step, $E^S = E^T$. Hence for every open normal subgroup V_i of T, if $L_i = E^{V_i}$, $L_i^{T/V_i} = K = L_i^{SV_i/V_i}$. By finite Galois theory, we conclude $T/V_i = SV_i/V_i$, i.e., $T = SV_i$. Hence S is dense in T. But S is closed by the first step and so $S = T$.

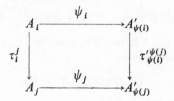

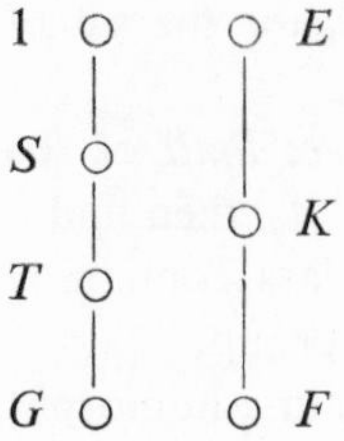

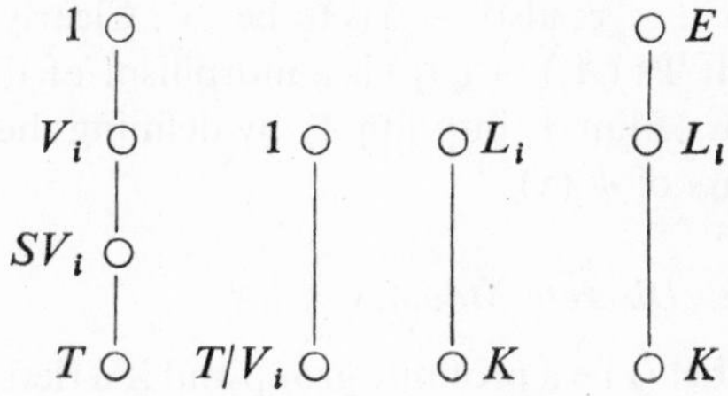

2. The Cohomology Theory

2.1. *Introduction*

In order to define the cohomology of profinite groups we make use of two facts: (i) a profinite group is put together from finite groups; and (ii) we know how to define the cohomology of finite groups.

2.2. *Direct Systems and Direct Limits*

We shall only be concerned here with the category of all discrete abelian groups (written additively).

We consider a family (A_i) of abelian groups, indexed by a directed set I. Assume that for each $i \le j$ in I we are given a homomorphism $\tau_i^j : A_i \to A_j$ and that (i) τ_i^i is the identity on A_i, (ii) if $i \le j \le k$, then $\tau_j^k \tau_i^j = \tau_i^k$. We call $(I; A_i; \tau_i^j)$ *a direct system* of abelian groups over I. Frequently we just write (A_i).

If $(A'_{i'})$ (over I') is a second direct system, let $\psi : I \to I'$ be an order preserving mapping and to each i in I, let ψ_i be a homomorphism: $A_i \to A'_{\psi(i)}$. If $i \le j$ always implies that

$$\begin{array}{ccc} A_i & \xrightarrow{\psi_i} & A'_{\psi(i)} \\ {\scriptstyle \tau_i^j}\downarrow & & \downarrow{\scriptstyle \tau'^{\psi(j)}_{\psi(i)}} \\ A_j & \xrightarrow{\psi_j} & A'_{\psi(j)} \end{array}$$

commutes, then we call $(\psi; \psi_i) = \Psi$ a morphism of direct systems: $(A_i) \to (A'_{i'})$.

Given (A_i), let S be the disjoint union of the groups A_i, $i \in I$. If $x \in A_i$, $y \in A_j$, write $x \sim y$ to mean that there exists $k \geq i, k \geq j$ such that $\tau_i^k x = \tau_j^k y$. Then $\sim$ is an equivalence relation on S. We write $\varinjlim A_i$ for the set of equivalence classes and $\tilde{x}$ for the class containing x.

Now $A = \varinjlim A_i$ is made into an abelian group (the *direct limit* of the groups A_i, $i \in I$) as follows. If $\tilde{x}, \tilde{y} \in A$, where $x \in A_i$, $y \in A_j$, then find k so that $k \geq i$ and $k \geq j$ and define $\tilde{x} + \tilde{y}$ to be the class containing $\tau_i^k x + \tau_j^k y$; also $-\tilde{x}$ is to be $\widetilde{-x}$. Clearly A is now an abelian group.

If $\Psi: (A_i) \to (A'_{i'})$ is a morphism of direct systems, we obtain a homomorphism of $\varinjlim A_i$ into $\varinjlim A'_{i'}$ by defining the image of $\tilde{x}$, where $x \in A_i$, to be the class of $\psi_i(x)$.

2.3. *Discrete Modules*

Let G be a profinite group and A a (left) G-module. If U is an open subgroup of G, we shall denote, as usual, the set of all fixed elements in A under U by A^U. We shall consider only G-modules A satisfying the condition

$$A = \bigcup A^U,$$

where the union is taken over all open normal subgroups of G. Such modules are called *discrete G-modules.*

It is not difficult to see that the following three conditions on the G-module A are equivalent:

(i) A is a discrete G-module;

(ii) the stabilizer in G of every module element is an open subgroup of G;

(iii) the pairing $G \times A \to A$ is continuous, where A is viewed as a discrete space and G has its usual topology as a profinite group.

2.4. *Cohomology of Profinite Groups*

Let A be a discrete G-module and let $(U_i; i \in I)$ be the family of all open normal subgroups of G. Then $G \cong \varprojlim G/U_i$ (Corollary 1 to Theorem 1) and $A \cong \varinjlim A^{U_i}$ (because $A = \bigcup A^{U_i}$ and $\bigcup A^{U_i}$ is naturally isomorphic to $\varinjlim A^{U_i}$).

Let q be a fixed non-negative integer. For every $i \leq j$, we obtain a homomorphism (inflation)

$$\lambda_i^j: H^q(G/U_i, A^{U_i}) \to H^q(G/U_j, A^{U_j})$$

in the standard way (cf. Chapter IV, Section 4). Clearly, we now have a direct system of abelian groups

$$(I; H^q(G/U_i, A^{U_i}); \lambda_i^j).$$

DEFINITION. $\varinjlim H^q(G/U_i, A^{U_i})$ is called the *q-th cohomology group* of G in A and written $H^q(G,A)$.

There is another way of defining these cohomology groups. We consider the additive group $C^n = C^n(G,A)$ of all *continuous* mappings of G^n into A and define a coboundary $d: C^n \to C^{n+1}$ by the standard formula:

$$(df)(g_1, \ldots, g_{n+1}) = g_1 \cdot f(g_2, \ldots, g_{n+1}) + \sum_{i=1}^{n} (-1)^i f(g_1, \ldots, g_i g_{i+1}, \ldots, g_{n+1}) + (-1)^{n+1} f(g_1, \ldots, g_n).$$

This yields a complex $C^{\cdot}(G,A)$ and the homology groups of it are precisely $H^q(G,A)$.

Of course, this must be proved. The argument is not difficult but (when written out in full) is both long and tedious. The crucial point is this. A mapping ϕ of a profinite group H into a discrete space S is continuous if, and only if, there exists an open normal subgroup K of H and a mapping ψ of the finite group H/K into S such that ϕ is the product of the natural projection $H \to H/K$ and ψ. It follows that if $f \in C^n(G,A)$, then there is an open normal subgroup U_1 of G such that f is

$$G^n \to (G/U_1)^n \to A.$$

Since f is finitely valued, the image of f lies in A^{U_2}, for some open normal U_2. If $U = U_1 \cap U_2$, then f is

$$G^n \to (G/U)^n \to A^U \to A$$

and $f'\colon (G/U)^n \to A^U$ is an element of $C^n(G/U, A^U)$. This makes it more than plausible that $C^n(G,A) = \varinjlim C^n(G/U, A^U)$.

2.5. *An Example: Generators of pro-p-Groups*

Let G be a pro-p-group and $\mathbf{F}_p$ the field of p elements, viewed as a discrete G-module with trivial action. The formula above for df shows immediately that

$$H^1(G,\mathbf{F}_p) = \mathrm{Hom}\,(G,\mathbf{F}_p).$$

If $G^* = G^p[G,G]$, then the right-hand side is Hom $(G/G^*, \mathbf{F}_p)$.

Assume G is finitely generated as a topological group. Then G/G^* is finite and its dimension d, as a vector space over $\mathbf{F}_p$, is the dimension of $H^1(G,\mathbf{F}_p)$. Let $x_1G^*, \ldots, x_dG^*$ be a basis of G/G^*. If U is any open normal subgroup of G contained in G^*, then $x_1, \ldots, x_d$ generate G modulo U (by the Burnside basis theorem for finite p-groups) and hence $x_1, \ldots, x_d$ generate G topologically. Thus $\dim_{\mathbf{F}_p} H^1(G,\mathbf{F}_p)$ *is the minimum number of generators of* G.

2.6. *Galois Cohomology I: Additive Theory*

[Our reference for elementary Galois cohomology is Chapter X of Serre: *Corps Locaux* (S).]

As in Section 1.6, let E/F be a Galois extension of fields with group $G = G(E/F)$. Denote by $(K_i; i \in I)$ the family of all finite Galois extensions of F contained in E and set $U_i = G(E/K_i)$. Then $G = \varprojlim G/U_i$.

The action of G on E turns the additive group of E into a G-module. Now $E^{U_i} = K_i$ and $E = \bigcup K_i$ so that E is a discrete G-module. Moreover, K_i is a $G(K_i/F)$ – module and $G(K_i/F) \cong G/U_i$. Thus we have

$$H^q(G,E) \cong \varinjlim H^q(G(K_i/F), K_i). \tag{1}$$

PROPOSITION 2. *$H^q(G,E) = 0$ for all $q \geq 1$.*

By equation (1) this is an immediate consequence of

LEMMA 1. *Let E/F be a finite Galois extension and $G = G(E/F)$. Then $H^q(G,E) = 0$ for all $q \geq 1$.*

Proof. The normal basis theorem states that E, as FG-module, is free on one generator (B, Section 10.8), i.e., is isomorphic to the induced module on F. Hence the result (cf. Chapter IV, Section 6).

Note that this argument yields the following stronger fact:

COROLLARY. *If E/F is a finite Galois extension, then the Tate cohomology groups $\hat{H}^q(G(E/F), E) = 0$ for all integers q.*

(Recall that $\hat{H}^q = H^q$ for $q \geq 1$.)

2.7. *Galois Cohomology II*: "*Hilbert* 90"

We continue with the notation of Section 2.6. We saw that E as a G-module turned out to be cohomologically uninteresting. The situation is very different when we look at E^* (the multiplicative group of E) as a G-module.

Again, since $(E^*)^{U_i} = K_i^*$ and $E^* = \bigcup K_i^*$, E^* is a discrete G-module; and

$$H^q(G,E^*) \cong \varinjlim H^q(G(K_i/F), K_i^*). \tag{2}$$

PROPOSITION 3. *$H^1(G,E^*) = 0$.*

Proof. By equation (2), we need only prove this when E/F is finite.

Let f be a 1-cocycle of G in E^*. By the theorem on the independence of automorphisms (B, Section 7.5), there exists c such that

$$b = \sum_{x \in G} f(x) \,.\, x(c) \neq 0.$$

Apply y in G to this:

$$y(b) = \sum_{x \in G} [yf(x)][yx(c)] = \sum_{x \in G} f^{-1}(y) f(yx) \,.\, yx(c)$$

$$\text{(since } f(yx) = f(y) \,.\, yf(x))$$

$$= f^{-1}(y) \sum_{z \in G} f(z) \,.\, z(c)$$

$$= f^{-1}(y) b.$$

Thus $f(y) = b.y(b)^{-1}$, i.e., f is a coboundary.

Corollary (Hilbert Theorem 90). *If $G = G(E/F)$ is finite cyclic with generator g and $a \in E^*$ is such that $N_{E/F}(a) = 1$, then there exists b in E^* such that $a = b/g(b)$.*

Proof. Since G is cyclic, $H^1(G, A) = {}_N A/(1 - g)A$ (cf. Chapter IV, Section 8). Here $A = E^*$ and so, in multiplicative notation, $(1 - g)A$ is $\{b/g(b), b \in E^*\}$. Since $H^1(G,E^*) = 0$, the result follows.

2.8. *Galois Cohomology III: Brauer Groups*

Let E_1/F, E_2/F be two Galois extensions and write $G_i = G(E_i/F)$.

Suppose j is an F-homomorphism: $E_1 \to E_2$. Then $j(E_1)/F$ is Galois and hence the restriction $g \to g|j(E_1)$ yields a morphism $\bar{j}$: $G_2 \to G_1$. Let $U = G(E_2/j(E_1))$. Now

$$H^q(G_1, E_1^*) \simeq H^q(G_2/U, E_2^{*U}) \xrightarrow{\text{inf}} H^q(G_2,E_2^*)$$

and we shall write j^* for the product of these two homomorphisms:

$$j^*: H^q(G_1,E_1^*) \to H^q(G_2,E_2^*).$$

We assert j^* is independent of j.

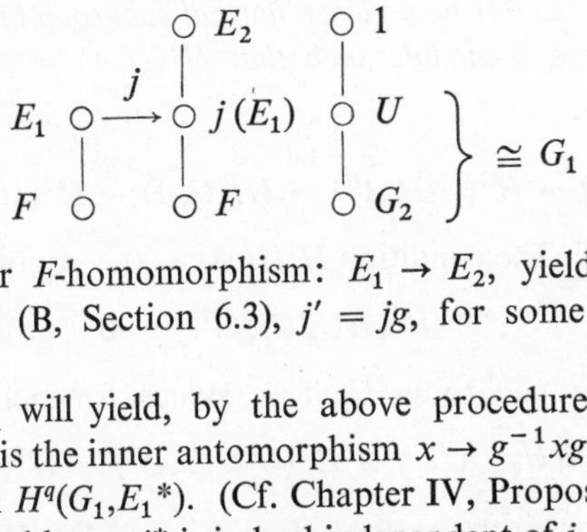

Let j' be another F-homomorphism: $E_1 \to E_2$, yielding $\bar{j}'$: $G_2 \to G_1$. Since $j'(E_1) = j(E_1)$ (B, Section 6.3), $j' = jg$, for some g in G_1. Hence $(j')^* = j^*g^*$.

Now g: $E_1 \to E_1$ will yield, by the above procedure, a morphism $\bar{g}$: $G_1 \to G_1$. Clearly $\bar{g}$ is the inner antomorphism $x \to g^{-1}xg$ of G_1. Therefore g^* is the identity on $H^q(G_1,E_1{}^*)$. (Cf. Chapter IV, Proposition 3.)

Thus $(j')^* = j^*$ and hence j^* is indeed independent of j.

Now suppose E_1, E_2 are two separable closures of F. Then there always exist F-isomorphisms: $E_1 \to E_2$ and all these yield the *same* isomorphism $H^q(G_1,E_1{}^*) \to H^q(G_2,E_2{}^*)$. From the cohomological point of view, it is therefore immaterial which separable closure one uses and we shall simply write $H^q(F)$ for the group $H^q(G(E/F),E^*)$, where E is any given separable closure of F. The groups $H^q(F)$ depend functorially on F.

Definition. The *Brauer group* of the field F is the group $H^2(F)$.

Theorem 3. *If E/F is a Galois extension containing a Galois extension K/F, then we have the exact sequence*

$$0 \to H^2(G(K/F),K^*) \to H^2(G(E/F), E^*) \to H^2(G(E/K),E^*).$$

COROLLARY 1. *If K/F is a Galois extension, the following sequence is exact:*

$$0 \to H^2(G(K/F),K^*) \to H^2(F) \to H^2(K).$$

Proof. Take E to be any separable closure of F containing K and apply Theorem 3.

An immediate consequence is the following corollary.

COROLLARY 2. *If (K_i) is the family of all finite Galois extensions of F in a separable closure of F, then $H^2(F) = \bigcup H^2(G(K_i/F),K_i^*)$.*

To prove the theorem, we first translate it into a result about abstract profinite groups.

Let $G = G(E/F)$, $H = G(E/K)$ and $A = E^*$. Then, by Galois theory, $G/H \cong G(K/F)$ and $A^H = K^*$. The mapping $H^2(G,A) \to H^2(H,A)$ is restriction and the mapping $H^2(G/H,A^H) \to H^2(G,A)$ is inflation. (Restriction and inflation for profinite groups are defined precisely as for abstract groups.) Theorem 3 is now seen as a consequence of the following result, together with Proposition 3.

PROPOSITION 4. *Let H be a closed normal subgroup of the profinite group G and A be a discrete G-module such that $H^1(H,A) = 0$. Then the following sequence is exact:*

$$0 \to H^2(G/H,A^H) \xrightarrow{\text{inf}} H^2(G,A) \xrightarrow{\text{res}} H^2(H,A).$$

Outline of proof. The condition $H^1(H,A) = 0$ is equivalent to

$$H^1(HU_i/U_i, A^{U_i}) = 0$$

for all open normal subgroups U_i of G. Hence, for each U_i,

$$0 \to H^2(G/HU_i, A^{HU_i}) \to H^2(G/U_i, A^{U_i}) \to H^2(HU_i/U_i, A^{U_i})$$

is exact (Chapter IV, Proposition 5 with $q = 1$). If $i \leq j$, we have an exact row for i, one for j and the inflation mappings connecting the two and producing a commutative diagram. All these diagrams together constitute an "exact sequence of direct systems". The result we want now follows by taking the direct limit and using two facts:

(1) $\varinjlim$ is an exact functor on the category of direct systems over a fixed indexing set (E–S, p. 225);

(2) $\varprojlim H/H \cap U_i \cong H$ and $\varprojlim G/HU_i \cong G/H$ (Corollaries 2 and 3 to Theorem 1, above).

Alternatively, one may prove the result directly by a method almost identical to that used for establishing the abstract case.

REFERENCES

The basic reference for profinite groups is

Serre, J-P., "Cohomologie Galoisienne". Springer Verlag, Berlin (1965).

Books referred to in this paper:

Bourbaki, N., "Algèbre," Chapter V Hermann, Paris (B) (1950).

Eilenberg, S. and Steenrod, N., "Foundations of Algebraic Topology" (E–S). Princeton University Press, Princeton, New Jersey, U.S.A. (1952).

Montgomery, D. and Zippin, L., "Topological Transformation Groups" (M–Z). Interscience, New York and London (1955).

Serre, J-P., "Corps Locaux". Hermann, Paris (S) (1962).

CHAPTER VI

Local Class Field Theory

J-P. SERRE

Introduction

We call a field K a *local field* if it is complete with respect to the topology defined by a discrete valuation v and if its residue field k is finite. We write $q = p^f = \text{Card}(k)$ and we always assume that the valuation v is normalized; that is, that the homomorphism $v: K^* \to \mathbf{Z}$ is surjective. The structure of such fields is known:

1. If K has characteristic 0, then K is a finite extension of the p-adic field $\mathbf{Q}_p$, the completion of $\mathbf{Q}$ with respect to the topology defined by the p-adic valuation. If $[K:\mathbf{Q}_p] = n$ then $n = ef$ where f is the residue degree (that is, $f = [k:\mathbf{F}_p]$ and e is the ramification index $v(p)$.

2. If K has characteristic p ("the equal characteristic case"), then K is isomorphic to a field $k((T))$ of formal power series, where T is a uniformizing parameter.

The first case is the one which arises in completions of a number field relative to a prime number p.

We shall study the Galois groups of extensions of K and would of course like to know the structure of the Galois group $G(K_s/K)$ of the separable closure K_s of K, since this contains the information about all such extensions. (In the case of characteristic 0, $K_s = \overline{K}$). We shall content ourselves with the following:

1. The cohomological properties of all galois extensions, whether abelian or not.

2. The determination of the abelian extensions of K, that is, the determination of G modulo its derived group G'.

Throughout this Chapter, we shall adhere to the notation already introduced above, together with the following. We denote the ring of integers of K by O_K, the multiplicative group of K by K^* and the group of units by U_K. A similar notation will be used for extensions L of K, and if L is a galois extension, then we denote the Galois group by $G(L/K)$ or $G_{L/K}$ or even by G. If $s \in G$ and $\alpha \in L$, then we denote the action of s on α by ${}^s\alpha$ or by $s(\alpha)$.

In addition to the preceding Chapters, the reader is referred to "Corps Locaux" (Actualités scientifiques et industrielles, 1296; Hermann, Paris, 1962) for some elided details. In what follows theorems etc. in the four sections are numbered independently.

1. The Brauer Group of a Local Field

1.1. *Statements of Theorems*

In this first section, we shall state the main results; the proofs of the theorems will extend over §§ 1.2–1.6.

We begin by recalling the definition of the Brauer group, Br (K), of K.

(See Chapter V, § 2.7.) Let L be a finite galois extension of K with Galois group $G(L/K)$. We write $H^2(L/K)$ instead of $H^2(G_{L/K}, L^*)$ and we consider the family $(L_i)_{i \in I}$ of all such finite galois extensions of K. The inductive (direct) limit $\varinjlim H^2(L_i/K)$ is by definition the Brauer group, Br(K), of K.

It follows from the definition that $\mathrm{Br}(K) = H^2(K_s/K)$. In order to compute Br (K) we look first at the intermediate field K_{nr}, $K \subset K_{nr} \subset K_s$, where K_{nr} denotes the maximal unramified extension of K. The reader is referred to Chapter I, § 7 for the properties of K_{nr}. We recall in particular, that the residue field of K_{nr} is $\bar{k}$, the algebraic closure of k, and that $G(K_{nr}/K) = G(\bar{k}/k)$. We denote by F the Frobenius element in $G(K_{nr}/K)$; the effect of F on the residue field $\bar{k}$ is given by $\lambda \mapsto \lambda^q$. The map $\upsilon \mapsto F^\upsilon$ is an isomorphism $\hat{\mathbf{Z}} \to G(K_{nr}/K)$ of topological groups. From Chapter V § 2.5, we recall that $\hat{\mathbf{Z}}$ is the projective (inverse) limit, $\varprojlim \mathbf{Z}/n\mathbf{Z}$, of the cyclic groups $\mathbf{Z}/n\mathbf{Z}$.

Since K_{nr} is a subfield of K_s, $H^2(K_{nr}/K)$ is a subgroup of $\mathrm{Br}(K) = H^2(K_s/K)$. In fact:

THEOREM 1. $H^2(K_{nr}/K) = \mathrm{Br}\,(K)$.

We have already noted above that $H^2(K_{nr}/K) = H^2(\hat{\mathbf{Z}}, K_{nr}^*)$.

THEOREM 2. *The valuation map* $v : K_{nr}^* \to \mathbf{Z}$ *defines an isomorphism* $H^2(K_{nr}/K) \to H^2(\hat{\mathbf{Z}}, \mathbf{Z})$.

We have to compute $H^2(\hat{\mathbf{Z}}, \mathbf{Z})$. More generally let G be a profinite group and consider the exact sequence

$$0 \to \mathbf{Z} \to \mathbf{Q} \to \mathbf{Q}/\mathbf{Z} \to 0$$

of G-modules with trivial action. The module $\mathbf{Q}$ has trivial cohomology, since it is uniquely divisible (that is, $\mathbf{Z}$-injective) and so the coboundary $\delta : H^1(\mathbf{Q}/\mathbf{Z}) \to H^2(\mathbf{Z})$ yields an isomorphism $H^1(\mathbf{Q}/\mathbf{Z}) \to H^2(G, \mathbf{Z})$. Now $H^1(\mathbf{Q}/\mathbf{Z}) = \mathrm{Hom}\,(G, \mathbf{Q}/\mathbf{Z})$ and so $\mathrm{Hom}\,(G, \mathbf{Q}/\mathbf{Z}) \cong H^2\,(G, \mathbf{Z})$.

We turn now to $\mathrm{Hom}\,(\hat{\mathbf{Z}}, \mathbf{Q}/\mathbf{Z})$. Let $\phi \in \mathrm{Hom}\,(\hat{\mathbf{Z}}, \mathbf{Q}/\mathbf{Z})$ and define a map $\gamma : \mathrm{Hom}\,(\hat{\mathbf{Z}}, \mathbf{Q}/\mathbf{Z}) \to \mathbf{Q}/\mathbf{Z}$ by $\phi \mapsto \phi(1) \in \mathbf{Q}/\mathbf{Z}$. It follows from Theorem 2 that we have isomorphisms

$$H^2(K_{nr}/K) \xrightarrow{v} H^2(\hat{\mathbf{Z}}, \mathbf{Z}) \xrightarrow{\delta^{-1}} \mathrm{Hom}\,(\hat{\mathbf{Z}}, \mathbf{Q}/\mathbf{Z}) \xrightarrow{\gamma} \mathbf{Q}/\mathbf{Z}.$$

The map $\mathrm{inv}_K : H^2(K_{nr}/K) \to \mathbf{Q}/\mathbf{Z}$ is now defined by

$$\mathrm{inv}_K = \gamma \circ \delta^{-1} \circ v.$$

For future reference, we state our conclusions in:

COROLLARY. *The map* $\mathrm{inv}_K = \gamma \circ \delta^{-1} \circ v$ *defines an isomorphism between the groups* $H^2(K_{nr}/K)$ *and* $\mathbf{Q}/\mathbf{Z}$.

Since, by Theorem 1, $H^2(K_{nr}/K) = \mathrm{Br}\,(K)$, we see that *we have defined an isomorphism* $\mathrm{inv}_K : \mathrm{Br}\,(K) \to \mathbf{Q}/\mathbf{Z}$.

If L is a finite extension of K, the corresponding map will be denoted by inv_L.

THEOREM 3. *Let L/K be a finite extension of degree n. Then*

$$\text{inv}_L \circ \text{Res}_{K/L} = n \,.\, \text{inv}_K.$$

In other words, the following diagram is commutative

$$\begin{array}{ccc} \text{Br}(K) & \xrightarrow{\text{Res}_{K/L}} & \text{Br}(L) \\ {\scriptstyle \text{inv}_K}\downarrow & & \downarrow{\scriptstyle \text{inv}_L} \\ \mathbf{Q}/\mathbf{Z} & \xrightarrow{\ n\ } & \mathbf{Q}/\mathbf{Z} \end{array}$$

(For the definition of $\text{Res}_{K/L}$, the reader is referred to Chapter IV § 4 and to Chapter V § 2.7.)

COROLLARY 1. *An element $\alpha \in \text{Br}(K)$ gives 0 in $\text{Br}(L)$ if and only if $n\alpha = 0$.*

COROLLARY 2. *Let L/K be an extension of degree n. Then $H^2(L/K)$ is cyclic of order n. More precisely, $H^2(L/K)$ is generated by the element $u_{L/K} \in \text{Br}(K)$, the invariant of which is $1/n \in \mathbf{Q}/\mathbf{Z}$.*

Proof. This follows from the fact that $H^2(L/K)$ is the kernel of Res.

1.2 *Computation of $H^2(K_{nr}/K)$*

In this section we prove Theorem 2. We have to prove that the homomorphism $H^2(K_{nr}/K) \to H^2(\hat{\mathbf{Z}}, \mathbf{Z})$ is an isomorphism.

PROPOSITION 1. *Let K_n be an unramified extension of K of degree n and let $G = G(K_n/K)$. Then for all $q \in \mathbf{Z}$ we have:*

(1). *$H^q(G, U_n) = 0$, where $U_n = U_{K_n}$;*

(2). *the map $v: H^q(G, K_n^*) \to H^q(G, \mathbf{Z})$ is an isomorphism.*

(Theorem 2 is evidently a consequence of (2) of Proposition 1, since $H^2(K_{nr}/K) = H^2(\hat{\mathbf{Z}}, K_{nr})$.)

Proof. The fact that (1) implies (2) follows from the cohomology sequence

$$H^q(G, U_n) \to H^q(G, K_n^*) \to H^q(G, \mathbf{Z}) \to H^{q+1}(G, U_n)$$

It remains to prove (1). Consider the decreasing sequence of open subgroups $U_n \supset U_n^1 \supset U_n^2 \supset \ldots$ defined as follows: $x \in U_n^i$ if and only if $v(x-1) \geqslant i$. Now let $\pi \in K$ be a uniformizing element; so that $U_n^i = 1 + \pi^i O_n$, where $O_n = O_{K_n}$. Then $U_n = \varprojlim U_n/U_n^i$. The proof will now be built up from the three following lemmas.

LEMMA 1. *Let k_n be the residue field of K_n. Then there are galois isomorphisms $U_n/U_n^1 \simeq k_n^*$ and, for $i \geqslant 1$, $U_n^i/U_n^{i+1} \simeq k_n^+$.*

(By a galois isomorphism we mean an isomorphism which is compatible with the action of the Galois group on either side.)

Proof. Take $\alpha \in U_n$ and map $\alpha \mapsto \bar{\alpha}$ where $\bar{\alpha}$ is the reduction of α into k_n. By definition, $U_n^1 = 1+\pi O_n$; so if $\alpha \in U_n^1$ then $\bar{\alpha} = 1$, and the first part of the lemma is proved.

To prove the second part, take $\alpha \in U_n^i$ and write $\alpha = 1+\pi^i\beta$ where $\beta \in O_n$. Now map $\alpha \mapsto \bar{\beta}$. We have to show that in this map a product $\alpha\alpha'$ corresponds to the sum $\bar{\beta}+\bar{\beta}'$. By definition, $\alpha\alpha' = 1+\pi^i(\beta+\beta')+\ldots$, whence $\alpha\alpha' \mapsto \bar{\beta}+\bar{\beta}'$.

Finally, the isomorphisms are galois since ${}^s\alpha = 1+\pi^i.{}^s\beta$.

LEMMA 2. *For all integers q and for all integers* $i \geqslant 0$, $H^q(G, U_n^i/U_n^{i+1}) = 0$.

Proof. For $i = 0$, $U_n^0 = U_n$, and the first part of Lemma 1 gives

$$H^q(G, U_n/U_n^1) = H^q(G, k_n^*) = H^q(G_{k_n/k}, k_n^*).$$

Now for $q = 1$, $H^1(G_{k_n/k}, k_n^*) = 0$ ("Hilbert Theorem 90", cf. Chapter V, § 2.6). For $q = 2$, observe that G is cyclic. Since k_n^* is finite, the Herbrand quotient $h(k_n^*) = 1$ (cf. Chapter IV, § 8, Prop. 11); hence the result for $q = 2$. For other values of q the result follows by periodicity.

For $i \geqslant 1$, the lemma follows from Lemma 1 and the fact that k_n^+ has trivial cohomology.

The proof of Theorem 2 will be complete if we can go from the groups U_n^i/U_n^{i+1} to the group U_n itself and the following lemma enables us to do this.

LEMMA 3. *Let G be a finite group and let M be a G-module. Let* M^i, $i \geqslant 0$ *and* $M^0 = M$, *be a decreasing sequence of G-submodules and assume that* $M = \varprojlim M/M^i$; (*more precisely, the map from M to the limit is a bijection*). *Then, if, for some* $q \in \mathbf{Z}$, $H^q(G, M^i/M^{i+1}) = 0$ *for all i, we have* $H^q(G, M) = 0$.

Proof. Let f be a q-cocycle with values in M. Since $H^q(G, M/M^1) = 0$, there exists a $(q-1)$-cochain ψ_1 of G with values in M such that $f = \delta\psi_1+f_1$, where f_1 is a q-cocycle in M^1. Similarly, there exists ψ_2 such that $f_1 = \delta\psi_2+f_2$, $f_2 \in M^2$, and so on. We construct in this way a sequence (ψ_n, f_n) where ψ_n is a $(q-1)$-cochain with values in M^{n-1} and f_n is a q-cocycle with values in M^n, and $f_n = \delta.\psi_{n+1}+f_{n+1}$. Set $\psi = \psi_1+\psi_2+\ldots$. In view of the hypotheses on M, this series converges and defines a $(q-1)$-cochain of G with values in M. On summing the equations $f_n = \delta\psi_{n+1}+f_{n+1}$, we obtain $f = \delta\psi$, and this proves the lemma.

We return now to the proof of Proposition 1. Take M in Lemma 3 to be U_n. It follows from Lemma 3 and from Lemma 2 that the cohomology of U_n is trivial and this completes the proof of Proposition 1 and so also of Theorem 2.

1.3 *Some Diagrams*

PROPOSITION 2. *Let L/K be a finite extension of degree n and let L_{nr} (resp. K_{nr}) be the maximal unramified extension of L (resp. K); so that $K_{nr} \subset L_{nr}$. Then the following diagram is commutative.*

$$\begin{array}{ccc} H^2(K_{nr}/K) & \xrightarrow{\text{Res}} & H^2(L_{nr}/L) \\ \downarrow{\scriptstyle \text{inv}_K} & & \downarrow{\scriptstyle \text{inv}_L} \\ \mathbf{Q}/\mathbf{Z} & \xrightarrow{n} & \mathbf{Q}/\mathbf{Z} \end{array}$$

Proof. Let $\Gamma_K = G(K_{nr}/K)$ and let F_K be the Frobenius element of Γ_K; let Γ_L and F_L be defined similarly. We have $F_L = (F_K)^f$ where $f = [l:k]$ is the residue field degree of L/K.

Let e be the ramification index of L/K, and consider the diagram:

$$\begin{array}{ccccccc} H^2(\Gamma_K, K^*_{nr}) & \xrightarrow{v_K} & H^2(\Gamma_K, \mathbf{Z}) & \xrightarrow{\delta^{-1}} & \text{Hom}(\Gamma_K, \mathbf{Q}/\mathbf{Z}) & \xrightarrow{\gamma_K} & \mathbf{Q}/\mathbf{Z} \\ \downarrow{\scriptstyle \text{Res}} & (1) & \downarrow{\scriptstyle e.\text{Res}} & (2) & \downarrow{\scriptstyle e.\text{Res}} & (3) & \downarrow{\scriptstyle n} \\ H^2(\Gamma_L, L^*_{nr}) & \xrightarrow{v_L} & H^2(\Gamma_L, \mathbf{Z}) & \xrightarrow{\delta^{-1}} & \text{Hom}(\Gamma_L, \mathbf{Q}/\mathbf{Z}) & \xrightarrow{\gamma_L} & \mathbf{Q}/\mathbf{Z}, \end{array}$$

where Res is induced by the inclusion $\Gamma_L \to \Gamma_K$, and γ_K (resp. γ_L) is given by $\varphi \mapsto \varphi(F_K)$ (resp. $\varphi \mapsto \varphi(F_L)$). The three squares (1), (2), (3) extracted from that diagram are *commutative*; for (1), this follows from the fact that v_L is equal to $e.v_K$ on K^*_{nr}; for (3), it follows from $F_L = F_K^f$, and $n = ef$; for (2), it is obvious.

On the other hand, the definition of $\text{inv}_K : H^2(\Gamma_K, K^*_{nr}) \to \mathbf{Q}/\mathbf{Z}$ is equivalent to:

$$\text{inv}_K = \gamma_K \circ \delta^{-1} \circ v_K,$$

and similarly:

$$\text{inv}_L = \gamma_L \circ \delta^{-1} \circ v_L.$$

Proposition 2 is now clear.

COROLLARY 1. *Let $H^2(L/K)_{nr}$ be the subgroup of $H^2(K_{nr}/K)$ consisting of those $\alpha \in H^2(K_{nr}/K)$ which are "killed by L" (that is, which give 0 in $Br(L)$). Then $H^2(L/K)_{nr}$ is cyclic of order n and is generated by the element $u_{L/K}$ in $H^2(K_{nr}/K)$ such that $\text{inv}_K(u_{L/K}) = 1/n$.*

Proof. Note that a less violent definition of $H^2(L/K)_{nr}$ is provided by $H^2(L/K)_{nr} = H^2(L/K) \cap H^2(K_{nr}/K)$.

Consider the exact sequence

$$0 \to H^2(L/K)_{nr} \to H^2(K_{nr}/K) \xrightarrow{\text{Res}} H^2(L_{nr}/L).$$

The kernel of the map $H^2(K_{nr}/K) \to H^2(L_{nr}/L)$ is $H^2(L/K)_{nr}$ and this goes to 0 under $\text{inv}_L : H^2(L_{nr}/L) \to \mathbf{Q}/\mathbf{Z}$. On the other hand, it follows from Proposition 2 that $\text{inv}_L \circ \text{Res} = n.\text{inv}_K$. The kernel of the latter is $(1/n)\mathbf{Z}/\mathbf{Z}$ and so $H^2(L/K)_{nr}$ is cyclic of order n, and is generated by $u_{L/K} \in H^2(K_{nr}/K)$ with $\text{inv}_K(u_{L/K}) = 1/n$.

Corollary 2. *The order of $H^2(L/K)$ is a multiple of n.*

Proof. $H^2(L/K)$ contains a cyclic subgroup of order n by Corollary 1.

1.4 *Construction of a Subgroup with Trivial Cohomology*

Let L/K be a finite galois extension with Galois group G, where L and K are local fields. According to the discussion in Proposition 1, the G-module U_L has trivial cohomology when L is unramified.

Proposition 3. *There exists an open subgroup, V, of U_L with trivial cohomology. That is, $H^q(G, V) = 0$ for all q.*

Proof. We shall give two proofs; the first one works only in characteristic 0, the second works generally.

Method 1. The idea is to compare the multiplicative and the additive groups of L. We know that L^+ is a free module over the algebra $K[G]$. That is, there exists $\alpha \in L$ such that $[{}^s\alpha]_{s\in G}$ is a basis for L considered as a vector space over K.

Now take the ring O_K of integers of K and define $A = \sum_{s\in G} O_K . {}^s\alpha$. This is free over G and so has trivial cohomology. Moreover, by multiplying α by a sufficiently high power of the local uniformizer π_K, we may take such an A to be contained in any given neighbourhood of 0.

It is a consequence of Lie theory that the additive group of L is locally isomorphic to the multiplicative group. More precisely, the power series $e^x = 1+x+\ldots+x^n/n!+\ldots$, converges for $v(x) > v(p)/(p-1)$. Thus in the neighbourhood $v(x) > v(p)/(p-1)$ of 0, L^* is locally isomorphic to L^+ under the map $x \mapsto e^x$. (Note that, in the same neighbourhood, the inverse mapping is given by $\log(1+x) = x - x^2/2 + x^3/3 - \ldots.$)

Now define $V = e^A$; it is clear that V has trivial cohomology.

The foregoing argument breaks down in characteristic p; namely at the local isomorphism of L^+ and L^*.

Method 2. We start from an A constructed as above: $A = \sum_{s\in G} O_K . {}^s\alpha$. We may assume that $A \subset O_L$. Since A is open in O_L, $\pi_K^N O_L \subset A$ for a suitable N. Set $M = \pi_K^i A$. Then $M.M \subset \pi_K M$ if $i \geqslant N+1$. For $M.M = \pi_K^{2i} A.A \subset \pi_K^{2i} O_L$ and if $i \geqslant N+1$ then

$$\pi_K^{2i} O_L \subset \pi_K . \pi_K^i A \subset \pi_K M.$$

Now let $V = 1+M$. Then V is an open subgroup of U_L. It remains to be proved that V has trivial cohomology. We define a filtration of V by means of subgroups $V^i = 1+\pi_K^i M$, $i \geqslant 0$. (Note that V^i is a subgroup since $(1+\pi_K^i x)(1+\pi_K^i y) = 1+\pi_K^i(x+y+\pi_K^i xy)$, etc.) This yields a decreasing filtration $V = V^0 \supset V^1 \supset V^2 \supset \ldots$. As in § 1.2, Lemma 2, we are reduced to proving that $H^q(G, V^i/V^{i+1}) = 0$ for all q. Take $x = 1+\pi_K^i\beta$, $\beta \in M$ and associate with this its image $\bar{\beta} \in M/\pi_K M$. This is a group isomorphism of V^i/V^{i+1} and $M/\pi_K M$ and we know that the latter has trivial cohomology, since it is free over G.

This completes our proofs of Proposition 3.

We recall the definition of the Herbrand quotient $h(M)$. Namely, $h(M) = \text{Card}(\hat{H}^0(M))/\text{Card}(H^1(M))$, when both sides are finite. (See Chapter IV, § 8.)

COROLLARY 1. *Let L/K be a cyclic extension of degree n. Then we have $h(U_L) = 1$ and $h(L^*) = n$.*

Proof. Let V be an open subgroup of U_L with trivial cohomology (cf. Prop. 3). Since h is multiplicative, $h(U_L) = h(V).h(U_L/V) = 1$.

Again, $L^*/U_L \cong \mathbf{Z}$. So $h(L^*) = h(\mathbf{Z}).h(U_L)$. Now $h(U_L) = 1$ and $h(\mathbf{Z}) = n$, since $\hat{H}^0(G, \mathbf{Z}) = n$ and $H^1(G, \mathbf{Z})$ is trivial. Hence $h(L^*) = n$.

COROLLARY 2. *Let L/K be a cyclic extension of degree n. Then $H^2(L/K)$ is of order $n = [L:K]$.*

Proof. We have

$$h(L^*) = \frac{\text{Card}(H^2(G, L^*))}{\text{Card}(H^1(G, L^*))}.$$

Now Corollary 1 gives $h(L^*) = n$. Moreover, $H^1(G, L^*) = 0$ (Hilbert Theorem 90). Hence $\text{Card}(H^2(G, L^*)) = n$. But $H^2(G, L^*)$ is $H^2(L/K)$, whence the result.

1.5 *An Ugly Lemma*

LEMMA 4. *Let G be a finite group and let M be a G-module and suppose that ρ, q are integers with $\rho \geqslant 0$, $q \geqslant 0$. Assume that:*

(a) *$H^i(H, M) = 0$ for all $0 < i < q$ and all subgroups H of G;*

(b) *if $H \subset K \subset G$, with H invariant in K and K/H cyclic of prime order, then the order of $H^q(H, M)$ (resp. $\hat{H}^0(H, M)$ if $q = 0$) divides $(K: H)^\rho$.*

Then the same is true of G. That is, $H^q(G, M)$ (resp. $\hat{H}^0(G, M)$ is of order dividing $(G:1)^\rho$.

Proof. Since the restriction map $\text{Res}: \hat{H}^q(G, M) \to \hat{H}^q(G_p, M)$ is injective on the p-primary components of $\hat{H}^q(G, M)$, where G_p denotes a Sylow p-subgroup of G, we may confine our attention to the case in which G is a p-group. We now argue by induction on the order of G.

Assume that G has order greater than 1. Choose a subgroup H of G which is invariant and of index p. We apply the induction hypothesis to G/H. We know from (b) that, for $q > 0$, the order of $H^q(G/H, M^H)$ divides $(G: H)^\rho = p^\rho$ and by the induction hypothesis $H^q(H, M)$ divides $(H: 1)^\rho$. Now it follows from (a) that we have an exact sequence (Chapter IV, § 5).

$$0 \longrightarrow H^q(G/H, M^H) \xrightarrow{\text{Inf}} H^q(G, M) \xrightarrow{\text{Res}} H^q(H, M).$$

Thus $H^q(G, M)$ has order dividing $p^\rho.(H:1)^\rho = (G:1)^\rho$.

For $q = 0$, we recall (see Chapter IV, § 6) that

$$\hat{H}^0(G, M) = M^G/N_G M.$$

Then we have the exact sequence

$$M^H/N_H M \xrightarrow{N_{G/H}} M^G/N_G M \longrightarrow (M^H)^{G/H}/N_{G/H} M^H$$

where $N_{G/H}$ denotes the norm map and the second map is induced by the identity. The remainder of the argument now runs as before.

1.6 *End of Proofs*

PROPOSITION 4. *Let L/K be a finite galois extension with Galois group G of order $n = [L:K]$. Then $H^2(L/K)$ is cyclic of order n and has a generator $u_{L/K} \in H^2(K_{nr}/K)$ such that $\mathrm{inv}_K(u_{L/K}) = 1/n$.*

Proof. In Lemma 4, take $M = L^*$, $\rho = 1$ and $q = 2$. Condition (a) is satisfied by "Theorem 90" and (b) is true by Prop. 3, Cor. 2. Hence $H^2(G, L^*)$ has order dividing $(G:1) = n$. But by Prop. 2, Cor. 1, $H^2(L/K)$ contains a cyclic subgroup of order n, generated by $u_{L/K} \in H^2(K_{nr}/K)$ and such that $\mathrm{inv}_K(u_{L/K}) = 1/n$. Whence Proposition 4.

It follows from this proposition that $H^2(L/K)$ is contained in $H^2(K_{nr}/K)$.

We turn now to the proof of Theorem 1. The theorem asserts that the inclusion $\mathrm{Br}(K) \supset H^2(K_{nr}/K)$ is actually equality. Now by definition, $\mathrm{Br}(K) = \cup H^2(L/K)$, where L runs through the set of finite galois extensions of K. But as remarked above, $H^2(L/K) \subset H^2(K_{nr}/K)$. Hence $\mathrm{Br}(K) \subset H^2(K_{nr}/K)$, as was to be proved.

Evidently, Theorem 3 follows from Theorem 1 and Proposition 2.

1.7 *An Auxiliary Result*

We have now proved all the statements in § 1.1 and we conclude the present chapter with a result which has applications to global fields.

Let A be an abelian group and let n be an integer $\geqslant 1$. Consider the cyclic group $\mathbf{Z}/n\mathbf{Z}$ with trivial action on A. We shall denote the corresponding Herbrand quotient by $h_n(A)$, whenever it is defined. We have

$$h_n(A) = \frac{\mathrm{Order}\,(A/nA)}{\mathrm{Order}\,{}_nA}$$

where ${}_nA$ is the set of $\alpha \in A$ such that $n\alpha = 0$. (Alternatively, we could begin with the map $A \xrightarrow{n} A$ and take $h_n(A)$ to be:

$$\mathrm{order}\,(\mathrm{Coker}\,(n))/\mathrm{order}\,(\mathrm{Ker}\,(n)).)$$

Now let K be a local field. Then for $\alpha \in K$ there is a normalized absolute value, denoted by $|\alpha|_K$ (see Chapter II, § 11). If $\alpha \in O_K$, then $|\alpha|_K = 1/\mathrm{Card}\,(O_K/\alpha O_K)$.

PROPOSITION 5. *Let K be a local field and let $n \geqslant 1$ be an integer prime to the characteristic of K. Then $h_n(K^*) = n/|n|_K$.*

Proof. Suppose that K has characteristic 0. We have $h_n(K^*) = h_n(\mathbf{Z}).h_n(U_K)$. Now $h_n(\mathbf{Z}) = n$; so we must compute $h_n(U_K)$. As in Proposition 3, we consider a subgroup V of U which is open and isomorphic to the additive group of O_K. We have $h_n(U_K) = h_n(V).h_n(U_K/V)$ and since U_K/V is finite, $h_n(U_K/V) = 1$. We have

$$h_n(V) = h_n(O_K)$$

and

$$h_n(O_K) = \text{Card}\,(O_K/nO_K) = 1/|n|_K.$$

Whence

$$h_n(K^*) = n.(1/|n|_K) = n/|n|_K.$$

Suppose now that K has characteristic p. We take the same steps as before. First, $h_n(K^*) = n.h_n(U_K)$. Now consider the exact sequence

$$0 \to U_K^1 \to U_K \to k^* \to 0$$

where U_K^1 is a pro-p-group (cf. Lemma 1). Since n is prime to p it follows that $h_n(U_K^1) = 1$ and that $h_n(k^*) = 1$. So $n.h_n(U_K) = n$. Whence the result.

We note that the statement of the proposition is also correct for **R** *or* **C**. In these cases we have $|n|_{\mathbf{R}} = |n|$, $|n|_{\mathbf{C}} = |n|^2$ and one can check directly that, for **R**, $h_n(\mathbf{R}^*) = n/|n| = 1$ and, for **C**, $h_n(\mathbf{C}^*) = n/|n|_{\mathbf{C}} = 1/n$.

APPENDIX

Division Algebras Over a Local Field

It is known that elements of Brauer groups correspond to skew fields (cf., for instance, "Séminaire Cartan", 1950/51, Exposés 6/7), and we are going to use this correspondence to give a description of skew fields and the corresponding invariants. Most results will be stated without proof.

Let K be a local field and let D be a division algebra over K, with centre K and $[D:K] = n^2$. The valuation v of K extends in a unique way from K to D (for example, by extending first to $K(\alpha)$, $\alpha \in D$, and then fitting the resulting extensions together). The field D is complete with respect to this valuation and, in an obvious notation, O_D is of degree n^2 over O_K. Let d be the residue field of D; we have $n^2 = ef$ where e is the ramification index and $f = [d:k]$.

Now $e \leqslant n$; for there exists $\alpha \in D$ such that $v_D(\alpha) = e^{-1}$ and α belongs to a commutative subfield of degree at most n over K. The residue field d is commutative, since k is a finite field, and $d = k(\bar{\alpha})$ for some $\alpha \in D$. Hence $f \leqslant n$. Together with $n^2 = ef$, the inequalities $e \leqslant n$ and $f \leqslant n$ yield $e = n$ and $f = n$.

Since $[d:k] = n$, we can find $\bar{\alpha} \in d$ such that $k(\bar{\alpha}) = d$. Now choose a corresponding $\alpha \in O_D$ and let $L = K(\alpha)$. Evidently $[L:K] \leqslant n$, since L is a commutative subfield of D. On the other hand, $\bar{\alpha}$ is an element of l (the residue field of L) and $l = d$; hence $[l:k] = n$. It follows that $[L:K] = n$ and L is unramified. We state this last conclusion as: *D contains a maximal commutative subfield L which is unramified over K.*

The element $\delta \in \mathrm{Br}(K)$ corresponding to D splits in L, that is $\delta \in H^2(L/K)$. So any element in $\mathrm{Br}(K)$ is split by an unramified extension and we have obtained a new proof of Theorem 1.

Description of the Invariant

The extension L of K constructed above is not unique, but the Skolem-Noether theorem (Bourbaki, "Algèbre", Chap. 8, § 10) shows that all such extensions are conjugate. The same theorem shows that any automorphism of L is induced by an inner automorphism of D. Hence there exists $\gamma \in D$ such that $\gamma L \gamma^{-1} = L$ and the inner automorphism $x \mapsto \gamma x \gamma^{-1}$ on L is the Frobenius F. Moreover γ is determined, up to multiplication by an element of L^*.

Let v_L be the valuation $v_L : L^* \to \mathbf{Z}$ of L; so that $v_D : D^* \to (1/n)\mathbf{Z}$ extends v_L on D. The image $i(D)$ of $v_D(\gamma)$ in $(1/n)\mathbf{Z}/\mathbf{Z} \subset \mathbf{Q}/\mathbf{Z}$ is independent of the choice of γ. One can prove that $i(D) = \mathrm{inv}_K(\delta)$, where $\delta \in \mathrm{Br}(K)$ is associated with D.

We can express the definition of $i(D)$ in a slightly different way. The map $x \mapsto \gamma^n x \gamma^{-n}$ is equal to F^n on L and so is the identity. It follows that γ^n commutes with L and $\gamma^n = c \in L^*$. Now

$$v_D(\gamma) = \frac{1}{n} v_D(\gamma^n) = \frac{1}{n} v_D(c) = \frac{1}{n} v_L(c).$$

Hence we have $v_D(\gamma) = (1/n)v_L(c) = i/n$ where $c = \pi_L^i u$.

Application

Suppose that K'/K is an extension of degree n. By Theorem 3, Cor. 2, an element $\delta \in \mathrm{Br}(K)$ is killed by K'. Hence: *any extension K'/K of degree n can be embedded in D as a maximal commutative subfield.* This may be stated more spectacularly as: any irreducible equation of degree n over K can be solved in D.

EXERCISE

Consider the 2-adic field $\mathbf{Q}_2$ and let H be the quaternion skew field over $\mathbf{Q}_2$. Prove that the ring of integers in H consists of the elements $a+bi+cj+dk$ where $a, b, c, d \in \mathbf{Z}_2$ or $a, b, c, d \equiv \frac{1}{2} \pmod{\mathbf{Z}_2}$. Make a list of the seven (up to conjugacy) quadratic subfields of H.

2. Abelian Extensions of Local Fields

2.1 *Cohomological Properties*

Let L/K be a finite galois extension of local fields with Galois group $G = G(L/K)$ of order n. We have seen (§ 1.1, Theorem 3, Cor. 2.) that the group $H^2(L/K) = H^2(G, L^*)$ is cyclic of order n and contains a generator $u_{L/K}$ such that $\operatorname{inv}_K(u_{L/K}) = 1/n \in \mathbf{Q}/\mathbf{Z}$. On the other hand, we know that $H^1(G, L^*) = 0$.

Now let H be a subgroup of G of order m. Since H is the Galois group of L/K' for some $K' \supset K$, we also have $H^1(H, L^*) = 0$ and $H^2(H, L^*)$ is cyclic of order m and generated by $u_{L/K'}$.

To go further, we need to know more about $u_{L/K'}$. Now we have the restriction map $\operatorname{Res}: \operatorname{Br}(K) \to \operatorname{Br}(K')$ and this suggests that $u_{L/K'} = \operatorname{Res}(u_{L/K})$. To see that this is the case, we simply check on invariants. We have

$$\operatorname{inv}_{K'}(\operatorname{Res} u_{L/K}) = [K' : K] \operatorname{inv}_K(u_{L/K}) = [K' : K] \,.\, \frac{1}{n} = \frac{1}{m} = \operatorname{inv}_{K'}(u_{L/K'} \,.$$

We can now apply Tate's theorem (Chapter IV, § 10) to obtain:

THEOREM 1. *For all $q \in \mathbf{Z}$, the map $\alpha \mapsto \alpha . u_{L/K}$ given by the cup-product is an isomorphism of $\hat{H}^q(G, \mathbf{Z})$ onto $\hat{H}^{q+2}(G, L^*)$.*

A similar statement holds if H is a subgroup of G corresponding to an extension L/K'. The mappings Res and Cor connect the two isomorphisms and we have a more explicit statement in terms of diagrams.

STATEMENT. *The diagrams*

$$\begin{array}{ccc} \hat{H}^q(G,\mathbf{Z}) & \xrightarrow{u_{L/K}} & \hat{H}^{q+2}(G,L^*) \\ \downarrow{\scriptstyle \mathrm{Res}} & & \downarrow{\scriptstyle \mathrm{Res}} \\ \hat{H}^q(H,\mathbf{Z}) & \xrightarrow{u_{L/K'}} & \hat{H}^{q+2}(H,L^*) \end{array} \qquad \begin{array}{ccc} \hat{H}^q(G,\mathbf{Z}) & \xrightarrow{u_{L/K}} & \hat{H}^{q+2}(G,L^*) \\ \uparrow{\scriptstyle \mathrm{Cor}} & & \uparrow{\scriptstyle \mathrm{Cor}} \\ \hat{H}^q(H,\mathbf{Z}) & \xrightarrow{u_{L/K'}} & \hat{H}^{q+2}(H,L^*) \end{array}$$

are commutative.

Proof. As above, $u_{L/K'} = \operatorname{Res}(u_{L/K})$. We must show that

$$\operatorname{Res}_{K/K'}(u_{L/K} . \alpha) = u_{L/K'} . \operatorname{Res}_{K/K'}(\alpha).$$

The left-hand side is $\operatorname{Res}_{K/K'}(u_{L/K}) . \operatorname{Res}_{K/K'}(\alpha)$ (see Cartan-Eilenberg, "Homological Algebra", Chap. XII, p. 256) and so commutativity with Res is proved.

For the second diagram we have to show that $\operatorname{Cor}(u_{L/K'} . \beta) = u_{L/K} . \operatorname{Cor}(\beta)$. Now $\operatorname{Cor}(u_{L/K'} . \beta) = \operatorname{Cor}(\operatorname{Res}(u_{L/K}) . \beta) = u_{L/K} . \operatorname{Cor}(\beta)$ (Cartan-Eilenberg, *loc. cit.*) and this proves the commutativity of the second diagram.

2.2 *The Reciprocity Map*

We shall be particularly concerned with the case $q = -2$ of the foregoing discussion. By definition $\hat{H}^{-2}(G, \mathbf{Z})$ is $H_1(G, \mathbf{Z})$ and we know that

$H_1(G, \mathbf{Z}) = G/G' = G^{ab}$. On the other hand, $\hat{H}^0(L/K) = K^*/N_{L/K}L^*$, where $N_{L/K}$ denotes the norm. In this case, Theorem 1 reads as follows.

THEOREM 2. *The cup-product by $u_{L/K}$ defines an isomorphism of $G^{ab}(L/K)$ onto $K^*/N_{L/K}L^*$.*

We give a name to the isomorphism just constructed, or rather to its inverse. Define $\theta = \theta_{L/K}$ to be the isomorphism of $K^*/N_{L/K}L^*$ on to G^{ab}, which is inverse to the cup-product by $u_{L/K}$. The map θ is called the *local reciprocity map* or the *norm residue symbol.*

If $\alpha \in K^*$ corresponds to $\bar{\alpha} \in K^*/N_{L/K}L^*$, then we write $\theta_{L/K}(\bar{\alpha}) = (\alpha, L/K)$. The norm residue symbol is so named since it tells whether or not $\alpha \in K^*$ is a norm from L^*. Namely, $(\alpha, L/K) = 0$ (remember that 0 means 1!) if and only if α is a norm from L^*.

Observe that if L/K is abelian, then $G^{ab} = G$ and we have an isomorphism $\theta : K^*/N_{L/K}L^* \to G$.

2.3 *Characterization of* $(\alpha, L/K)$ *by Characters*

Let L/K be a galois extension with group G. We start from an $\alpha \in K^*$ and we seek a characterization of $(\alpha, L/K) \in G^{ab}$. For ease of writing we set $s_\alpha = (\alpha, L/K)$. Let $\chi \in \mathrm{Hom}(G, \mathbf{Q}/\mathbf{Z}) = H^2(G, \mathbf{Z})$ be a character of degree 1 of G and let $\delta\chi \in H^2(G, \mathbf{Z})$ be the image of χ by the coboundary map $\delta : H^1(G, \mathbf{Q}/\mathbf{Z}) \to H^2(G, \mathbf{Z})$ (cf. § 1.1) Let

$$\bar{\alpha} \in K^*/N_{L/K}(L^*) = \hat{H}^0(G, L^*)$$

be the image of α. The cup-product $\bar{\alpha}.\delta\chi$ is an element of $H^2(G, L^*) \subset \mathrm{Br}(K)$.

PROPOSITION 1. *With the foregoing notation, we have the formula*

$$\chi(s_\alpha) = \mathrm{inv}_K(\bar{\alpha}.\delta\chi).$$

Proof. By definition $s_\alpha.u_{L/K} = \bar{\alpha} \in \hat{H}^0(G, L^*)$, s_α being identified with an element of $H^{-2}(G, \mathbf{Z})$. Using the associativity of the cup-product, this gives $\bar{\alpha}.\delta\chi = u_{L/K}.s_\alpha.\delta\chi = u_{L/K}.(s_\alpha.\delta\chi) = u_{L/K}.\delta(s_\alpha.\chi)$ with $s_\alpha.\chi \in \hat{H}^{-1}(G, \mathbf{Q}/\mathbf{Z})$. Now $\hat{H}^{-1}(G, \mathbf{Q}/\mathbf{Z}) \xrightarrow{\delta} \hat{H}^0(G, \mathbf{Z}) = \mathbf{Z}/n\mathbf{Z}$ and we identify $\hat{H}^{-1}(G, \mathbf{Q}/\mathbf{Z})$ with $\mathbf{Z}/n\mathbf{Z}$. Moreover, the identification between $H^{-2}(G, \mathbf{Z})$ and G^{ab} has been so made in order to ensure that $s_\alpha.\chi = \chi(s_\alpha)$ (see "Corps Locaux", Chap. XI, Annexe pp. 184–186). Write $s_\alpha.\chi = r/n$, $r \in \mathbf{Z}$. Then $\delta(r/n) \in \hat{H}^0(G, \mathbf{Z})$ and $\delta(r/n) = r$. Hence $u_{L/K}.(s.\delta\chi) = r.u_{L/K}$ and the invariant of this cohomology class is just $r/n = \chi(s_\alpha)$. So Proposition 1 is proved.

As an application we consider the following situation. Consider a tower of galois extensions $K \subset L' \subset L$ with $G = G(L/K)$ and $H = G(L/L')$. Then, if χ' is a character of $(G/H)^{ab}$ and χ is the corresponding character of G^{ab}, and if $\alpha \in K^*$ induces $s_\alpha \in G^{ab}$ and $s'_\alpha \in (G/H)^{ab}$ under the natural map $s_\alpha \mapsto s'_\alpha$, we have $\chi(s_\alpha) = \chi'(s'_\alpha)$. This follows from Prop. 2 and the fact that the inflation map transforms χ' (resp. $\delta\chi'$) into χ (resp. $\delta\chi$).

This compatibility allows us to define s_α for any abelian extension; in particular, taking $L = K^{ab}$, the maximal abelian extension of K, we get a homomorphism $\theta_K : K^* \to G(K^{ab}/K)$ defined by $\alpha \mapsto (\alpha, K^{ab}/K)$.

2.4 *Variations with the Fields Involved*

Having considered the effect on $(\alpha, L/K)$ of extensions of L we turn now to consider extensions of K. Let K'/K be a separable extension and let K^{ab}, K'^{ab} be the maximal abelian extensions of K, K' respectively.

We look at the first of the diagrams in the Statement of § 2.1 and the case $q = -2$. Taking the projective limit of the groups involved, we obtain a commutative diagram:

$$\begin{array}{ccc} K^* & \xrightarrow{\theta_K} & G_K^{ab} \\ {\scriptstyle \text{incl}}\downarrow & & \downarrow{\scriptstyle V} \\ K'^* & \xrightarrow{\theta_{K'}} & G_{K'}^{ab} \end{array}$$

Here V denotes the transfer (Chapter IV, § 6), $G_{K'}^{ab}$ denotes $G(K'^{ab}/K)$ and G_K^{ab} denotes $G(K^{ab}/K) = G^{ab}(K'^{ab}/K)$.

Similarly, using the second of the diagrams in the Statement, we obtain a commutative diagram:

$$\begin{array}{ccc} K'^* & \xrightarrow{\theta'_K} & G_{K'}^{ab} \\ {\scriptstyle N_{K'/K}}\downarrow & & \downarrow{\scriptstyle i} \\ K^* & \xrightarrow{\theta_K} & G_K^{ab} \end{array}$$

where i is induced by the inclusion of $G_{K'}$ into G_K.

[Note that if K'/K is an inseparable extension, then in the first of these diagrams the transfer, V, should be replaced by qV where q is the inseparable factor of the degree of the extension K'/K. The second diagram holds even in the inseparable case.]

2.5 *Unramified Extensions*

In this case it is possible to compute the norm residue symbol explicitly in terms of the Frobenius element:

PROPOSITION 2. *Let L/K be an unramified extension of degree n and let $F \in G_{L/K}$ be the Frobenius element. Let $\alpha \in K^*$ and let $v(\alpha) \in Z$ be its normalized valuation. Then $(\alpha, L/K) = F^{v(\alpha)}$.*

Proof. Let χ be an element of Hom $(G_{L/K}, \mathbf{Q}/\mathbf{Z})$. By Prop. 1, we have:

$$\chi((\alpha, L/K)) = \text{inv}_K(\bar{\alpha}.\delta\chi).$$

The map $\text{inv}_K : H^2(G_{L/K}, L^*) \to \mathbf{Q}/\mathbf{Z}$ has been defined as a composition:

$$H^2(G_{L/K}, L^*) \xrightarrow{v} H^2(G_{L/K}, \mathbf{Z}) \xrightarrow{\delta^{-1}} H^1(G_{L/K}, \mathbf{Q}/\mathbf{Z}) \xrightarrow{\gamma} \mathbf{Q}/\mathbf{Z}.$$

We have $v(\bar{\alpha}.\delta\chi) = v(\alpha).\delta\chi$, hence:

$$\text{inv}_K(\bar{\alpha}.\delta\chi) = \gamma \circ \delta^{-1} \circ v(\bar{\alpha}.\delta\chi) = v(\alpha).\gamma(\chi) = v(\alpha)\chi(F) = \chi(F^{v(\alpha)}).$$

This shows that

$$\chi((\alpha, L/K)) = \chi(F^{v(\alpha)})$$

for any character χ of $G_{L/K}$; hence $(\alpha, L/K) = F^{v(\alpha)}$.

COROLLARY. *Let E/K be a finite abelian extension. The norm residue symbol $K^* \to G_{E/K}$ maps U_K onto the inertia subgroup T of $G_{E/K}$.*

Proof. Let L be the sub-extension of E corresponding to T. By Prop. 2, the image of U_K in $G_{L/K}$ is trivial; this means that the image of U_K in $G_{E/K}$ is contained in T. Conversely, let $t \in T$, and let $f = [L:K]$; there exists $a \in K^*$ such that $t = (a, E/K)$. Since $t \in T$, Prop. 2 shows that f divides $v_K(a)$; hence, there exists $b \in E^*$ such that $v_K(a) = v_K(Nb)$. If we put $u = a.Nb^{-1}$, we have $u \in U_K$ and $(u, E/K) = (a, E/K) = t$.

2.6 *Norm Subgroups*

DEFINITION. *A subgroup M of K^* is called a norm subgroup if there exists a finite abelian extension L/K with $M = N_{L/K}L^*$.*

Example: Let $m \geqslant 1$ be an integer, and let M_m be the set of elements $a \in K^*$ with $v_K(a) \equiv 0 \bmod m$; it follows from Prop. 2 (or from a direct computation of norms) that M_m is the norm group of the unramified extension of K of degree m.

Norm subgroups are closely related to the reciprocity map

$$\theta_K : K^* \to G_K^{ab} = G(K^{ab}/K)$$

defined in § 2.3. By construction, θ_K is obtained by projective limit from the isomorphisms $K^*/NL^* \to G_{L/K}$, where L runs through all finite abelian extensions of K. If we put:

$$\tilde{K} = \varprojlim . K^*/NL^*,$$

we see that θ_K can be factored into

$$K^* \xrightarrow{i} \tilde{K} \xrightarrow{\tilde{\theta}} G_K^{ab}.$$

where i is the natural map, and $\tilde{\theta}$ is an *isomorphism.* Note that $\tilde{K}$ is just the *completion* of K^* with respect to the topology defined by the norm subgroups.

This shows that norm subgroups of K^* and open subgroups of G_K^{ab} correspond to each other in a one–one way: if U is an open subgroup of G_K^{ab}, with fixed field L, we attach to U the norm subgroup $\theta_K^{-1}(U) = N_{L/K}L^*$; if M is a norm subgroup of K^*, we attach to it the adherence of $\theta_K(M)$; the corresponding field L_M is then the set of elements in K^{ab} which are invariant by the $\theta_K(a)$, for $a \in M$. We thus get a "Galois correspondence" between norm subgroups and finite abelian extensions; we state it as a proposition:

PROPOSITION 3. (a) *The map $L \mapsto NL^*$ is a bijection of the set of finite abelian extensions of K onto the set of norm subgroups of K^*.*

(b) *This bijection reverses the inclusion.*

(c) $N(L.L') = NL \cap NL'$ *and* $N(L \cap L') = NL.NL'$.

(d) *Any subgroup of* K^* *which contains a norm subgroup is a norm subgroup.*

(For a direct proof, see "Corps Locaux", Chap. XI, § 4.)

Non-abelian extensions give the same norm subgroups as the abelian ones:

PROPOSITION 4. *Let* E/K *be a finite extension, and let* L/K *be the largest abelian extension contained in* E. *Then we have:*

$$N_{E/K}E^* = N_{L/K}L^*.$$

Proof. This follows easily from the properties of the norm residue symbol proved in § 2.4; for more details, see Artin-Tate, "Class Field Theory", pp. 228–229, or "Corps Locaux", p. 180. (These two books give only the case where E/K is separable; the general case reduces to this one by observing that $NL = K$ when L is a purely inseparable extension of K.)

COROLLARY ("Limitation theorem"). *The index* $(K^* : NE^*)$ *divides* $[E:K]$. *It is equal to* $[E:K]$ *if and only if* E/K *is abelian.*

Proof. This follows from the fact that the index of NL^* in K^* is equal to $[L:K]$.

2.7 *Statement of the Existence Theorem*

It gives a characterization of the norm subgroups of K^*:

THEOREM 3. *A subgroup* M *of* K^* *is a norm subgroup if and only if it satisfies the following two conditions:*

(1) *Its index* $(K^* : M)$ *is finite.*

(2) M *is open in* K^*.

(Note that, if (1) is satisfied, (2) is equivalent to " M is closed".)

Proof of necessity. If $M = NL^*$, where L is a finite abelian extension of K, we know that K^*/M is isomorphic to $G_{L/K}$; hence $(K^* : M)$ is finite. Moreover, one checks immediately that $N : L^* \to K^*$ is continuous and *proper* (the inverse image of a compact set is compact); hence $M = NL^*$ is closed, cf. Bourbaki, "Top. Gén.", Chap. I, § 10. As remarked above, this shows that M is open. [This last property of the norm subgroups may also be expressed by saying that the reciprocity map

$$\theta_K : K^* \to G_K^{ab}$$

is *continuous*.]

Proof of sufficiency. See § 3.8, where we shall deduce it from Lubin Tate's theory. The usual proof, reproduced for instance in "Corps Locaux", uses Kummer and Artin-Schreier equations.

We give now some equivalent formulations.

Consider the reciprocity map $\theta_K : K^* \to G_K^{ab}$. By Prop. 2, the composition

$$K^* \xrightarrow{\theta_K} G_K^{ab} \to G(K_{nr}/K) = \hat{\mathbf{Z}}$$

is just the valuation map $v : K^* \to Z$. Hence we have a commutative diagram:

$$\begin{array}{ccccccccc} 0 & \to & U_K & \to & K^* & \to & \mathbf{Z} & \to & 0 \\ & & \downarrow \theta & & \downarrow \theta & & \downarrow \text{id.} & & \\ 0 & \to & I_K & \to & G_K^{ab} & \to & \hat{\mathbf{Z}} & \to & 0, \end{array}$$

where $I_K = G(K^{ab}/K_{nr})$ is the *inertia subgroup* of G_K^{ab}, and $G(K_{nr}/K)$ is identified with $\hat{\mathbf{Z}}$.

The map $\theta : U_K \to I_K$ is continuous, and its image is dense (cf. Cor. to Prop. 2); since U_K is compact, it follows that it is *surjective*.

We can now state two equivalent formulations of the existence theorem.

THEOREM 3a. *The map* $\theta : U_K \to I_K$ *is an isomorphism.*

THEOREM 3b. *The topology induced on* U_K *by the norm subgroups is the natural topology of* U_K.

The group I_K is just $\varprojlim U_K/(M \cap U_K)$, where M runs through all norm subgroups of K^*; the equivalence of Theorem 3a and Theorem 3b follows from this and a compacity argument. The fact that Theorem 3 $\Rightarrow$ Theorem 3b is clear; the converse is easy, using Prop. 2.

COROLLARY. *The exact sequence* $0 \to U_K \to K^* \to \mathbf{Z} \to 0$ *gives by completion the exact sequence:*

$$0 \to U_K \to \tilde{K} \to \hat{\mathbf{Z}} \to 0.$$

Loosely speaking, this means that $\tilde{K}$ is obtained from K^* by "replacing $\mathbf{Z}$ by $\hat{\mathbf{Z}}$".

2.8 *Some Characterizations of* $(\alpha, L/K)$

Let L be an abelian extension of K containing K_{nr}, the maximal unramified extension. We want to give characterizations of the reciprocity map $\theta : K^* \to G_{L/K}$.

Since $K_{nr} \subset L$, we have an exact sequence $0 \to H \to G_{L/K} \to \hat{\mathbf{Z}} \to 0$ where $H = G(L/K_{nr})$ and $\hat{\mathbf{Z}}$ is identified with $G(K_{nr}/K)$. Choose a local uniformizer π in K and write $\sigma_\pi = \theta(\pi) = (\pi, L/K) \in G_{L/K}$. We know that σ_π maps onto the Frobenius element $F \in G_{K_{nr}/K}$. Moreover, we can write $G_{L/K}$ as a direct product of subgroups $G_{L/K} = H.I_\pi$ where I_π is generated by σ_π. Corresponding to this we have $L = K_{nr} \otimes K_\pi$, where K_π is the fixed field of $\sigma_\pi = \theta(\pi)$. In terms of a diagram, the interrelationship between the fields is expressed by

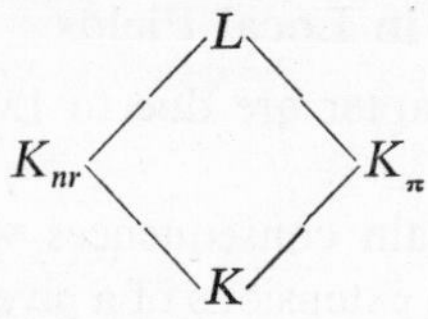

where K_{nr} and K_π are linearly disjoint.

PROPOSITION 5. *Let $f: K^* \to G$ be a homomorphism and assume that:*

(1) *the composition $K^* \xrightarrow{f} G \to G(K_{nr}/K)$, where $G \to G(K_{nr}/K)$ is the natural map, is the valuation map $v: K^* \to \mathbf{Z}$;*

(2) *for any uniformizing element $\pi \in K$, $f(\pi)$ is the identity on the corresponding extension K_π.*

Then f is equal to the reciprocity map θ.

Proof. Note that condition (1) can be restated as: for $\alpha \in K^*$, $f(\alpha)$ induces on K_{nr} the power of the Frobenius element, $F^{v(\alpha)}$.

We know that $f(\pi)$ is F on K_{nr} and that $\theta(\pi)$ is F on K_{nr}. On the other hand, $f(\pi)$ is 1 on K_π and $\theta(\pi)$ is 1 on K_π. Hence $f(\pi) = \theta(\pi)$ on L.

Now K^* is generated by its uniformizing elements πu (write $\pi^n u$ as $(\pi u).\pi^{n-1}$). Hence $f = \theta$.

PROPOSITION 6. *Let $f: K^* \to G$ be a homomorphism and assume that* (1) *of Proposition* 3 *holds, whilst* (2) *is replaced by:*

(2′) *if $\alpha \in K^*$, if K'/K is a finite sub-extension of L and if α is a norm from K'^*, then $f(\alpha)$ is trivial on K'.*

Then f is equal to the reciprocity map θ.

Proof. It suffices to prove that (2′) implies (2). That is, we have to prove that if π is a uniformizing element, then $f(\pi)$ is trivial on K_π. Let K'/K be a finite sub-extension of K_π. We want to prove that $\pi \in NK'^*$. But $\theta(\pi)$ is trivial on K_π and so on K'. This implies $\pi \in NK'^*$.

2.9 *The Archimedean Case*

For global class-field theory it is necessary to extend these results to the (trivial) cases in which K is either $\mathbf{R}$ or $\mathbf{C}$. Let $G = G(\mathbf{C}/\mathbf{R})$. In the case $K = \mathbf{C}$, the Brauer group is trivial, $\mathrm{Br}(\mathbf{C}) = 0$. On the other hand, $\mathrm{Br}(\mathbf{R}) = H^2(G, \mathbf{C}^*) = \mathbf{R}^*/\mathbf{R}^*_+$ and so $\mathrm{Br}(\mathbf{R})$ is of order 2.

The invariant $\mathrm{inv}_R: \mathrm{Br}(\mathbf{R}) \to \mathbf{Q}/\mathbf{Z}$ has image $\{0, 1/2\}$ in $\mathbf{Q}/\mathbf{Z}$ and $\mathrm{inv}_C: \mathrm{Br}(\mathbf{C}) \to \mathbf{Q}/\mathbf{Z}$ has image $\{0\}$. The group $H^2(G, \mathbf{C}^*) = H^2(\mathbf{C}/\mathbf{R})$ is cyclic of order 2 and is generated by $u \in \mathrm{Br}(\mathbf{R})$ such that $\mathrm{inv}_R(u) = 1/2$.

Under the reciprocity map (or rather its inverse) we have an isomorphism $G = H^{-2}(G, \mathbf{Z}) \to H^0(G, \mathbf{C}^*) = \mathbf{R}^*/\mathbf{R}^*_+$.

3. Formal Multiplication in Local Fields

The results given in this chapter are due to Lubin-Tate, *Annals of Mathematics*, **81** (1965), 380–387.

For our purposes, the main consequences will be: (1) the construction of a cofinal system of abelian extensions of a given local field K; (2) a formula giving $(\alpha, L/K)$ explicitly in such extensions; (3) the Existence Theorem of § 2.7.

In order to illustrate the ideas involved, we begin with the case $K = \mathbf{Q}_p$. The results to be proved were already known in this case (but were not easily obtained) and they will be shown to be trivial consequences of Lubin-Tate theory.

3.1 *The Case* $K = \mathbf{Q}_p$

THEOREM 1. *Let* $\mathbf{Q}_p^{cycl}$ *be the field generated over* $\mathbf{Q}_p$ *by all roots of unity. Then* $\mathbf{Q}_p^{cycl}$ *is the maximal abelian extension of* $\mathbf{Q}_p$.

In order to determine $(\alpha, L/K)$ it is convenient to split $\mathbf{Q}_p^{cycl}$ into parts. Define $\mathbf{Q}_{nr}$ to be the field generated over $\mathbf{Q}_p$ by roots of unity of order prime to p (so $\mathbf{Q}_{nr}$ is the maximal unramified extension of $\mathbf{Q}_p$) and define $\mathbf{Q}_{p^\infty}$ to be the field generated over $\mathbf{Q}_p$ by p^υth roots of unity, $\upsilon = 1, 2, \ldots$ (so $\mathbf{Q}_{p^\infty}$ is totally ramified). Then $\mathbf{Q}_{nr}$ and $\mathbf{Q}_{p^\infty}$ are linearly disjoint and

$$\mathbf{Q}_p^{cycl} = \mathbf{Q}_{nr} \cdot \mathbf{Q}_{p^\infty} = \mathbf{Q}_{nr} \otimes \mathbf{Q}_{p^\infty}.$$

We have a diagram:

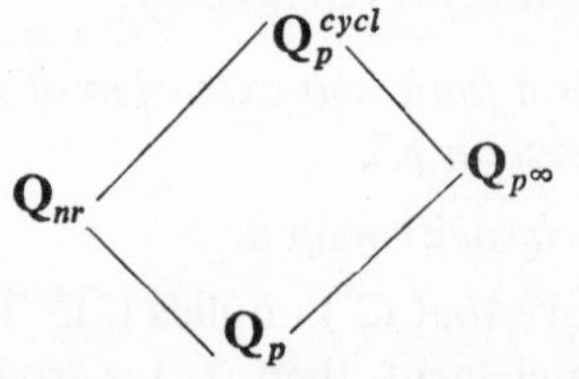

Now $G(\mathbf{Q}_{nr}/\mathbf{Q}_p) = \hat{\mathbf{Z}}$ and if $\sigma \in G(\mathbf{Q}_{p^\infty}/\mathbf{Q}_p)$ then σ is known by its action on the roots of unity. Let E be the group of p^υth roots of unity, $\upsilon = 1, 2, \ldots$. As an abelian group, E is isomorphic to $\varinjlim \mathbf{Z}/p^\upsilon\mathbf{Z} = \mathbf{Q}_p/\mathbf{Z}_p$. We shall view E as a $\mathbf{Z}_p$-module. There is a canonical map $\mathbf{Z}_p \to \operatorname{End}(E)$, defined in an obvious way and this map is an isomorphism. The action of the Galois group on E defines a homomorphism $G(\mathbf{Q}_{p^\infty}/\mathbf{Q}_p) \to \operatorname{Aut}(E) = U_p$ and it is known that this is an isomorphism. (See Chapter III, and "Corps Locaux", Chap. IX, § 4, and Chap. XIV, § 7.) If $u \in U_p$, we shall denote by $[u]$ the corresponding automorphism of $\mathbf{Q}_{p^\infty}/\mathbf{Q}_p$.

THEOREM 2. *If* $\alpha = p^n . u$ *where* $u \in U_p$, *then* $(\alpha, \mathbf{Q}_p^{cycl}/\mathbf{Q}_p) = \sigma_\alpha$ *is described by:*

(1) *on* $\mathbf{Q}_{nr}$, σ_α *induces the nth power of the Frobenius automorphism;*

(2) *on* $\mathbf{Q}_{p^\infty}$, σ_α *induces the automorphism* $[u^{-1}]$.

Of these (1) is trivial and has already been proved in § 2.5, Prop. 2. The assertion (2) can be proved by (a) global methods, or (b) hard local methods (Dwork), or (c) Lubin-Tate theory (see § 3.4, Theorem 3).

Remark. Assertion (2) of Theorem 2 is equivalent to the following: if w is a primitive p^vth root of unity and if $u \in U_p$ then

$$\sigma_u(w) = w^{u^{-1}} = 1 + \sum_{n=1}^{\infty} \binom{u^{-1}}{n} x^n,$$

where $w = 1+x$.

3.2 *Formal Groups*

The main game will be played with something which replaces the multiplicative group law $F(X, Y) = X+Y+XY$ and something instead of the binomial expansion. The group law will be a formal power series in two variables and we begin by studying such group laws.

DEFINITION. *Let A be a commutative ring with* 1 *and let $F \in A[[X, Y]]$. We say that F is a commutative formal group law if:*

(a) $F(X, F(Y, Z)) = F(F(X, Y), Z)$;
(b) $F(0, Y) = Y$ *and* $F(X, 0) = X$;
(c) *there is a unique* $G(X)$ *such that* $F(X, G(X)) = 0$;
(d) $F(X, Y) = F(Y, X)$;
(e) $F(X, Y) \equiv X+Y \pmod{\deg 2}$.

(In fact one can show that (c) and (e) are consequences of (a), (b) and (d).

Here, two formal power series are said to be congruent (mod deg n) if and only if they coincide in terms of degree strictly less than n.

Take $A = O_K$. Let $F(X, Y)$ be a commutative formal group law defined over O_K and let $\mathfrak{m}_K$ be the maximal ideal of O_K. If $x, y \in \mathfrak{m}_K$ then $F(x, y)$ converges and its sum $x*y$ belongs to O_K. Under this composition law, $\mathfrak{m}_K$ is a *group* which we denote by $F(\mathfrak{m}_K)$.

The same argument applies to an extension L/K and the maximal ideal $\mathfrak{m}_L$ in O_L. We then obtain a group $F(\mathfrak{m}_L)$ defined for any algebraic extension of K by passage to the inductive limit from the finite case.

If $F(X, Y) = X+Y+XY$ then we recover the multiplicative group law of $1+\mathfrak{m}_K$.

The elements of finite order of $F(\mathfrak{m}_{K_s})$ form a torsion group and $G(K_s/K)$ operates on this group. The structure of this Galois module presents an interesting problem which up to now has been solved only in special cases.

3.3 *Lubin-Tate Formal Group Laws*

Let K be a local field, $q = \text{Card}\,(k)$ and choose a uniformizing element $\pi \in O_K$. Let $\mathfrak{F}_\pi$ be the set of formal power series f with:

(1) $f(X) \equiv \pi X \pmod{\text{deg. } 2}$;
(2) $f(X) \equiv X^q \pmod{\pi}$.

(Two power series are said to be congruent (mod. π) if and only if each coefficient of their difference is divisible by π. So the second condition means that if we go to the residue field and denote by $\bar{f}(X)$ the corresponding element of $k[[X]]$ then $\bar{f}(X) = X^q$.)

Examples.

(*a*) $f(X) = \pi X + X^q$;

(*b*) $K = \mathbf{Q}_p, \quad \pi = p, \quad (X) = pX + \binom{p}{2} X^2 + \ldots + pX^{p-1} + X^p.$

The following four propositions will be proved in § 5 as consequences of Prop. 5.

PROPOSITION 1. *Let $f \in \mathfrak{F}_\pi$. Then there exists a unique formal group law F_f with coefficients in A for which f is an endomorphism.*

(This means $f(F_f(X, Y)) = F_f(f(X), f(Y))$, that is $f \circ F_f = F_f \circ (f \times f)$.)

PROPOSITION 2. *Let $f \in \mathfrak{F}_\pi$ and F_f the corresponding group law of Prop.* 1. *Then for any $a \in A = O_K$ there exists a unique $[a]_f \in A[[X]]$ such that:*

(1) $[a]_f$ *commutes with* f;

(2) $[a]_f \equiv aX \quad$ (mod. deg. 2).

Moreover, $[a]_f$ is then an endomorphism of the group law F_f.

From Prop. 2 we obtain a mapping $A \to \text{End}(F_f)$ defined by $a \mapsto [a]_f$. For example, consider the case

$$K = \mathbf{Q}_p, \quad f = pX + \binom{p}{2} X^2 + \ldots + X^p;$$

then F is the multiplicative law $X + Y + XY$, and

$$[a]_f = (1+X)^a - 1 = \sum_{i=1}^{\infty} \binom{a}{i} X^i.$$

PROPOSITION 3. *The map $a \mapsto [a]_f$ is an injective homomorphism of the ring A into the ring* End (F_f).

PROPOSITION 4. *Let f and g be members of $\mathfrak{F}_\pi$. Then the corresponding group laws are isomorphic.*

3.4 *Statements*

Let K be a local field and let π be a uniformizing element. Let $f \in \mathfrak{F}_\pi$ and let F_f be the corresponding group law (of Prop. 1). We denote by $M_f = F_f(\mathfrak{m}_{K_s})$ the group of points in the separable closure equipped with the group law deduced from F. Let $a \in A$, $x \in M_f$ and put $ax = [a]_f x$. By Prop. 3, this defines a structure of an A-module on M_f. Let E_f be the torsion sub-module of M_f; that is the set of elements of M_f killed by a power of π.

THEOREM 3. *The following statements hold.*

(a) *The torsion sub-module E_f is isomorphic (as an A-module) with K/A.*

(b) *Let $K_\pi = K(E_f)$ be the field generated by E_f over K. Then K_π is an abelian extension of K.*

(c) *Let u be a unit in K^*. Then the element $\sigma_u = (u, K_\pi/K)$ of $G(K_\pi/K)$ acts on E_f via $[u^{-1}]_f$.*

(d) *The operation described in* (c) *defines an isomorphism $U_K \to G(K_\pi/K)$.*

(e) *The norm residue symbol $(\pi, K_\pi/K)$ is 1.*

(f) *The fields K_{nr} and K_π are linearly disjoint and $K^{ab} = K_{nr}.K_\pi$.*

We may express the results of Theorem 3 as follows. We have a diagram:

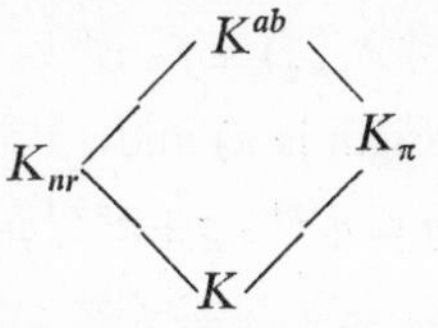

Here $G(K_{nr}/K) = \hat{\mathbf{Z}}$ and $G(K_\pi/K) = U_K$. Moreover every $\alpha \in K^*$ can be written in the form $\alpha = \pi^n.u$ and σ_π gives σ (the Frobenius) on K_{nr}/K whilst σ_u gives $[u^{-1}]$ on K_π/K.

Example. Take $K = \mathbf{Q}_p$, $\pi = p$ and $f = pX + \binom{p}{2} X^2 + \ldots + X^p$. The formal group law is the multiplicative group law; E_f is the set of p^νth roots of unity; K_π is the field denoted by $\mathbf{Q}_{p^\infty}$ in § 3.1—and we recover Theorems 1 and 2.

3.5 *Construction of* F_f, $[a]_f$

In this section we shall construct the formal group law F_f and the map $a \mapsto [a]_f$.

PROPOSITION 5. *Let $f, g \in \mathfrak{F}_\pi$, let n be an integer and let $\phi_1(X_1, \ldots, X_n)$ be a linear form in $X_1, \ldots, X_n$ with coefficients in A. Then there exists a unique $\phi \in A[[X_1, \ldots, X_n]]$ such that:*

(a) $\phi \equiv \phi_1$ (mod deg 2);

(b) $f \circ \phi = \phi \circ (g \times \ldots \times g)$.

Remarks. (1) The property (b) may be written

$$f(\phi(X_1, \ldots, X_n)) = \phi(g(X_1), \ldots, g(X_n)).$$

(2) The completeness of A will not be used in the proof. Moreover, the proof shows that ϕ is the only power series with coefficients in an extension of A, which is torsion free as an A-module, satisfying (a) and (b).

Proof. We shall construct ϕ by successive approximations. More precisely, we construct a sequence $(\phi^{(p)})$ such that $\phi^{(p)} \in A[[X_1, \ldots, X_n]]$, $\phi^{(p)}$ satisfies (a) and (b) (mod deg $p+1$), and $\phi^{(p)}$ is unique (mod deg $p+1$).

We shall then define $\phi = \lim \phi^{(p)}$ and this will be the ϕ whose existence is asserted.

We take $\phi^{(1)} = \phi_1$.

Suppose that the approximation $\phi_1 + \ldots + \phi_p = \phi^{(p)}$ has been constructed. That is, $f \circ \phi^{(p)} \equiv \phi^{(p)} \circ (g \times \ldots \times g)$ (mod deg $p+1$). For convenience of writing, we shall replace $g \times \ldots \times g$ by the single variable g. Now write $\phi^{(p+1)} = \phi^{(p)} + \phi_{p+1}$. Then we may write

$$f \circ \phi^{(p)} \equiv \phi^{(p)} \circ g + E_{p+1} \quad (\text{mod deg } p+2),$$

where E_{p+1} ("the error") satisfies $E_{p+1} \equiv 0$ (mod deg $p+1$). Consider $\phi^{(p+1)}$; we have

$$f \circ \phi^{(p+1)} = f \circ (\phi^{(p)} + \phi_{p+1}) \equiv f \circ \phi^{(p)} + \pi \phi_{p+1} \quad (\text{mod deg } p+2)$$

(the derivative of f at the origin is π) and

$$\phi^{(p)} \circ g + \phi_{p+1} \circ g \equiv \phi^{(p)} \circ g + \pi^{p+1} \phi_{p+1} \quad (\text{mod deg } p+2).$$

Thus

$$f \circ \phi^{(p+1)} - \phi^{(p+1)} \circ g \equiv E_{p+1} + (\pi - \pi^{p+1}) \phi_{p+1} \quad (\text{mod deg } p+2).$$

These equations show that we must take

$$\phi_{p+1} = -E_{p+1}/\pi(1-\pi^p).$$

The unicity is now clear and it remains to show that ϕ_{p+1} has coefficients in A. That is, $E_{p+1} \equiv 0 \pmod{\pi}$. Now for $\phi \in \mathbf{F}_q[[X]]$, we have $\phi(X^q) = (\phi(X))^q$ and together with $f(X) \equiv X^q \pmod{\pi}$ this gives

$$f \circ \phi^{(p)} - \phi^{(p)} \circ f \equiv (\phi^{(p)}(X))^q - \phi^{(p)}(X^q) \equiv 0 \quad (\text{mod } \pi).$$

So, given $\phi^{(p)}$ we can construct a unique $\phi^{(p+1)}$ and the proof is completed by induction and passage to the limit.

Proof of Proposition 1. For each $f \in \mathfrak{F}_\pi$, let $F_f(X, Y)$ be the unique solution of $F_f(X, Y) \equiv X + Y$ (mod deg 2) and $f \circ F_f = F_f \circ (f \times f)$ whose existence is assured by Prop. 5. That F_f is a formal group law now requires the verification of the rules (a) to (e) above. But this is an exercise in the application of Prop. 5: in each case we check that the left-and the right-hand sides are solutions to a problem of the type discussed there and we use the unicity statement of Prop. 5. For example, to prove associativity note that both $F_f(F_f(X, Y), Z)$ and $F_f(X, F_f(Y, Z))$ are solutions of

$$H(X, Y, Z) \equiv X + Y + Z \quad (\text{mod deg } 2)$$

and

$$H(f(X), f(Y), f(Z)) = f(H(X, Y, Z)).$$

Proof of Proposition 2. For each $a \in A$ and $f, g \in \mathfrak{F}_\pi$ let $[a]_{f,g}(T)$ be the unique solution of

$$[a]_{f,g}(T) \equiv aT \quad (\text{mod deg } 2)$$

and

$$f([a]_{f,g}(T)) = [a]_{f,g}(g(T)),$$

(that is $f \circ [a]_{f,g} = [a]_{f,g} \circ g$). Write $[a]_f = [a]_{f,f}$.

Now we have

$$F_f([a]_{f,g}(X), [a]_{f,g}(Y)) = [a]_{f,g}(F_g(X, Y)).$$

For each side is congruent to $aX+aY$ (mod deg 2) and if we replace X by $g(X)$ and Y by $g(Y)$ in either side, then the result is the same as if we substitute the sides in question in f. Thus $[a]_{f,g}$ is a formal homomorphism of F_g into F_f. If we take $g = f$, this shows that the $[a]_f$'s are endomorphisms of F_f.

Proof of Proposition 3. In the same way as outlined above, one proves that

$$[a+b]_{f,g} = F_f \circ ([a]_{f,g} \times [a]_{f,g})$$

and

$$[ab]_{f,h} = [a]_{f,g} \circ [b]_{g,h}.$$

It follows from this that the composition of two homomorphisms of the type just established is reflected in the product of corresponding elements of A. Taking $f = g$, we see that the map $a \mapsto [a]_f$ is a ring homomorphism of A into End (E_f). It is injective because the term of degree 1 of $[a]_f$ is aX.

Proof of Proposition 4. If a is a unit in A, then $[a]_{f,g}$ is invertible (cf. the proof of Prop. 2) and so $F_g \cong F_f$ by means of the isomorphism $[a]_{f,g}$.

Note that $[\pi]_f = f$ and $[1]_f$ is the identity (proved as before).

This completes the proofs of the propositions 1, 2, 3, 4.

3.6 *First Properties of the Extension K_π of K*

From now on, we confine our attention to subfields of a fixed separable closure K_s of K. Given $f \in \mathfrak{F}_\pi$, let F_f be the corresponding formal group law and let E_f be the torsion submodule of the A-module $F_f(\mathfrak{m}_{K_s})$. Let E_f^n be the kernel of $[\pi^n]_f$; so that $E_f = \cup E_f^n$. Let $K_\pi^n = K(E_f^n)$ and $K_\pi = \cup K_\pi^n$. If $G_{\pi,n}$ denotes the Galois group of $K(E_f^n)$ over K, then $G(K_\pi/K) = \varprojlim G_{\pi,n}$.

PROPOSITION 6. (a) *The A-module E_f is isomorphic to K/A;*

(b) *the natural homomorphism $G(K_\pi/K) \to \text{Aut}(E_f)$ is an isomorphism.*

Proof. We are free to choose f as we please, since, by Prop. 4, different choices give isomorphic group laws. We take $f = \pi X + X^q$. Then $\alpha \in E_f^n$ if and only if $f^{(n)}(\alpha) = 0$, where $f^{(n)}$ denotes the composition $f \circ \ldots \circ f$ n times; that is $f^{(n)} = [\pi^n]_f$.

If $\alpha \in \mathfrak{m}_{K_s}$ then the equation $\pi X + X^q = \alpha$ is separable and so solvable in K_s, its solution belonging indeed to $\mathfrak{m}_{K_s}$. This shows that M_f is divisible.

Hence E_f is divisible also. This already implies that E_f is a direct sum of modules isomorphic to K/A.

Let us consider the submodule E_f^1 of E_f consisting (see above) of those $\alpha \in M_f$ such that $[\pi]_f \alpha = 0$. The submodule E_f^1 is isomorphic with $A/\mathfrak{m}_{K_s}$, since it is an A-module with q elements. This is enough to show that E_f is isomorphic to K/A.

An automorphism $\sigma \in G(K_\pi/K)$ induces an automorphism of the A-module E_f. But since $E_f \cong K/A$ and $\mathrm{End}_A(K/A) = A$ this gives a map $G(K_\pi/K) \to \mathrm{Aut}(E_f) = U_K$. This map is injective by the definition of K_π and it remains to be proved that it is surjective.

Take $n \geqslant 1$ and define E_f^n and K_π^n as above. We have an injection $G(K_\pi^n/K) \to U_K/U_K^n$, where $U_K^n = 1+\pi^n A$. Let $\alpha \in E_f^n$ be a primitive element; that is an element of E_f^n such that $[\pi^n]_f \alpha = 0$, but $[\pi^{n-1}]_f \alpha \neq 0$. Finally, we define ϕ as follows:

$$\phi = f^{(n)}/f^{(n-1)} = f(f^{(n-1)})/f^{(n-1)}.$$

Now $f = X^q + \pi X$; so $f/X = X^{q-1} + \pi$. Hence

$$\frac{f(f^{(n-1)})}{f^{(n-1)}} = (f^{(n-1)}(X))^{q-1} + \pi,$$

which is of degree $q^n - q^{n-1}$ and which is irreducible, since it is an Eisenstein polynomial. All primitive elements α are roots of ϕ. Thus the order of $G(K_\pi^n/K)$ is at least $(q-1)q^{n-1}$. On the other hand, this is actually the order of the group U_K/U_K^n. Hence $G(K^n/K) = U_K/U_K^n$. It follows that

$$G(K_\pi/K) = \varprojlim G(K_\pi^n/K) = \varprojlim U_K/U_K^n = U_K,$$

and this completes the proof of Prop. 6.

The same proof also yields:

Corollary. *The element π is a norm from $K(\alpha) = K_\pi^n$.*

Proof. The polynomial ϕ constructed above is monic and ends with π. Hence $N(-\alpha) = \pi$.

3.7 *The Reciprocity Map*

We shall study the compositum $L = K_{nr}K_\pi$ of K_{nr} and K_π, and the symbol $(\alpha, L/K)$, $\alpha \in K^*$. We need to compare two uniformizing elements π and $\omega = \pi u$, $u \in U_K$.

Let $\hat{K}_{nr}$ be the completion of K_{nr} (remember: K_{nr} is an increasing union of complete fields but is not itself complete) and denote by $\hat{A}_{nr}$ the ring of integers of $\hat{K}_{nr}$. By definition $\hat{K}_{nr}$ is complete; it has an algebraically closed residue field and π is a uniformizing parameter in $\hat{K}_{nr}$. We take $f \in \mathfrak{F}_\pi$ and $g \in \mathfrak{F}_\omega$.

LEMMA 1. *Let $\sigma \in G(K_{nr}/K)$ be the Frobenius automorphism and extend it to $\hat{K}_{nr}$ by continuity. Then there exists a power series $\phi \in \hat{A}_{nr}[[X]]$ with $\phi(X) \equiv \varepsilon X$ (mod deg 2) and ε a unit, such that*

(a) ${}^{\sigma}\phi = \phi \circ [u]_f$;

(b) $\phi \circ F_f = F_g \circ (\phi \times \phi)$;

(c) $\phi \circ [a]_f = [a]_g \circ \phi$ *for all* $a \in A$.

Proof. Since $\sigma - 1$ is surjective on $\hat{A}_{nr}$ and on $\hat{U}_{nr}$ (cf. "Corps Locaux", p. 209), there exists a $\phi \in \hat{A}_{nr}[[X]]$ such that $\phi(X) \equiv \varepsilon X$ (mod deg 2) where ε is a unit and ${}^{\sigma}\phi = \phi \circ [u]_f$. This is proved by successive approximation and we refer the reader to Lubin-Tate for the details. This particular ϕ does not necessarily give (b) and (c) but can be adjusted to do so; the computations are given in Lubin-Tate (where they appear as (17) and (18) in Lemma 2 on p. 385). Note that together the above conditions express the fact that ϕ is an A-module isomorphism of F_f into F_g.

Computation of the norm reciprocity map in L/K.

Let $L_\pi = K_{nr}.K_\pi$. Since K_{nr} and K_π are linearly disjoint over K, the Galois group $G(L_\pi/K)$ is the product of the Galois groups $G(K_\pi/K)$ and $G(K_{nr}/K)$. For each uniformizing element $\pi \in A$ we define a homomorphism $r_\pi : K^* \to G(L_\pi/K)$ such that:

(a) $r_\pi(\pi)$ is 1 on K_π and is the Frobenius automorphism σ on K_{nr};

(b) for $u \in U_K$, $r_\pi(u)$ is equal to $[u^{-1}]_f$ on K_π and is 1 on K_{nr}.

We want to prove that *the field L_π and the homomorphism r_π are independent of π*. Let $\omega = \pi u$ be a second uniformizing element.

First, $L_\pi = L_\omega$. For by Lemma 1, F_f and F_g are isomorphic over $\hat{K}_{nr}$. Hence, the fields generated by their division points are the same. So $\hat{K}_{nr}.K_\pi = \hat{K}_{nr}.K_\omega$. On taking completions we find that $\widehat{K_{nr}.K_\pi} = \widehat{K_{nr}.K_\omega}$. In order to deduce that $K_{nr}.K_\pi = K_{nr}.K_\omega$ from this, we require the following:

LEMMA 2. *Let E be any algebraic extension (finite or infinite) of a local field and let $\alpha \in \hat{E}$. Then, if α is separable algebraic over E, α belongs to E.*

Proof. Let E_s be the separable closure of E and let E' be the adherence of E in E_s. We can view α as an element of E'. Hence it is enough to show that $E' = E$.

Let $s \in G(E_s/E)$. Since s is continuous and is the identity on E, it is also the identity on E'. Hence $G(E_s/E) = G(E_s/E')$ and by Galois theory we have $E' = E$.

It follows from Lemma 2 that $L_\pi = L_\omega$ and so $L_\pi = L$ is independent of π.

We turn now to the homomorphism $r_\pi : K^* \to G(L/K)$. *We shall show* *that* $r_\pi(\omega) = r_\omega(\omega)$. This will imply that $r_\pi(\omega)$ is independent of π and so the r_π's coincide on the local uniformizers. Since these generate K^*, the result will follow.

We look first at $r_\omega(\omega)$. On K_{nr}, $r_\omega(\omega)$ is the Frobenius automorphism σ. On K_ω it is 1. On the other hand, $r_\pi(\omega)$ is σ on K_{nr}; so we must look at $r_\pi(\omega)$ on K_ω.

Now $K_\omega = K(E_g)$, where $g \in \mathfrak{F}_\omega$. Let $\phi \in \hat{A}[[X]]$ be as in Lemma 1; ϕ determines an isomorphism of E_f onto E_g. So if $\lambda \in E_g$, then we can write $\lambda = \phi(\mu)$ with $\mu \in E_f$. We look at $r_\pi(\omega)\lambda$ and we want to show that this is λ. As already remarked, $r_\pi(\omega)(\lambda) = r_\pi(\omega)\phi(\mu)$. Write $s = r_\pi(\omega)$. We want to show that ${}^s\lambda = \lambda$; that is ${}^s\phi(\mu) = \phi(\mu)$. Now, $r_\pi(\omega) = r_\pi(\pi).r_\pi(u)$ and the effects of $r_\pi(\pi)$ and $r_\pi(u)$ are described in (a) and (b) above. Since ϕ has coefficients in $\hat{K}_{nr}$, ${}^s\phi = {}^\sigma\phi = \phi \circ [u]_f$ by (a) of Lemma 1. But

$${}^s(\phi(\mu)) = {}^s\phi({}^s\mu) = {}^s\phi([u^{-1}]_f(\mu)).$$

Hence

$${}^s\phi(\mu) = \phi \circ [u]_f \circ [u^{-1}]_f(\mu) = \phi(\mu).$$

So r_π is the identity on K_ω and it follows that r_π is independent of π. Thus $r: K^* \to G(L/K)$ is the reciprocity map θ (§ 2.8, Prop. 5).

All assertions of Theorem 3 have now been proved except the equality $L = K^{ab}$, which we are now going to prove.

3.8 *The Existence Theorem*

Let K^{ab} be the maximal abelian extension of K; it contains K_{nr}. The Existence Theorem is equivalent to the following assertion (§ 2.3, Theorem 3a). If $I_K = G(K^{ab}/K_{nr})$ is the inertia subgroup of $G(K^{ab}/K)$, then *the reciprocity map* $\theta: U_K \to I_K$ *is an isomorphism.*

Let L be the compositum $K_\pi.K_{nr}$ and let $I_K' = G(L/K_{nr})$ be the inertia subgroup of $G(L/K)$. Consider the maps

$$U_K \xrightarrow{\theta} I_K \xrightarrow{e} I_K'$$

where θ is the reciprocity map and e is the canonical map $I_K \to I_K'$. Both θ and e are surjections.

On the other hand, the composition $e \circ \theta: U_K \to I_K$ has just been computed. If we identify I_K' with U_K it is $u \mapsto u^{-1}$. Hence the composed map $e \circ \theta$ is an isomorphism. It follows that both θ and e are isomorphisms.

As we have already noted, the first isomorphism is equivalent to the Existence Theorem. The second means that $L = K^{ab}$, since both L and K^{ab} contain K_{nr}.

[*Alternative Proof.* Let us prove directly that every open subgroup M of K^*, which is of finite index, is a norm subgroup corresponding to a finite subextension of L. This will prove both the existence theorem (§ 2.7, Theorem 3) and the fact that $L = K^{ab}$.

Since M is open, there exists $n \geqslant 1$ such that $U_K^n \subset M$; since M is of finite index, there exists $m \geqslant 1$ such that $\pi^m \in M$; hence M contains the subgroup $V_{n,m}$ generated by U_K^n and π^m. Now let K_m be the unramified extension of K of degree m, and consider the subfield $L_{n,m} = K_\pi^n . K_m$ of L. If $u \in U_K$, and $a \in \mathbf{Z}$, we know that $(u\pi^a, L_{n,m}/K)$ is equal to $[u^{-1}]$ on K_π^n and to the a-th power of the Frobenius element on K_m; hence $(u\pi^a, L_{n,m}/K)$ is trivial if and only if $u \in U_K^n$ and $a \equiv 0 \bmod m$, i.e. if and only if $u\pi^a \in V_{n,m}$. This shows that $V_{n,m} = NL_{n,m}$, and, since M contains $V_{n,m}$, M is the norm group of a subextension of $L_{n,m}$, Q.E.D.]

4. Ramification Subgroups and Conductors

4.1 *Ramification Groups*

Let L/K be a galois extension of local fields with Galois group $G(L/K)$. We recall briefly the definition of the upper numbering of the ramification groups. (For details, the reader should consult Chapter I, § 9, or "Corps Locaux", Chap. IV.)

Let the function $i_G : G(L/K) \to \{\mathbf{Z} \cup \infty\}$ be defined as follows. For $s \in G(L/K)$, let x be a generator of O_L as an O_K algebra and put $i_G(s) = v_L(s(x)-x)$. Now define G_u for all positive real numbers u by: $s \in G_u$ if and only if $i_G(s) \geqslant u+1$. The groups G_u are called the ramification groups of $G(L/K)$ (or of L/K). In order to deal with the quotient groups, it is necessary to introduce a second enumeration of the ramification groups called the "upper numbering". This new numbering is given by $G^v = G_u$, where $v = \phi(u)$ and where the function ϕ is characterized by the properties:

(a) $\phi(0) = 0$;
(b) ϕ is continuous;
(c) ϕ is piecewise linear;
(d) $\phi'(u) = 1/(G_0 : G_u)$ when u is not an integer.

The G^v's so defined are compatible with passage to the quotient: $(G/H)^v$ is the image of G^v in G/H ("Herbrand's theorem"). This allows one to define the G^v's even for infinite extensions.

On the other hand, we have a filtration on U_K defined by $U_K^n = 1+\mathfrak{m}_K^n$. We extend this filtration to real exponents by $U_K^v = U_K^n$ if $n-1 < v \leqslant n$. (It should be noted that v in this context is a real number and is not to be confused with the valuation map!)

THEOREM 1. *Let L/K be an abelian extension with Galois group G. Then the local reciprocity map $\theta : K^* \to G$ maps U_K^v onto G^v for all $v \geqslant 0$.*

Proof. (1) *Verification for the extensions K_π^n of* § 3.6.

Let $u \in U_K^i$ with $i < n$ and $u \notin U_K^{i+1}$. Let $s = \theta(u) \in G(K_\pi^n/K)$. We have

$i(s) = v_{K_\pi^n}(s\lambda - \lambda)$, where λ is a uniformizing element. We choose a primitive root α for λ; that is, an α satisfying $[\pi^n]_f\alpha = 0$ but $[\pi^{n-1}]_f\alpha \neq 0$. Observe that $s_u(\alpha) = [u^{-1}]_f\alpha$ and $u^{-1} = 1+\pi^i v$ (see § 3.3, Theorem 3), where v is a unit. These imply that

$$s_u\alpha = [1+\pi^i v]_f\alpha = F_f(\alpha, [\pi^i v]_f\alpha).$$

If we write $\beta = [\pi^i v]_f\alpha$, then β is a primitive $(n-i)$th root (that is, $[\pi^{n-i}]_f\beta = 0$, $[\pi^{n-1-i}]_f\beta \neq 0$), and we have

$$F_f(\alpha, [\pi^i v]_f\alpha) = \alpha+\beta+\sum_{i>1,\, j>1} \gamma_{ij}\alpha^i\beta^j$$

for some $\gamma_{ij} \in O_K$. Accordingly,

$$s_u(\alpha)-\alpha = \beta+\sum \gamma_{ij}\alpha^i\beta_j$$

and

$$v_{K_\pi^n}(s_u(\alpha)-\alpha) = v_{K_\pi^n}(\beta).$$

Now α is a uniformizing element in K_π^n whilst β is a uniformizing element

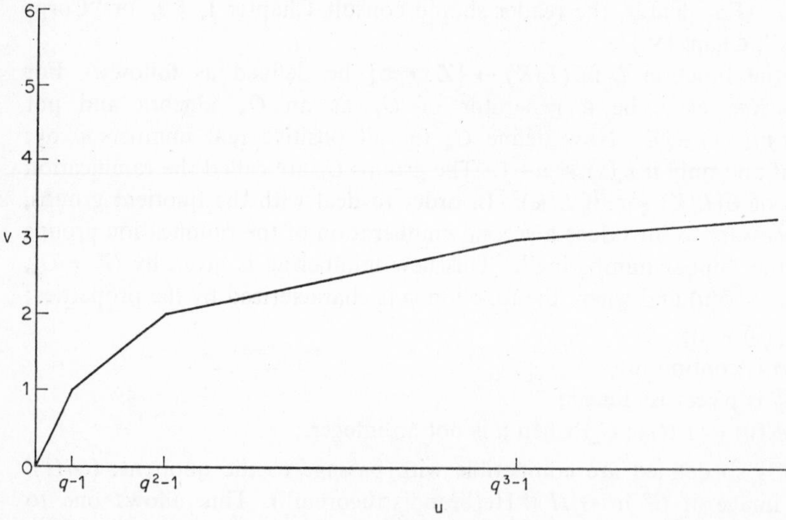

Figure 1.

in K_π^{n-i} and K_π^n/K_π^{n-i} is totally ramified. Its degree is q^i. So we have determined the i function of $\theta(u)$; namely, if $u \in U^i$ but $u \notin U^{i+1}$, then $i(\theta(u)) = q^i$. This says that if $q^{i-1}-1 < u \leqslant q^i-1$ then the ramification group G_u is $\theta(U_K^i)$.

We turn now to the upper numbering of the G_u's. That is, we define a function $\phi = \phi_{K_\pi^n/K}$, corresponding to the extension K_π^n, which satisfies the conditions (a) to (d) above. Namely,

$$\phi(u) = \phi_{K_\pi^n/K}(u) = \int_0^u \frac{dt}{(G : G_t)}.$$

Then $G^v = G_u$ with $v = \phi(u)$. The graph of $\phi(u)$ is shown in Figure 1.

If $q^{i-1}-1 < u \leqslant q^i-1$, then $\phi'(u) = 1/(q^i-q^{i-1})$ and $(U_K : U_K^i) = q^i-q^{i-1}$. So if $i-1 < v \leqslant i$, then $G^v = \theta(U_K^v)$ for $v \leqslant n$.

The general case

(2) *Verification in the general case.*

Having proved Theorem 1 for K_π^n it follows for $K_\pi = \cup K_\pi^n$ by taking projective limits. Hence also for $K_\pi . K_{nr}$, since both extensions have the same intertia subgroup. Since $K_\pi . K_{nr}$ is the maximal abelian extension, the result is true in general.

This concludes the proof of Theorem 1.

COROLLARY. *The jumps in the filtration $\{G^v\}$ of G occur only for integral values of v.*

Proof. This follows from Theorem 1, since it is trivial for filtrations of U_K and Theorem 1 transforms one into the other.

[This result is in fact true for any field which is complete with respect to a discrete valuation and which has perfect residue field (theorem of Hasse-Arf), cf. "Corps Locaux", Chap. IV, V.]

4.2 *Abelian Conductors*

Let L/K be a finite extension and let $\theta : K^* \to G(L/K)$ be the corresponding reciprocity map. There is a smallest number n such that $\theta(U_K^n) = 0$. This number n is called the *conductor* of the extension L/K and is denoted by $f(L/K)$.

PROPOSITION 1. *Let c be the largest integer such that the ramification group G_c is not trivial. Then $f(L/K) = \phi_{L/K}(c)+1$.*

Proof. This is a trivial consequence of Theorem 1 and the fact that the upper numbering is obtained by applying ϕ.

Now let L/K be an arbitrary galois extension. Let $\chi : G \to \mathbf{C}^*$ be a one-dimensional character and let L_χ be the subfield of L corresponding to Ker (χ). The field L_χ is a cyclic extension of K and $f(L_\chi/K)$ is called *the conductor of* χ and is denoted by $f(\chi)$.

PROPOSITION 2. *Let $\{G_i\}$ be the ramification subgroups of $G = G(L/K)$ and write $g_i =$ Card (G_i). Then*

$$(\chi) = \sum_{i=0}^{\infty} \frac{g_i}{g_0}(1-\chi(G_i))$$

where $\chi(G_i) = g_i^{-1} \sum_{s \in G_i} \chi(s)$ is the "mean value" of χ on G_i.

Proof. We have $\chi(G_i) = 1$ if χ is trivial on G_i (that is, equal to 1 everywhere) and $\chi(G_i) = 0$ if χ is non-trivial on G_i. Hence (the reader is referred to "Corps Locaux", Chaps. IV and VI for the details)

$$\sum_{i=0}^{\infty} \frac{g_i}{g_0}(1-\chi(G_i)) = \sum_{i=0}^{c_\chi} \frac{g_i}{g_0} = \phi_{L/K}(c_\chi)+1,$$

where c_χ is the largest number such that the restriction $\chi|G_{c_\chi} \neq 1$. Now $f(\chi) = f(L_\chi/K)$ is equal to $\phi_{L_\chi/K}(c)+1$, where c is defined as in Prop. 1 for the extension L_χ/K. Since $\phi_{L/K}$ is transitive, it suffices to show that $c = \phi_{L/L_\chi}(c_\chi)$ and this is a consequence of Herbrand's theorem (§ 4.1).

4.3 *Artin's Conductors*

Let L/K be a finite galois extension with Galois group $G = G(L/K)$. Let χ be a character of G (that is, an integral combination of irreducible characters). Artin defined the *conductor* of χ as the number

$$f(\chi) = \sum_{i=0}^{\infty} \frac{g_i}{g_0}(\chi(1)-\chi(G_i)).$$

If χ is irreducible of degree 1, this $f(\chi)$ coincides with the previous $f(\chi)$. We define *Artin's character* a_G as follows. For $s \in G$, set

$$a_G(s) = -f.i_G(s) \quad \text{if } s \neq 1$$
$$a_G(1) = f\sum_{s\neq 1} i_G(s).$$

Here f is the residue degree $[l:k]$ (not to be confused with the conductor!), and i_G is the function defined above.

PROPOSITION 3. *Let* $g = \text{Card}(G)$. *Then*

$$f(\chi) = (a_G, \chi) = \frac{1}{g}\sum_{s\in G} \chi(s)a_G(s).$$

Proof. The proof depends on summation on successive differences $G_i - G_{i+1}$ and is left as an exercise. (See "Corps Locaux", Chap. VI, § 2.)

PROPOSITION 4. (a) *Let $K \subset L' \subset L$ be a tower of galois extensions, let χ' be a character of $G(L'/K)$ and let χ be the corresponding character of $G(L/K)$. Then $f(\chi) = f(\chi')$.*

(b) *Let $K \subset K' \subset L$ and let ψ be a character of $G(L/K')$ and let ψ^* be the corresponding induced character of $G(L/K)$. Then*

$$f(\psi^*) = \psi(1).v_K(\mathfrak{d}_{K'/K})+f_{K'/K}.f(\psi),$$

where $f_{K'/K}$ is the residue degree of K'/K and $\mathfrak{d}_{K'/K}$ is the discriminant of K'/K.

Proof. The proof depends on properties of the i_G function and on the relation between the different and the discriminant, and can be found in "Corps Locaux", Chap. VI.

THEOREM 2 (Artin). *Let χ be the character of a representation of G. Then $f(\chi)$ is a positive integer.*

Proof. Let χ be the character of the rational representation M of G. It follows from representation theory that

$$\chi(1) = \dim M$$

and

$$\chi(G_i) = \dim M^{G_i}.$$

Thus in

$$\sum \frac{g_i}{g_0}(\chi(1) - \chi(G_i)),$$

each term is positive ($\geqslant 0$) and so $f(\chi) \geqslant 0$.

It remains to be proved that $f(\chi)$ is an integer. According to a theorem of Brauer, χ can be written $\chi = \sum m_i \psi_i^*$ where $m_i \in \mathbf{Z}$ and ψ_i^* is induced by a character ψ_i of degree 1 of a subgroup H_i of G.

Hence, since $f(\psi_i^*) = \psi_i(1)v_K(\mathfrak{d}_{K'/K}) + f_{K'/K}.f(\psi_i)$, $f(\psi_i^*)$ is an integer provided that $f(\psi_i)$ is. But since ψ_i has degree 1, $f(\psi_i)$ may be interpreted as an abelian conductor and so is obviously an integer. This proves Theorem 2.

4.4 *Global Conductors*

Let L/K be a finite galois extension of *number fields* and let $G = G(L/K)$ be the Galois group. If χ is a character of G, then we define an ideal $\mathfrak{f}(\chi)$ of K, the *conductor of* χ, as follows. Let $\mathfrak{p}$ be a prime ideal in K and choose a prime ideal $\mathfrak{P}$ in L which divides $\mathfrak{p}$. Let $G_{\mathfrak{p}} = G(L_{\mathfrak{P}}/K_{\mathfrak{p}})$ be the corresponding decomposition subgroup. Let $f(\chi, \mathfrak{p})$ be the Artin conductor of the restriction of χ to $G_{\mathfrak{p}}$ as defined above. We have $f(\chi, \mathfrak{p}) = 0$ when $\mathfrak{p}$ is unramified. The ideal

$$\mathfrak{f}(\chi) = \prod_{\mathfrak{p}} \mathfrak{p}^{f(\chi, \mathfrak{p})}$$

is called the (global) conductor of χ.

In this notation, Prop. 4 gives:

PROPOSITION 5. *Let K'/K be a sub-extension of L/K. Let ψ be a character of $H = G(L/K')$ and let ψ^* be the induced character of $G(L/K)$. Then*

$$\mathfrak{f}(\psi^*) = \mathfrak{d}_{K'/K}^{\psi(1)}.N_{K'/K}(\mathfrak{f}(\psi)),$$

where $\mathfrak{d}_{K'/K}$ is the discriminant of K'/K.

We apply Prop. 5 to the case $\psi = 1$ and we denote the induced character ψ^* by $s_{G/H}$ (it corresponds to the permutation representation of G/H). Since $\mathfrak{f}(\psi) = (1)$ we obtain:

COROLLARY. *We have $\mathfrak{f}(s_{G/H}, L/K) = \mathfrak{d}_{K'/K}$.*

In the case $H = 1$ we have $s_{G/H} = r_G$, the character of the regular representation of G, and the corollary reads

$$\mathfrak{d}_{L/K} = \prod_{\chi} \mathfrak{f}(\chi)^{\chi(1)},$$

where χ runs through the set of irreducible characters of G. This is the "Führerdiskriminantenproduktformel" of Artin and Hasse, which was first proved by analytical methods (L functions). In the abelian case it reads:

$$\mathfrak{d}_{L/K} = \prod_{\chi : G \to \mathbf{C}^*} \mathfrak{f}(\chi).$$

In the quadratic case it reduces to the fact that the discriminant is equal to the conductor.

4.5 *Artin's Representation*

We return to the local case.

THEOREM 3. *Let L/K be a finite galois extension of local fields with Galois group G. Let a_G be the Artin character of G defined above* (*cf.* § 4.3). *Then a_G is the character of a complex linear representation of G called "the" Artin representation.*

Proof. The character a_G takes the same values on conjugate elements and so is a class function. It follows that a_G is a combination $\sum_\chi m_\chi \chi$, with complex coefficients m_χ, of the irreducible characters χ. Since

$$m_\chi = (a_G, \chi) = f(\chi),$$

we know (Prop. 3 and Theorem 2) that m_χ is a positive integer. Hence the result.

Now let V_χ be an irreducible representation corresponding to χ. We can define Artin's representation A_G by:

$$A_G = \sum f(\chi) . V_\chi,$$

where the summation is over all irreducible characters χ.

Remark. This construction of A_G is rather artificial. Weil has posed the problem of finding a "natural" A_G.

THEOREM 4. *Let l be a prime number not equal to the residue characteristic. Then the Artin representation can be realized over $\mathbf{Q}_l$.*

Proof. See J-P. Serre, *Annals of Mathematics*, **72** (1960), 406–420, or "Introduction à la théorie de Brauer" *Séminaire I.H.E.S.*, 1965/66.

Examples exist where the Artin representation cannot be realized over $\mathbf{Q}$, $\mathbf{R}$ or $\mathbf{Q}_p$, where p is the residue characteristic. This suggests that there is no trivial definition of the Artin representation.

Assume now that L/K is totally ramified. Let $u_G = r_G - 1$; we have

$u_G(s) = -1$ if $s \neq 1$ and $u_G(s) = \text{Card}(G)-1$ if $s = 1$. Now $a_G = u_G + b_G$ where b_G is a character of some representation.

Note: $a_G = u_G$ if and only if L/K is tamely ramified. So b_G is a measure of how wild the ramification is.

THEOREM 5. *Let l be a prime number not equal to the residue characteristic. Then there exists a finitely generated, projective $\mathbf{Z}_l[G]$ module $B_{G,l}$ with character b_G and this module is unique up to isomorphism.*

Proof. This follows from a theorem of Swan, "Topology", 2 (1963), Theorem 5, combined with Theorem 4 above and the remark that $b_G(s) = 0$ when the order of s is divisible by l. [See also the I.H.E.S. seminar quoted above.]

For applications of Theorem 5 to the construction of invariants of finite G-modules, see M. Raynaud, "Sém. Bourbaki", 1964/65, exposé 286. These invariants play an important role in the functional equation of the zeta functions of curves.

CHAPTER VII

Global Class Field Theory

J. T. TATE

Throughout these lectures, K will be a global field, as has been defined in Chapter II, § 12. We treat the number field case completely, but in the function field case there is one big gap in our proofs, in that the second inequality and the accompanying key lemma for the existence theorem are proved only for extensions of degree prime to the characteristic. (The reader interested in filling the gap can consult the Artin-Tate notes,† pp. 29–38.)

As in Local Class Field theory, there are several aspects: (1) The cohomology theory of Galois extensions of K. (2) The determination of the abelian extensions of K. (3) L-series analysis.

We will discuss the first two, leaving the third to Heilbronn (Chapter VIII), except for a few remarks.

Sections 1–6 constitute a statement and discussion of the reciprocity law and the main theorems on abelian extensions, with no mention of cohomology. We hope that this preliminary discussion will serve both as orientation and bait for the reader. In sections 7–12 we give the main proofs, based on the determination of the Galois cohomology of idèle classes and the Brauer group of K.

This chapter is strictly limited to the central theorems. In the exercises at the end of the book the reader will find a few concrete examples and further

† Harvard, Dept. of Mathematics, 1961.

results. There are some references to recent literature scattered in the text but we have made no attempt to give a systematic bibliography. A list of symbols used in this chapter is given at the end.

1. Action of the Galois Group on Primes and Completions

Let L be a finite Galois extension field of K with Galois group $G = G(L/K)$.

1.1. First of all we have a few lines on our notation and language. If $a \in L$ and $\sigma \in G$, then the action of σ on a will be denoted by σa or a^σ, according to the situation. If $\tau \in G$ we use the convention $\sigma(\tau a) = (\sigma\tau)a$ and so $(a^\tau)^\sigma = a^{(\sigma\tau)}$.

A *prime* is an equivalence class of valuations, or a normalized valuation, of K; we usually denote a prime by the letter v or w. A prime may be either *archimedean* or *discrete*; if v is discrete we write $\mathfrak{O}_v$ for its valuation ring and $\mathfrak{P}_v$ for the maximal ideal of $\mathfrak{O}_v$. We reserve the symbol $\mathfrak{P}$ for prime ideals.

Let w be a prime of L, then with the definition $|a|_{\sigma w} = |\sigma^{-1}a|_w$ it follows that σw is another prime of L and $\sigma(\tau w) = (\sigma\tau)w$. If $\mathfrak{O}_w$ is the valuation ring of w, then $\sigma\mathfrak{O}_w = \mathfrak{O}_{\sigma w}$. A Cauchy sequence for w, acted on by σ, gives a Cauchy sequence for σw and conversely a Cauchy sequence for σw, acted on by σ^{-1}, gives a Cauchy sequence for w; so σ induces by continuity an isomorphism $\sigma_w : L_w \xrightarrow{\sim} L_{\sigma w}$ of the completions of L with respect to the primes w and σw respectively. If w is over the prime v of K so is σw and this map is a K_v-isomorphism. Clearly, $\sigma_{\tau w} \circ \tau_w = (\sigma\tau)_w$.

The *decomposition group* G_w of w is the subgroup

$$G_w = \{\sigma \in G \mid \sigma w = w\}$$

of G. Note that

$$(1) \qquad G_{\tau w} = \{\sigma \in G \mid \sigma\tau w = \tau w\} = \tau G_w \tau^{-1},$$

thus the decomposition group of w is determined up to conjugacy by the prime v. By what we have said σ is a K_v-automorphism of L_w if $\sigma \in G_w$ and so we have an injection i of G_w into $G(L_w/K_v)$.

1.2. Proposition. (i) *L_w/K_v is Galois and the injection $i: G_w \to G(L_w/K_v)$ is an isomorphism.*

(ii) *If w and w' are two primes of L over the prime v of K, there exists a $\sigma \in G$ such that $\sigma w = w'$.*

Proof. Letting $[X]$ denote the cardinality of a set X, we have

$$[G_w] \leqslant G(L_w/K_v) \leqslant [L_w : K_v],$$

and these inequalities are equalities if and only if (i) is true. Let $r = (G : G_w)$ and let (σ_i), $1 \leqslant i \leqslant r$, be a system of representatives for the cosets $\sigma_i G_w$ of G_w in G. Put $w_i = \sigma_i w$ for $1 \leqslant i \leqslant r$. These are distinct primes of L lying over v; let w_i for $r+1 \leqslant i \leqslant s$ be the remaining such, if any. Then

$$[G] = r[G_w] = \sum_{i=1}^{r}[G_{w_i}] \leqslant \sum_{i=1}^{r}[L_{w_i}:K_v] \leqslant \sum_{i=1}^{s}[L_{w_i}:K_v] = [L:K] = [G],$$

so we have equality throughout. Hence $r = s$, which implies (ii) and $[G_w] = [L_w : K_v]$, which implies (i). [The fact that the sum of the local degrees is equal to the global degree follows from the bijectivity of the map $L \otimes_K K_v \to \prod_{i=1}^{s} L_{w_i}$ on taking dimensions over K_v; see Chapter II § 10. The surjectivity, which is all we have used, is an easy consequence of the weak approximation theorem.]

Write $\mathfrak{M}_K$ for the set of primes of K. Then, since $\mathfrak{M}_L \to \mathfrak{M}_K$ is surjective (every prime v of K can be extended to a prime w of L), Proposition 1.2 amounts to saying that $\mathfrak{M}_K \simeq \mathfrak{M}_L/G$, i.e. the primes of K are in 1–1 correspondence with the orbits under G of the primes of L, and for each prime w of L, its stabilizer G_w is isomorphic to the Galois group of the corresponding local field extension L_w/K_v.

2. Frobenius Automorphisms

2.1. Suppose that w is a discrete, unramified prime of L over the prime v of K. (This is true of "almost all" primes v, w, i.e. for all but finitely many.) Then

$$G \supset G_w \simeq G(L_w/K_v) \simeq G(k(w)/k(v)), \tag{1}$$

where $k(v)$ (resp. $k(w)$) denotes the residue class field of K (resp. L) with respect to v (resp. w). Since these residue class fields are finite the Galois group $G(k(w)/k(v))$ is cyclic with a canonical generator,

$$F: x \mapsto x^{Nv},$$

where $Nv = [k(v)]$ is the "absolute norm". Hence we see from (1) that there is a unique element $\sigma_w \in G_w$ which is characterized by the property

$$\sigma_w \in G_w \quad \text{and} \quad a^{\sigma_w} \equiv a^{Nv} \pmod{\mathfrak{P}_w}$$

for all $a \in \mathfrak{O}_w$. This automorphism σ_w is called the *Frobenius automorphism* associated with the prime w. An immediate consequence of this definition is

2.2. Proposition

$$\sigma_{\tau w} = \tau^{-1}\sigma_w \tau.$$

Thus the Frobenius automorphism is determined by v *up to conjugacy* and we define

$$F_{L/K}(v) = (\text{conjugacy class of } \sigma_w, w \text{ over } v) = (\text{the set of } \sigma_w\text{'s for } w \text{ over } v).$$

If S is a finite set of primes of K containing the archimedean primes and the primes ramified in the extension L/K, then $F_{L/K}$ is a map of $\mathfrak{M}_K - S$ into the conjugacy classes of $G(L/K)$.

2.3. PROPOSITION. *Let $\sigma \in F_{L/K}(v)$ have order f, so that it generates the subgroup $<\sigma> = \{1, \sigma, \ldots, \sigma^{f-1}\}$. Then in L, v splits into $[G : <\sigma>]$ factors, each of degree $f = [k(w) : k(v)]$. In particular, v splits completely if and only if $F_{L/K}(v) = 1$, the identity element of G.*

2.4. *Remarks.* This proposition tells us that knowledge of $F_{L/K}$ gives the decomposition law for unramified primes, and more, since it chooses a definite generator for the decomposition group.

Since $F_{L/K}$ is a function to classes of G, to know $F_{L/K}$ it is enough to know $\chi(F_{L/K}(v))$ for all characters χ of G. Accordingly, Artin was led to define his non-abelian L-series in terms of $\chi(F)$, by means of which one can prove the fundamental *Tchebotarev* (= *Čebotarev*) *Density Theorem: Let* $\mathscr{C}$ *be a conjugacy class in* G; *the primes* v *with* $F(v) = \mathscr{C}$ *have density* $[\mathscr{C}]/[G]$. In particular, for each conjugacy class $\mathscr{C}$, there exists an infinite number of primes v of K such that $F_{L/K}(v) = \mathscr{C}$.

In the cyclotomic case Tchebotarev's theorem is equivalent to the Dirichlet theorem on primes in arithmetic progressions (see 3.4 below).

From Tchebotarev's theorem it follows almost trivially that a finite Galois extension L of K is uniquely determined (up to isomorphism) by the set Spl (L/K) of primes of K which split completely in L (cf. exercise 6). Unfortunately one knows no way to characterize directly, in terms of the arithmetic of K itself, those sets T of primes of K which are of the form Spl (L/K), except in case L is abelian. The decomposition law for abelian extensions, together with the complete classification of such extensions, is given by the main theorem below (§ 5); but no such theorem is known for non-abelian extensions, i.e. "non-abelian class field theory" does not exist. From the abelian theory one can derive decomposition laws of sorts for some soluble extensions (cf. Exercise 2) but this is not what is sought. Recently Shimura ("A reciprocity law in non-solvable extensions", *Crelle's Journal*, **221** (1966), 209–220) has given an explicit decomposition law for certain non-soluble extensions obtained by adjoining to **Q** the points of order l on a certain elliptic curve. The idea is to relate the behaviour of primes in those extensions to the zeta-function of the curve, and to identify that zeta-function with a modular function, the coefficient of whose q-expansion can be calculated explicitly. The degree of generality of such examples, and whether they will point the way to a general theory, is unclear; but at any rate they are there to test hypotheses against.

3. Artin's Reciprocity Law

3.1. First of all we give some notation. S will usually denote a *finite* set of primes of K including all the archimedean primes. If we are considering a particular finite extension L/K, then S will also include the primes of K

ramified in L. We will denote by I^S the free abelian group on the elements of $\mathfrak{M}_K - S$ (a subgroup of the group of ideals, see Chapter II § 17).

Assume now that L/K is a finite abelian extension. Then the conjugacy classes of $G = G(L/K)$ are single elements and so $F_{L/K}$ is a map from $\mathfrak{M}_K - S$ into G. By linearity we can extend this to a homomorphism (to be denoted by $F_{L/K}$ also) of I^S into G, putting

$$F_{L/K}\left(\sum_{v \notin S} n_v v\right) = \prod_{v \notin S} F_{L/K}(v)^{n_v},$$

where the n_v are integers and $n_v = 0$ except for a finite number of the v.

The first proposition of this section concerns the change in the map $F_{L/K}$ when the fields are changed. Suppose that L'/K' and L/K are abelian field extensions with Galois group G' and G respectively, such that $L' \supset L$ and $K' \supset K$, and let θ be the natural map $G' \to G$ (every automorphism of L'/K' induces one of L/K). Let S denote a finite set of primes of K including the archimedean ones and those primes ramified in L' and let S' be the set of primes of K' above those in S. Then

3.2. Proposition. *The diagram*

$$\begin{array}{ccc} I^{S'} & \xrightarrow{F_{L'/K'}} & G' \\ \downarrow{\scriptstyle N_{K'/K}} & & \downarrow{\scriptstyle \theta} \\ I^S & \xrightarrow{F_{L/K}} & G \end{array}$$

commutes, where N denotes "norm".

Proof. By linearity, it is clear that it is enough to check that

$$\theta F_{L'/K'}(v') = F_{L/K}(N_{K'/K}v')$$

for an arbitrary prime v' of K' such that $v' \notin S'$. Let $N_{K'/K}v' = fv$, where v is the prime of K below v'; thus $f = [k(v'):k(v)]$. Let $\sigma' = F_{L'/K'}(v')$ and $\sigma = F_{L/K}(v)$. We must show $\theta(\sigma') = \sigma^f$. Now σ and σ' are determined by their effect on the residue fields. Let w' be a prime of L' above v' and let w be the prime of L below w'. For $x \in k(w) \subset k(w')$ we have

$$x^{\sigma'} = x^{Nv'} = x^{(Nv)^f} = x^{\sigma^f},$$

as required.

If $a \in K^*$ (i.e. a is a non-zero element of K), then we write

$$(a)^S = \sum_{v \notin S} n_v v,$$

where $n_v = v(a)$ for all $v \notin S$; thus $(a)^S$ is an element of I^S.

We can now state the reciprocity law in its crudest form

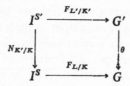

3.3. Reciprocity Law (Crude form). *If L/K is a finite abelian extension, and S is the set of primes of K consisting of the archimedean ones and those*

ramified in L, then there exists $\varepsilon > 0$ *such that if* $a \in K^*$ *and* $|a-1|_v < \varepsilon$ *for all* $v \in S$, *then* $F((a)^S) = 1$.

In words, if $a \in K^*$ is sufficiently near to 1 at all primes in a large enough set S, then $F((a)^S) = \prod_{v \notin S} F(v)^{v(a)} = 1$.

In the number field case the subgroup $(K_v^*)^n$ is open in K^* for all $n > 0$, and we claim that the condition $|a-1|_v < \varepsilon$ can be replaced by $a \in (K_v^*)^n$ for $v \in S$, where $n = [L:K]$. Indeed if the latter is satisfied then, by the weak approximation theorem, there exists $b \in K^*$ such that $|ab^{-n}-1|_v < \varepsilon$ for all $v \in S$, and then

$$F((a)^S) = F((b^n ab^{-n})^S) = F((b)^S)^n F((ab^{-n})^S) = 1.$$

Thus, in the case of number fields, although the set S depends on L, the neighbourhoods of 1 at the primes of S depend only on the degree n of L over K. In particular, for archimedean primes there is no condition needed unless v is real and n is even, in which case the condition $a > 0$ in K_v is sufficient.

Using the approximation theorem in L instead of K, one can replace the condition "a is a local $[L:K]$-th power in S" by "a is a local norm from L to K in S", but for that we shall use the technique of idèles (see 4.4 and 6.4 below). The shift in emphasis from n-th powers to norms was decisive, and is due to Hilbert.

3.4. *Example. The reciprocity law for cyclotomic extensions.* This reciprocity law may be verified directly in the cyclotomic case $k = \mathbf{Q}$, $L = \mathbf{Q}(\zeta)$, where ζ is a primitive m-th root of unity. This particular result will be used later in one of our proofs of the general result (see § 10, below) so we give some details. In the rational case it is conventional to denote primes by p and the associated valuations by v_p. The set S will consist of the archimedean prime and those primes p which divide m (see Chapter III). For $p \notin S$ and w above p, the powers of ζ have *distinct* images in the residue class field $k(w)$. so we have

PROPOSITION.

$$F(v_p)\zeta = \zeta^p \textit{ for all } p \notin S.$$

From this we deduce

COROLLARY. *If* $a \in \mathbf{Z}$, $a > 0$ *and* $(a, m) = 1$, *then* $F((a)^S)\zeta = \zeta^a$.

Consequently, if a is a positive rational number with $|a-1|_p < |m|_p$ for all $p \in S$, then a is a p-adic integer for all p dividing m, and we can write $a = b/c$ with $(b, m) = (c, m) = 1$, and $b \equiv c \pmod{m}$; hence $\zeta^b = \zeta^c$ and so $F((b)^S)\zeta = \zeta^b = \zeta^c = F((c)^S)\zeta$. By linearity this gives $F((a)^S)\zeta = \zeta$ so that $F((a)^S) = 1$.

For another example of an explicit description of $F_{L/K}$, and for the connection between Artin's general reciprocity law and the classical quadratic reciprocity law, see exercise 1.

3.5. *Remark.* The cyclotomic case was easy because one can use the roots of unity to "keep book" on the effect of the F(v)'s for variable v. A similar direct proof works for abelian extensions of complex quadratic fields using division points and modular invariants of elliptic curves with complex multiplication, instead of roots of unity. In the general case no such proof is known (cf. the 12th problem of Hilbert), although Shimura and Taniyama and Weil have made a great contribution, using abelian varieties instead of elliptic curves. (See Shimura-Taniyama, "Complex Multiplication of Abelian Varieties and its Applications to Number Theory", *Publ. Math. Soc. Japan*, No. 6, 1961, and more recently Shimura, "On the Field of Definition for a Field of Automorphic Functions: II", *Annals of Math*, **81** (1965), 124–165.) The proof of the reciprocity law in the general case is very indirect, and can fairly be described as showing that the law holds "because it could not be otherwise".

3.6. *Remark.* In the function field case, as Lang has shown ("Sur les séries L d'une variété algébrique", *Bull. Soc. Math. Fr.* **84** (1956), 385–407), the reciprocity law relates to a geometric theorem about the field $K = k(C)$ of a curve C. Serre has carried out in detail the program initiated by Lang. In his book, "Groupes algébriques et corps de classes", Hermann, Paris (1959), an analogue of the reciprocity law is described as follows. Let $f : C \to G$ be a rational map of a non-singular curve C into a commutative algebraic group G; let S be the finite set of points of C where f is not regular. Then f induces a homomorphism of the group of divisors I^S into G and

THEOREM. *If $\phi \in K$ takes the value 1 to a high order at each point of S, then $f((\phi)) = 1$.*

This theorem is due to Rosenlicht, and independently, but later, Serre. It was Serre and Lang who applied it to class field theory.

3.7. *Definition.* Let K be a global field, S be a finite set of primes of K including all the archimedean ones and G a commutative topological group. A homomorphism $\phi : I^S \to G$ is said to be *admissible* if for each neighbourhood N of the identity element 1 of G there exists $\varepsilon > 0$ such that $\phi((a)^S) \in N$ whenever $a \in K^*$ and $|a-1|_v < \varepsilon$ for all $v \in S$.

If G is a discrete group, we simply take N to be (1). Thus

3.8. *Reformulation of the Reciprocity law: $F_{L/K}$ is admissible.*

In this context the finite group $G = G(L/K)$ is discrete. If G is the circle group, then ϕ is admissible if and only if it is a Grössencharakter (if it maps into a finite subgroup, it is a Dirichlet character). Dirichlet and Hecke formed their L-series with such characters; Artin was originally forced to produce his reciprocity law in order to show that in the abelian case his L-series defined in terms of characters of the Galois group were really Weber L-series, in other words that $\chi(F(v))$ was admissible for each linear character χ of the abelian Galois group.

4. Chevalley's Interpretation by Idèles

The set of elements of the idèle group J_K (see Chapter II § 16) which have the value 1 at all the v-th components, $v \in S$, is denoted by J_K^S. If $x \in J_K$ it has a non-unit component at only a finite number of v-components; if the (additive) valuation of the v-th component x_v of x is $n_v \in \mathbf{Z}$ we write

$$(x)^S = \sum_{v \notin S} n_v v \in I^S.$$

4.1. PROPOSITION. *Let K and S be as before, G be a complete commutative topological group and ϕ an admissible homomorphism of I^S into G.*

Then there exists a unique homomorphism ψ of $J_K \to G$ such that

(i) *ψ is continuous;*
(ii) $\psi(K^*) = 1$;
(iii) $\psi(x) = \phi((x)^S)$ *for all* $x \in J_K^S$.

Conversely, if ψ is a continuous homomorphism of $J_K \to G$ such that $\psi(K^*) = 1$, then ψ comes from some admissible pair S, ϕ as defined above, provided there exists a neighbourhood of 1 *in G in which* (1) *is the only subgroup.*

Remark. It is clear that if such a ψ exists then it induces a continuous homomorphism of the idèle class group $C_K \simeq J_K/K^*$ into G. This induced homomorphism will also be denoted by ψ. Furthermore, if such a ψ exists for a given ϕ and S, then by the unicity statement, it is unchanged if S is enlarged to a bigger set S' and ϕ replaced by its restriction ϕ' to $I^{S'} \subset I^S$. Similarly, two ϕ's on I^S which coincide on $I^{S'}$ for some finite $S' \supset S$ are actually equal on I^S (cf. Exercise 7).

For applications G can be thought of as a discrete group or the circle group.

Proof. Suppose we have an admissible map $\phi : I^S \to G$. If such a ψ were to exist, for any $a \in K^*$ and $x \in J_K$ we would have

$$\psi(x) = \psi(ax) = \psi((ax)_1)\psi((ax)_2),$$

where $(ax)_1$ is the idèle with the same v-component as ax for all $v \in S$ and value 1 elsewhere and $(ax)_2$ is the idèle with the same v-component as ax for all $v \notin S$ and whose v-component is 1 at all $v \in S$ (thus $(ax)_2 \in J_K^S$). By the (weak) approximation theorem (see Chapter II, §6) we can find a sequence

$\{a_n\}$ of elements $a_n \in K^*$, such that $a_n \to x^{-1}$, as $n \to \infty$, at all $v \in S$. Then

$$\psi(x) = \lim_{n\to\infty} \psi((a_n x)_1) . \phi((a_n x)^S) = \lim_{n\to\infty} \phi((a_n x)^S).$$

Hence given ϕ we define a function ψ by

$$\psi(x) = \lim_{n\to\infty} \phi((a_n x)^S). \tag{1}$$

As $n, m \to \infty$ we have $a_n/a_m \to 1$ at all primes $v \in S$, and consequently

$$\frac{\phi((a_n x)^S)}{\phi((a_m x)^S)} = \phi\left(\left(\frac{a_n}{a_m}\right)^S\right) \to 1$$

in G, because ϕ is admissible. Thus the limit exists, since G is complete, and the limit is independent of the sequence $\{a_n\}$, because it exists for all such sequences. Moreover ψ is continuous. If the components of x are units at primes $v \notin S$, then we have $\psi(x) = \lim \phi((a_n)^S)$; and if in addition the components of x are sufficiently close to 1 at primes $v \in S$, then so will be those of a_n for large n, and by admissibility, $\phi((a_n)^S)$ will be close to 1 in G. The last two conditions (ii) and (iii) are trivially verified by taking $a_n = x^{-1}$ and 1 for all n respectively.

Now suppose we are given a continuous homomorphism $\psi : J_K \to G$ such that $\psi(K^*) = 1$. We will find a set S so that (a) the restriction of ψ to J_K^S comes from a function on I^S and (b) if we call this function ϕ, then ϕ is admissible.

For any finite set S of primes of K let U^S be the set of idèles in J_K for which the v-component is 1 at all $v \in S$ and a unit of K_v for $v \notin S$. By taking S arbitrarily large we can make U^S an arbitrarily small neighbourhood of the identity of J_K. If N is a neighbourhood of (1) we can choose S sufficiently large so that $\psi(U^S) \subseteq N$, since ψ is continuous. Then taking N small enough, we see that $\psi(U^S) = (1)$ for some set S by the "no-small-subgroup" hypothesis. We choose such a set S. Now J_K^S/U^S is canonically isomorphic to I^S and so ψ, when restricted to J_K^S, induces a continuous homomorphism ϕ of I^S into G.

It remains to verify that ϕ is admissible; in words, given a neighbourhood N, then $\psi((a)^S) \in N$ whenever $a \in K^*$ is near enough to 1 at all $v \in S$. But in this case $(a)^S$ is near to a in J_K and so by continuity $\psi((a)^S)$ is near to $\psi(a)$, which is 1 since $a \in K^*$.

4.2. Corollary. *The reciprocity law holds for a finite abelian extension L of K if and only if there exists a continuous homomorphism ψ of $J_K \to G(L/K)$ such that*

(i) *ψ is continuous.*

(ii) *$\psi(K^*) = 1$.*

(iii) *$\psi(x) = F_{L/K}((x)^S)$ for all $x \in J_K^S$, where S consists of the archimedean primes of K and those ramified in L.*

Such a map $\psi = \psi_{L/K}$ whose existence we have just postulated is called the *Artin map* associated with the extension L/K. It has been defined as a map $J_K \to G(L/K)$; but since it acts trivially on K^* it may be viewed as a map of the idèle class group $C_K = J_K/K^*$ into $G(L/K)$.

The reciprocity law for finite abelian extensions will be proved later (see § 10). In the meantime certain propositions will be proved and remarks made which depend on its validity. Suppose that L'/K' and L/K are abelian field extensions with Galois groups G' and G respectively and that $L' \supset L$, $K' \supset K$. Let θ be the natural map $G' \to G$. Then in terms of idèles and Artin maps Proposition 3.1 becomes

4.3. **Proposition.** *If the reciprocity law holds for L/K and L'/K', then*

$$\begin{array}{ccc} J_{K'} & \xrightarrow{\psi_{L'/K'}} & G' \\ {\scriptstyle N_{K'/K}}\downarrow & & \downarrow{\scriptstyle \theta} \\ J_K & \xrightarrow{\psi_{L/K}} & G \end{array}$$

is a commutative diagram.

Proof. Let S be a large finite set of primes of K, and S' the set of primes of K' above S. We have then a diagram

(2)

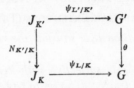

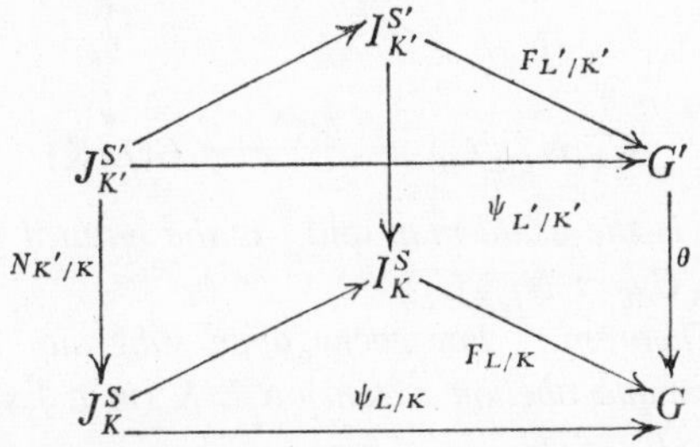

The non-rectangular parallelograms are commutative by the compatibility of ideal and idèle norms, and by Proposition 3.2. The triangles are commutative by (4.2)(iii). Thus the rectangle is commutative, i.e. the restrictions of $\psi_{L/K} \circ N_{K'/K}$ and $\theta \circ \psi_{L'/K'}$ to $J_{K'}^{S'}$ coincide. But those two homomorphisms take the value 1 on principal idèles by 4.2 (ii), so they coincide on $(K')^* J_{K'}^{S'}$, which is a dense subset of $J_{K'}$ by the weak approximation theorem (Chapter II, § 6). Since the two homomorphisms are continuous, they coincide on all of $J_{K'}$ which is what we wished to prove.

For proving Proposition 6.2 below, which is in turn needed for the first of our two proofs of the reciprocity law in §10.4, we need the following

Variant. *Suppose L/K satisfies the reciprocity law, and $K \subset M \subset L$. Then* $\psi_{L/K}(N_{M/K} J_M) \subset G(L/M)$.

Consider diagram (2) with $L' = L$, $K' = M$, but with the upper horizontal arrow $\psi_{L'/K'} = \psi_{L/M}$ removed. It shows that

$$\psi_{L/K}(N_{M/K}J_M^{S'}) \subset G' = G(L/M).$$

Consequently the same is true with $J_M^{S'}$ replaced by $M^*J_M^{S'}$, and since that set is dense in J_M we are done.

4.4. COROLLARY. *If the reciprocity law holds for L/K, then*

$$\psi_{L/K}(N_{L/K}J_L) = 1.$$

It follows that $\psi_{L/K}(K^*N_{L/K}J_L) = 1$; the next theorem states (among other things) that $K^*N_{L/K}J_L$ is the kernel of $\psi_{L/K}$.

5. Statement of the Main Theorems on Abelian Extensions

5.1. MAIN THEOREM ON ABELIAN EXTENSIONS (Takagi-Artin).

(A) *Every abelian extension L/K satisfies the reciprocity law* (*i.e. there is an Artin map* $\psi_{L/K}$).

(B) *The Artin map $\psi_{L/K}$ is surjective with kernel $K^*N_{L/K}(J_L)$ and hence induces an isomorphism of $C_K/N_{L/K}(C_L)$ on to $G(L/K)$.*

(C) *If $M \supset L \supset K$ are abelian extensions, then the diagram*

$$\begin{array}{ccc} C_K/N_{M/K}C_M & \xrightarrow{\psi_{M/K}} & G(M/K) \\ \downarrow j & & \downarrow \theta \\ C_K/N_{L/K}C_L & \xrightarrow{\psi_{L/K}} & G(L/K) \end{array}$$

commutes (*where θ is the usual map and j is the natural surjective map which exists because $N_{M/K}C_M \subset N_{L/K}C_L$*).

(D) (*Existence Theorem.*) *For every open subgroup N of finite index in C_K there exists a unique abelian extension L/K* (*in a fixed algebraic closure of K*) *such that $N_{L/K}C_L = N$.*

The subgroups N of (D) are called *Norm groups*, and the abelian extension L such that $N_{L/K}C_L = N$ is called the *class field* belonging to N. In the number field case every open subgroup of C_K is of finite index in C_K.

5.2. A certain amount of this theorem may be deduced readily from the rest. First, given (A) and (B), then (C) is a special case of 4.3 (put $K' = K$ and $L' = M$).

5.3. Secondly, the uniqueness, though not the existence, of the correspondence given in (D) follows from the rest. Given the existence, let L and L' be two finite abelian extensions of K in a fixed algebraic closure of K and let M be the compositum of L and L' (which is again a finite abelian extension of K). Now consider the commutative diagram above, under (C). Since the horizontal arrows are isomorphisms (by (B)) we see that Ker $\theta = G(M/L)$ is the isomorphic image, under $\psi_{M/K}$, of the group $N_{L/K}C_L/N_{M/K}C_M$. Thus L, as the fixed field of the group Ker θ, is uniquely determined as a subfield of M, by $N_{L/K}C_L$. Applying the same reasoning with L replaced by L', we see that if $N_{L'/K'}C_{L'} = N_{L/K}C_L$, then $L = L'$.

For some special examples of class fields (Hilbert class fields) see exercise 3.

For the functorial properties of the Artin map when the ground field K is changed, see 11.5 below.

5.4. The commutative diagram of (C) allows us to pass to the inverse limit (see Chapter III, §1), as L runs over all finite abelian extensions of K. We obtain a homomorphism

$$\psi_K : C_K \to \varprojlim_L G(L/K) \simeq G(K^{\mathrm{ab}}/K),$$

where K^{ab} is the maximal abelian extension of K; and then, by (D),

$$G(K^{\mathrm{ab}}/K) \simeq \varprojlim_N (C_K/N),$$

where the limit is taken over all open subgroups N of finite index in C_K. Thus we know the Galois groups of all abelian extensions of K from a knowledge of the idèle class group of K. The nature of the homomorphism $\psi_K : C_K \to G(K^{\mathrm{ab}}/K)$ is somewhat different in the function field and number field cases. The facts, which are not hard to derive from the main theorem, but whose proofs we omit, are as follows:

5.5. *Function Field Case.* Here the map ψ_K is injective and its image is the dense subgroup of $G(K^{\mathrm{ab}}/K)$ consisting of those automorphisms whose restriction to the algebraic closure $\bar{k}$ of the field of constants k is simply an integer power of the Frobenius automorphism F_k (see Artin-Tate notes, p. 76).

5.6. *Number Theory Case.* Here ψ_K is surjective and its kernel is the connected component D_K of C_K. So we have obtained a canonical isomorphism $C_K/D_K \simeq G(K^{\mathrm{ab}}/K)$.

However, as Weil has stressed ("Sur la théorie du corps de classes", *J. Math. Soc. Japan*, 3, 1951), we really want a Galois-theoretic interpretation of the *whole* of C_K. The connected component D_K can be very complicated (see Artin-Tate, p. 82).

5.7. *Example. Cyclotomic Fields.* Consider $\mathbf{Q}^{\mathrm{mc}}/\mathbf{Q}$, the maximal cyclotomic extension of $\mathbf{Q}$. Let $\hat{\mathbf{Z}} = \varprojlim_n \mathbf{Z}/n\mathbf{Z}$; by the Chinese remainder theorem this is isomorphic to $\prod_p \mathbf{Z}_p$, where $\mathbf{Z}_p$ is the ring of p-adic integers. $\hat{\mathbf{Z}}$ acts on any abelian torsion group (for $\mathbf{Z}/n\mathbf{Z}$ operates on any abelian group whose exponent divides n) and the invertible elements of $\hat{\mathbf{Z}}$ are those in $\prod_p U_p$, where U_p is the set of p-adic units in $\mathbf{Z}_p$.

Now consider the torsion group μ consisting of all roots of unity. If $\zeta \in \mu$ we can define ζ^u for all $u \in \prod_p U_p$; u induces an automorphism on μ. The idèle group $J_{\mathbf{Q}}$ is isomorphic to the direct product $\mathbf{Q}^* \times \mathbf{R}_+^* \times \prod_p U_p$. (In fact, if $x = \{x_\infty, x_2, x_3, \ldots\} \in J_{\mathbf{Q}}$ we have $x = a.\{t, u_2, u_3, \ldots\}$, where

$$a = (\operatorname{sign} x_\infty) \prod_p p^{v_p(x_p)} \in \mathbf{Q}^*,$$

and where $t > 0$, and $u_p \in U_p$ for $p = 2, 3, \ldots$; moreover, this decomposition is unique, because 1 is the only positive rational number which is a p-adic unit for all primes p.) Hence $C_{\mathbf{Q}}$ is canonically isomorphic to $\mathbf{R}_+^* \times \prod_p U_p$, so there is a map of $C_{\mathbf{Q}}$ onto $\prod_p U_p$, which is the Galois group of the maximal cyclotomic extension.

What in fact happens is the following. If $x \in C_{\mathbf{Q}}$ and $x \mapsto u$ by this map, then $\zeta^{\psi(x)} = \zeta^{u^{-1}}$ (this result is an easy exercise, starting from 3.4, and is independent of parts (B) and (D) of the main theorem). Thus the kernel of ψ is $\mathbf{R}_+^*$, which is the connected component $D_{\mathbf{Q}}$ of $C_{\mathbf{Q}}$. We have now used up the whole of $C_{\mathbf{Q}}/D_{\mathbf{Q}}$; so if we grant part (B) of the main theorem, we see that every abelian extension of $\mathbf{Q}$ must already have appeared as a subfield of $\mathbf{Q}^{mc}$, and that part (D) holds for abelian extensions of $\mathbf{Q}$.

The connected component $\mathbf{R}_+^*$ of $C_{\mathbf{Q}}$ is uninteresting; similarly, C_K has an uninteresting connected component when K is complex quadratic, essentially because there is only one archimedean prime. It may well be that it is the connected component that prevents a simple proof of the reciprocity law in the general case.

6. Relation Between Global and Local Artin Maps

We continue to deduce results on the assumption that the reciprocity law (but not necessarily the whole main theorem of § 5) is true for an abelian extension L/K.

6.1. For each prime v of K, we let K_v denote the completion of K at v. If L/K is a finite Galois extension, then the various completions L_w with w over v are isomorphic. It is convenient to write L^v for "any one of the completions L_w for w over v", and we write $G^v = G(L^v/K_v)$ for the local Galois group, which we can identify with a decomposition subgroup of G (see 1.2). In the abelian case this subgroup is unique, i.e. independent of the choice of w.

Assume that L/K is abelian and that there is an Artin map

$$\psi_{L/K}: J_K \to G(L/K) = G.$$

For each prime v of K we have

$$K_v^* \underset{j_v}{\overset{i_v}{\rightleftarrows}} J_K \xrightarrow{\psi_{L/K}} G,$$

where i_v is the mapping of an $x \in K_v^*$ onto the element of J_K whose v component is x and whose other components are 1, and j_v is the projection onto the v-th component. Call $\psi_v = \psi_{L/K} \circ i_v$; so $\psi_v : K_v^* \to G$. In fact

6.2. PROPOSITION. *If $K_v \subset \mathcal{M} \subset L^v$, then $\psi_v(N_{\mathcal{M}/K_v}\mathcal{M}^*) \subset G(L^v/\mathcal{M})$. In particular, $\psi_v(K_v^*) \subset G^v$, and $\psi_v(N_{L^v/K_v}(L^v)^*) = 1$.*

Proof. Let $M = L \cap \mathcal{M}$ be the fixed field of $G(L^v/\mathcal{M})$ in L, so that $G(L/M)$ is identified with $G(L^v/\mathcal{M})$ under our identification of the decomposition group with the local Galois group. Then $\mathcal{M} = M_w$, where w is a prime above v, and the diagram

$$\begin{array}{ccc} \mathcal{M} = M_w & \xrightarrow{\;i_w\;} & J_M \\ {\scriptstyle N_{\mathcal{M}/K_v}}\downarrow & & \downarrow{\scriptstyle N_{M/K}} \\ K_v & \xrightarrow{\;i_v\;} & J_K \end{array}$$

is commutative. By the 'variant" of 4.3 we conclude that

$$\psi_v(N_{\mathcal{M}/K_v}\mathcal{M}^*) \subset \psi_{L/K}N_{M/K} \subset G(L/M) \simeq G(L^v/\mathcal{M}),$$

6.3. We shall call $\psi_v : K_v^* \to G^v$ the *local Artin homomorphism*, or by its classical name: *norm residue homomorphism.* If $x = (x_v) \in J_K$, then we have

$$x = \lim_S \left\{\prod_{v \in S} i_v(x_v)\right\}$$

and consequently, by continuity, we have

$$\psi_{L/K}(x) = \prod_v \psi_v(x_v)$$

(this product is actually finite since if x_v is a v-unit and v is not ramified, then it is a norm of L^v/K_v). Thus knowledge of all the local Artin maps ψ_v is equivalent to knowledge of the global Artin map $\psi_{L/K}$. Classically, the local maps ψ_v were studied via the global theory and, in particular, were shown to depend only on the local extension L^v/K_v, and not on the global extension L/K from which they were derived. Nowadays one reverses the procedure, giving first a purely local construction (cf. Chapter VI) of maps $\theta_v : K_v^* \to G_v = G(L^v/K_v)$. We will take these maps θ_v from Serre and show that $\prod_v \theta_v$ satisfies the characterizing properties for ψ, in particular, that $\prod_v \theta_v(a) = 1$ for all $a \in K^*$ (see § 10).

The local theory tells us that the Main Theorem of 5.1 is true locally if we replace C_K by K_v^*, ψ by ψ_v and $G(L/K)$ by $G(L^v/K_v)$. In particular

$$K_v^*/NL^{v*} \simeq G(L^v/K_v)$$

and in this isomorphism the ramification groups correspond to the standard filtration of K_v^*/NL^{v*}. Going back to the global theory we get a complete description of prime decomposition in terms of idèle classes, even in the ramified case.

For the question of abelian and cyclic extensions with given local behaviour and the Grunwald-Wang theorem, see Artin-Tate notes Chapter 10, and Wang, "On Grunwald's Theorem", *Annals*, **51** (1950), pp. 471–484.

6.4. We can now give an apparently stronger statement of the reciprocity law formulated in 3.3.

RECIPROCITY LAW (Strong form). *Let L/K be abelian, and let S consist of the archimedean primes of K and those ramified in L. If an element $a \in K^*$ is a norm from L^v for all $v \in S$, then $F_{L/K}((a)^S) = 1$.*

For if $j_v(a)$ is a norm for $v \in S$ we can write $j_v(a) = N_{L^v/K_v}(b_v)$ for some $b_v \in L^v$. Then by Corollary 4.2

$$1 = \psi((a)^S).\prod_{v \in S} \psi_v(j_v(a)) = F_{L/K}((a)^S).\prod_{v \in S} \psi_v(N_{L^v/K_v}(b_v)) = F_{L/K}((a)^S),$$

by 6.2.

For the concrete description of the local Artin maps ψ_v by means of the norm residue symbols $(a, b)_v$ in case of Kummer extensions, and the application to the general n-th power reciprocity law, see exercise 2.

7. Cohomology of Idèles

7.1. L/K is a finite Galois extension (not necessarily abelian) with Galois group G. Write A_L for the adèle ring of L; then J_L is the group of invertible elements in $A_L = L \otimes_K A_K$, and G acts on $L \otimes_K A_K$ by $\sigma \mapsto \sigma \otimes 1$; so G acts on J_L.

However, we want to look at the action of G on the cartesian product structure of J_L. Suppose $x \in J_L$, then $x = (x_w)$, where w runs through $\mathfrak{M}_L$; $\sigma \in G$ induces $\sigma_w : L_w \to L_{\sigma w}$ (see 1.1) and $(\sigma x)_{\sigma w} = \sigma_w x_w$, that is, the diagrams

$$\begin{array}{ccc} L_w^* & \xrightarrow{\sigma_w} & L_{\sigma w}^* \\ {\scriptstyle i_w}\downarrow & & \downarrow{\scriptstyle i_{\sigma w}} \\ J_L & \xrightarrow{\sigma} & J_L \end{array} \qquad\qquad \begin{array}{ccc} L_w^* & \xrightarrow{\sigma_w} & L_{\sigma w}^* \\ {\scriptstyle j_w}\uparrow & & \uparrow{\scriptstyle j_{\sigma w}} \\ J_L & \xrightarrow{\sigma} & J_L \end{array}$$

commute. (Note that the image of L_w^* in J_L is not a G-invariant subgroup; the smallest such subgroup containing L_w^* is $\prod_{w/v} L_{w'}^*$.)

7.2. PROPOSITION. *Let $v \in \mathfrak{M}_K$ and $w_0 \in \mathfrak{M}_L$ with w_0 over v. Then there are mutually inverse isomorphisms*

$$H^r\Big(G, \prod_{w/v} L_w^*\Big) \underset{j_{w_0}\,.\,\mathrm{res}}{\overset{\mathrm{cores}\,.\,i_{w_0}}{\rightleftarrows}} H^r(G_{w_0}, L_{w_0}^*)$$

and

$$H^r\left(G, \prod_{w/v} U_w\right) \underset{j_{w_0}\,.\,\mathrm{res}}{\overset{\mathrm{cores}\,.\,i_{w_0}}{\rightleftarrows}} H^r(G_{w_0}, U_{w_0}),$$

where U_w denotes the group of units in L_w.

The assertions remain valid when H^r is replaced by $\hat{H}^r$.

The proof is immediate from Shapiro's lemma (see Chapter IV, § 4) in view of Proposition 1.2 of § 1.

Thus the cohomology groups $H^r(G_w, L_w^*)$ are canonically isomorphic for all w over v, so it is permissible to use the notation $H^r(G^v, (L^v)^*)$ for any one of these.

7.3. PROPOSITION. (a) $J_K \simeq J_L^G$, *the group of idèles of L left fixed by all elements of G.*

(b) $\hat{H}^r(G, J_L) \simeq \coprod_{v \in \mathfrak{M}_K} \hat{H}^r(G^v, (L^v)^*)$,

where $\coprod$ denotes the direct sum.

Proof. (a) is clear from Chapter II, § 19. To prove (b) we observe that

(1) $$J_L = \varinjlim_{S} J_{L,S}, \text{ where } J_{L,S} = \prod_{v \in S}\left(\prod_{w/v} L_w^*\right) \times \prod_{v \notin S}\left(\prod_{w/v} U_w\right)$$

and S is a finite set of primes of K containing all the ramified primes in L/K and the archimedean primes. The limit is taken over an increasing sequence of S with $\lim S = \mathfrak{M}_K$. The cohomology of finite groups commutes with direct limits, and any cohomology theory commutes with products, so it is enough to look at the cohomology of the various parts. By 7.2 and Chapter VI, § 1.4, $\prod_{v \notin S}\left(\prod_{w/v} U_w\right)$ has trivial cohomology if S contains all the ramified primes. Hence

$$\hat{H}^r(G, J_{L,S}) \simeq \prod_{v \in S} \hat{H}^r(G^v, (L^v)^*),$$

by 7.2. Let $S \to \mathfrak{M}_K$; we find

$$\hat{H}^r(G, J_L) \simeq \coprod \hat{H}^r(G^v, (L^v)^*).$$

7.4. COROLLARY.

(a) $H^1(G, J_L) = 0$.

(b) $H^2(G, J_L) \simeq \coprod_v \left(\frac{1}{n_v}\mathbf{Z}/\mathbf{Z}\right)$, *where $n_v = [L^v : K_v]$.*

Here, the determination of H^1 is just Hilbert's "Theorem 90" for the local fields (see Chapter V, § 2.6 and Chapter VI, § 1.4). The second part follows from the determination of the Brauer group of K_v in Chapter VI, § 1.6.

8. Cohomology of Idèle Classes (I), The First Inequality

We recollect the exact sequence $0 \to L^* \to J_L \to C_L \to 0$. The action of G on C_L is that induced by its action on J_L.

8.1. PROPOSITION. $C_K \simeq C_L^G$.

Proof. The above exact sequence gives rise to the homology sequence

$$0 \to H^0(G, L^*) \to H^0(G, J_L) \to H^0(G, C_L) \to H^1(G, L^*),$$

that is

$$0 \to K^* \to J_K \to C_L^G \to 0.$$

8.2. *Remark.* Our object in the abelian case is to define

$$\psi_{L/K}: C_K/N_{L/K}C_L \to G(L/K) = G.$$

By the Proposition above $C_K/N_{L/K}C_L = \hat{H}^0(G, C_L)$, and on the other hand $G = \hat{H}^{-2}(G, \mathbf{Z})$. Comparison with Chapter VI, § 2.1, suggests that the global theorem we want to prove about the cohomology of C_L is essentially the same as the local theorem Serre proves about the cohomology of L^*. This is in fact the case. Abstracting the common features, one gets the general notion of a "class formation". [cf. the Artin-Tate notes.]

We recollect that if G is cyclic and A a G-module the *Herbrand quotient* is defined by $h(G, A) = [H^2(G, A)]/[H^1(G, A)]$ if both these cardinalities $[H^2(G, A)]$ and $[H^1(G, A)]$ are finite (see Chapter IV, § 8).

8.3. THEOREM. *Let L/K be a cyclic extension of degree n. Then $h(G, C_L) = n$.*

Proof. We take a finite set S of primes of K so large that we can write $J_L = L^*.J_{L,S}$, where

$$J_{L,S} = \prod_{v \in S}\Big(\prod_{w/v} L_w^*\Big) \times \prod_{v \notin S}\Big(\prod_{w/v} U_w\Big).$$

More precisely, S is to include the archimedean primes of K, the primes of K ramified in L and all primes of K which "lie below" some primes whose classes generate the ideal class group of L. Denote by T the set of primes of L which are above primes in S. Hence

$$C_L \simeq J_L/L^* \simeq J_{L,S}/(L^* \cap J_{L,S}) = J_{L,S}/L_T$$

where $L_T = L^* \cap J_{L,S}$ is the set of T-units of L, i.e. those elements of L which are units of L_w for $w \notin T$. It follows that

$$h(C_L) = h(J_{L,S})/h(L_T),$$

if the right-hand side is defined (we note that it is impossible to use the above equation with the S missing, since then the right-hand side is not defined).

First of all we determine $h(J_{L,S})$. Since S contains all ramified primes, the group $\prod_{v \notin S}\Big(\prod_{v/w} U_w\Big)$ has trivial cohomology, as remarked in 7.3. Hence

$$h(J_{L,S}) = h\Big(\prod_{v \in S}\Big(\prod_{w/v} L_w^*\Big)\Big) = \prod_{v \in S} h\Big(\prod_{w/v} L_w^*\Big);$$

so by 7.2 we have $h(J_{L,S}) = \prod_{v \in S} n_v$, where the n_v are the local degrees (see Chapter VI, § 1.4). This was the "local part" of the proof.

The "global part" consists in determining $h(L_T)$; in order to prove that

$h(C_L) = n$ we have to show that $nh(L_T) = \prod_{v \in S} n_v$. We do this by constructing a real vector space, on which G operates, with two lattices such that one has Herbrand quotient $nh(L_T)$ and the other has quotient $\prod_{v \in S} n_v$.

Let V be the real vector space of maps $f: T \to \mathbf{R}$, so $V \simeq \mathbf{R}^t$, where $t = [T]$, the cardinality of T. We make G operate on V by defining $(\sigma f)(w) = f(\sigma^{-1}w)$ (so that $(\sigma f)(\sigma w) = f(w)$), for all $f \in V$, $\sigma \in G$ and $w \in T$.

Put $N = \{f \in V | f(w) \in \mathbf{Z}$ for all $w \in T\}$. Clearly, N spans V and is G-invariant. We have $N \simeq \prod_{v \in S}\left(\prod_{w/v} \mathbf{Z}_w\right)$, where $\mathbf{Z}_w \simeq \mathbf{Z}$ for all w, and the action of G on N is to permute the $\mathbf{Z}_w$ for all w over a given $v \in S$. Hence.

$$\hat{H}^r(G, N) \simeq \prod_{v \in S} \hat{H}^r\left(G, \prod_{w/v} \mathbf{Z}_w\right) \simeq \prod_{v \in S} \hat{H}^r(G^v, \mathbf{Z})$$

by Shapiro's lemma again. Therefore

$$h(N) = \prod_{v \in S} ([\hat{H}^0(G^v, \mathbf{Z})]/[H^1(G^v, \mathbf{Z})] = \prod_{v \in S} n_v.$$

Now define another lattice. Let λ be a map: $L_T \to V$ given by $\lambda(a) = f_a$, where $f_a(w) = \log |a|_w$ for all $w \in T$. The unit theorem (or at any rate its proof!) tells us that the kernel of λ is finite and its image is a lattice M^0 of V spanning the subspace $V^0 = \{f \in V | \sum f(w) = 0\}$.

Since the kernel of λ is finite, $h(L_T) = h(M^0)$ (see Chapter IV, § 8). Now $V = V^0 + \mathbf{R}g$, where g is defined by $g(w) = 1$ for all $w \in S_L$. We define the second lattice M as $M^0 + \mathbf{Z}g$. Then M spans V and both M^0 and $\mathbf{Z}g$ are invariant under G. Hence $h(M) = h(M^0).h(\mathbf{Z}) = nh(M^0) = nh(L_T)$.

Now M, N are lattices spanning the same vector space, so $h(N) = h(M)$ by Chapter IV, § 8. Hence $\prod_v n_v = h(N) = h(M) = nh(L_T)$, as required.

8.4. Consequence. *If L/K is cyclic of degree n, then*

$$[J_K/K^* N_{L/K} J_L] \geqslant n.$$

This inequality, called in the old days the second inequality, was always proved by non-analytic methods having their origins in Gauss' theory of the genera of quadratic forms, of which our present ones are an outgrowth. For us it is the *first inequality*, since the other inequality is deduced with the aid of this one.

8.5. Consequence. *If L/K is a finite abelian extension and D is a subgroup of J_K such that*

(a) $D \subset N_{L/K} J_L$,

(b) *K^*D is dense in J_K,*

then $L = K$.

Proof. We may suppose that L/K is cyclic, since if $L \supset L' \supset K$ and L'/K is cyclic, then $D \subset N_{L/K} J_L \subset N_{L'/K} J_{L'}$. Serre has proved that locally the norms $N_{L_w/K_v}L_w^*$ are open subsets of K_v^* which contain U_v for almost all v; so $N_{L/K}J_L$ (which is simply $\prod_w N_{L_w/K_v}L_w^*$) and $K^*N_{L/K}J_L$ are open, hence closed in J_K, and the latter is dense since its subset K^*D is dense. So it is the whole of J_K, that is, $[J_K/K^*N_{L/K}J_L] = 1$; so $n = 1$ by the previous consequence.

8.6. *Remark.* We emphasize that in the Galois case an element $x = (x_v) \in J_K$ is in $N_{L/K}J_L$ if and only if it is a local norm everywhere, i.e. $x_v \in N_{L^v/K_v}(L^v)^*$ for all $v \in \mathfrak{M}_K$.

8.7. CONSEQUENCE. *If S is a finite subset of $\mathfrak{M}_K$ and L/K is a finite abelian extension, then $G(L/K)$ is generated by the elements $F_{L/K}(v)$ for $v \notin S$* (i.e. *the map $F_{L/K}: I^S \to G(L/K)$ is surjective; cf.* 3.3).

Proof. Take G' as the subgroup of $G(L/K)$ generated by the $F_{L/K}(v)$ with $v \notin S$; let M be the fixed field of G'. For $v \notin S$, the $F_{L/K}(v)$ viewed in $G(M/K) \simeq G/G'$ are all trivial, so for all $v \notin S$, $M_w = K_v$ if $w \in \mathfrak{M}_M$ is over v. Trivially, every element of K_v^* is a norm of this extension.

Take $D = J_K^S$ (idèles with $x_v = 1$ for $v \in S$); every element of D is a local norm, i.e. $D \subseteq N_{M/K}J_M$. By the weak approximation theorem (see Chapter II, § 6) $K^*J_K^S$ is dense in J_K. So by 8.5 we have $M = K$ and G' is the whole of G.

8.8. COROLLARY. *If L is a non-trivial abelian extension of K, there are infinitely many primes v of K that do not split completely* (*i.e. for which $F_{L/K}(v) \neq 1$*).

For we have just seen that such primes exist outside of any finite set S.

9. Cohomology of Idèle Classes (II), The Second Inequality

Here we deduce what in the non-analytic treatment is the *second inequality*. This inequality can be proved very quickly and easily by analysis (see Chapter VIII, Theorem 5), and classically was called the first inequality. We give Chevalley's proof (*Annals*, 1940).

9.1. THEOREM. *Let L/K be a Galois extension of degree n, with Galois group G. Then*

(1) $[\hat{H}^0(G, C_L)]$ *and* $[\hat{H}^2(G, C_L)]$ *divide* n,
(2) $\hat{H}^1(G, C_L) = (0)$.

Proof. The proof will be in several steps.

Step 1. Suppose that the theorem has been proved when G is cyclic and n is prime. By the Ugly Lemma (see Chapter VI, § 1.5) it follows that $[\hat{H}^0(G, C_L)]$ divides n and $\hat{H}^1(G, C_L) = (0)$. Using this triviality of $\hat{H}^1$, it follows, again by the ugly lemma, that $[\hat{H}^2(G, C_L)]$ divides n.

Step 2. Now we assume that G is cyclic of prime order n; in this case we know that $\hat{H}^0 \simeq \hat{H}^2$ and by the first inequality 8.3 that $[\hat{H}^2] = n[\hat{H}^1]$; so it will be enough to show that $[\hat{H}^0(G, C_L)] = [C_K : N_{L/K} C_L]$ divides n.

We will make the one assumption that in the function field case n is not equal to the characteristic of K. (The other case is treated in the Artin-Tate notes, Chapter 6.)

Step 3. We now show that we may further assume that K contains the n-th roots of unity.

In fact, if we adjoin a primitive n-th root of unity ζ to K, we get an extension $K' = K(\zeta)$ whose degree m divides $(n-1)$, and so is prime to the prime n. So

$$\begin{array}{ccc} L' = LK' & \overset{n}{\text{———}} & K' = K(\zeta) \\ \Big| {\scriptstyle m} & & \Big| {\scriptstyle m} \\ L & \underset{n}{\text{———}} & K \end{array}$$

The degree of LK' over K' is n, and L and K' are linearly disjoint over K. So there is a commutative diagram with exact rows (we drop the subscripts since they are obvious):

$$\begin{array}{ccccccc} C_L & \longrightarrow & C_K & \longrightarrow & C_K/NC_L & \longrightarrow & 0 \\ \downarrow{\scriptstyle \text{Con}} & & \downarrow{\scriptstyle \text{Con}} & & \downarrow{\scriptstyle \text{Con}} & & \\ C_{L'} & \longrightarrow & C_{K'} & \longrightarrow & C_{K'}/NC_{L'} & \longrightarrow & 0 \\ \downarrow{\scriptstyle N} & & \downarrow{\scriptstyle N} & & \downarrow{\scriptstyle N} & & \\ C_L & \longrightarrow & C_K & \longrightarrow & C_K/NC_L & \longrightarrow & 0 \end{array}$$

Here Con is the Conorm map; and the composite map $N.\text{Con}$ is simply raising to the mth power (see Chapter II, § 19, for this and the definition of the Conorm map). The group C_K/NC_L is a torsion group in which each element has order n, for if $a \in C_K$, then a^n is a norm, i.e. $a^n \in NC_L$. Thus the map $N_{K'/K} \text{Con}_{K'/K} : C_K/NC_L \to C_K/NC_L$ is surjective since $(m, n) = 1$. Hence the map $N_{K'/K} : C_{K'}/NC_{L'} \to C_K/NC_L$ is surjective; so if $[C_{K'} : NC_{L'}]$ divides n so does $[C_K : NC_L]$.

Step 4. We are thus reduced to the case where n is a prime and K contains the n-th roots of unity. In fact we shall prove directly in this case the more general result:

Let K contain the n-th roots of unity and L/K be an abelian extension of prime exponent n, with say $G(L/K) = G \simeq (\mathbf{Z}/n\mathbf{Z})^r$. Then

(1) $$[C_K : N_{L/K} C_L] \text{ divides } [L : K] = n^r.$$

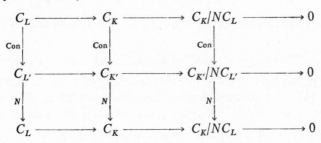

For although, as we have just seen, the case of arbitrary r does follow from the case $r = 1$, yet the method to be used does not simplify at all if one puts $r = 1$, and some of the constructions in the proof are useful for large r (see 9.2 and 9.5).

By Kummer Theory (see Chapter III), we know that $L = K(\sqrt[n]{a_1}, \ldots, \sqrt[n]{a_r})$ for some $a_1, a_2, \ldots, a_r \in K$. Take S to be a finite set of (bad) primes, such that

(2) (i) S contains all archimedean primes,
(ii) S contains all divisors of n,
(iii) $J_K = K^* J_{K,S}$ (by making S contain representatives of a system of generators for the ideal class group),
(iv) S contains all factors of the numerator and denominator of any a_i.

Condition (iv) just means that all the a_i are S-units, that is, they belong to $K_S = K \cap J_{K,S}$: they are units for all $v \notin S$.

Write $M = K(\sqrt[n]{K_S})$ for the field obtained from K by adjoining n-th roots of *all* S-units. By the unit theorem the group K_S has a finite basis, so this extension is finite, and M is unramified outside S by Kummer Theory and condition (ii). Now $M \supset L \supset K$ and

$$K_S = M^{*n} \cap K_S \supset L^{*n} \cap K_S \supset K^{*n} \cap K_S = K_S^n.$$

By Kummer theory with $[M : L] = n^t$, $[L : K] = n^r$ (given) and $[M : K] = n^s$ we have

(3) $[K_S : L^{*n} \cap K_S] = n^t, \quad [L^{*n} \cap K_S : K_S^n] = n^r \quad \text{and} \quad [K_S : K_S^n] = n^s$

respectively. We claim that $s = [S]$, the cardinality of S. By the unit theorem, there are $[S]-1$ fundamental units, and the roots of unity include the n-th roots; so $K_S \simeq \mathbf{Z}^{[S]-1} \times$(cyclic group of order divisible by n) and

(4) $$[K_S : K_S^n] = n^{[S]} = n^s, \quad \text{where } s = t+r.$$

We recall we want to show that $[C_K : N_{L/K} C_L]$ divides n^r, i.e. divides $[L^{*n} \cap K_S : K_S^n]$. So we need to show that $N_{L/K} C_L$ is fairly large—we have to provide a lot of norms.

If w is a prime of L above a $v \notin S$, then, since M/K is unramified outside S, the Frobenius map $F_{M/L}(w)$ is well-defined. By consequence 8.7, the $F_{M/L}(w)$ generate $G(M/L)$. Choose $w_1, \ldots, w_t$ so that $F_{M/L}(w_i)$ $(i = 1, \ldots, t)$ are a basis for $G(M/L)$, and let $v_1, \ldots, v_t$ be primes of K below them. We assert that $F_{M/L}(w_i) = F_{M/K}(v_i)$ $(i = 1, \ldots, t)$. (In fact, each of the v's is unramified, so $F_{M/K}(v_i)$ is defined). The M/K decomposition group $G_v(M/K)$ is a cyclic subgroup of $(\mathbf{Z}/n\mathbf{Z})^s$, so is either of prime order n or trivial. The w's were chosen so that the $F_{M/L}(w)$ were non-trivial, so the M/L decomposition group $G_w(M/L)$ is non-trivial; so the L/K decomposition group

$$G_v(L/K) \simeq G_v(M/K)/G_w(M/L)$$

is trivial, i.e. v splits completely in L (see Proposition 2). Therefore, $G_{v_i} = G_{w_i}$ and it is generated by the $F_{M/L}(v_i) = F_{M/K}(w_i)$.) Notice also that we have $L_{w_i} = K_{v_i}$ for all $i = 1, \ldots, t$.

Write $T = \{v_1, \ldots, v_t\}$. We claim that

$$(5) \qquad (L^*)^n \cap K_S = \{a \in K_S | a \in K_v^n \quad \text{for all } v \in T\}.$$

In fact, since $L_w = K_v$ for all $v \in T$ and w above v, it follows trivially that $L^{*n} \cap K_S$ is contained in the right-hand side. Conversely, if $a \in K_S$, then $\sqrt[n]{a} \in M$. If further $a \in K_v^n$ for all $v \in T$, then $\sqrt[n]{a} \in K_v$ for all $v \in T$ and so is left fixed by all $F_{M/K}(v) = F_{M/L}(w)$; these generate $G(M/L)$ so $\sqrt[n]{a} \in L$. This proves (5).

Let

$$(6) \qquad E = \prod_{v \in S} K_v^{*n} \times \prod_{v \in T} K_v^* \times \prod_{v \notin S \cup T} U_v,$$

where U_v is the set of v-units in K_v; so $E \subset J_{K,S \cup T}$. Also $E \subset N_{L/K} J_L$ (see Remark 8.6)—for every element of K_v^{*n} is a norm, since $K_v^*/NL_w^* \simeq G_v$ (see Chapter VI, § 2.1), which is killed by n; we have $K_v^* = L_w^*$ for all $v \in T$, and so all the elements of these K_v^* are norms, and the elements of U_v are all norms for v unramified (see Chapter VI, § 1.2, Prop. 1).

Now

$$[C_K/N_{L/K}C_L] = [J_K/K^*N_{L/K}J_L]$$

divides $[J_K : K^*E]$ because $E \subset N_{L/K}J_L$. The set S was chosen ((2)(iii)) so that

$$J_K = K^*J_{K,S} = K^*J_{K,S \cup T}$$

therefore $[C_K/N_{L/K}C_L]$ divides $[K^*J_{K,S \cup T} : K^*E]$. A general formula for indices of groups is

$$[CA : CB][C \cap A : C \cap B] = [A : B],$$

so to prove (1) it will be enough to show that

$$(7) \qquad [J_{K,S \cup T} : E]/[K_{S \cup T} : K \cap E] = n^r$$

(where $K_{S \cup T} = K^* \cap J_{K,S \cup T}$).

First, we calculate $[J_{K,S \cup T} : E]$.

$$J_{K,S \cup T} = \prod_{v \in S} K_v^* \prod_{v \in T} K_v^* \prod_{v \notin S \cup T} U_v,$$

so $[J_{K,S \cup T} : E] = \prod_{v \in S} [K_v^* : (K_v^*)^n]$, by (5). From Chapter VI, § 1.7 (cf. also the Artin-Tate notes, p. xii), we see that the "trivial action" Herbrand quotient $h(K_v^*) = n/|n|_v$ where $|\ |_v$ denotes the normed absolute value. But also $h(K_v^*) = [K_v^* : K_v^{*n}]/n$ because the n-th roots of unity are in K_v^*. This means that $[K_v^* : K_v^{*n}] = n^2/|n|_v$ and

$$(8) \qquad [J_{K,S \cup T} : E] = n^{2s} \prod_{v \in S} |n|_v^{-1} = n^{2s}, \text{ by the product formula}$$

since $|n|_v = 1$ if $v \notin S$.

We will also need in a moment the formula

$$(9) \qquad [U_v : U_v^n] = n/|n|_v.$$

which follows from the fact that $h(U_v) = 1/|n|_v$ (see Chapter VI, § 1.7).

By (8) we see that to prove (7), it will be enough to show that

$$(10) \qquad [K_{S \cup T} : K^* \cap E] = n^{2s-r} = n^{s+t}.$$

As in (4), replacing S by $S \cup T$, we have $[K_{S \cup T} : K_{S \cup T}^n] = n^{s+t}$, so it will be enough to show that $K^* \cap E = K_{S \cup T}^n$.

Trivially, $K^* \cap E \supset K_{S \cup T}^n$, so it remains to prove

$$(11) \qquad K^* \cap E \subset K_{S \cup T}^n,$$

and this will result from the following lemma.

9.2. Lemma. *Let K contain the n-th roots of unity. Let S be a subset of $\mathfrak{M}_K$ satisfying parts* (i), (ii), (iii) *of* (2) *in the above proof, and let T be a set of primes disjoint from S, and independent for K_S in the sense that the map $K_S \to \prod_{v \in T} U_v/U_v^n$ is surjective.*

Suppose that $b \in K^*$ is an n-th power in S, arbitrary in T, and a unit outside $S \cup T$. Then $b \in K^{*n}$.

Proof of Lemma. Consider the extension $K' = K(\sqrt[n]{b})$; it will be enough to deduce that $K' = K$. Put

$$D = \prod_{v \in S} K_v^* \times \prod_{v \in T} U_v^n \times \prod_{v \notin S \cup T} U_v;$$

by arguments similar to ones used before (see after (6)), $D \subset N_{K'/K} J_{K'}$. Therefore, by the first inequality in the form of consequence 8.5, in order to prove that $K' = K$ it is sufficient to prove that $K^* D = J_K$. But by hypothesis, the map $K_S \to \prod_{v \in T} (U_v/U_v^n) \simeq J_{K,S}/D$ is surjective. Hence $J_{K,S} = K_S D$, and $J_K = K^* J_{K,S} = K^* D$ as required.

To deduce (11) from the lemma, we have to check that T is independent for S in the sense of the lemma. Let H denote the kernel of the map $K_S \to \prod_{v \in T} (U_v/U_v^n)$. To prove that map is surjective it suffices to show that $(K_S : H) = \prod_{v \in T} (U_v : U_v^n)$. This latter product is just n^t by (9), because $|n|_v = 1$ for $v \in T$. On the other hand, by (5) we have $H = K_S \cap (L^*)^n$, and consequently $(K_S : H) = n^t$ by (3).

The proof of the theorem is now complete.

9.3. *Remark.* Even the case of the Lemma 9.2 with T empty is interesting. "*If S satisfies conditions* (i), (ii), (iii) *of* (2), *then an S-unit which is a local n-th power at all primes in S is an n-th power*".

9.4. Consequence. *If L/K is abelian with Galois group G, and there is an Artin map $\psi : \hat{H}^0(G, C_L) = C_K/NC_L \to G$, then ψ must be an isomorphism.*

In fact, consequence 8.7 of the first inequality already tells us that ψ has to be surjective; if now $[\hat{H}^0(G, C_L)] \leqslant [G]$, then ψ can only be an isomorphism!

9.5. CONSEQUENCE. (Extracted from the proof of Theorem 9.1.) *Let n be a prime and let K be a field, not of characteristic n, containing the n-th roots of unity. Let S be a finite set of primes of K satisfying the conditions* (i), (ii), (iii) *of* (2), *and let $M = K(\sqrt[n]{K_S})$. Then, if the reciprocity law holds for M/K, we have*

$$(12) \qquad K^* N_{M/K} J_M = K^* E, \text{ where } E = \prod_{v \in S} (K_v^*)^n \times \prod_{v \notin S} U_v.$$

Consider the case $L = M$ of the proof of 9.1 (so that T is empty, $t = 0$ and $s = r$). Then the E of that proof is as given in (12), and $E \subset N_{M/K} J_M$. By (7) with $L = M$, we have $[J_K : K^* E] = n^s = [M : K]$. On the other hand, if the reciprocity law holds, we know that

$$[C_K : N_{M/K} C_M] = [J_K : K^* N_{M/K} J_M] = n^s;$$

hence (12) must hold.

This result we put into the refrigerator; we will pull it out for the proof of the "existence theorem" in the final section § 12.

9.6. CONSEQUENCE. Let L/K be a finite (not necessarily abelian) Galois extension. Since $H^1(G, C_L) = 0$, the exact sequence $0 \to L^* \to J_L \to C_L \to 0$ gives rise to a very short exact sequence $0 \to H^2(G, L^*) \to H^2(G, J_L)$. Now $H^2(G, J_L) = \coprod_{v \in \mathfrak{M}_K} H^2(G^v, (L^v)^*)$, by Proposition 7.3, so there is an injection

$$(13) \qquad 0 \to H^2(G, L^*) \to \coprod_{v \in \mathfrak{M}_K} H^2(G^v, (L^v)^*).$$

We shall see later (from the fact that the arrow β_1 in diagram (9) of § 11 is an isomorphism, for example) that the image of this injection consists of those elements in the direct sum, the sum of whose local invariants is 0. We thus obtain a complete description of the structure of the group $H^2(G, L^*)$.

In terms of central simple algebras, (13) gives the *Brauer-Hasse-Noether Theorem, that a central simple algebra over K splits over K if and only if it splits locally everywhere.* In particular, if G is cyclic, $\hat{H}^2 \simeq \hat{H}^0$, and we have the *Hasse Norm Theorem:*

If $a \in K^*$, and L/K is cyclic, then $a \in N_{L/K} L^*$ if and only if $a \in N_{L^v/K_v} L^{v*}$ or all $v \in \mathfrak{M}_K$.

Specializing further, take G of order 2, so $L = K(\sqrt{b})$.

$$N_{L/K}(x + y\sqrt{b}) = x^2 - by^2,$$

so (if the characteristic is not 2) we deduce that a has the form $x^2 - by^2$ if and only if it has this form locally everywhere. It follows that *a quadratic form $Q(x, y, z)$ in three variables over K has a non-trivial zero in K if and only if it has a non-trivial zero in every completion of K.* Extending to n variables, we may obtain the *Minkowski-Hasse Theorem*, that a quadratic form has a zero if and only if it has a zero locally everywhere, see exercise 4.

One may consider the general problem, "if $a \in K^*$ and $a \in NL^{v*}$ for all v, is $a \in NL^*$?" Unfortunately, the answer is not always yes! (See 11.4.)

9.7. We return to the sequence (13). We write $H^2(L/K)$ for $H^2(G, L^*)$ and $H^2(L^v/K_v)$ for $H^2(G^v, L^{v*})$. Thus (13) becomes

$$0 \to H^2(L/K) \to \coprod_v H^2(L^v/K_v). \tag{13'}$$

Serre (Chapter VI, § 1.1, Theorem 3, Corollary 2) has determined $H^2(L^v/K_v)$; it is cyclic of order $n_v = [L^v : K_v]$, with a canonical generator. Thus

$$H^2(G, J_L) = \coprod_v H^2(L^v/K_v) \simeq \coprod_v \left(\frac{1}{n_v}\mathbf{Z}/\mathbf{Z}\right).$$

and

$$0 \to H^2(L/K) \to \coprod_v \left(\frac{1}{n_v}\mathbf{Z}/\mathbf{Z}\right).$$

If $\alpha \in \coprod_v H^2(L^v/K_v)$, or $\alpha \in H^2(L/K)$, we can find its local invariants $\mathrm{inv}_v(\alpha)$ (more precisely $\mathrm{inv}_v(j_v(\alpha))$, where j_v is the projection on the v-component of α), which will determine it precisely.

We are interested in the functorial properties of the map inv_v. Let $L' \supset L \supset K$ be finite Galois extensions with groups

$$G' = G(L'/K),$$

and

$$G = G(L/K) \simeq G'/H,$$

where $H = G(L'/L)$. If $\alpha \in H^2(G, J_L)$, then $\mathrm{infl}(\alpha) \in H^2(G', J_{L'})$ and

$$\mathrm{inv}_v(\mathrm{infl}\,\alpha) = \mathrm{inv}_v(\alpha). \tag{14}$$

Indeed, choosing a prime w' of L' above a prime w of L above v, one reduces this to the corresponding local statement for the tower $L'_{w'} \supset L_w \supset K_v$; cf. Chapter VI, § 1.1.

Thus nothing changes under inflation so we can pass in an invariant manner to the *Brauer group* of K, and get the *local invariants* for $\alpha \in \mathrm{Br}(K) = H^2(\bar{K}/K)$, where $\bar{K}$ is the algebraic closure of K (see Chapter VI, § 1), and more generally for

$$\alpha \in H^2(G_{\bar{K}/K}, J_{\bar{K}}) = \varinjlim_L H^2(G_{L/K}, J_L),$$

where $J_{\bar{K}} = \varinjlim_L J_L$, by definition, the limits being taken over all finite Galois extensions L of K; cf. Chapter V.

If now $\alpha \in H^2(G', J_{L'})$, then $\operatorname{res}^{G'}_H \alpha \in H^2(H, J_{L'})$ and

$$\operatorname{inv}_w(\operatorname{res}^{G'}_H \alpha) = n_{w/v} \operatorname{inv}_v(\alpha), \tag{15}$$

where $w \in \mathfrak{M}_L$ lies above $v \in \mathfrak{M}_K$ and $n_{w/v} = [L_w : K_v]$ (again one reduces immediately to the local case, for which see Chapter VI, § 1.1, or Serre's "Corps Locaux", Hermann, (1962), p. 175). Moreover, L/K need not be Galois here.

Finally we mention the result for corestriction, though we will not use it. Again, L/K need not be Galois. If $\alpha' \in H^2(H, J_{L'})$, then $\operatorname{cor}^{G'}_H \alpha' \in H^2(G', J_{L'})$ and

$$\operatorname{inv}_v(\operatorname{cor}^{G'}_H \alpha') = \sum_{w/v} \operatorname{inv}_w(\alpha'), \tag{16}$$

where the sum is over all primes $w \in \mathfrak{M}_L$ over $v \in \mathfrak{M}_K$ (see "Corps Locaux", p. 175).

9.8. Corollary. *Let $\alpha \in \operatorname{Br}(K)$ or $H^2(G(\bar{K}/K), J_{\bar{K}})$, where $\bar{K}$ is the separable algebraic closure of K. Let L be an extension of K in $\bar{K}$. Then $\operatorname{res}^{K}_{L}(\alpha) = 0$ if and only if $[L_w : K_v] \operatorname{inv}_v(\alpha) = 0$ for every w over v (this is only a finite condition, since almost all the $\operatorname{inv}_v(\alpha)$ are zero).*

In the case when L/K is Galois, there is an exact sequence

$$0 \longrightarrow H^2(L/K) \xrightarrow{\text{infl}} \operatorname{Br}(K) \xrightarrow{\text{res}} \operatorname{Br}(L),$$

and $\alpha \in H^2(L/K)$ if and only if the denominator of $\operatorname{inv}_v(\alpha)$ divides $[L_w : K_v]$ for all w over v.

10. Proof of the Reciprocity Law

10.1. Now let L/K be a finite abelian extension with Galois group G. We recall our discussion in § 6 on local symbols in which we noted that if a global Artin map existed we were able to reduce it to the study of local symbols and remarked that, conversely, if the local Artin maps are defined we could obtain a global Artin map. We propose to carry out this latter program here using the local Artin ("norm residue") maps defined in Chapter VI, § 2.2.

Let the local Artin maps be denoted by $\theta_v : K_v^* \to G^v$; we define a map

$$\theta : J_K \to G$$

by

$$\theta(x) = \prod_{v \in \mathfrak{M}_K} \theta_v(x_v), \quad x \in J_K.$$

This is a proper definition, since (by Chapter VI, § 2.3) $\theta_v(x_v) = F_{L^v/K_v}(v)^{v(x_v)}$ ($v(x_v)$ being the normalized valuation of x_v) when v is unramified, and $v(x_v) = 0$ if $x_v \in U_v$; so $\theta_v(x_v) = 1$ for all but finitely many v. (Indeed, even if L/K were an infinite extension, the product for $\theta(x)$ would be convergent.) It is clear that θ is a continuous map.

Take $S_0 \subseteq \mathfrak{M}_K$ as the set of archimedean primes plus the primes ramified in L/K; then $x \in J_K^{S_0}$ implies $\theta(x) = F((x)^{S_0})$. Thus, θ satisfies two of the conditions for an Artin map ((i) and (iii) of Corollary 4.2); the other condition ((ii) of 4.2) is that

$$\theta(a) = \prod_{v \in \mathfrak{M}_K} \theta_v(a) = 1 \quad \text{for all a} \in K^*.$$

So if we can prove this, we will have proved the reciprocity law.

10.2. To prove the reciprocity law, it will be convenient to state two related theorems, and to prove them both at once, gradually extending the cases for which they are true.

THEOREM A. *Every finite abelian extension L/K satisfies the reciprocity law, and the Artin map $\theta : J_K \to G(L/K)$ is given by $\theta = \prod_v \theta_v$.*

THEOREM B. *If $\alpha \in \mathrm{Br}(K)$, then* $\sum_{v \in \mathfrak{M}_K} \mathrm{inv}_v(\alpha) = 0$.

Remarks. After what has been said above, Theorem A has been whittled down to the assertion that

(1) $$\prod_{v \in \mathfrak{M}_K} \theta_v(a) = 1 \quad \text{for all } a \in K^*.$$

The sum of Theorem B is finite since $\mathrm{inv}_v(\alpha) = \mathrm{inv}_v(j_v . \alpha) = 0$ for all but finitely many α.

If $\alpha \in \mathrm{Br}(K)$, then $\alpha \in H^2(L/K)$ for some finite extension L/K, i.e. α is split by a finite extension of K.

Logically, the proof is in four main steps.

Step 1. Prove A for an arbitrary finite cyclotomic extension L/K.
Step 2. Deduce B for α split by a cyclic cyclotomic extension.
Step 3. Deduce B for arbitrary $\alpha \in \mathrm{Br}(K)$.
Step 4. Deduce A for all abelian extensions.

In practice, we first clarify the relation between Theorems A and B and deduce (step 2) that A implies B for cyclic extensions and (step 4) that B implies A for arbitrary abelian extensions. Then we prove Step 1 directly, and finally push through Step 3, by showing that every element of Br (K) has a cyclic cyclotomic splitting field.

10.3. *Steps 2 and 4. The relation between* A *and* B. A is about $\hat{H}^0$ and B is about H^2, so we need a lemma connecting them.

Let L/K be a finite abelian extension with Galois group G. Let χ be a character of G, thus $\chi \in \mathrm{Hom}(G, \mathbf{Q}/\mathbf{Z}) = H^1(G, \mathbf{Q}/\mathbf{Z})$, where $\mathbf{Q}/\mathbf{Z}$ is a trivial G-module. If $v \in \mathfrak{M}_K$, denote by χ_v the restriction of χ to the decomposition group G^v. Let δ be the connecting homomorphism

$$\delta : H^1(G, \mathbf{Q}/\mathbf{Z}) \to H^2(G, \mathbf{Z}).$$

If $x = (x_v) \in J_K$, let $\bar{x}$ be its image in $J_K/N_{L/K}J_L \simeq \hat{H}^0(G, J_L)$. Then the cup product (see Chapter IV, § 7) $\bar{x} . \delta\chi \in H^2(G, J_L)$.

LEMMA. *For each v we have*

$$\mathrm{inv}_v(\bar{x}.\delta\chi) = \chi_v(\theta_v(x_v)),$$

and so

$$\sum_v \mathrm{inv}_v(\bar{x}.\delta\chi) = \chi(\theta(x)).$$

Proof. We refer to Chapter VI, § 2.3. The projection $j_v: J_L \to (L^v)^*$ induces a map

$$j_v.\mathrm{res}^G_{G_v}: H^2(G, J_L) \to H^2(G_v, J_L) \to H^2(G_v, (L^v)^*),$$

and as restriction commutes with the cup product, so

$$\begin{aligned}\mathrm{inv}_v(\bar{x}.\delta\chi) &= \mathrm{inv}_v(j_v.\mathrm{res}^G_{G_v}(\bar{x}.\delta\chi))\\ &= \mathrm{inv}_v((j_v.\bar{x}).\delta\chi_v)\\ &= \mathrm{inv}_v(\bar{x}_v.\delta\chi_v)\\ &= \chi_v(\theta_v(x_v)),\end{aligned}$$

the final step coming from Chapter VI, § 2.3.

It follows immediately that

$$\chi(\theta(x)) = \chi\Big(\prod_v \theta_v(x_v)\Big) = \sum_v \chi_v(\theta_v(x_v)) = \sum_v \mathrm{inv}_v(\bar{x}.\delta\chi).$$

To check Step 4, apply the lemma with $x = a \in K^* \subseteq J_K$. Denote by $\tilde{a}$ the image of a in $\hat{H}^0(G, L^*)$. Then $\tilde{a}.\delta\chi \in \hat{H}^2(G, L^*) \subseteq \mathrm{Br}(K)$, as we need. The image of $\tilde{a}.\delta\chi$ in $H^2(G, J_L)$ is $\bar{a}.\delta\chi$, where $\bar{a}$ is the image of a in $\hat{H}^0(G, J_L)$, and by the above lemma, $\sum_v \mathrm{inv}_v(\bar{a}.\delta\chi) = \chi(\theta(a))$; so if Theorem B is true for all $\alpha \in \mathrm{Br}(K)$, it follows that $\chi(\theta(a)) = 0$, and since this is true for all χ, that $\theta(a) = 0$. This is Theorem A.

To check Step 2, take L/K cyclic. Choose χ as a generating character, i.e. as an injection of G into $\mathbf{Q}/\mathbf{Z}$. Then cupping with $\delta\chi$ gives an isomorphism $\hat{H}^0 \xrightarrow{\sim} H^2$, so every element of $H^2(L/K, L^*)$ is of the form $\tilde{a}.\delta\chi$. If Theorem A is true, then by the above lemma

$$\sum_v \mathrm{inv}_v(\bar{a}.\delta\chi) = \chi(\theta(a)) = 0$$

for all $a \in K^*$, which is Theorem B.

10.4. *Step 1.* (*Number Field Case.*) We want to prove that if L/K is a cyclotomic extension, then $\prod_v \theta_v(a) = 1$ for all $a \in K^*$.

Let L/K be a finite cyclotomic extension. Then we have $L \subset K(\zeta)$ for some root of unity ζ, and it will suffice to treat the case $L = K(\zeta)$ because of the compatibility of the local symbols θ_v relative to the extensions $(K(\zeta))^v/K_v$ and L^v/K_v; cf. Chapter VI, § 2.4.

Next we reduce to the case $K = \mathbf{Q}$. Suppose that $M = K(\zeta)$, with Galois group G'; define $L = \mathbf{Q}(\zeta)$, with Galois group G. Then $M = LK$, and there is a natural injection $i: G' \to G$ and norm map $N: J_K \to J_{\mathbf{Q}}$. The diagram

$$\begin{array}{ccc} J_K & \xrightarrow{\theta'} & G' \\ {\scriptstyle N_{K/\mathbf{Q}}}\downarrow & & \downarrow{\scriptstyle i} \\ J_{\mathbf{Q}} & \xrightarrow{\theta} & G \end{array}$$

(where $\theta' = \prod_v \theta'_v$, and $\theta = \prod_p \theta_p$) is commutative, since

$$(N_{K/\mathbf{Q}}x)_p = \prod_{v/p} N_{K_v/\mathbf{Q}_p} x_v$$

(see Chapter II, § 11, last display formula) and since the diagrams

$$\begin{array}{ccc} K_v & \longrightarrow & G'_v \\ {\scriptstyle N}\downarrow & & \downarrow{\scriptstyle i} \\ \mathbf{Q}_p & \longrightarrow & G_p \end{array}$$

are commutative whenever v is above p (see Chaper VI, § 2.1, cf. Proposition 3.1 above). Thus $i \circ \theta'(x) = \theta(N_{K/\mathbf{Q}}(x))$ for all $x \in J_K$ and so, in particular, $i \circ \theta'(a) = \theta(N_{K/\mathbf{Q}}(a))$ for all $a \in K$. If Theorem A is true for $L/\mathbf{Q}$, then $\theta(b) = 1$ for all $b \in \mathbf{Q}$, so $\theta'(a) = 1$ for all $a \in K$, because i is injective.

First Proof for $L/\mathbf{Q}$ cyclotomic. We know that the reciprocity law, in the sense of 3.8, holds for $L/\mathbf{Q}$ by computation (see 3.4), i.e. we have an admissible map $F: I^S \to G(L/\mathbf{Q}) = G$, for some S. Using the Chevalley interpretation (Proposition 4.1) we get an Artin map $\psi: J_{\mathbf{Q}} \to G$, and we obtain induced local maps $\psi_p: \mathbf{Q}_p^* \to G_p$ (see § 6). Using Proposition 4.3 we can pass to the limit and take L as the maximal cyclotomic extension $\mathbf{Q}^{\text{mc}}$ of $\mathbf{Q}$. This gives us local maps $\psi_p: \mathbf{Q}_p^{\text{mc}} \to G(\mathbf{Q}_p^{\text{mc}}/\mathbf{Q}_p)$, for all primes p. We want to show that these ψ_p's are the same as the θ_p's of Chapter VI, § 2.2; we do this by using the characterization given by Chapter VI, § 2.8, Proposition 3.

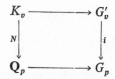

We have to check three things. Firstly, that $\mathbf{Q}_p^{\text{mc}}$ contains the maximal unramified extension $\mathbf{Q}_p^{\text{nr}}$ of $\mathbf{Q}_p$; this follows from Chapter I, § 7, Application. Secondly, if $\alpha \in \mathbf{Q}_p$, then $\psi_p(\alpha) \,|\, \mathbf{Q}_p = F^{v_p(\alpha)}$, where $v_p(\alpha)$ is the normalized valuation of α, and F the Frobenius element of $G(\mathbf{Q}_p^{\text{nr}}/\mathbf{Q}_p)$; this is clear. Thirdly, if $\mathcal{M}/\mathbf{Q}_p$ is a finite subextension in $\mathbf{Q}_p^{\text{mc}}$, and $\alpha \in N_{\mathcal{M}/\mathbf{Q}_p}\mathcal{M}^*$, then $\psi_p(\alpha)$ leaves $\mathcal{M}$ pointwise-fixed; this follows from Proposition 6.2. Hence $\psi_p = \theta_p$ for all finite primes p. We must not forget to check that ψ_∞ is the same as θ_∞ (see Chapter VI, § 2.9). By Proposition 6.2, ψ_∞ is a continuous homomorphism of $\mathbf{R}^*$ into $G_\infty = G(\mathbf{C}/\mathbf{R}) \simeq \{\pm 1\}$, and $\psi_\infty(N_{\mathbf{C}/\mathbf{R}}\mathbf{C}^*) = 1$. Hence ψ_∞ and θ_∞ induce maps of $\mathbf{R}^*/\mathbf{R}^*_+$ into $G(\mathbf{C}/\mathbf{R})$ and θ_∞ is onto, so we just have to check that ψ_∞ is onto—in other words, we have to check that ψ_∞ is not the null map.

$\mathbf{C} = \mathbf{R}(i)$, so consider the effect of ψ on $\mathbf{Q}(i) \supset \mathbf{Q}$; the only ramification is at 2 and ∞. Therefore

$$1 = \psi(-7) = \psi_2(-7)\psi_7(-7)\psi_\infty(-7) = \psi_7(7).\psi_\infty(-1),$$

since -7 is a 2-adic norm and so $\psi_2(-7) = 1$. Now $\psi_7(7)$ is the map $i \to i^7 = -i$, so $\psi_\infty(-1)$ is also the map $i \to -i$, i.e. is non-trivial.

Second Proof for $L/\mathbf{Q}$ cyclotomic. We may proceed entirely locally, without using our results of the early sections, but using the explicit local computation of the norm residue symbol in cyclotomic extensions, due originally to Dwork.

Let ζ be a root of unity; by Chapter VI, § 2.9

$$(1) \qquad \zeta^{\theta_\infty(x)} = \zeta^{\mathrm{sign}\,(x)}, \quad \text{for } x \in \mathbf{R}^*,$$

and by Chapter VI, § 3.1, if $x \in \mathbf{Q}_p^*$, $x = p^\nu u$, with u a unit in $\mathbf{Q}_p$ and ν an integer

$$(2) \qquad \zeta^{\theta_p(p^\nu u)} = \begin{cases} \zeta^{p^\nu}, & \text{when } \zeta \text{ has order prime to } p. \\ \zeta^{u^{-1}}, & \text{when } \zeta \text{ has } p\text{-power order.} \end{cases}$$

We need to check that $\prod_p \theta_p(a) = 1$ for all $a \in \mathbf{Q}^*$ and to do this it is sufficient to show that $\prod_p \theta_p(q) = 1$ for all primes $q > 0$, and that $\prod_p \theta_p(-1) = 1$. Furthermore, it is enough to consider the effect on ζ, an l-th power root of unity (l a prime). One checks explicitly that the effect is trivial, using the tables

$$\zeta^{\theta_p(-1)} = \begin{cases} \zeta^{-1}, & p = \infty \\ \zeta^{-1}, & p = l \\ \zeta, & p \neq l, \infty \end{cases}$$

$$\zeta^{\theta_p(q)} = \begin{cases} \zeta, & p = q = \\ \zeta, & p \neq l, p \neq q \text{ (including the case } p = \infty) \\ \zeta^{q^{-1}}, & p = l, p \neq q \\ \zeta^q, & p \neq l, p = q \end{cases}$$

(Since the Galois group is abelian, it does not matter in what order one applies the automorphisms $\theta_p(-1)$, resp. $\theta_p(q)$.)

10.5. *Step 3.* (*Number Field Case.*) It is enough to show that every element of Br (K) has a cyclic, cyclotomic splitting field. In other words, for every $\alpha \in$ Br (K), there is a cyclic, cyclotomic extension L/K such that for every

$v \in \mathfrak{M}_K$, the local degree $[L^v : K_v]$ is a multiple of the denominator of $\text{inv}_v(\alpha)$ (see Corollary 9.8). Now $\text{inv}_v(\alpha) = 0$ for all but a finite number of primes and so we need only prove the

LEMMA. *Given a number field K of finite degree over $\mathbf{Q}$, a finite set of primes S of K, and a positive integer m, there exists a cyclic, cyclotomic extension L/K whose local degrees are divisible by m at the non-archimedean primes v of S and divisible by 2 at real archimedean primes v of S (in other words, L is complex).*

Proof. It is sufficient to construct L in the case $K = \mathbf{Q}$ (multiply m by the degree $[K:\mathbf{Q}]$). Take r very large and q an odd prime. The extension $L(q) = \mathbf{Q}(\sqrt[q^r]{1})$ has a Galois group isomorphic to the direct sum of a cyclic group of order $(q-1)$ and cyclic group of order q^{r-1}, so has a subfield $L'(q)$ which is a cyclic cyclotomic extension of $\mathbf{Q}$ of degree q^{r-1}. Now

$$[L(q) : L'(q)] = q-1,$$

and so on localizing at a fixed prime $p \neq \infty$ of $\mathbf{Q}$ we have

$$[L(q)^{(p)} : L'(q)^{(p)}] \leqslant (q-1);$$

since $[L(q)^{(p)} : \mathbf{Q}_p] \to \infty$ as $r \to \infty$ (this follows for example from the fact that each finite extension of $\mathbf{Q}_p$ contains only a finite number of roots of unity), it follows that $[L'(q)^{(p)} : \mathbf{Q}_p] \to \infty$ as $r \to \infty$. Therefore, since $[L'(q)^{(p)} : \mathbf{Q}_p]$ is always a power of q, it is divisible by a sufficiently large power of q if we take r large enough.

Now let $q = 2$, and put $L(2) = \mathbf{Q}(\sqrt[2^r]{1})$ for r large. $L(2)$ has a Galois group isomorphic to the direct sum of a cyclic group of order 2 and a cyclic group of order 2^{r-2}. Let ζ be a primitive 2^r-th root of unity and set $\xi = \zeta - \zeta^{-1}$ and $L'(2) = \mathbf{Q}(\xi)$. The automorphisms of $\mathbf{Q}(\zeta)$ over $\mathbf{Q}$ are of the form $\sigma_\mu : \zeta \mapsto \zeta^\mu$ for μ odd, and $\sigma_\mu(\xi) = \zeta^\mu - \zeta^{-\mu}$. Since $\zeta^{2^{r-1}} = -1$, one sees that $\sigma_{-\mu+2^{r-1}}(\xi) = \sigma_\mu(\xi)$; since either μ or $-\mu + 2^{r-1}$ is $\equiv 1 \pmod 4$, this implies that the automorphisms of $\mathbf{Q}(\xi)/\mathbf{Q}$ are induced by those σ_μ where $\mu \equiv 1 \pmod 4$ and that they form a cyclic group of order 2^{r-2}. Also, since $\sigma_{-1}\xi = -\xi$, $\mathbf{Q}(\xi)$ is not real, and so its local degree at an infiinte real prime is 2.

Now $[L(2) : L'(2)] = 2$, and the same argument as above shows that for $p \neq \infty$ we can make $[L'(2)^{(p)} : \mathbf{Q}_p]$ divisible by as large a power of 2 as we like by taking r large enough.

If now the prime factors of m are $q_1, \ldots, q_n$ and possibly 2, then for large enough r the compositum of $L'(q_1), \ldots, L'(q_n)$ and possibly $L'(2)$ is a complex cyclic cyclotomic extension of $\mathbf{Q}$ whose local degree over $\mathbf{Q}_p$ is divisible by m for all p in a finite set S.

Cyclic cyclotomic extensions seem to be at the heart of all proofs of the general reciprocity law. We have been able to get away with a very trivial existence lemma for them, because we have at our disposal both cohomology and the local theory. In his original proof Artin used a more subtle lemma; see for example Lang, "Algebraic Numbers", Addison Wesley, 1964, p. 60. (But notice that the necessary hypothesis that $\mathfrak{p}$ be unramified is omitted from the statement there.)

We may prove the reciprocity law for function fields on the same lines, but the special role of "cyclic cyclotomic extensions" in the proof is taken over by "constant field extensions".

Step 3 goes through, if we replace "cyclic cyclotomic extension" by "constant field extension"; we have only to take for the L in the lemma the constant field extension whose degree is m times the least common multiple of the degrees of the primes in S.

For step 1, we check the reciprocity law directly for constant field extensions; in fact, if we denote by σ the Frobenius automorphism of $\bar{k}/k$, where k is the constant field of K, then for each prime v of K the effect of $F(v)$ on $\bar{k}$ is just $\sigma^{\deg v}$, where $\deg v = [k(v) : k]$ is the degree of v. Hence the effect on $\bar{k}$ of $\theta(a)$ is $\prod_v \sigma^{v(a) \deg v} = \sigma^{\sum v(a) \deg v} = \sigma^{\deg a} = 1$, since $\deg a = 0$ for all $a \in K^*$ (the number of zeros of an algebraic function a is equal to the number of poles).

11. Cohomology of Idèle Classes (III), The Fundamental Class

11.1 Let $E/L/K$ be finite Galois extensions of K; then we have an exact commutative diagram

$$\begin{array}{ccccccc}
 & & 0 & & 0 & & 0 \\
 & & \downarrow & & \downarrow & & \downarrow \\
0 & \longrightarrow & H^2(L/K, L^*) & \longrightarrow & H^2(L/K, J_L) & \longrightarrow & H^2(L/K, C_L) \\
 & & \downarrow & & \downarrow & & \downarrow \\
(1) \quad 0 & \longrightarrow & H^2(E/K, E^*) & \longrightarrow & H^2(E/K, J_E) & \longrightarrow & H^2(E/K, C_E) \\
 & & \downarrow & & \downarrow & & \downarrow \\
0 & \longrightarrow & H^2(E/L, E^*) & \longrightarrow & H^2(E/L, J_E) & \longrightarrow & H^2(E/L, C_E),
\end{array}$$

where we have written $H^2(L/K, L^*)$ for $H^2(G(L/K), L^*)$, etc. In this diagram, the vertical lines are inflation-restriction sequences; these are exact since $H^1(E/L, E^*) = (0)$ (Hilbert Theorem 90, Chapter V, § 2.6), $H^1(E/L, J_E) = (0)$ (Corollary 7.4) and $H^1(E/L, C_E) = (0)$ (Theorem 9.1) [see Chapter IV, § 5, Proposition 5]. The horizontal sequences are exact, and come from the sequence $0 \to L^* \to J_L \to C_L \to 0$, since again $H^1(L/K, C_L) = (0)$, etc.

We pass to the limit and let $E \to \bar{K}$, where $\bar{K}$ is the algebraic closure of K, to obtain the new commutative diagram

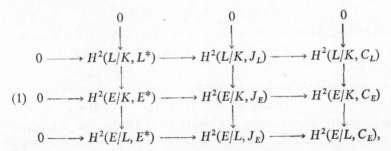

$$
\begin{array}{ccccccc}
 & & 0 & & 0 & & 0 \\
 & & \downarrow & & \downarrow & & \downarrow \\
0 & \longrightarrow & H^2(L/K, L^*) & \xrightarrow{\gamma_1} & H^2(L/K, J_L) & \xrightarrow{\varepsilon_1} & H^2(L/K, C_L) \\
 & & \downarrow & & \downarrow & & \downarrow \\
(2)\quad 0 & \longrightarrow & H^2(K, \bar{K}^*) & \xrightarrow{\gamma_2} & H^2(K, J_{\bar{K}}) & \xrightarrow{\varepsilon_2} & H^2(K, C_{\bar{K}}) \\
 & & \downarrow & & \downarrow & & \downarrow \\
0 & \longrightarrow & H^2(L, \bar{K}^*) & \xrightarrow{\gamma_3} & H^2(L, J_{\bar{K}}) & \xrightarrow{\varepsilon_3} & H^2(L, C_{\bar{K}}),
\end{array}
$$

where we have written $H^2(K, \bar{K}^*)$ for $H^2(G(\bar{K}/K), \bar{K}^*)$, etc. Certain of the maps with which we shall be concerned below have been labelled in the diagram.

11.2. We are going to enlarge the above commutative diagram.

For the Galois extension L/K we have the map

$$\text{inv}_1 = \sum_v \text{inv}_v : H^2(L/K, J_L) \to \mathbf{Q}/\mathbf{Z},$$

and Theorem B of 10.2 tells us that the sequence

$$(3) \qquad 0 \longrightarrow H^2(L/K, L^*) \xrightarrow{\gamma_1} H^2(L/K, J_L) \xrightarrow{\text{inv}_1} \mathbf{Q}/\mathbf{Z}$$

is a complex.†

Since $\text{inv}_v(\text{infl}\,\alpha) = \text{inv}_v(\alpha)$ for all $\alpha \in H^2(L/K, J_L)$ (see 9.7, (14)), we have a map $\text{inv}_2 : H^2(K, J_{\bar{K}}) \to \mathbf{Q}/\mathbf{Z}$ such that the diagram

$$
(4) \qquad
\begin{array}{ccc}
H^2(L/K, J_L) & \xrightarrow{\text{inv}_1} & \mathbf{Q}/\mathbf{Z} \\
\text{infl}\downarrow & & \downarrow i \\
H^2(K, J_{\bar{K}}) & \xrightarrow{\text{inv}_2} & \mathbf{Q}/\mathbf{Z}
\end{array}
$$

is commutative, where i is the identity map. Furthermore, the sequence

$$(5) \qquad 0 \longrightarrow H^2(K, \bar{K}^*) \xrightarrow{\gamma_2} H^2(K, J_{\bar{K}}) \xrightarrow{\text{inv}_2} \mathbf{Q}/\mathbf{Z}$$

is a complex.

In a similar manner we have a complex

$$(6) \qquad 0 \longrightarrow H^2(L, \bar{K}^*) \xrightarrow{\gamma_3} H^2(L, J_{\bar{K}}) \xrightarrow{\text{inv}_3} \mathbf{Q}/\mathbf{Z}.$$

But now, $\text{inv}_w(\text{res}\,\alpha) = n_{w/v}\,\text{inv}_v(\alpha)$, where $\alpha \in H^2(K, J_{\bar{K}})$ and w is a prime of L over v of K, and $n_{w/v} = [L_w : K_v]$ (see § 9.7, (15)). Thus we have the commutative diagram

$$
(7) \qquad
\begin{array}{ccc}
H^2(K, J_{\bar{K}}) & \xrightarrow{\text{inv}_2} & \mathbf{Q}/\mathbf{Z} \\
\text{res}\downarrow & & \downarrow n \\
H^2(L, J_{\bar{K}}) & \xrightarrow{\text{inv}_3} & \mathbf{Q}/\mathbf{Z},
\end{array}
$$

as the sum of the local degrees $\sum_{w/v} n_{w/v} = n = [L : K]$.

† i.e. the image of each map is in the kernel of the next.

Now let Image of $\varepsilon_2 = \operatorname{Im} \varepsilon_2$ in $H^2(K, C_{\bar{K}})$ be denoted by $H^2(K, C_{\bar{K}})_{\mathrm{reg}}$ and $\operatorname{Im} \varepsilon_3$ by $H^2(L, C_{\bar{K}})_{\mathrm{reg}}$. It follows that we have a map β_2 (resp. β_3) induced by inv_2 (resp. inv_3) of $H^2(K, C_{\bar{K}})_{\mathrm{reg}}$ into $\mathbf{Q}/\mathbf{Z}$ (resp. $H^2(L, C_{\bar{K}})_{\mathrm{reg}}$ into $\mathbf{Q}/\mathbf{Z}$). Thus for $a \in H^2(K, C_{\bar{K}})_{\mathrm{reg}}$, we have $\beta_2(a) = \mathrm{inv}_2(b)$, where $\varepsilon_2(b) = a$ (this is independent of the choice of b). We have now explained the two lower layers in diagram (9) below.

We define

$$\text{(8)} \qquad H^2(L/K, C_L)_{\mathrm{reg}} = \{a \in H^2(L/K, C_L) \mid \mathrm{infl}\, a \in H^2(K, C_{\bar{K}})_{\mathrm{reg}}\}.$$

Then $n\beta_2\, \mathrm{infl}\, a = 0$, and so β_2 induces a homomorphism

$$\beta_1 : H^2(L/K, C_L)_{\mathrm{reg}} \to \frac{1}{n}\mathbf{Z}/\mathbf{Z}$$

such that

$$\beta_1(a) = \beta_2(\mathrm{infl}\, a).$$

If $a = \varepsilon_1 b$ with $b \in H^2(L/K, J_L)$ then

$$\beta_1(a) = \beta_2(\mathrm{infl}\, b) = \mathrm{inv}_2(\mathrm{infl}\, b) = \mathrm{inv}_1(b).$$

(Note the difference in construction of β_1 and β_2; the point is that $H^2(L/K, C_L)_{\mathrm{reg}} \supset \operatorname{Im} \varepsilon_1$ but they will not in general be equal.)

We put all the information from (3)–(8) into (2) to obtain a new commutative (three-dimensional) diagram

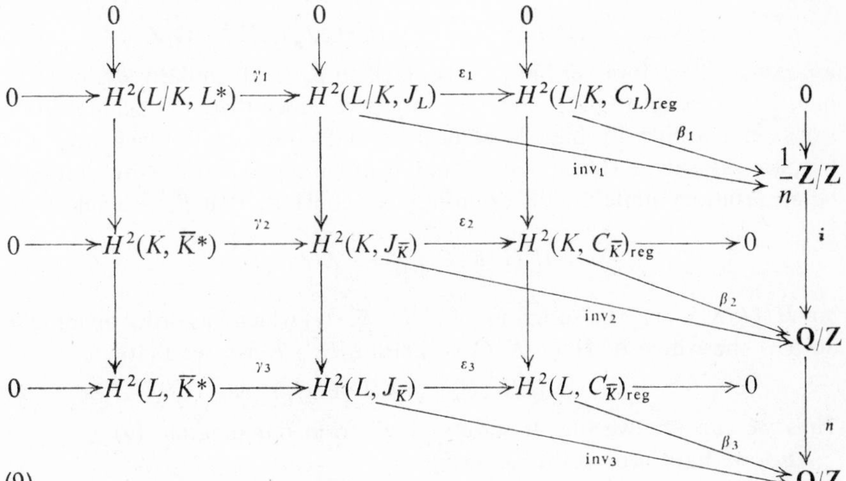

(9)

in which i is the inclusion map, n is multiplication by n and the "bent" sequences are *complexes*, and the horizontal and vertical sequences are exact.

11.2. (*bis*) We propose to show that

$$H^2(K, C_{\bar{K}})_{\text{reg}} = H^2(K, C_{\bar{K}}) \simeq \mathbf{Q}/\mathbf{Z}. \tag{10}$$

Now Im (inv_1) in $\frac{1}{n}\mathbf{Z}/\mathbf{Z}$ is the subgroup $\frac{1}{n_0}\mathbf{Z}/\mathbf{Z}$, where n_0 is the lowest common multiple of all the local degrees of L/K, by Corollary 7.4, and so since Im $\beta_1 \supset (\text{inv}_1)$ we have the inequalities

$$n \geqslant [H^2(L/K, C_L)] \geqslant [H^2(L/K, C_L)_{\text{reg}}] \geqslant [\text{Im}\,\beta_1] \geqslant [\text{Im}\,(\text{inv}_1)] = n_0,$$

by the second inequality, Theorem 9.1. It follows that *if* $n = n_0$ for this particular finite extension L/K, *then* we have equality throughout, so that β_1 is bijective and the sequence

$$0 \longrightarrow H^2(L/K, L^*) \xrightarrow{\gamma_1} H^2(L/K, J_L) \xrightarrow{\text{inv}_1} \mathbf{Q}/\mathbf{Z} \tag{11}$$

is *exact* (for if $0 = \text{inv}_1\,(b) = \beta_1 \varepsilon_1 b$, then $\varepsilon_1 b = 0$, and $b \in \text{Im}\,\gamma_1$).

Now if L/K is a finite cyclic extension, then $n = n_0$ because the Frobenius elements $F_{L/K}(v)$, whose orders are equal to the local degrees n_v, generate the cyclic group $G(L/K)$ by Consequence 8.7. So if, in particular, the extension L/K is cyclic cyclotomic, then (11) is an exact sequence. But the Lemma of § 10.5 says that the groups $H^2(K, \bar{K}^*)$ and $H^2(K, J_{\bar{K}})$ are the unions (of the isomorphic images under inflation) of the groups $H^2(L/K, L^*)$ and $H^2(L/K, J_L)$ respectively, where L runs over all cyclic cyclotomic extensions of K. Consequently, in our commutative diagram (9) the complexes

$$0 \longrightarrow H^2(K, \bar{K}^*) \xrightarrow{\gamma_2} H^2(K, J_{\bar{K}}) \xrightarrow{\text{inv}_2} \mathbf{Q}/\mathbf{Z}$$

and

$$0 \longrightarrow H^2(L, \bar{K}^*) \xrightarrow{\gamma_3} H^2(L, J_{\bar{K}}) \xrightarrow{\text{inv}_3} \mathbf{Q}/\mathbf{Z}$$

are exact. Therefore ker (inv_2) = ker (ε_2), so β_2 (and similarly β_3) must be injective maps into $\mathbf{Q}/\mathbf{Z}$. They are surjective, since there exist finite extensions with arbitrarily high local degrees and consequently even inv_2 and inv_3 are surjective. Hence both β_2 and β_3 are bijective maps. Now, letting L be an arbitrary finite Galois extension, we conclude that β_1 is a bijection:

$$H^2(L/K, C_L)_{\text{reg}} \simeq \frac{1}{n}\mathbf{Z}/\mathbf{Z};$$

but $H^2(L/K, C_L)_{\text{reg}}$ is a subgroup of $H^2(L/K, C_L)$ which has order dividing n. So it is the whole of $H^2(L/K, C_L)$. Letting $L \to \bar{K}$ we see that

$$H^2(L/K, C_{\bar{K}})_{\text{reg}} = H^2(L, C_{\bar{K}}).$$

Thus we can remove the subscripts "reg" from our diagram (9).

Also, we have proved the following

RESULT. *$H^2(L/K, C_L)$ is cyclic of order n, and it has a canonical generator $u_{L/K}$ with invariant $\frac{1}{n}$, i.e.* $\text{inv}_1\,(u_{L/K}) = \frac{1}{n}$.

This element $u_{L/K}$ is called the *fundamental class* of the extension L/K. It was first exhibited by Weil (see the discussion in 11.6 below). The complete determination of the structure of $H^2(L/K, C_L)$ is due to Nakayama. He and Hochschild were the first to give a systematic cohomological treatment of class field theory; see G. Hochschild and T. Nakayama "Cohomology in Class Field Theory", *Annals*, 1952, and the references contained therein.

The two lower layers of diagram (9) and the vertical arrows between them make sense for an arbitrary finite separable extension L/K of finite degree n, and in this more general case, that much of the diagram is still commutative, because the argument showing the commutativity of (7) did not require L/K to be Galois. Using this, and replacing L by K', we see that if $L \supset K' \supset K$ with L/K Galois, then restricting $u_{L/K}$ from L/K to L/K' gives the fundamental class $u_{L/K'}$.

11.3. *Applications.* The results we have obtained show that the idèle classes constitute a class formation. In particular (cf. Chapter IV, § 10) the cup product with the fundamental class $u_{L/K}$ gives isomorphisms

$$\hat{H}^r(G(L/K), \mathbf{Z}) \simeq \hat{H}^{r+2}(G(L/K), C_L),$$

for $-\infty < r < \infty$, such that for $L \supset K' \supset K$ with L/K Galois the diagrams

$$(12)\qquad \begin{array}{ccc} \hat{H}^r(G,\mathbf{Z}) & \simeq & \hat{H}^{r+2}(G,C_L) \\ \text{res}\downarrow & & \text{res}\downarrow \\ \hat{H}^r(G',\mathbf{Z}) & \simeq & \hat{H}^{r+2}(G',C_L) \end{array} \qquad \text{and} \qquad \begin{array}{ccc} \hat{H}^r(G,\mathbf{Z}) & \simeq & \hat{H}^{r+2}(G,C_L) \\ \text{cor}\uparrow & & \text{cor}\uparrow \\ \hat{H}^r(G',\mathbf{Z}) & \simeq & \hat{H}^{r+2}(G',C_L) \end{array}$$

are commutative, where $G = G(L/K)$ and $G' = G(L/K')$.

Case $r = -2$. There is a canonical isomorphism (see Chapter IV, § 3)

$$G(L/K)^{\text{ab}} \to C_K/N_{L/K}C_L,$$

which is inverse to the Artin map. Using this as a *definition* in the local case, Serre deduced the formula $\text{inv}\,(\bar{a}.\delta\chi) = \chi(\theta(a))$ in Chapter VI, § 2.3; we have proved the formula in the global case, so one can reverse the argument. (The isomorphism $G^{\text{ab}} \simeq H^{-2}(G, \mathbf{Z})$ is to be chosen in such a manner that for $\chi \in \text{Hom}\,(G, \mathbf{Q}/\mathbf{Z}) \simeq H^1(G, \mathbf{Q}/\mathbf{Z})$ and $\sigma \in G$, we have $\chi.\sigma = \chi(\sigma)$ upon identifying $\frac{1}{n}\mathbf{Z}/\mathbf{Z}$ with $H^{-1}(G, \mathbf{Q}/\mathbf{Z})$ as usual.)

Reversing the horizontal arrows in (12), with $r = -2$, and letting $L \to \bar{K}$, we obtain the commutative diagrams

$$(13)\qquad \begin{array}{ccc} C_K & \xrightarrow{\psi} & G(K^{\text{ab}}/K) \\ \text{con}\downarrow & & \downarrow V \\ C_{K'} & \xrightarrow{\psi'} & G((K')^{\text{ab}}/K') \end{array} \qquad \text{and} \qquad \begin{array}{ccc} C_K & \xrightarrow{\psi} & G(K^{\text{ab}}/K) \\ N\uparrow & & \uparrow \\ C_{K'} & \xrightarrow{\psi'} & G((K')^{\text{ab}}/K'), \end{array}$$

where the ψ's are the Artin maps and V is the "Verlagerung†". The right-hand

† Called the "transfer" in Chapter IV, § 6, *Note* after Prop. 7.

diagram expresses the so-called *translation theorem*, and in fact results also directly from 4.3, which in turn came from an almost obvious property 3.2 of the Frobenius automorphisms $F(v)$. The commutativity of the left-hand diagram (13) can also be proved by a straightforward but somewhat more complicated computation with the Frobenius automorphisms which was first made by Artin in connection with the "principal ideal theorem" (see exercise 3, and Serre, "Corps Locaux", p. 130).

Case $r = -3$. This leads to an isomorphism used by Roquette in Chapter IX, § 2.

11.4. *Application to the Cohomology of* L^*. The general idea is to determine the cohomology of L^* from a knowledge of the cohomology of the idèles and the idèle classes.

Let L/K be a finite extension, with Galois group G. Then the exact sequence $0 \to L^* \to J_L \to C_L \to 0$ gives an exact sequence

$$\to \hat{H}^{r-1}(G, J_L) \xrightarrow{g} \hat{H}^{r-1}(G, C_L) \to \hat{H}^r(G, L^*) \xrightarrow{f} \hat{H}^r(G, J_L) \to \dots$$

in which the kernel of f is isomorphic to the cokernel of g. We know

$$\hat{H}^{r-1}(G, J_L) = \coprod_{v \in \mathfrak{M}_K} \hat{H}^{r-1}(G^v, L^{v*}) = \coprod_{v \in \mathfrak{M}_K} \hat{H}^{r-3}(G^v, \mathbf{Z}).$$

(see Proposition 7.3), and

$$\hat{H}^{r-1}(G, C_L) = \hat{H}^{r-3}(G, \mathbf{Z});$$

so the kernel of

$$f : \hat{H}^r(G, L^*) \to \coprod \hat{H}^r(G^v, L^{v*})$$

is isomorphic to the cokernel of

$$g_1 : \coprod \hat{H}^{r-3}(G^v, \mathbf{Z}) \to \hat{H}^{r-3}(G, \mathbf{Z}).$$

It is easy to see that the map g_1 is given by

$$g_1\Big(\sum_v z_v\Big) = \sum_v \operatorname{cor}_G^{G_v} z_v.$$

Using the fundamental duality theorem in the cohomology of finite groups, which states that the cup product pairing

$$\hat{H}^r(G, \mathbf{Z}) \times \hat{H}^{-r}(G, \mathbf{Z}) \to \hat{H}^0(G, \mathbf{Z}) \approx \mathbf{Z}/n\mathbf{Z}$$

is a perfect duality of finite groups, one sees that the cokernel of g_1 is the dual of the kernel of the map

$$h : \hat{H}^{3-r}(G, \mathbf{Z}) \to \prod_v \hat{H}^{3-r}(G^v, \mathbf{Z})$$

which is defined by $(h(z))_v = \operatorname{res}_{G_v}^{G}(z)$ for all $v \in \mathfrak{M}_K$.

Case $r = 0$.

$$\operatorname{Ker} f = \left(\frac{a \mid a \in K^*, \ a \text{ is a local norm everywhere}}{a \mid a \in K^*, \ a \text{ is a global norm}}\right),$$

and coker g is dual to $\ker\big(H^3(G, \mathbf{Z}) \xrightarrow{\text{res}} \prod_v H^3(G^v, \mathbf{Z})\big)$. For example, if

$G = G^v$ for some v, then this is an injection, so local norms are global norms. If G is cyclic, then $H^3(G, \mathbf{Z}) \approx H^1(G, \mathbf{Z}) = 0$, so local norms are global norms and we recover Hasse's theorem, 9.6. On the other hand, if for instance G is the Vierergruppe, it is possible that G^v is always one of the subgroups of order 2, so $\hat{H}^3(G^v, \mathbf{Z}) = 0$ but $H^3(G, \mathbf{Z}) = \mathbf{Z}/2\mathbf{Z}$. Explicitly, we can consider $\mathbf{Q}(\sqrt{13}, \sqrt{17})/\mathbf{Q}$; here $\left(\frac{13}{17}\right) = \left(\frac{17}{13}\right) = 1$, and the extension is unramified at 2 because $13 \equiv 17 \equiv 1 \pmod 4$, so all the decomposition groups are cyclic. Thus the set of elements of K^* which are local norms everywhere is not the same as the set of elements of K^* which are global norms (see exercise 5).

Case r = 3. $H^3(G, L^*)$ is cyclic of order n/n_0, the global degree divided by the lowest common multiple of the local degrees, generated by $\delta u_{L/K}$ ($\delta : H^2(C_L) \to H^3(L^*)$), the "Teichmüller 3-class". This can be killed by inflation (replace L by a bigger L' so that the n_0 for L' is divisible by n); so $H^3(\bar{K}/K, \bar{K}^*) = 0$.

For a more precise description of the situation, announced at the Amsterdam Congress (*Proc.* II,66-67), see Tate: "The cohomology groups of tori in finite galois extensions of number fields", *Nagoya Math. J.* **27** (1966), 709–719.

Group Extensions. Consider extensions $M/L/K$, where L/K is Galois with group G, and M/K is Galois with group E and M is a class field over L with abelian Galois group A. So $1 \to A \to E \to G \to 1$ is exact. By the Artin isomorphism $A \simeq C_L/N_{M/L}C_M$ (see Theorem A of 10.2 and Consequence 9.4). We want to know about E.

11.5. THEOREM. (i) *Let* $\sigma \in E$ *have image* $\bar{\sigma} \in G$. *Let* $x \in C_L$; *then* $\psi(\bar{\sigma}x) = \sigma\psi(x)\sigma^{-1}$, *where* ψ: $C_L \to A$ *is the Artin map.*

(ii) *Let* $v \in H^2(G, A)$ *be the class of the group extension* E; *then* $v = \psi_*(u_{L/K})$, *where* ψ_* *is the map:* $H^2(G, C_L) \to H^2(G, A)$ *induced by* $\psi : C_L \to A$, *and where* $u_{L/K}$ *is the fundamental class for* L/K.

It is straightforward to see (i). As usual in such cases the situation becomes clearer if we consider an arbitrary field isomorphism $\sigma : M \to M'$ rather than an automorphism. Denoting σL by L' and the restriction of σ to L by $\bar{\sigma}$, we have the picture

$$\begin{array}{ccc} M & \xrightarrow{\ \sigma\ } & M' \\ | & & | \\ L & \xrightarrow{\ \bar{\sigma}\ } & L', \end{array}$$

and by transporting the structure of M/L to M'/L' we see that, if $x \in C_L$ and $y \in M$, then $(\psi'(\bar{\sigma}x))(\sigma y) = \sigma(\psi(x)(y))$.

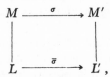

(ii) is non-trivial; Šafarevič did the local case ("On Galois Groups of P-adic Fields", *Doklady*, 1946), but it is really a general theorem about class formations (see Artin-Tate notes, p. 246). We do not prove it here, and will not make any use of the result in these notes.

11.6. Before the structure of $H^2(G, C_L)$ was known, Weil ("Sur la Théorie du Corps de Classes", *J. Math. Soc. Japan*, **3** (1951), 1–35) looked at this situation from the opposite point of view. Taking M to be L^{ab}, the maximal abelian extension of K (so that now $A = G(L^{ab}/L)$ is a profinite abelian group), Weil asked himself whether there was a group extension $\mathscr{E}$ of $G = G(L/K)$ by C_L which fits into a commutative diagram of the sort

$$\begin{array}{ccccccccc} 1 & \longrightarrow & C_L & \longrightarrow & \mathscr{E} & \longrightarrow & G & \longrightarrow & 1 \\ & & \downarrow{\scriptstyle \psi_L} & & \downarrow{\scriptstyle W} & & \downarrow{\scriptstyle \mathrm{id}} & & \\ 1 & \longrightarrow & A & \longrightarrow & E & \longrightarrow & G & \longrightarrow & 1, \end{array} \tag{14}$$

where $E = G(L^{ab}/K)$, and if so, to what extent was it unique? In the function field case, ψ_L is for all practical purposes an isomorphism, and the existence of such a diagram is obvious. Moreover, in that case, the group-theoretical transfer map V (Verlagerung) from $\mathscr{E}$ to C_L (which has its image in C_K) gives a commutative diagram

$$\begin{array}{ccc} \mathscr{E} & \xrightarrow{V} & C_K \subset C_L \\ \downarrow{\scriptstyle W} & & \downarrow{\scriptstyle \psi_K} \\ E & \longrightarrow & E^{ab}, \end{array} \tag{15}$$

as follows from the commutativity of the left-hand diagram (13). Inspired by the case of function fields, Weil proved that also in the number field case a diagram (14) did indeed exist, and was essentially uniquely determined by the condition that (15) (together with its analogues when K is replaced by an arbitrary intermediate field K' between K and L) should be commutative. In particular, the class $u \in H^2(G, C_L)$ of such an extension $\mathscr{E}$ was unique, and that is the way the fundamental class was discovered.

Nowadays one can proceed more directly, simply constructing $\mathscr{E}$ as a group extension of G by C_L corresponding to the fundamental class $u_{L/K}$, and interpreting the unicity as reflecting the fact that $H^1(G, C_L) = 0$ (cf. Artin-Tate, Ch. 14).

The kernel of the map $W: \mathscr{E} \to E$ is the connected component D_L of C_L. As Weil remarks, the search for a Galois-like interpretation of $\mathscr{E}$ (or even a "natural" construction, without recourse to factor systems, of a group $\mathscr{E}$ furnished with a "natural" map $W: \mathscr{E} \to E$) seems to be one of the fundamental problems of number theory.

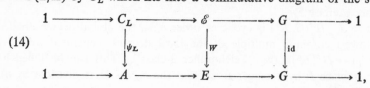

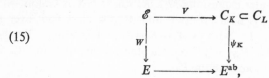

In support of the idea that $\mathscr{E}$ behaves like a Galois group, Weil also describes how to attach L-series to characters χ of unitary representations of $\mathscr{E}$. These L-series of Weil generalize simultaneously Hecke's L-series "mit Grössencharakteren" (which are obtained from representations which factor through C_K via the arrow V in (15)) and Artin's "non-abelian" L-series (which are obtained from representations which factor through E, or in particular through $G \simeq E/A$, via the arrow W in (15)). (The intersection of Hecke's and Artin's L-series are those of Weber obtained from representations of $E^{ab} \simeq C_K/D_K$, i.e. from ordinary congruence characters.) Using Brauer's theorem on group characters, Weil shows that his L-series can be expressed as products of (positive or negative) integral powers of Hecke L-series, and are therefore meromorphic.

12. Proof of the Existence Theorem

We still have to prove the Existence Theorem (D) of 5.1. Our proof, more traditional than that used by Serre in Chapter VI, works just as well in the local case.

If H is an open subgroup of C_K of finite index $[C_K : H]$, we say temporarily that H is *normic* if and only if there is an abelian extension L/K such that $H = N_{L/K} C_L$. The existence theorem asserts that every open subgroup H of finite index in C_K is normic. (We have already shown that if L/K is abelian, then $N_{L/K} C_L$ is an open subgroup of C_K of finite index; in fact the normic subgroups are just the inverse images of the open subgroups of $G(K^{ab}/K)$ under the Artin map $\psi_k : C_K \to G(K^{ab}/K)$.)

First, two obvious remarks: If $H_1 \supset H$, and H is normic, then H_1 is normic (the field L corresponding to H has a subfield L_1 corresponding to H_1). If H_1, H_2 are normic, so is $H_1 \cap H_2$ (take as the field the compositum $L_1 L_2$).

Next, we go to 9.5 in order to prove

Key Lemma. *Let n be a prime, and K a field not of characteristic n containing the n-th roots of unity. Then every open subgroup H of index n in C_K is normic.*

Proof. In fact, suppose H is open in C_K with $[C_K : H] = n$. Let H' be the inverse image of H in J_K. Then H' is open in J_K, so there is a finite set $S \subset \mathfrak{M}_K$ such that $H' \supset \prod_{v \in S} (1) \times \prod_{v \notin S} U_v = U^S$. Furthermore, H is of index n in C_K, so $H' \supset J_K^n$. Therefore $H' \supset \prod_{v \in S} K^{*n} \times \prod_{v \notin S} U_v = E$, say. Thus $H = H'/K^* \supset EK^*/K^*$, and from consequence 9.5, it follows that H is normic.

If L is an extension of K, there is a norm map $N : C_L \to C_K$; conversely, if we start with $H \subset C_K$ we get a subgroup $N^{-1}(H) \subset C_L$.

Lemma. *If L/K is cyclic and $H \subset C_K$, and if $N_{L/K}^{-1}(H) \subset C_L$ is normic for L, then H is normic for K.*

Proof. Write H' for $N_{L/K}^{-1}(H)$ and let M/L be the class field of H'. We claim that M is abelian over K, and $N_{M/K}C_M \subset H$, so H is normic. That $N_{M/K}C_M \subset H$ is clear, since N is transitive; the difficulty is to show that M/K is abelian.

(In point of fact, if something is the norm group from a non-abelian extension, then it is already the norm group from the maximal abelian sub-extension (see exercise 8). But this has not been proved here—if it had, we would not need L/K to be cyclic, and we would be already finished with the proof of the lemma.)

M/K is a Galois extension since H' is invariant under $G(L/K)$. The Galois group E of M/K is a group extension, $0 \to A \to E \to G \to 1$; since $E/A \simeq G$ is cyclic, it is enough to show that $A = G(M/L)$ is in the centre of E.

We can use the first part of Theorem 11.5. Let ψ be the Artin map $C_L \to A$. To show that A is in the centre, it is enough to check that

$$\psi(x) = \sigma\psi(x)\sigma^{-1} = \psi(\sigma x)$$

for all $x \in C_L$ and $\sigma \in E$. Now $\psi : C_L \to A$ has kernel H', so we want to check that $\sigma x/x \in H'$, which is clear since $N(\sigma x/x) = 1$.

Proof of the Theorem. (In the function field case we can only treat the case in which the index is prime to the characteristic; for the general case, see Artin-Tate, p. 78.)

We use induction on the index of H. If the index is 1 everything is clear.

Now let n be a prime dividing the index. Adjoin the n-th roots of unity to K to get K', and replace H by $H' = N_{K'/K}^{-1}(H)$. By the last lemma, it suffices to consider H'. The index of H' divides the index of H; we can assume $(C_{K'} : H') = (C_K : H)$, otherwise H' is normic by induction hypothesis.

So n divides $(C_{K'} : H')$. Take H_1' so that $H_1' \supset H$ and $(C_{K'} : H') = n$. By the above Key Lemma, H_1' is normic. Let L be its class field, i.e. $H_1' = N_{L/K'}C_L$. Put $H'' = N_{L/K'}^{-1}(H')$. Then

$$[C_L : H''] < [C_{K'} : H'] = [C_K : H].$$

(For $C_L/H'' \xrightarrow{N_{L/K'}} C_{K'}/H'$ is an injection, whose image is H_1'/H', properly contained in $C_{K'}/H'$.)

Hence H'' is normic by induction hypothesis; L/K' is cyclic, so we can apply the above lemma again; so H' is normic.

List of Symbols

The numbering refers to the section of this Chapter where the symbol was first used.

Note (i) $[A]$ is the cardinality of the set A.
(ii) "$\supset$" denotes inclusion with the possibility of equality.

1.1. K, K^* (non-zero elements of K)
$G(L/K)$, G
$v, v_1 \ldots; w, w_1, \ldots$
$\mathfrak{O}_v$, $\mathfrak{O}_w$
$\mathfrak{P}_v$
K_v, L_w
G_w

1.2. $\mathfrak{M}_K$

2.1. $k(v)$
Nv

2.2. $F_{L/K}(v)$
S

3.1. I^S

3.2. $N_{K'/K}$
$(a)^S$

4. J_K, J_K^S
$(x)^S$

4.1. ψ
C_K
$(x)_S$
U^S

4.2. $\psi_{L/K}$
$\mathrm{Im}\, \psi$

5.1. Norm group

5.5. $\hat{\mathbf{Z}}$

5.7. $\mathbf{Q}^{\mathrm{mc}}$, $\mathbf{R}_+^*$

6.1. ψ_v

7.1. w/v, $\prod_{w/v}$

7.2. G^v
L^v

7.3. $\coprod$
$J_{K,S}$, $S \subset \mathfrak{M}_K$
$J_{L,S}$, $S \subset \mathfrak{M}_K$
N_v

8.1. $h(G, A)$, $h(A)$
S-units $= K_S$

9.1. Conorm = Con

9.7. inv_v
inv_v (infl)
inv_v (res)
inv_v (cor)
Br (K)

10.1. θ_v, θ Artin maps.

10.3. ., cup-product
G^{ab}

CHAPTER VIII

Zeta-Functions and L-Functions

H. HEILBRONN

The object of this Chapter is to study the distribution of prime ideals in various algebraic number fields, the principal results being embodied in several so-called "density theorems" such as the Prime Ideal Theorem (Theorem 3) and Čebotarev's Theorem (Section 3). As in the study of the distribution of rational primes, L-series formed with certain group characters play an important part in such investigations.

Much of what we have to say goes back to the early decades of this century and is described in Hasse's "Bericht über neuere Untersuchungen und Probleme aus der Theorie der algebraischen Zahlenkörper" (Hasse 1926, 1927 and 1930), henceforward to be referred to as Hasse's Bericht.

1. Characters

Throughout, let k be a finite extension of $\mathbf{Q}$, of degree ν. Let S denote a set consisting of the infinite primes (archimedean valuations) of k together with a finite number of other primes (non-archimedean valuations) of k. S is sometimes referred to as the *exceptional* set.

In slight modification of earlier notation, an idèle x of k will be written as

$$x = (x_{\mathfrak{p}_1}, \ldots, x_{\mathfrak{p}_a}; x_{\mathfrak{p}_{a+1}}, \ldots, x_{\mathfrak{p}_b}; x_{\mathfrak{p}_{b+1}}, \ldots),$$

where $\mathfrak{p}_1, \ldots, \mathfrak{p}_a$ are the infinite primes, $\mathfrak{p}_{a+1}, \ldots, \mathfrak{p}_b$ are the finite primes of S, and the remaining $\mathfrak{p}_i$ are the primes not in S. Let J denote the idèle group.

By a character ψ of the idèle class group we understand a homomorphism from J into the unit circle of the complex plane satisfying

(1) $\psi(x) = 1$ if $x \in k^*$ (i.e. $x_\mathfrak{p} = x$ for all $\mathfrak{p}$);
(2) $\psi(x)$ is continuous on J (in the idèle topology);
(3) $\psi(x) = 1$ if $x_\mathfrak{p} = 1$ for $\mathfrak{p} \in S$ and $|x_\mathfrak{p}|_\mathfrak{p} = 1$ for $\mathfrak{p} \notin S$.

As was pointed out in Chapter VII, "Global Class Field Theory", §4, ψ generates a character of the ideal group I^S (the free abelian group on the set of all $\mathfrak{p} \notin S$) in the following way:

Let

$$\mathfrak{a} = \prod_{i>b} \mathfrak{p}_i^{\alpha_i} \qquad (\alpha_i \in \mathbf{Z})$$

be a general element of I^S (so that almost all the exponents α_i are 0). For each $i > b$, let π_i be an element of k with $|\pi_i|_{\mathfrak{p}_i} < 1$ and maximal. With $\mathfrak{a}$ we associate the idèle $x^{\mathfrak{a}}$ having

$$(x^{\mathfrak{a}})_{\mathfrak{p}_i} = \begin{cases} 1, & i = 1, 2, \ldots, b, \\ \pi_i^{\alpha_i}, & i = b+1, \ldots; \end{cases}$$

then we define

$$\chi(\mathfrak{a}) = \psi(x^{\mathfrak{a}}).$$

We observe that although $x^{\mathfrak{a}}$ is not unique, $\chi(\mathfrak{a})$ is, nevertheless, well-defined in view of property (3) above. Clearly χ is a multiplicative function in the sense that for all ideals $\mathfrak{a}, \mathfrak{b}$ coprime with S,

$$\chi(\mathfrak{a}\mathfrak{b}) = \chi(\mathfrak{a})\chi(\mathfrak{b}).$$

Any ideal character χ defined in this way is called a Grössencharacter, and such characters were first studied by Hecke (1920) and later, in the idèle setting, by Chevalley (1940).

Let S, S' be two exceptional sets and χ, χ' characters of $I^S, I^{S'}$ respectively. We say that χ and χ' are *co-trained* if $\chi(\mathfrak{a}) = \chi'(\mathfrak{a})$ whenever both $\chi(\mathfrak{a}), \chi'(\mathfrak{a})$ are defined. This definition determines an equivalence relation† among characters. In the equivalence class of χ there is a unique χ' corresponding to the least possible exceptional set S' (S' being the intersection of all exceptional sets corresponding to the characters co-trained with χ); we refer to this character χ' as the *primitive* character co-trained with χ.

The principal character χ_0 of I^S is defined by $\chi_0(\mathfrak{a}) = 1$ for all $\mathfrak{a} \in I^S$. The principal characters form a co-trained equivalence class, and the primitive member of this class is 1 for all non-zero finite ideals.

We shall now look more closely into the structure of a character of the ideal group I^S, with a view to describing the important class of Hilbert and Dirichlet characters.

We can write each idèle x in the form

$$x = \prod_{\mathfrak{p}} x(\mathfrak{p})$$

where each factor $x(\mathfrak{p})$ is the idèle defined by

$$x(\mathfrak{p})_{\mathfrak{p}_i} = \begin{cases} x_{\mathfrak{p}_i}, & \mathfrak{p} = \mathfrak{p}_i \\ 1, & \mathfrak{p} \neq \mathfrak{p}_i. \end{cases}$$

† To prove the transitivity of the relation it suffices to show that if $\psi(y) = 1$ for all idèles y for which $y_{\mathfrak{p}_i} = 1$, $i = 1, 2, \ldots, m$, then $\psi(x) = 1$ for all idèles x. However, for any $\varepsilon > 0$ there is an $\alpha \in k^*$ such that

$$|\alpha - x_{\mathfrak{p}_i}|_{\mathfrak{p}_i} < \varepsilon, \qquad i = 1, 2, \ldots, m,$$

by the Chinese Remainder theorem and thus $\psi(x) = \psi(\alpha^{-1}x)$ tends to 1 as $\varepsilon \to 0$.

Then

$$\psi(x) = \prod_{\mathfrak{p}} \psi_{\mathfrak{p}}(x),$$

where $\psi_{\mathfrak{p}}$ is a character of J defined by

$$\psi_{\mathfrak{p}}(x) = \psi(x(\mathfrak{p}))$$

and is referred to as a *local component* of ψ (Chevalley, 1940). We note that $\psi_{\mathfrak{p}}$ is continuous and satisfies (3). We first follow up some consequences of the continuity of ψ.

Let $\mathcal{N}$ be a neighbourhood of 1 containing no subgroup of $\psi(J)$ except 1. By continuity of ψ, there exists a neighbourhood $\mathcal{N}'$ of 1 in J, say

$$|x_{\mathfrak{p}} - 1|_{\mathfrak{p}} < \varepsilon_{\mathfrak{p}}, \qquad \mathfrak{p} \in E, \tag{1.1}$$

$$|x_{\mathfrak{p}}|_{\mathfrak{p}} = 1, \qquad \mathfrak{p} \notin E, \tag{1.2}$$

where E is some finite set of valuations, such that

$$\psi(\mathcal{N}') \subset \mathcal{N}.$$

We choose $\mathcal{N}'$ first to make the set E minimal, and then to make the $\varepsilon_{\mathfrak{p}}$'s maximal; so that for the finite $\mathfrak{p}$ in E we have $\varepsilon_{\mathfrak{p}} \leqslant 1$. For finite $\mathfrak{p}$, (1.1) is now equivalent to saying that $x_{\mathfrak{p}} \in 1 + \mathfrak{p}^{\mu_{\mathfrak{p}}}$ where $\mu_{\mathfrak{p}}$ is a positive integer. But since $1 + \mathfrak{p}^{\mu_{\mathfrak{p}}}$ is a group, so is $\psi_{\mathfrak{p}}(1 + \mathfrak{p}^{\mu_{\mathfrak{p}}})$, whence $\psi_{\mathfrak{p}}(1 + \mathfrak{p}^{\mu_{\mathfrak{p}}}) = 1$, and this holds for no smaller integer than $\mu_{\mathfrak{p}}$. We write

$$\mathfrak{f}_{\chi} = \prod_{\substack{\mathfrak{p}\ \mathrm{finite} \\ \mathfrak{p} \in E}} \mathfrak{p}^{\mu_{\mathfrak{p}}}$$

and we refer to $\mathfrak{f}_{\chi}$ as the *conductor* of the character χ derived from ψ. If $\mathfrak{p}$ is finite and belongs to E, (1.1) implies, by virtue of (3), that $\mathfrak{p} \in S$. Moreover, if $\mathfrak{p}$ is finite and not in E, (1.2) shows that it is not necessary, in view of (3), to include $\mathfrak{p}$ in S. Thus the finite $\mathfrak{p}$ in E are just those non-archimedean primes in the exceptional set of the primitive character co-trained with χ.

Let $\mathfrak{m}$ be a given integral ideal of k and let χ be any character such that $\mathfrak{f}_{\chi} | \mathfrak{m}$. Then if $\mathfrak{a} = (\alpha)$ where $\alpha \equiv 1 \pmod{\mathfrak{m}}$,

$$\chi(\mathfrak{a}) = \psi(1, \ldots, 1; 1, \ldots, 1; \alpha, \alpha, \ldots)$$

$$= \psi(\alpha^{-1}, \ldots, \alpha^{-1}; \alpha^{-1}, \ldots, \alpha^{-1}; 1, 1, \ldots$$

by (1),

$$= \psi(\alpha^{-1}, \ldots, \alpha^{-1}; 1, \ldots, 1; 1, 1, \ldots$$

since $\alpha^{-1} \in 1 + \mathfrak{p}^{\mu_{\mathfrak{p}}}$ for finite $\mathfrak{p} \in S$. Hence

$$\chi(\mathfrak{a}) = \prod_{\mathfrak{p} \in S_0} \psi_{\mathfrak{p}}(\alpha^{-1})$$

where S_0 is the set of archimedean primes.

We now restrict attention to those characters χ for which $\psi_{\mathfrak{p}}(J)$ is a discrete sub-set of the unit circle for all $\mathfrak{p} \in S_0$. Consider a particular $\mathfrak{p} \in S_0$. There exists an integer m such that

$$\psi_{\mathfrak{p}}(x^m) = 1 \qquad \text{for all } x \in J,$$

and, in particular, for all $x \in k^*$. The completion $k_{\mathfrak{p}}$ is $\mathbf{R}$ or $\mathbf{C}$ according as $\mathfrak{p}$ is real or complex, with each x of k^* mapped onto the $\mathfrak{p}$-conjugate $x_{\mathfrak{p}}$ of x. However, a homomorphic mapping of $\mathbf{C}^*$ into the unit circle and having finite order must map $\mathbf{C}^*$ onto 1 and similarly, a homomorphic map of $\mathbf{R}^*$, of finite order, into the unit circle either maps $\mathbf{R}^*$ onto 1 or maps $\mathbf{R}^*$ onto ± 1 by $x \to \operatorname{sgn} x$. Thus, if $\mathfrak{p}$ is complex, $\psi_{\mathfrak{p}}$ is identically 1, and if $\mathfrak{p}$ is real $\psi_{\mathfrak{p}}$ is either identically 1 or is ± 1; in the latter case, for $x \in k^*$ we have

$$\psi_{\mathfrak{p}}(x) = \begin{cases} 1, & x^{(\mathfrak{p})} > 0, \\ -1, & x^{(\mathfrak{p})} < 0. \end{cases}$$

If $x^{(\mathfrak{p})} > 0$ for all real $\mathfrak{p} \in S_0$, x is said to be *totally positive* and we write $x \gg 0$. Thus, if ψ has discrete infinite components, χ is a character determined by the subgroup of totally positive principal ideals $\equiv 1 \pmod{\mathfrak{m}}$. Such a character is called a *Dirichlet character modulo* $\mathfrak{m}$; if $\mathfrak{m} = 1$, χ is called a *Hilbert character*.

Conversely, we shall now show that any character χ of the ideal group I^S which is 1 on the subgroup $H^{(\mathfrak{m})}$ of totally positive principal ideals congruent 1 modulo $\mathfrak{m}$ (where S consists of the archimedean primes together with the primes dividing $\mathfrak{m}$) arises in this way from an idèle class character ψ with exceptional set S. Let χ be such a character, and let χ^*, χ_1 be the restrictions of χ to the group A^S of principal ideals coprime with $\mathfrak{m}$, and to the group $B^{(\mathfrak{m})}$ of principal ideals $\equiv 1 (\text{mod } \mathfrak{m})$ respectively. Then $\chi_1(\alpha)$ is determined by the signs of the real conjugates of α. We extend this definition to all elements α of k^* in the obvious way. Then we write $\chi_2 = \chi^* \chi_1^{-1}$; clearly χ_2 is a character of A^S equal to 1 on $B^{(\mathfrak{m})}$.

We define ψ corresponding to χ by stages. For any idèle x, and each $\mathfrak{p}$ not in S, define

$$\psi_{\mathfrak{p}}(x) = \chi(\mathfrak{p}^{v_{\mathfrak{p}}}) \qquad \text{where}\dagger\ \mathfrak{p}^{v_{\mathfrak{p}}} \| x_{\mathfrak{p}}. \tag{1.3}$$

This part of the definition ensures that ψ satisfies (3).

We next consider together all the finite primes of S, that is, all $\mathfrak{p} \in S - S_0$. We choose $y \in k^*$ such that $y \equiv x_{\mathfrak{p}} \pmod{\mathfrak{p}^{\nu_{\mathfrak{p}}}}$ for each $\mathfrak{p} \in S - S_0$, where $\mathfrak{p}^{\nu_{\mathfrak{p}}} \| \mathfrak{m}$ (this is possible by the Chinese Remainder Theorem). We then define

$$\prod_{\mathfrak{p} \in S - S_0} \psi_{\mathfrak{p}}(x) = \chi_2^{-1}(y) \tag{1.4}$$

for those idèles x having $|x_{\mathfrak{p}}|_{\mathfrak{p}} = 1$ for all $\mathfrak{p} \in S - S_0$.

† $\mathfrak{p}^v \| x_{\mathfrak{p}}$ means that $x_{\mathfrak{p}} \in \mathfrak{p}^v - \mathfrak{p}^{v+1}$.

To complete the definition of ψ on this sub-set of J, we need to define $\psi_{\mathfrak{p}}(x)$ for $\mathfrak{p} \in S_0$. For real $\mathfrak{p} \in S_0$ let $\chi^{(\mathfrak{p})}$ be the character on k^* defined by $\chi^{(\mathfrak{p})}(\alpha) = \operatorname{sgn} \alpha_{\mathfrak{p}}$. Then χ_1 is the product of some sub-set of these characters $\chi^{(\mathfrak{p})}$, say

$$\chi_1 = \prod_{\mathfrak{p} \in T} \chi^{(\mathfrak{p})} \qquad (T \subset S_0) \tag{1.5}$$

and we define $\psi_{\mathfrak{p}}(x)$ for $\mathfrak{p} \in S_0$ by

$$\psi_{\mathfrak{p}}(x) = \begin{cases} \chi^{(\mathfrak{p})}(x_{\mathfrak{p}})^{-1} & \text{if } \mathfrak{p} \in T \\ 1 & \text{if } \mathfrak{p} \in S_0 - T, \end{cases} \tag{1.6}$$

provided $x_{\mathfrak{p}} \in k^*$, and we extend this definition to $k_{\mathfrak{p}}^*$ by continuity.

We postpone defining ψ for those idèles x for which $|x_{\mathfrak{p}}|_{\mathfrak{p}} \neq 1$ for some $\mathfrak{p} \in S - S_0$.

It is clear from our construction that ψ is multiplicative. We proceed to verify that ψ satisfies (1) and (2), (3) having been satisfied by construction. Consider (1) first. Then

$$\prod_{\mathfrak{p} \in S_0} \psi_{\mathfrak{p}}(\alpha) = \chi_1^{-1}(\alpha)$$

by (1.5) and (1.6),

$$\prod_{\mathfrak{p} \in S - S_0} \psi_{\mathfrak{p}}(\alpha) = \chi_2^{-1}(\alpha)$$

by (1.4), and

$$\prod_{\mathfrak{p} \notin S} \psi_{\mathfrak{p}}(\alpha) = \chi(\alpha) = \chi^*(\alpha)$$

by (1.3). Since $\chi^* = \chi_1 \chi_2$, ψ is seen to be 1 on k^*.

It remains to consider (2). But $\psi(x) = 1$ if

$$\begin{aligned} |x_{\mathfrak{p}} - 1|_{\mathfrak{p}} &< 1, & \mathfrak{p} &\in S_0, \\ x_{\mathfrak{p}} &\in 1 + \mathfrak{p}^{u_{\mathfrak{p}}}, & \mathfrak{p} &\in S - S_0, \\ |x_{\mathfrak{p}}|_{\mathfrak{p}} &= 1, & \mathfrak{p} &\notin S, \end{aligned}$$

and this is an open set in the idèle topology.

Finally, we need to extend the definition of ψ to idèles x for which, for some $\mathfrak{p} \in S - S_0$, $|x_{\mathfrak{p}}|_{\mathfrak{p}} \neq 1$. Let x be such an idèle and suppose that $\mathfrak{p} \in S - S_0$. If $\mathfrak{p}^{u_{\mathfrak{p}}} \| x_{\mathfrak{p}}$ (where $u_{\mathfrak{p}}$ is, of course, not necessarily positive), choose $\alpha \in k^*$ such that

$$\mathfrak{p}^{-u_{\mathfrak{p}}} \| \alpha \qquad \text{for each } \mathfrak{p} \in S - S_0.$$

We now define

$$\psi(x) = \psi(\alpha x),$$

noting that the right-hand side has already been defined. Hence ψ is well defined; for, if β is another element of k^* such that $\mathfrak{p}^{-u_{\mathfrak{p}}} \| \beta$ for each $\mathfrak{p} \in S - S_0$,

$$\psi(\beta x) = \psi(\beta/\alpha)\psi(\alpha x) = \psi(\alpha x),$$

since $\beta/\alpha \in k^*$ and ψ is multiplicative. This completes the definition of ψ as an idèle class character.

We recall that I^S is the group of all ideals of k relatively prime to S, A^S denotes the subgroup of principal ideals in I^S, $B^{(\mathfrak{m})}$ the subgroup of A^S consisting of those principal ideals (α) where $\alpha \equiv 1 \pmod{\mathfrak{m}}$, and $H^{(\mathfrak{m})}$ the subgroup of $B^{(\mathfrak{m})}$ consisting of those principal ideals (α) which satisfy

$$\alpha \equiv 1 \pmod{\mathfrak{m}}, \qquad \alpha \gg 0.$$

We note that $H^{(\mathfrak{m})}$ is the intersection of the kernels of all the distinct Dirichlet characters modulo $\mathfrak{m}$, and the number $h_{\mathfrak{m}}$ of such characters is thus the index of $H^{(\mathfrak{m})}$ in I^S.

The index of A^S in I^S is equal to the so-called *absolute class number* h. The index of $B^{(\mathfrak{m})}$ in A^S is the number of units in the residue class ring mod $\mathfrak{m}$, denoted by $\phi(\mathfrak{m})$; and the index of $H^{(\mathfrak{m})}$ in $B^{(\mathfrak{m})}$ is the number of totally positive units $\equiv 1 \pmod{\mathfrak{m}}$, equal to $H/(h\phi_1(\mathfrak{m}))$ where $\phi_1(\mathfrak{m})$ is the number of residue classes mod $\mathfrak{m}$ containing totally positive units and H is the number of ideal classes in the "narrow" sense, i.e. relative to the subgroup of I^S consisting of all totally positive principal ideals of k. Thus the number $h_{\mathfrak{m}}$ of distinct Dirichlet characters mod $\mathfrak{m}$ is given by

$$h_{\mathfrak{m}} = \frac{H}{\phi_1(\mathfrak{m})}\phi(\mathfrak{m}).$$

2. Dirichlet L-series and Density Theorems

In this section we shall take "character" to mean "Dirichlet character". If χ is a character, we define χ on S by $\chi(\mathfrak{p}) = 0$ if $\mathfrak{p} \in S$.

Let $\mathfrak{a}$ denote a general integral ideal, with the prime decomposition of $\mathfrak{a}$ in k given by

$$\mathfrak{a} = \prod_{\mathfrak{p}} \mathfrak{p}^{v_{\mathfrak{p}}}, \qquad v_{\mathfrak{p}} \geqslant 0,\ v_{\mathfrak{p}} = 0 \text{ for almost all } \mathfrak{p}.$$

By $N(\mathfrak{a})$ we shall understand the absolute norm of $\mathfrak{a}$, i.e. $N_{k/\mathbf{Q}}(\mathfrak{a})$.

We define the Dedekind zeta-function $\zeta_k(s)$ by

$$\zeta_k(s) = \sum_{\mathfrak{a}\neq 0} \frac{1}{N(\mathfrak{a})^s} = \prod_{\mathfrak{p}} \left(1 - \frac{1}{N(\mathfrak{p})^s}\right)^{-1} \qquad (s = \sigma + it),$$

and with each character χ we associate a so-called L-series

$$L(s,\chi) = \sum_{\mathfrak{a}\neq 0} \frac{\chi(\mathfrak{a})}{N(\mathfrak{a})^s} = \prod_{\mathfrak{p}} \left(1 - \frac{\chi(\mathfrak{p})}{N(\mathfrak{p})^s}\right)^{-1}.$$

Since each rational prime p is the product of at most $[k:\mathbf{Q}]$ primes $\mathfrak{p}$, the convergence of both sum and product in each case, and the equality between them, for $\sigma > 1$ all follow from the absolute convergence of sum and product for $\sigma > 1$.

We observe that $L(s, \chi_0)$ and $\zeta_k(s)$ differ only by the factors corresponding to the ramified primes, and that $\zeta_k(s)$ is the L-series corresponding to the primitive character co-trained with χ_0.

As in classical rational number theory, L-functions are introduced as a means of proving various density theorems (such as Theorem 3 below). An important property of these functions is that their range of definition can be extended analytically to the left of the line $\sigma = 1$. The continuation into the region $\sigma > 1 - \frac{1}{\nu}$ can be effected in an elementary way (using only Abel summation and the fact that $\zeta(s)$ is regular apart from a simple pole at $s = 1$) by virtue of the following

THEOREM 1

$$\sum_{N(\mathfrak{a}) \leqslant x} \chi(\mathfrak{a}) = \begin{cases} O(x^{1-1/\nu}), & \chi \neq \chi_0, \\ \kappa x + O(x^{1-1/\nu}), & \chi = \chi_0, \end{cases}$$

where κ *depends on the degree, class number, discriminant and units of* k.

We indicate briefly the proof of this result. Let C denote a typical coset of $H^{(\mathfrak{m})}$ in I^S. Then the sum considered in the theorem is equal to

$$\sum_C \chi(C) \sum_{\substack{N(\mathfrak{a}) \leqslant x \\ \mathfrak{a} \in C}} 1,$$

and since

$$\sum_C \chi(C) = \begin{cases} h_{\mathfrak{m}}, & \chi = \chi_0, \\ 0 \text{ otherwise}, \end{cases}$$

it suffices to estimate the inner sum. Let $\mathfrak{b}$ be a fixed ideal in C^{-1}. Then $\mathfrak{ab} = (a)$ where a is a totally positive element of k such that $a \equiv 1 \pmod{\mathfrak{m}}$. As $\mathfrak{a}$ varies, a is a variable integer in the ideal $\mathfrak{b}$. Also,

$$|N(a)| = |N((a))| = N(\mathfrak{a})N(\mathfrak{b}),$$

so that the inner sum may be written in the form

$$\sum_{\substack{|N(a)| \leqslant xN(\mathfrak{b}) \\ a \in \mathfrak{b}}}^{*} 1$$

where the asterisk indicates that $a \equiv 1 \pmod{\mathfrak{m}}$, $a \gg 0$, and that in each set of associates only one element is to be counted. The integers a of the ideal $\mathfrak{b}$ may be represented by the points of a certain n-dimensional lattice, and the problem is essentially the classical one of estimating the number of these points in a certain simplex (Dedekind, 1871–94; Weber, 1896 and Hecke, 1954). The estimate takes the form†

$$\frac{\kappa}{h_{\mathfrak{m}}} x + O(x^{1-1/\nu}).$$

† A better error term can be derived as in Landau (1927), Satz 210.

A result of this type may also be derived for Grössencharacters, but the proof is complicated (Hecke, 1920).

As in classical theory, deeper methods lead to analytic continuation of L-functions into the whole complex plane, and thence to a functional equation for such functions. In the case of the ordinary ζ-function, one obtains†

$$\pi^{-s/2}\Gamma\left(\frac{s}{2}\right)\zeta(s)=\frac{1}{s-1}-\frac{1}{s}+\int_1^{\infty}(x^{-\frac{1}{2}s-\frac{1}{2}}+x^{\frac{1}{2}s-1})\tfrac{1}{2}(\theta(x)-1)\,dx=\Phi(s),$$

where

$$\theta(x)=\sum_{m=-\infty}^{\infty}e^{-\pi m^2 x},$$

and one derives at once the functional equation

$$\Phi(s)=\Phi(1-s).$$

Hecke (1920) extended this classical result in a far-reaching way to L-series formed with Grössencharacters; and, more recently, Tate (Chapter XV) generalized Hecke's result to general spaces. For Dirichlet characters, Hecke's result is summarized below (Hasse's Bericht, 1926, 1927 and 1930).

Let

$$\Phi(s,\chi)=\prod_{q=1}^{r_1}\Gamma\left(\frac{s+a_q}{2}\right).\Gamma(s)^{r_2}\left\{\frac{|d|N(\mathfrak{f}_\chi)}{4^{r_2}\pi^{\nu}}\right\}^{s/2}L(s,\chi);$$

then $\Phi(s,\chi)$ is meromorphic and satisfies the functional equation

$$\Phi(s,\chi)=W(\chi)\Phi(1-s,\bar{\chi})$$

where W is a constant of absolute value 1, and

d denotes the discriminant;

r_1, r_2 are the numbers of real and complex valuations respectively;

$a_q=0$ or 1 according as the value of χ in the domain of all principal ideals (α) with $\alpha\equiv 1 \pmod{\mathfrak{f}_\chi}$ does or does not depend on the sign of the qth real conjugate of α.

An explicit expression for W is given, e.g. in Hasse's Bericht (Section 9, Satz 15); its presence in the functional equation leads to interesting information of an algebraic nature, for instance, about generalized Gaussian sums (Bericht, Section 9.2 *et seq*). It follows from the proof of the functional equation that $L(s,\chi)$ is an integral function, except for a simple pole at $s=1$ when $\chi=\chi_0$.

We shall see that information about the zeros of L-functions plays an important part in applications to density results. The distribution of zeros in the "critical" strip $0<\sigma\leqslant 1$ is particularly important. According to the

† Titchmarsh (1951).

generalized Riemann hypothesis, $L(s,\chi) \neq 0$ if $\sigma > \frac{1}{2}$; but this conjecture is far from being settled.

Nevertheless, significant information can be extracted from the much weaker

THEOREM 2

$$L(s,\chi) \neq 0 \qquad \text{if} \quad \sigma \geqslant 1.$$

Proof. In view of the product representation of L for $\sigma > 1$ we may restrict ourselves to the case $\sigma = 1$. The proof falls into two parts, the first due to Hadamard, the second to Landau. We suppose on the contrary that $1+it$ is a zero of $L(s,\chi)$.

(i) (Hadamard) Assume that $\chi^2 \neq \chi_0$ if $t = 0$. If $\sigma > 1$, we have, from the product representation, that

$$L(s,\chi) = \exp\left\{\sum_{\mathfrak{p}} \sum_{m=1}^{\infty} \frac{1}{m} N(\mathfrak{p})^{-m\sigma} e^{-itm\log N(\mathfrak{p})} \chi(\mathfrak{p}^m)\right\}.$$

When $\mathfrak{p}$ is prime to $\mathfrak{f}_\chi$, we write $\chi(\mathfrak{p}) = e^{ic_\mathfrak{p}}$, $\beta_\mathfrak{p} = t\log N(\mathfrak{p}) + c_\mathfrak{p}$ and consider the function

$$\begin{aligned}|L^3(\sigma,\chi_0)L^4(\sigma+it,\chi)L(\sigma+2it,\chi^2)| &= \exp\left\{\sum_{\mathfrak{p}\text{ prime to }\mathfrak{f}_\chi} \sum_{m=1}^{\infty} \frac{1}{m} N(\mathfrak{p})^{-m\sigma}(3+4\cos m\beta_\mathfrak{p} + \cos 2m\beta_\mathfrak{p})\right\} \\ &\geqslant 1\end{aligned}$$

since $3+4\cos\omega+\cos 2\omega \geqslant 0$ for all real ω. Keeping t fixed, we now let $\sigma \to 1+0$. Of the terms on the left, the first is $O((\sigma-1)^{-3})$, the second is $O((\sigma-1)^4)$ by hypothesis and the third is $O(1)$ because if $t = 0$, $\chi^2 \neq \chi_0$. Hence the expression on the left tends to 0 as $\sigma \to 1+0$, and we arrive at a contradiction.

(ii) (Landau) It remains to consider the case when $\chi^2 = \chi_0$ (so that χ is real) and, if possible, $L(1,\chi) = 0$. We consider the product

$$\zeta_k(s)L(s,\chi) = \sum_{\mathfrak{a}} N(\mathfrak{a})^{-s}\lambda(\mathfrak{a}) = \sum_{u=1}^{\infty} a_u . u^{-s}$$

where

$$a_u = \sum_{N(\mathfrak{a})=u} \lambda(\mathfrak{a})$$

and

$$\begin{aligned}\lambda(\mathfrak{a}) = \sum_{\mathfrak{b}|\mathfrak{a}} \chi(\mathfrak{b}) &= \prod_{\mathfrak{p}^m\|\mathfrak{a}} \{1+\chi(\mathfrak{p})+\ldots\chi(\mathfrak{p}^m)\} \\ &\geqslant 0,\end{aligned}$$

where $\mathfrak{p}^m\|\mathfrak{a}$ signifies that $m = m_\mathfrak{p}$ is the highest exponent to which $\mathfrak{p}$ divides $\mathfrak{a}$. Moreover, if $m_\mathfrak{p}$ is even for all $\mathfrak{p}$ dividing $\mathfrak{a}$,

$$\lambda(\mathfrak{a}) \geqslant 1.$$

Hence, if σ is real and both series converge,

$$\sum_{\mathfrak{a}} N(\mathfrak{a})^{-\sigma}\lambda(\mathfrak{a}) \geqslant \sum_{\mathfrak{a}} N(\mathfrak{a})^{-2\sigma}. \tag{2.1}$$

We now utilize the following simple result from the theory of Dirichlet series:

A Dirichlet series of type

$$f(s) = \sum_{u=1}^{\infty} a_u . u^{-s}, \qquad a_u \geqslant 0 \quad (u = 1, 2, \ldots),$$

has a half-plane $\operatorname{Re} s > \sigma_0$ *as its domain of convergence, and if* σ_0 *is finite, then* $f(s)$ *is non-regular at* $s = \sigma_0$. (Titchmarsh, 1939, see the theorem of Section 9.2.)

By hypothesis, $f(s) = \zeta_k(s)L(s, \chi)$ is everywhere regular (the hypothetical zero of $L(s, \chi)$ at $s = 1$ counteracting the pole of $\zeta_k(s)$); hence the series on the left of (2.1) converges for all real σ. However, the series on the right of (2.1) is equal to $\zeta_k(2\sigma)$ which tends to $+\infty$ as $\sigma \to \frac{1}{2}+0$. Hence we arrive at a contradiction.

The Landau proof is purely existential, whereas Hadamard's argument can be used to yield quantitative results about zero-free regions and orders of magnitude of L-functions.†

We are now in a position to prove

THEOREM 3 (*Prime Ideal Theorem*)

$$\sum_{N(\mathfrak{p}) \leqslant x} \chi(\mathfrak{p}) = \begin{cases} \dfrac{x}{\log x}\{1+o(1)\}, & \chi = \chi_0, \\[2ex] o\left(\dfrac{x}{\log x}\right), & \chi \neq \chi_0. \end{cases}$$

Proof. For $\operatorname{Re} s > 1$, form the logarithmic derivative of $L(s, \chi)$, namely

$$-\frac{L'(s,\chi)}{L(s,\chi)} = \sum_{\mathfrak{p}} \sum_{m=1}^{\infty} N(\mathfrak{p})^{-ms} \log N(\mathfrak{p}) . \chi(\mathfrak{p}^m)$$

$$= \sum_{\mathfrak{p}} \chi(\mathfrak{p}) \frac{\log N(\mathfrak{p})}{N(\mathfrak{p})^s} + g(s,\chi)$$

where g is a function regular for $\operatorname{Re} s > \frac{1}{2}$. Our first, and major, step will be to estimate the coefficient sum

$$\sum_{N(\mathfrak{p}) \leqslant x} \chi(\mathfrak{p}) \log N(\mathfrak{p}).$$

One way of doing this is to express the sum as a contour integral of

$$\frac{x^s}{s} \frac{L'(s,\chi)}{L(s,\chi)}$$

† See Estermann (1952) and Landau (1907).

along the line $(c-i\infty, c+i\infty)$ with some $c > 1$, and then to shift the line of integration to the parallel line $\operatorname{Re} s = 1$, with an indent round $s = 1$. This we now know to be the only point at which a pole can occur (and does occur precisely when $\chi = \chi_0$, the residue in this case then leading to the dominant term). For an account of this treatment, see Landau (1927). It is clear from even this sketch that the non-vanishing of $L(s, \chi)$ on $\operatorname{Re} s = 1$ is vital.

An alternative approach is via the Wiener–Ikehara tauberian theorem: *Suppose that*

$$f(s) = \sum_{m=1}^{\infty} \frac{a_m}{m^s} \quad (a_m \geqslant 0), \qquad g(s) = \sum_{m=1}^{\infty} \frac{b_m}{m^s}$$

are Dirichlet series, convergent for $\operatorname{Re} s > 1$, *regular on* $\operatorname{Re} s = 1$ *with simple poles at* $s = 1$, *of residue* 1 *in the case of* f, *and* η *in the case of* g, *where* η *may be* 0. *Assume that there exists a constant* c *such that* $|b_m| \leqslant c a_m$. *Then*

$$\sum_{m \leqslant x} b_m \sim \eta x, \quad \textit{as } x \to \infty.$$

We apply this result with

$$f(s) = -\frac{\zeta'(s)}{\zeta(s)}, \qquad g(s) = -\frac{L'(s,\chi)}{L(s,\chi)}, \qquad c = [k:$$

Clearly $\eta = 1$ when $\chi = \chi_0$, and otherwise $\eta = 0$.

Finally, it is an easy matter to show that

$$\frac{1}{\log x} \sum_{N(\mathfrak{p}) \leqslant x} \chi(\mathfrak{p}) \log N(\mathfrak{p}) \sim \sum_{N(\mathfrak{p}) \leqslant x} \chi(\mathfrak{p}),$$

e.g. by partial summation; and this proves the theorem. (The tauberian approach is described in Lang (1964).)

It is worth remarking that the analytic method can be made to give sharper estimates of the error terms (Hecke, 1920). Both methods extend to Grössencharacters.

In close analogy to Dirichlet's famous proof of the infinitude of rational primes in arithmetic progressions, one can show that every Dirichlet ideal class C contains infinitely many primes $\mathfrak{p}$ of k. Indeed, by means of the prime ideal theorem we can show that the primes $\mathfrak{p}$ are equally distributed among the classes C; we have, in particular, that

THEOREM 4

$$\sum_{\substack{N(\mathfrak{p}) \leqslant x \\ \mathfrak{p} \in C}} 1 \sim \frac{1}{h_{\mathfrak{m}}} \frac{x}{\log x}, \qquad x \to \infty.$$

Proof. We have only to remark that

$$\sum_{\chi} \bar{\chi}(C)\chi(\mathfrak{p}) = \begin{cases} h_{\mathfrak{m}}, & \mathfrak{p} \in C, \\ 0 & \text{otherwise.} \end{cases}$$

By virtue of this orthogonality formula, we have

$$h_{\mathfrak{m}} \sum_{\substack{N(\mathfrak{p}) \leqslant x \\ \mathfrak{p} \in C}} 1 = \sum_{\chi} \bar{\chi}(C) \sum_{N(\mathfrak{p}) \leqslant x} \chi(\mathfrak{p});$$

on the other hand, the sum on the right is asymptotic to $x/\log x$ as $x \to \infty$ by the prime ideal theorem.

If B is any set of ideals in k, and

$$\lim_{x \to \infty} \frac{\log x}{x} \operatorname{card}\{\mathfrak{p} \in B \mid N(\mathfrak{p}) \leqslant x\} =$$

exists, then l is called the *density* of primes in B. Thus the density of the set of all primes of k is 1.

To investigate the density of primes in a given set, it suffices to consider only primes $\mathfrak{p}$ of absolute first degree, that is, those $\mathfrak{p}$ for which $N_{k/\mathbf{Q}}(\mathfrak{p})$ is a rational prime; for all primes $\mathfrak{p}$ whose norms $N(\mathfrak{p})$ are powers of rational primes greater than the first, and satisfy $N(\mathfrak{p}) \leqslant x$, are $O(x^{\frac{1}{2}})$ in number. For the same reason we may clearly disregard the finite number of ramified primes.

We shall use this remark in proving the next result, known in classical parlance as the *first fundamental inequality of class field theory* (see Chapter VII, "Global Class Field Theory", §9, and Chapter XI, "The History of Class Field Theory", §1).

THEOREM 5. *Let K be a finite normal extension of k, and denote $[K : k]$ by n. Let S be the exceptional set in k. K determines the subgroup H_S of I^S, of finite index h_S in I^S, composed of those cosets of $H^{\mathfrak{m}}$ which contain norms (relative to k) of ideals of K coprime with S. Then*

$$h_s \leqslant n.$$

Proof. We identify $1/n$ and $1/h_S$ as the densities of two sets of primes in k.

First of all, if C is the set of all primes $\mathfrak{p}$ (of k) in H_S, then, by the preceeding theorem, the density of C is $1/h_S$.

Next, since K/k is normal, the prime decomposition of any $\mathfrak{p}$ in K is of the form

$$\mathfrak{p} = (\mathfrak{P}_1 \dots \mathfrak{P}_r)^e$$

where all the primes $\mathfrak{P}_i$ have the *same* degree f relative to $\mathfrak{p}$, and

$$efr = n.$$

Since the number of ramified $\mathfrak{p}$ is finite, we need consider only primes $\mathfrak{p}$ for which $e = 1$. Now consider the set B of all primes $\mathfrak{p}$ whose prime decomposition in K is characterized by $e = f = 1$, that is, by $r = n$. On the one hand, by the prime ideal theorem for K (noting that the primes $\mathfrak{P}_i$ are all the primes of K of absolute first degree) the density of B is clearly $1/n$; on the other hand, if $\mathfrak{p} \in B$ and $\mathfrak{P} | \mathfrak{p}$, then $N_{K/k}(\mathfrak{P}) = \mathfrak{p}$, so that $B \subset H_S$. The result follows at once.

Note. It is worth remarking that Theorem 5 can be proved without appeal to the relatively deep Theorems 3 and 4 and, in particular, to the non-vanishing of $L(s, \chi)$ on Re $s = 1$. A more elementary argument, using only real variable theory, runs as follows:

Let s be real and > 1. By Theorem 1 and partial summation we have

(a) $$\lim_{s \to 1} (s-1)L(s, \chi_0) = \kappa$$

and

(b) $$\lim_{s \to 1} L(s, \chi) \text{ exists and is finite if } \chi \neq \chi_0.$$

From the product representation of $L(s, \chi)$ it follows that

$$\log L(s, \chi) = \sum \frac{\chi(\mathfrak{p})}{N(\mathfrak{p})^s} + g(s, \chi)$$

where $g(s, \chi)$ is a Dirichlet series absolutely convergent for $s > \frac{1}{2}$. Using the orthogonality properties of the characters χ, we conclude that

(c) $$\sum_{\mathfrak{p} \in H_s} \frac{1}{N(\mathfrak{p})^s} = \frac{1}{h_s} \log \frac{1}{s-1} + f(s)$$

where

$$h_s f(s) = \sum_{\chi \neq \chi_0} \{\log L(s, \chi) - g(s, \chi)\} + \log (s-1)L(s, \chi_0) - g(s, \chi_0).$$

By (a) and (b), $\limsup_{s \to 1} f(s)$ is not $+\infty$ and, indeed, is finite unless one of the $L(s, \chi)\,(\chi \neq \chi_0)$ vanishes at $s = 1$.

Now let K be as described in the statement of Theorem 5. We have, analogously to (a), that $\lim_{s \to 1} \zeta_K(s).(s-1)$ exists and is finite. Taking logarithms of the product representation of $\zeta_K(s)$, gives

(d) $$\sum_{\mathfrak{p} \in B} \frac{1}{N(\mathfrak{p})^s} = \frac{1}{n} \log \frac{1}{s-1} + G(s)$$

where $\lim_{s \to 1} G(s)$ exists and is finite. Subtracting (d) from (c), and using $B \subset H_S$, we obtain

$$\left(\frac{1}{h_s} - \frac{1}{n}\right) \log \frac{1}{s-1} + f(s) - G(s) \geqslant 0$$

for all $s > 1$. Letting $s \to 1+0$, the result follows.

For the next theorem we require some results from class-field theory.

THEOREM 6. *If K is a finite abelian extension of k, then*

$$\zeta_K(s) = \prod_{\chi} L(s, \chi, k) \tag{2.2}$$

where, in the notation of the preceding theorem, the product on the right extends over the primitive characters co-trained with the characters of the class group I^S/H_S.

Proof. The proof is carried out in terms of local factors, and we consider separately non-ramified and ramified primes $\mathfrak{p}$ of k.

(i) Let $\mathfrak{p}$ be a non-ramified prime of k, so that

$$\mathfrak{p} = \mathfrak{P}_1 \ldots \mathfrak{P}_l$$

where $\mathfrak{P}_1, \ldots, \mathfrak{P}_l$ are distinct primes of K. From class field theory,

$$N_{K/\mathbf{Q}}(\mathfrak{P}_i) = N_{k/\mathbf{Q}}(\mathfrak{p})^f$$

where $lf = [K:k] = n$.

Thus the corresponding local factor on the left is

$$(1 - N(\mathfrak{p})^{-fs})^{-n/f},$$

whilst the corresponding local factor on the right is

$$\prod_{\chi} (1 - \chi(\mathfrak{p}) N(\mathfrak{p})^{-s})^{-1}.$$

Since f is the least positive integer such that $\chi(\mathfrak{p}^f) = 1$ for all χ, we have the easily verifiable identity (take logs of both sides and use $h_S = n$)

$$(1 - y^f)^{-n/f} = \prod_{\chi} (1 - \chi(\mathfrak{p}).y)^{-1};$$

from this, with $y = N(\mathfrak{p})^{-s}$, equality of the local factors follows at once.

(ii) The proof for ramified primes is more difficult, and depends on the functional equations satisfied by the various L-functions. We begin by writing

$$\zeta_K(s) = g(s) \prod_{\chi} L(s, \chi, k),$$

and prove that $g(s)$ is identically 1. From above, $g(s)$ is equal to the finite product over ramified $\mathfrak{p}$ of the expressions

$$\frac{\prod_{\chi} \{1 - \chi(\mathfrak{p}) N(\mathfrak{p})^{-s}\}}{\prod_{\mathfrak{P}|\mathfrak{p}} \{1 - N(\mathfrak{P})^{-s}\}}.$$

If this product is not constant, then it has a pole or zero at a pure imaginary point it_0, $t_0 \neq 0$. In view of the functional equations, $g(1-s)/g(s)$ is a quotient of gamma functions and so can have only real poles and zeros. Thus $1 - it_0$ is also a pole or zero of g. But we know that $1 - it_0$ is not a singularity or zero of any of the L-series or of $\zeta_K(s)$. Hence g is constant, and so equal to 1.

Example 1.† Let $k = \mathbf{Q}$, $K = \mathbf{Q}(\omega)$ where ω is a primitive mth root of unity. Then

$$\zeta_K(s) = \zeta(s) \prod_{\chi} L(s, \chi)$$

where the product on the right extends over the primitive characters co-trained with all non-principal rational characters mod m.

Proof. See Chapter III, §1.

Example 2. Let $k = \mathbf{Q}$, $K = \mathbf{Q}(\sqrt{d})$ where d is the discriminant of K. Then

$$\zeta_K(s) = \zeta(s) \sum_{m=1}^{\infty} \left(\frac{d}{m}\right) m^{-s},$$

where $\left(\frac{d}{m}\right)$ denotes the Kronecker symbol (Hecke, 1954, Chapter VII).

We touch upon another consequence of this theorem. We recall that the functional equation of an L-function contains a factor

$$\{|d| N(\mathfrak{f}_\chi)\}^{s/2}.$$

Applying the functional equation to $\zeta_K(s)$ on the left of (2.2) and to each of the L-series on the right, one can derive the relation

$$\prod_{\chi} |d| N(\mathfrak{f}_\chi) = |D|,$$

where D is the discriminant of K (Hasse's Bericht, Section 9.3). If we assume for the moment that $k = \mathbf{Q}$, we obtain

$$\prod_{\chi} \mathfrak{f}_\chi = \mathrm{Disc}(K/k). \tag{2.3}$$

This inference is not as easy to justify in the general case when $k \neq \mathbf{Q}$, because two distinct ideals in k can have equal norms. However, it can be proved (Hasse's Bericht, Section 9.3, formula (12) and Note 44) that (2.3) is valid in general.

3. L-functions for Non-abelian Extensions

Suppose now that K is a finite, normal but not necessarily abelian extension of k of degree n. The problem is to develop in this case an analogue of the above theory of L-series formed with abelian group characters.

As usual, let G be the Galois group of K over k. Let $\{M(\mu)\}_{\mu \in G}$ be a representation of G into matrices over the complex field. Thus to each element μ of G corresponds a matrix $M(\mu)$. The character $\chi(\mu)$ of μ is defined to be

† By (2.2), since $\zeta_K(s)$ and $L(s, \chi_0, k) = \zeta_k(s)$ have simple poles at $s = 1$, and the remaining $L(s, \chi, k)$ on the right are regular there, it follows that these $L(s, \chi, k)$ do not vanish at $s = 1$. In particular, in the situation of Example 1, it follows that all the L-functions formed with non-principal Dirichlet characters mod m do not vanish at $s = 1$. This is an alternative proof of the key step in the proof of Dirichlet's theorem on the infinitude of primes in arithmetic progressions mod m.

the trace of $M(\mu)$ and depends only on the conjugacy class $\langle\mu\rangle$ in which μ lies.

Two representations† $\{M(\mu)\}_{\mu\in G}$, $\{N(\mu)\}_{\mu\in G}$ are said to be *equivalent* if there exists a non-singular matrix P such that

$$PM(\mu)P^{-1} = N(\mu) \qquad \text{for all } \mu \in G.$$

A representation $\{M(\mu)\}$ is said to be *reducible* if and only if it is equivalent to a representation $\{N(\mu)\}$ such that

$$N(\mu) = \begin{pmatrix} N^{(1)}(\mu) & 0 \\ 0 & N^{(2)}(\mu) \end{pmatrix} \qquad \text{for all } \mu \in G,$$

where $\{N^{(1)}(\mu)\}$, $\{N^{(2)}(\mu)\}$ are themselves representations of G.

The character of an *irreducible* representation is said to be *simple.* From the general theory of group representations (for an account of this theory see e.g. Hall, 1959) the number g of simple characters of G is equal to the number of conjugacy classes of G, and the following orthogonality relations are known to hold:

$$\sum_{\mu\in G} \chi(\mu)\bar{\chi}'(\mu) = \begin{cases} n, & \chi = \chi', \\ 0, & \chi \neq \chi'; \end{cases} \tag{3.1}$$

in particular

$$\sum_{\mu\in G} \chi(\mu) = \begin{cases} n, & \chi \text{ principal}, \\ 0, & \text{otherwise}, \end{cases}$$

where the *principal* character is the character of the representation $M(\mu) = 1$ for all $\mu \in G$, to be denoted henceforward by χ_0. Also, if $\psi_1, \psi_2, \ldots, \psi_g$ are the simple characters of G, then

$$\sum_{i=1}^{g} \psi_i(\mu)\bar{\psi}_i(\mu') = \begin{cases} n/l_\mu, & \mu' \in \langle\mu\rangle, \\ 0, & \mu' \notin \langle\mu\rangle, \end{cases} \tag{3.2}$$

where l_μ is the number of elements in the conjugacy class $\langle\mu\rangle$ of μ. In particular, taking $\mu' = \mu = 1$,

$$\sum_{i=1}^{g} n_i^2 = n, \tag{3.3}$$

where n_i is the degree of ψ_i (that is, ψ_i is the character of a representation by $n_i \times n_i$ matrices).

If G is abelian, then each $l_\mu = 1$, so that $g = n$ and each $n_i = 1$. Thus each character ψ_i is a homomorphism of G into the unit circle, and so an abelian character.

Let $\mathfrak{P}$ be a non-ramified prime of K, and let $\mathfrak{p}$ be the prime of k lying under $\mathfrak{P}$. We shall denote the Frobenius automorphism of K/k relative to $\mathfrak{P}$ (for

† It should be clear from the context that N is not used here to denote a norm!

definition see Chapter VII §2) by $\left[\frac{K/k}{\mathfrak{P}}\right]$. If

$$|I-M(\mu)x|$$

is the characteristic polynomial of $M(\mu)$—so that I denotes the unit matrix—we take as local factor of our L-function the expression

$$\left|I-M\left(\left[\frac{K/k}{\mathfrak{P}}\right]\right)N_{k/\mathbf{Q}}(\mathfrak{p})^{-s}\right|^{-1}.$$

We note that this definition cannot be extended to ramified $\mathfrak{P}$ since there is no corresponding Frobenius automorphism.

It is important to note that this local factor depends only on the character χ of the representation, and not on the explicit representation matrix. For any similarity transformation of $M(\mu)$ leaves its characteristic polynomial invariant and, since $M(\mu)$ has finite order, the Jordan canonical form of $M(\mu)$ must therefore be a diagonal matrix all of whose diagonal elements are roots of unity. Thus, without loss of generality,

$$M\left(\left[\frac{K/k}{\mathfrak{P}}\right]\right)$$

may be taken to be

$$M\left(\left[\frac{K/k}{\mathfrak{P}}\right]\right)=\begin{pmatrix}\varepsilon_1 & & 0\\ & \ddots & \\ 0 & & \varepsilon_b\end{pmatrix}.$$

The local factor is then equal to

$$\begin{aligned}\prod_{i=1}^{b}(1-\varepsilon_i N(\mathfrak{p})^{-s})^{-1} &= \exp\left\{\sum_{i=1}^{b}\sum_{m=1}^{\infty}\frac{1}{m}\varepsilon_i^m N(\mathfrak{p})^{-ms}\right\}\\ &= \exp\left\{\sum_{m=1}^{\infty}\frac{1}{m}\chi\left(\left[\frac{K/k}{\mathfrak{P}}\right]^m\right)N(\mathfrak{p})^{-ms}\right\} \qquad (3.4)\end{aligned}$$

since $\sum_{i=1}^{b}\varepsilon_i^m$ is equal to the trace of $\left\{M\left[\frac{K/k}{\mathfrak{P}}\right]\right\}^m$ which, by definition, is equal to $\chi\left(\left[\frac{K/k}{\mathfrak{P}}\right]^m\right)$.

We collect up the local factors corresponding to non-ramified $\mathfrak{P}$ and define the so-called Artin L-function† essentially by

$$L(s,\chi)=L(s,\chi,K/k)=\prod_{\substack{\text{non-ram.}\\ \mathfrak{p}}}\left|I-M\left(\left[\frac{K/k}{\mathfrak{P}}\right]\right)N(\mathfrak{p})^{-s}\right|^{-1};$$

we shall introduce later a factor derived from the ramified primes.

† See also Artin (1930).

We now list a number of observations about $L(s, \chi)$:

(I) $L(s, \chi)$ is regular for $\sigma > 1$, since the product is absolutely and uniformly convergent in every closed sub-set of the half-plane $\operatorname{Re} s > 1$.

(II) If K/k is abelian, and if χ is simple then, apart from the factor corresponding to the ramified primes, this definition coincides with that given in Section 2 above.

(III) Suppose that Ω is a field intermediate between K and k, normal over k. Let $H = \operatorname{Gal}(K/\Omega)$, so that H is a normal subgroup of G and

$$G/H = \operatorname{Gal}(\Omega/k).$$

Then if χ is a character of G/H, it can be regarded in an obvious way as a character of G, and

$$L(s, \chi, K/k) = L(s, \chi, \Omega/k).$$

Proof. Take the character over G defined by the representation

$$M'(\mu) = M(\mu H).$$

We have

$$X^{\left[\frac{K/k}{\mathfrak{P}}\right]} \equiv X^{N(\mathfrak{p})} \pmod{\mathfrak{P}} \tag{3.5}$$

for all integers $X \in K$, and in particular for all integers $X \in \Omega$. Since Ω is a normal extension of k,

$$X \in \Omega \Rightarrow X^{\mu} \in \Omega \qquad \text{for all } \mu \in G.$$

Hence (3.5) is a congruence in Ω, and since $\mathfrak{P}$ is unramified, if $\mathfrak{P}$ lies over $\mathfrak{q}$ in Ω we have

$$X^{\left[\frac{K/k}{\mathfrak{P}}\right]} \equiv X^{N(\mathfrak{p})} \pmod{\mathfrak{q}}.$$

Hence also

$$X^{\left[\frac{K/k}{\mathfrak{P}}\right]H} \equiv X^{N(\mathfrak{p})} \pmod{\mathfrak{q}},$$

i.e. $\left[\frac{K/k}{\mathfrak{P}}\right]H$ is the Frobenius automorphism in Ω.

Thus

$$\left|I - M'\left(\left[\frac{K/k}{\mathfrak{P}}\right]\right) N(\mathfrak{p})^{-s}\right| = \left|I - M\left(\left[\frac{K/k}{\mathfrak{P}}\right] H\right) N(\mathfrak{p})^{-s}\right|$$
$$= \left|I - M\left(\left[\frac{\Omega/k}{\mathfrak{P}}\right]\right) N(\mathfrak{p})^{-s}\right|.$$

(IV) Suppose that χ is a non-simple character of G, say $\chi = \chi_1 + \chi_2$. Then

$$L(s, \chi) = L(s, \chi_1) L(s, \chi_2),$$

since $\log L$ is linear in χ by (3.4).

(V) Suppose again that Ω is a field intermediate between K and k, this time not necessarily normal over k. Let $H = \mathrm{Gal}(K/\Omega)$, and suppose that

$$G = \sum_i H\alpha_i$$

is the partition of G into right cosets of H. To each character χ of H there corresponds an *induced* character χ^* of G, given by

$$\chi^*(\mu) = \sum_{\substack{i \\ \alpha_i\mu\alpha_i^{-1} \in H}} \chi(\alpha_i \mu \alpha_i^{-1}), \qquad \mu \in G; \tag{3.6}$$

then

$$L(s, \chi^*, K/k) = L(s, \chi, K/\Omega).$$

Proof.† Let $\mathfrak{P}$ be a non-ramified prime of K, and $\mathfrak{p}$ the prime of k under $\mathfrak{P}$. Suppose that, in Ω, $\mathfrak{p}$ has the prime decomposition

$$\mathfrak{p} = \prod_{i=1}^{r} \mathfrak{q}_i, \qquad N_{\Omega/\mathbf{Q}}(\mathfrak{q}_i) = (N_{k/\mathbf{Q}}\mathfrak{p})^{f_i}; \tag{3.7}$$

and suppose that τ_i is an element of G such that $\mathfrak{q}_i$ lies under $\tau_i\mathfrak{P}$. Then (Hasse's Bericht, Section 23, I) G can be decomposed in the form

$$G = \sum_{i=1}^{r} \sum_{x_i=0}^{f_i-1} H\tau_i\mu_0^{x_i},$$

where

$$\mu_0 = \left[\frac{K/k}{\mathfrak{P}}\right].$$

From the definition of induced character given above, we have

$$\begin{aligned} \chi^*(\mu^m) &= \sum_{i=1}^{r} \sum_{\substack{x_i=0 \\ \tau_i\mu_0^{x_i}(\mu_0^m)\mu_0^{-x_i}\tau_i^{-1} \in H}}^{f_i-1} \chi(\tau_i\mu_0^{x_i}\mu_0^m\mu_0^{-x_i}\tau_i^{-1}) \\ &= \sum_{\substack{i=1 \\ \tau_i\mu_0^m\tau_i^{-1} \in H}}^{r} f_i\chi(\tau_i\mu_0^m\tau_i^{-1}) \\ &= \sum_{\substack{i=1 \\ f_i \mid m}}^{r} f_i\chi(\tau_i\mu_0^m\tau_i^{-1}) \end{aligned}$$

since $(\tau_i\mu_0\tau_i^{-1})^m \in H$ if and only if $f_i \mid m$.

The logarithm of the $\mathfrak{p}$-component ($\mathfrak{p}$ non-ramified) of $L(s, \chi^*, K/k)$ is

$$\begin{aligned} \sum_{m=1}^{\infty} \frac{1}{m}\chi^*(\mu_0^m)N(\mathfrak{p})^{-ms} &= \sum_{m=1}^{\infty} \frac{1}{m} N(\mathfrak{p})^{-ms} \sum_{\substack{i=1 \\ f_i \mid m}}^{r} f_i\chi(\tau_i\mu_0^m\tau_i^{-1}) \\ &= \sum_{i=1}^{r} \sum_{\substack{m=1 \\ f_i \mid m}}^{\infty} \frac{f_i}{m}\chi(\tau_i\mu_0^m\tau_i^{-1})N(\mathfrak{p})^{-ms} \\ &= \sum_{i=1}^{r} \sum_{t=1}^{\infty} t^{-1}\{\chi(\tau_i\mu_0^{f_i}\tau_i^{-1})\}^t N(\mathfrak{q}_i)^{-ts} \end{aligned}$$

† For an alternative proof see Hasse's Bericht, Section 27, VII.

by (3.7), on writing $m = f_i t$ in the inner summation; and this is nothing but the sum of the logarithms of those $\mathfrak{q}$-components of $L(s, \chi, K/\Omega)$ which, by (3.7), correspond to $\mathfrak{p}$.

We proceed to consider some special cases of (V).

V(i) $\Omega = K$. Then $H = \mathrm{Gal}(K/\Omega) = (1)$ and we have only one character, the principal character χ_0. In this case, then, $L(s, \chi_0, K/\Omega)$ reduces to $\zeta_K(s)$. By (3.6) the corresponding induced character, $\chi_0{}^*$, of G is given by

$$\chi_0^*(\mu) = \begin{cases} n \text{ if } \mu \text{ is the unit element of } G, \\ 0 \text{ otherwise.} \end{cases} \tag{3.8}$$

Let $\psi_1, \psi_2, \ldots, \psi_g$ be all the simple characters of G. By (3.2), with $\mu' = 1$, we have $l_1 = 1$ and arrive, by (3.8), at

$$\sum_{i=1}^{g} \psi_i(\mu)\psi_i(1) = \chi_0^*(\mu). \tag{3.9}$$

We observe that, of course, $\psi_i(1)$ must be a positive integer. By repeated application of (IV), it follows that

$$\zeta_K(s) = \prod_{i=1}^{g} L(s, \psi_i, K/k)^{\psi_i(1)}. \tag{3.10}$$

V(ii) $\Omega = k$. By (III) (with $\Omega = k$ and therefore $G = H$),

$$\begin{aligned} L(s, \chi_0, K/k) &= L(s, \chi_0, k/k) \\ &= \zeta_k(s). \end{aligned}$$

We shall now deduce from the preceding theorems the remarkable result that a general Artin L-function $L(s, \chi, K/k)$ can be expressed as a product of rational powers of abelian L-functions $L(s, \psi, K/\Omega)$, where the Ω's are fields intermediate between k and K with K/Ω abelian.

With the notation used in (i), each character χ of G can be written in the form

$$\chi = \sum_{i=1}^{g} r_i \psi_i, \tag{3.11}$$

where the r_i's are non-negative rational integers. Hence, by repeated application of (IV), it suffices to consider the *simple* Artin L-functions

$$L(s, \psi_i, K/k).$$

Let H be any subgroup of G, and let ξ_j run through the simple characters of H. Each ξ_j induces a character ξ_j^* of G, given, let us say, by

$$\xi_j^*(\mu) = \sum_i r_{ji} \psi_i(\mu) \qquad \text{for all } \mu \in G, \tag{3.12}$$

in accordance with (3.11).

The restriction of ψ_i to H is, itself, a character of H and therefore has an expression of type (3.11) in terms of the ξ_j's. Moreover, by the theory of induced characters, this representation actually takes the form

$$\psi_i(\tau) = \sum_j r_{ji}\xi_j(\tau), \qquad \text{all } \tau \in H, \tag{3.13}$$

where the coefficients r_{ji} are the *same* as in (3.12).

Now take H to be a *cyclic* subgroup of G. Then if Ω is the subfield of K consisting of elements invariant under H, K/Ω is abelian and so, by (V),

$$L(s, \xi_j^*, K/k) = L(s, \xi_j, K/\Omega),$$

which is an abelian L-function. To prove our result, it therefore suffices to express each ψ_i as a linear combination of characters of type ξ_j^*.

Each element γ of G generates a cyclic subgroup H_γ of G and so, by (3.12), denoting the simple characters of H_γ by $\xi_{\gamma;\,j}$, we have

$$\xi_{\gamma;\,j}^*(\mu) = \sum_{i=1}^{g} r_{\gamma;\,ji}\psi_i(\mu), \qquad \text{all } \mu \in G. \tag{3.14}$$

The system of equations (3.14) is described by a matrix with each fixed pair (γ, j) determining a row and each i a column and we shall prove that its rank is equal to g.

Suppose on the contrary that the rank is less than g. Then the columns are linearly dependent, i.e. there exist integers $c_1, c_2, \ldots, c_g$ not all zero, such that

$$\sum_{i=1}^{g} c_i r_{\gamma;\,ji} = 0 \qquad \text{for all } \gamma \in G \text{ and all } j.$$

Thus, by (3.13), interpreted in relation to a particular H_γ,

$$\begin{aligned}\sum_i c_i\psi_i(\tau) &= \sum_i c_i \sum_j r_{\gamma;\,ji}\xi_{\gamma;\,j}(\tau), &\qquad \text{all } \tau \in H_\gamma,\\ &= 0, &\qquad \text{all } \tau \in H_\gamma.\end{aligned}$$

In particular, taking $\tau = \gamma$, we arrive at

$$\sum_i c_i\psi_i(\gamma) = 0 \qquad \text{for all } \gamma \in G, \tag{3.15}$$

contradicting the linear independence of the simple characters $\psi_1, \psi_2, \ldots, \psi_g$. Following on from (3.15), multiply this relation by $\bar{\psi}_k(\gamma)$ and sum over all the elements γ of G. From (3.1) it follows that

$$nc_k = 0 \qquad (k = 1, 2, \ldots, g) \tag{3.16}$$

whence $c_1 = c_2 = \ldots = c_g = 0$ (so that, incidentally, we have here another way of arriving at a contradiction). Either way, we have now that the system of equations (3.14) can be solved for ψ_i, giving

$$\psi_i = \sum_{\gamma \in G} \sum_j u_{\gamma;\,ji}\xi_{\gamma;\,j}^*$$

where the coefficients $u_{\gamma;\,ji} \in \mathbf{Q}$.

The argument centering on (3.16) can be carried out modulo any prime p which does not divide n, whence it follows that the coefficients $u_{\gamma;\, ji}$ have denominators composed of prime factors of n.

We have thus proved the following

THEOREM 7. *For any character χ of G, the Artin L-function $L(s, \chi, K/k)$ is given by*

$$L(s, \chi, K/k) = \prod_{l} \prod_{j} L(s, \xi_{lj}, K/\Omega_l)^{n_{lj}}$$

where each Gal (K/Ω_l) *is cyclic, the ξ_{lj}'s are (abelian) characters of* Gal (K/Ω_l) *and each n_{lj} is rational with denominator composed of prime factors of n.*

It has been proved by Brauer (1947) that the exponents in the above theorem can be taken to be rational integers, and it follows, in particular, that the Artin L-functions are meromorphic. Furthermore, if χ is non-principal, then the ξ's in the above product representation of $L(s, \chi, K/k)$ can also be chosen non-principal. Hence Artin L-functions formed with non-principal characters are, in addition, regular and non-zero for $\sigma \geqslant 1$.

If, on the other hand, $\chi = \chi_0$ is the principal character, then $L(s, \chi_0, K/k)$ has a simple pole at $s = 1$. Artin has conjectured that, apart from this simple pole, in the case $\chi = \chi_0$, the $L(s, \chi, K/k)$ are integral functions.

This conjecture would imply that $\zeta_K(s)/\zeta_k(s)$ is an integral function whenever $k \subset K$. If K/k is normal, this is true by (3.10), (V(ii)) and a fundamental theorem on group characters due to Brauer (see Lang, 1964 p. 139).

Artin's conjecture has been verified when G is one of the following special groups: S_3 and, more generally, any group of squarefree order; any group of prime power order; any group whose commutator subgroup is abelian (Speiser, 1927); S_4 (Artin, 1924). The conjecture has not been confirmed for $G = A_5$.

By Theorem 7, each Artin's L-function $L(s, \chi)$ is seen to satisfy a functional equation by virtue of the fact that each abelian L-function occuring on the right satisfies its own functional equation. This equation will be of the form

$$\Phi(s, \chi) = W(\chi)\Phi(1-s, \bar{\chi})$$

where W is a constant of absolute value 1, and Φ is of the form

$$\Phi(s, \chi) = A(\chi)^s \Gamma\left(\frac{s}{2}\right)^{a(\chi)} \Gamma\left(\frac{s+1}{2}\right)^{b(\chi)} L(s, \chi)$$

with a, b in $\mathbf{Q}$ and A a positive constant.

At this point we recall that, in the definition of Artin's L-function, we omitted to include a factor corresponding to the ramified primes. Now we introduce on the right-hand side of (3.17) the ramified local factors corresponding to the abelian L-functions (see beginning of Section 2), and take the new product as the definition of L. Then the above functional equation is satisfied automatically by the redefined L-function.

What is lacking in the theory of Artin L-functions is a non-local approach (provided, in the abelian case, by a series definition of L-functions). This lack causes the difficulties in extending these L-functions to the complex plane.

Example: The case $G = S_3$.

The elements of S_3 fall into three conjugacy classes

$$C_1\colon (1);\quad C_2\colon (1,2,3),(3,2,1);\quad C_3\colon (1,2),(2,3),(3,1).$$

Hence there are three simple characters. Let ψ_1 be the principal character and ψ_2 the other character determined by the subgroup $C_1 \cup C_2$. These are both of first degree and so, by (3.3), ψ_3 is of degree 2. Thus, by (3.2) with $\mu' = 1$, we have that

$$\psi_1(\mu)+\psi_2(\mu)+2\psi_3(\mu) = \begin{cases} 6, & \mu = 1, \\ 0, & \text{otherwise.} \end{cases}$$

Hence the table of simple characters of S_3 can be set out as follows:

	ψ_1	ψ_2	ψ_3
C_1	1	1	2
C_2	1	1	−1
C_3	1	−1	0.

Working from (3.6), we obtain the induced characters χ^* corresponding to the characters χ of

(i) $H = A_3$:

	χ_1^*	χ_2^*	χ_3^*
C_1	2	2	2
C_2	2	−1	−1
C_3	0	0	0;

(ii) $H = \{1,(1,2)\}$:

	χ_4^*	χ_5^*
C_1	3	3
C_2	0	0
C_3	1	−1;

(iii) $H = \{1\}$:

	χ_6^*
C_1	6
C_2	0
C_3	0.

From these tables we see that

$$\chi_1^* = \psi_1+\psi_2, \qquad \chi_2^* = \chi_3^* = \psi_3,$$
$$\chi_4^* = \psi_1+\psi_3, \qquad \chi_5^* = \psi_2+\psi_3,$$
$$\chi_6^* = \psi_1+\psi_2+2\psi_3.$$

S_3 is the Galois group of any non-abelian normal extension K of k of degree 6. Let Ω_1, Ω_2 be the two intermediate fields fixed under the subgroups $A_3, \{(1), (1,2)\}$ respectively. Thus Ω_1 is a quadratic extension and Ω_2 a cubic extension of k, and K is therefore an abelian extension of each of them. Also, Ω_1 is an abelian extension of k. Thus, by (V(ii)), and (IV),

$$\begin{aligned}\zeta_K(s) &= L(s, \chi_0, K/K) = L(s, \psi_1+\psi_2+2\psi_3, K/k)\\ &= L_{\psi_1}L_{\psi_2}L_{\psi_3}^2,\\ \zeta_{\Omega_1}(s) &= L(s, \chi_0, K/\Omega_1) = L(s, \psi_1+\psi_2, K/k)\\ &= L_{\psi_1}L_{\psi_2},\\ \zeta_{\Omega_2}(s) &= L(s, \chi_0, K/\Omega_2) = L(s, \psi_1+\psi_3, K/k)\\ &= L_{\psi_1}L_{\psi_3},\end{aligned}$$

and

$$\zeta_k(s) = L(s, \chi_0, K/k) = L_{\psi_1}.$$

We remark that

$$L_{\psi_2} = L(s, \psi_2, K/k) = L(s, \chi_5, \Omega_1/k)$$

by (III) and that

$$L_{\psi_3} = L(s, \psi_3, K/k) = L(s, \chi_2, K/\Omega_1)$$

by (V). Hence L_{ψ_2} and L_{ψ_3} are integral functions.

Incidentally, this example verifies Artin's conjecture for $\mathrm{Gal}(K/k) = S_3$.

We conclude this brief survey of the non-abelian case by quoting *Čebotarev's density theorem:*

Let K/k be normal and let $G = \mathrm{Gal}(K/k)$. Let C denote a given conjugacy class in G. Then the class of all non-ramified primes $\mathfrak{p}$, each having the property that $\left[\frac{K/k}{\mathfrak{P}}\right] \in C$ for some† prime $\mathfrak{P}$ of K lying over $\mathfrak{p}$, has density equal to

$$\frac{\mathrm{card}\, C}{\mathrm{card}\, G}.$$

Using arguments of the kind described above (see Section 2), this result follows from the fact than an Artin L-function has no zeros on the line $\mathrm{Re}\, s = 1$.

Example. As an illustration of the theorem, let us consider the case of a non-normal cubic extension K_3/k. A (non-ramified) prime $\mathfrak{p}$ in k factorizes in K_3 in one of the following three ways:

(1) $\mathfrak{p} = \mathfrak{P}_1\mathfrak{P}_2\mathfrak{P}_3$
(2) $\mathfrak{p} = \mathfrak{P}_1\mathfrak{P}_2$ where the $\deg \mathfrak{P}_1/\mathfrak{p} = 1$, $\deg \mathfrak{P}_2/\mathfrak{p} = 2$
(3) $\mathfrak{p} = \mathfrak{P}$.

† In fact, C consists of the Frobenius automorphisms $\left[\frac{K/k}{\mathfrak{P}}\right]$ corresponding to those $\mathfrak{P}_i$ lying over $\mathfrak{p}$.

We wish to determine the density of primes $\mathfrak{p}$ falling into each of these categories.

Let K_6 denote the minimal extension of K_3 that is *normal* over k. We study the factorization of $\mathfrak{p}$ in K_6, bearing in mind that in any decomposition of $\mathfrak{p}$ into primes of K_6, these all have equal order. Thus in (1) $\mathfrak{p}$ decomposes either in six primes (in K_6) of degree 1, or $\mathfrak{P}_1, \mathfrak{P}_2, \mathfrak{P}_3$ are themselves primes of K_6, each of degree 2. The latter possibility is ruled out because K_3/k is not normal.

[Suppose, on the contrary that, each $\mathfrak{P}_i$ remains a prime in K_6, and hence is of degree 2 in K_6. Write

$$\sigma_i = \left[\frac{K/k}{\mathfrak{P}_i}\right].$$

Then each σ_i is of order 2, and hence is a 2-cycle (note that Gal $(K_6/k) = S_3$). Further, the σ_i's span a conjugacy class, and hence are distinct transpositions.

Now K_3 is the set of elements of K_6 invariant under some 2-cycle, say σ_1. Thus

$$\sigma_1(\mathfrak{P}_i \cap K_3) = \mathfrak{P}_i \cap K_3.$$

But since there are three distinct prime ideals in K_3, and since each has a unique extension to K_6 (for each remains a prime in K_6),

$$\sigma_1 \mathfrak{P}_i = \mathfrak{P}_i \qquad (i = 1, 2, 3).$$

Let the subfields invariant under σ_2 and σ_3 be K_3' and K_3''. Then, in a similar way we have (since K_3' and K_3'' are the conjugates of K_3)

$$\sigma_j \mathfrak{P}_i = \mathfrak{P}_i \qquad (i, j, = 1, 2, 3).$$

But the transpositions generate S_3. Hence

$$S_3 \mathfrak{P}_i = \mathfrak{P}_i.$$

Thus there is no automorphism τ such that

$$\tau \mathfrak{P}_1 = \mathfrak{P}_2,$$

and this is impossible.]

In (2), we must have $\mathfrak{p} = \mathfrak{q}_1 \mathfrak{q}_2 \mathfrak{P}_1$ as the prime factorization over K_6, each factor being of degree 2, with $\mathfrak{q}_1 \mathfrak{q}_2 = \mathfrak{P}_2$. In (3), either $\mathfrak{p}$ remains prime, or $\mathfrak{p}$ decomposes into two primes of degree 3. The former would imply that $\left[\frac{K_6/k}{\mathfrak{p}}\right]$ generates S_3, which is impossible. Hence the latter decomposition must hold.

We now apply the fact (Chapter VII, §2) that the order of $\left[\frac{K_6/k}{\mathfrak{q}}\right]$ equals the degree of $\mathfrak{q}$. From this it follows for each prime $\mathfrak{q}$ of K_6 lying over $\mathfrak{p}$ that $\left[\frac{K_6/k}{\mathfrak{q}}\right]$ is an i-cycle in case (i) ($i = 1, 2, 3$). Hence, by Čebotarev's theorem, the required densities in cases (1), (2) and (3) are $\frac{1}{6}$, $\frac{1}{2}$ and $\frac{1}{3}$ respectively.

The following result is a direct consequence of Kummer's theorem (see Chapter III, Appendix, or Weiss (1963), 4.9 and in particular 4.9.2).

"Suppose $f \in k[x]$, is irreducible, and θ is a zero of f. Let $\mathfrak{p}$ denote a prime of k. Then, for almost all primes $\mathfrak{p}$ of k, $\mathfrak{p}$ splits in $k(\theta)$ as $f(x)$ splits over the residue class field of k modulo $\mathfrak{p}$."

Now let $n(\mathfrak{p},f)$ denote the number of solutions of the congruence

$$f(x) \equiv 0 \pmod{\mathfrak{p}};$$

then, for almost all $\mathfrak{p}$, $n(\mathfrak{p},f)$ may be regarded, alternatively, as the number of prime factors from $k(\theta)$ of $\mathfrak{p}$ having degree 1 relative to k. Applying the prime ideal theorem (Theorem 3) to primes of $k(\theta)$, we arrive therefore at the following

THEOREM 8. *Using the notation defined above,*

$$\sum_{N(\mathfrak{p}) \leq x} n(\mathfrak{p},f) \sim \frac{x}{\log x} \qquad \text{as } x \to \infty.$$

Corollary 1. More generally, if f is the product of l distinct irreducible factors, then

$$\sum_{N(\mathfrak{p}) \leq x} n(\mathfrak{p},f) \sim l\frac{x}{\log x} \qquad \text{as } x \to \infty.$$

Corollary 2. If, for almost all $\mathfrak{p}$, f splits completely mod $\mathfrak{p}$, then f factorizes completely over $k[x]$.

Proof. If n' denotes the degree of f, then we are given that $n(\mathfrak{p},f) = n'$ for almost all $\mathfrak{p}$. Hence, by the prime ideal theorem for k, $l = n'$.

It would seem plausible that if f has at least one linear factor mod $\mathfrak{p}$ for almost all $\mathfrak{p}$, then f has at least one linear factor in $k[x]$. However, the following counter-examples show this to be false.

(i) $$f(x) = (x^2-a)(x^2-b)(x^2-c)$$

where abc is a perfect square in $\mathbf{Z}$, with none of a, b, c a perfect square.

For, if a, b are quadratic non-residues mod p, then c is a quadratic residue mod p and hence f has two linear factors mod p.

(ii) $$f(x) = (x^2+3)(x^3+2).$$

For if $p \equiv 1 \pmod 3$, x^2+3 factorizes mod p, and if $p \equiv 2 \pmod 3$, x^3+2 factorizes mod p.

However, we do have the following,

THEOREM 9. *If f is a non-linear polynomial over k which has at least one linear factor modulo $\mathfrak{p}$ for almost all $\mathfrak{p}$, then f is reducible in $k[x]$.*

Proof. Assume that f is irreducible. Then it follows from Theorem 8 and the prime ideal theorem for k (Theorem 3) that

$$\sum_{N(\mathfrak{p})\leqslant x} (n(\mathfrak{p},f)-1) = o\left(\frac{x}{\log x}\right).$$

Hence, since $n(\mathfrak{p},f) \geqslant 1$ almost everywhere, $n(\mathfrak{p},f) = 1$ almost everywhere.

Let K be the root field of f over k, and $\mathfrak{q}$ a prime ideal in k which splits totally in K. Then $\mathfrak{q}$ splits totally in $k(\theta)$ and $n(\mathfrak{q},f)$ is equal to the degree of f, with a finite number of exceptions. These $\mathfrak{q}$ have positive density by the prime ideal theorem (Theorem 3) in K. Hence f is linear.

REFERENCES

Artin, E. (1923). Über eine neue Art von *L*-Reihen. *Abh. math. Semin. Univ. Hamburg*, **3**, 89–108. (Collected Papers (1965), 105–124. Addison-Wesley.)

Artin, E. (1930). Zur Theorie der *L*-Reihen mit allgemeinen Gruppencharakteren. *Abh. math. Semin. Univ. Hamburg*, **8**, 292–306. (Collected Papers (1965), 165–179. Addison-Wesley.)

Brauer, R. (1947). On Artin's *L*-series with general group characters. *Ann. Math.* (2) **48**, 502–514.

Chevalley, C. (1940). La théorie du corps de classes. *Ann. Math.* (2) **41**, 394–418; and other papers referred to in the above.

Dedekind, R. Vorlesungen über Zahlentheorie von P. G. Lejeune Dirichlet. Braunschweig, 1871–1894. Supplement 11.

Estermann, T. (1952). Introduction to modern prime number theory. *Camb. Tracts in Math.* **41.**

Hall, M., Jr. (1959). "The Theory of Groups". Macmillan, New York.

Hasse, H. Bericht über neuere Untersuchungen und Probleme aus der Theorie der algebraischen Zahlkörper. *Jber. dt. Mat Verein.*, **35** (1926), **36** (1927) and **39** (1930).

Hecke, E. (1920). Eine neue Art von Zetafunktionen und ihre Beziehungen zur Verteilung der Primzahlen (Zweite Mitteilung). *Math. Z.* **6,** 11–51 (Mathematische Werke (1959), 249–289. Vandenhoeck und Ruprecht).

Hecke, E. (1954). Vorlesungen über die Theorie der algebraischen Zahlen, 2. Unveränderte Aufl., Leipzig.

Landau, E. (1907). Über die Verteilung der Primideale in den Idealklassen eines algebraischen Zahlkörpers. *Math. Annln*, **63,** 145–204.

Landau, E. (1927). Einführung in die elementare und analytische Theorie der algebraischen Zahlen und der Ideale, 2. Aufl. Leipzig.

Lang, S. (1964). "Algebraic Numbers". Addison-Wesley.

Speiser, A. (1927). "Die Theorie der Gruppen von endlicher Ordnung", 2. Aufl. Berlin.

Titchmarsh, E. C. (1939). "The Theory of Functions", 2nd edition. Oxford University Press, London.

Titchmarsh, E. C. (1951). "The Theory of the Riemann Zeta-function". Oxford University Press, London.

Weber, H. (1896). Über einen in der Zahlentheorie angewandten Satz der Integralrechnung. *Göttinger Nachrichten*, 275–281.

Weiss, E. (1963). "Algebraic Number Theory". McGraw-Hill, New York.

CHAPTER IX

On Class Field Towers

PETER ROQUETTE

1. Introduction

Let k be an algebraic number field of finite degree and h_k its class number, i.e. the order of the finite group Cl_k of divisor classes of k. One of the most striking features of algebraic number theory—as compared to rational number theory—is the existence of fields k with class number $h_k > 1$, i.e. whose ring of integers is not a principal ideal ring.

There arises the question as to whether every such k can be imbedded into an algebraic number field K of finite degree with $h_K = 1$. We refer to this problem as the imbedding problem for k, and to K as a solution of the imbedding problem.

Let k_1 be the Hilbert class field of k. It can be defined as the maximal unramified abelian field extension of k. The Galois group of k_1/k is isomorphic to Cl_k via the reciprocity isomorphism of class field theory. In particular,

$$(k_1 : k) = h_k.$$

The principal divisor theorem states that every divisor of k becomes a principal divisor in k_1. But there may be divisors of k_1 which are not principal; so let k_2 be the Hilbert class field of k_1. Continuing, we obtain a tower of fields

$$k \subset k_1 \subset k_2 \subset k_3 \subset \ldots$$

in which each field is the Hilbert class field of its predecessor. This is called the *Hilbert class field tower* of k. We denote by k_∞ the union of the fields k_i. This is an algebraic number field whose degree may be finite or infinite.

PROPOSITION 1. *If the imbedding problem $k \subset K$ with $h_K = 1$ has a solution* K, then $k_\infty \subset K$. *In particular, the degree of k_∞ is then finite.*

Conversely, if the degree of k_∞ is finite, then $h_{k_\infty} = 1$ and hence k_∞ is then the smallest solution of the imbedding problem for k.

Proof. (i) First we show $k_i \subset K$ for all i. Using induction we may assume $i = 1$. The field extension k_1/k is unramified and has abelian Galois group.

Both these properties carry over to the composite field extension $k_1 K/K$. Hence $k_1 K$ is contained in the Hilbert class field K_1 of K. By assumption, $(K_1 : K) = h_K = 1$. It follows $k_1 \subset K$.

(ii) Now we assume k_∞ of finite degree. Then $k_i = k_\infty$ if i is large. Hence

$$h_{k_\infty} = h_{k_i} = (k_{i+1} : k_i) = 1. \text{ QED.}$$

By Proposition 1 we see that the imbedding problem for k is equivalent to the problem of whether the Hilbert class field tower of k is finite. This problem has been posed by Furtwängler and it is mentioned in Hasse's Klassenkörperbericht 1926, in connection with the (then yet unsolved) principal divisor theorem for k. Although the principal divisor theorem was proved already in 1930 (Furtwängler), it was not until 1964 that the finiteness problem of the Hilbert class field tower could be solved. The solution has been given by Šafarevič (together with Golod) who showed that the answer in general is negative, i.e. the Hilbert class field tower can be infinite.

The purpose of this course is to give a report about Šafarevič's results, together with the related work of Brumer.

Let p be a prime number. A field extension K/k is called a *p-extension* if it is Galois and if its Galois group is a p-group. (Warning: if K/k is not Galois it is not called a p-extension, even if its degree is a p-power.)

Let $k_1^{(p)}$ be the maximal p-extension of k contained in k_1; this is called the *Hilbert p-class field* of k. Let $k_2^{(p)}$ be the Hilbert p-class field of $k_1^{(p)}$. We obtain a field tower

$$k \subset k_1^{(p)} \subset k_2^{(p)} \subset k_3^{(p)} \subset \ldots$$

in which each field is the Hilbert p-class field of its predecessor. This is called the *Hilbert p-class field tower* of k. The union of the $k_i^{(p)}$ is called $k_\infty^{(p)}$.

It is easy to see that $k_i^{(p)} \subset k_i$ and in fact $k_i^{(p)}$ is the *maximal* p-extension of k which is contained in k_i. It follows $k_\infty^{(p)} \subset k_\infty$. In particular, if $k_\infty^{(p)}$ is of infinite degree we see that k_∞ is of infinite degree too.

Hence we ask: Under what conditions is $k_\infty^{(p)}$ of finite degree, if p is a fixed prime? The fact that we shall deal with $k_\infty^{(p)}$ rather than with k_∞ is due only to the fact that p-groups are easier to handle than arbitrary solvable groups.

The following proposition is the analogue to Proposition 1 for the p-class field tower and is proved similarly, using the fact that $(k_1^{(p)} : k) = h_k^{(p)}$ is the p-power part of the class number h_k. The proof is left to the reader.

PROPOSITION 2. *Let p be a prime number. If the imbedding problem* $k \subset K$ *with* $p \nmid h_K$ *has a solution K, then* $k_\infty^{(p)} \subset K$. *In particular, the degree of* $k_\infty^{(p)}$ *is then finite.*

Conversely, if the degree of $k_\infty^{(p)}$ *is finite, then its class number is not divisible by p and hence* $k_\infty^{(p)}$ *is then the smallest solution of the imbedding problem for k with respect to p.*

Now we state our main result. First a definition: If G is any group, we denote by G/p the maximal abelian factor group of G of exponent p, regarded as a vector space over the field of p elements. We define the p-rank $d^{(p)}G$ to be the dimension of G/p:

$$d^{(p)}G = \dim G/p.$$

If G is finite abelian, then $d^{(p)}G$ is the number of factors of p-power order which occur in a direct decomposition of G into cyclic primary components.

THEOREM 3 (Golod–Šafarevič). *There exists a function $\gamma(n)$ such that*

$$d^{(p)}\,\mathrm{Cl}_k < \gamma(n)$$

for any algebraic number field k of degree n whose p-class field tower is finite.

Remark 4. As we shall see in the proof of Theorem 3, we have

$$d^{(p)}\,\mathrm{Cl}_k < 2+2\sqrt{(r_k+\delta_k^{(p)})} \tag{1}$$

where r_k denotes the number of infinite primes of k and $\delta_k^{(p)} = 1$ or 0 according to whether the pth roots of unity are contained in k or not. Since $r_k \leqq n$ and $\delta_k^{(p)} \leqq 1$ we see that we can take

$$\gamma(n) = 2+2\sqrt{(n+1)}.$$

In order to formulate our next theorem, we introduce the following notation. Let q be a finite prime in the rational number field Q, and let $\mathfrak{Q}$ be any extension of q to k with the corresponding ramification degree $e(\mathfrak{Q})$. Let us put

$$e_k(q) = \gcd_{\mathfrak{Q}|q} e(\mathfrak{Q})$$

where $\mathfrak{Q}$ ranges over the extensions of q to k (gcd means "greatest common divisor"). We shall call q *completely ramified in k* if $e_k(q) > 1$. Let $t_k^{(p)}$ be the number of completely ramified q such that p divides $e_k(q)$.

THEOREM 5 (Brumer). *There exists a function $c(n)$ such that*

$$d^{(p)}\,\mathrm{Cl}_k \geqq t_k^{(p)} - c(n)$$

for every algebraic number field k of degree n.

Remark 6. One can show that

$$d^{(p)}\,\mathrm{Cl}_k \geqq t_k^{(p)} - r_k n$$

where r_k has the same meaning as in Remark 4. Since $r_k \leqq n$ we see that we can take

$$c(n) = n^2.$$

Actually, following Brumer, we are going to prove here Theorem 5 only in a somewhat weaker version, insofar as we shall consider only Galois extensions k of $\mathbf{Q}$. We shall exhibit a function $c'(n)$ such that for every Galois extension $k/\mathbf{Q}$ of degree n the following inequality holds:

$$d^{(p)}\,\mathrm{Cl}_k \geqq t_k^{(p)} - c'(n).$$

Our proof of Theorem 5 in the general case requires the use of the Amitsur cohomology in number fields which we do not want to assume known in this Chapter. For Galois extensions, we shall show that

(2) $$d^{(p)}\,\mathrm{Cl}_k \geqq t_k^{(p)} - \left(\frac{r_k-1}{p-1} + w_p(n).\delta_k^{(p)}\right)$$

where $w_p(n)$ denotes the exponent of p occurring in n. Since $w_p(n) \leqq n-1$ we see that we can take

$$c'(n) = (n-1)+(n-1) = 2(n-1).$$

Combining Theorems 3 and 5 we obtain the

COROLLARY 7. *If k is an algebraic number field of degree n and if*

$$t_k^{(p)} \geqq \gamma(n)+c(n)$$

then the p-class field tower of k is infinite.

In particular, for any given degree $n > 1$ and any prime p dividing n, there exist infinitely many algebraic number fields k of degree n with an infinite p-class field tower, for instance the fields

$$k = \mathbf{Q}(\sqrt[n]{(q_1 \ldots q_N)}) \text{ with } N \geqq \gamma(n)+c(n)$$

where the $q_i > 0$ are different prime numbers in **Q**.

Numerical examples: We consider the case $n = p = 2$ and use the estimates given by formulae (1) and (2). We have $\delta_k^{(2)} = 1$, $w_2(2) = 1$. Furthermore, $t_k^{(2)}$ is just the number of finite primes of Q which ramify in k. It follows: *A quadratic field k has an infinite 2-class field tower if the number of finite primes of* **Q** *which are ramified in k is* $\geqq 2+2\sqrt{(r_k+1)}+r_k$.

If k is imaginary, we have $r_k = 1$. Since $2+2\sqrt{2}+1 < 6$ it follows that any imaginary quadratic field with at least six ramified finite primes has an infinite 2-class field tower. A small numerical example is

$$k = \mathbf{Q}(\sqrt{(-2.3.5.7.11.13)}) = \mathbf{Q}(\sqrt{(-30030)}).$$

If k is real, we have $r_k = 2$. Since $2+2\sqrt{3}+2 < 8$ we see that in the real case we must have at least eight finite ramified primes in order to deduce the infinity of the 2-class field tower. A small numerical example is

$$k = \mathbf{Q}(\sqrt{(2.3.5.7.11.13.17.19)})$$
$$= \mathbf{Q}(\sqrt{(9699690)}).$$

2. Proof of Theorem 3

We consider the following situation:

- k an algebraic number field of finite degree;
- Cl_k its divisor class group;
- C_k its idèle class group;
- U_k the group of idèle units;
- E_k $= U_k \cap k$ the group of units in k;

W_k the group of roots of unity in k;
p a fixed prime number
K $= k_\infty^{(p)}$ as explained in Section 1;
G $= G(K/k)$ the corresponding Galois group.

Under the assumption that $(K:k)$ is finite we are going to prove the inequality (1) of Section 1.

The proof will be divided into two parts. In the first part, we shall reduce Theorem 3 to a purely group theoretical statement about finite p-groups. In the second part, we shall prove this group theoretical statement.

The unit theorem says that E_k is a direct product of the finite cyclic group W_k and a free abelian group with $r_k - 1$ free generators. (See Chapter II, § 18.) This gives

$$d^{(p)} E_k = (r_k - 1) + d^{(p)} W_k = (r_k - 1) + \delta_k^{(p)}.$$

Therefore the inequality (1) to be proved can also be written as

$$d^{(p)} \mathrm{Cl}_k < 2 + 2\sqrt{(d^{(p)} E_k + 1)}$$

or equivalently, in rational form:

$$\tfrac{1}{4}(d^{(p)} \mathrm{Cl}_k)^2 - d^{(p)} \mathrm{Cl}_k < d^{(p)} E_k. \tag{3}$$

First we observe that

$$d^{(p)} \mathrm{Cl}_k = d^{(p)} G.$$

Namely, we have

$$d^{(p)} G = d^{(p)}(G^{ab})$$

where G^{ab} is the maximal abelian factor group of G. This follows directly from the definition of the p-rank of G as given in Section 1. Now, G^{ab} is the Galois group of the maximal subfield of K which is abelian over k; this subfield is the Hilbert p-class field $k_1^{(p)}$. By the reciprocity isomorphism of class field theory, we have therefore

$$G^{ab} = \mathrm{Cl}_k^{(p)}$$

where $\mathrm{Cl}_k^{(p)}$ is the p-Sylow group of Cl_k. By definition of the p-rank,

$$d^{(p)} \mathrm{Cl}_k^{(p)} = d^{(p)} \mathrm{Cl}_k.$$

This proves our contention.

Therefore the inequality (3) to be proved may be written as

$$\tfrac{1}{4}(d^{(p)} G)^2 - d^{(p)} G < d^{(p)} E_k. \tag{4}$$

Any factor group of E_k has p-rank $\leqq d^{(p)} E_k$. In particular, this is true for the norm factor group:

$$E_k / N_{K/k}(E_K) = \hat{H}^0(G, E_K).$$

Hence it suffices to show that

$$\tfrac{1}{4}(d^{(p)} G)^2 - d^{(p)} G < d^{(p)} \hat{H}^0(G, E_K). \tag{5}$$

To determine the right-hand side, we use the exact sequence

$$1 \to E_K \to U_K \to U_K/E_K \to 1.$$

Since K/k is unramified, U_K is cohomologically trivial as a G-module. (For the proof, decompose U_K into its local components and prove the similar fact for a local Galois extension and its unit group, cf. Chapter VI, § 2.5.)†

It follows that

$$\hat{H}^0(G, E_K) = H^{-1}(G, U_K/E_K).$$

Now we use the exact sequence

$$1 \to U_K/E_K \to C_K \to \mathrm{Cl}_K \to 1.$$

Here, the group Cl_K is of order prime to p. This follows from the fact that $K = k_\infty^{(p)}$ is the maximal field in the Hilbert p-class tower; see Proposition 2 in Section 1. Since G is a p-group, we conclude that Cl_K is cohomologically trivial as a G-module. Therefore

$$H^{-1}(G, U_K/E_K) = H^{-1}(G, C_K) = H^{-3}(G, \mathbf{Z}).$$

using Tate's fundamental theorem of cohomology in class field theory (Chapter VII, § 11.3).

It follows that the inequality (5) to be proved may be written as

$$\tfrac{1}{4}(d^{(p)}G)^2 - d^{(p)}G < d^{(p)}H_2(G, \mathbf{Z}). \tag{6}$$

using the fact that

$$H_2(G, \mathbf{Z}) = H^{-3}(G, \mathbf{Z})$$

by definition of the cohomology groups with negative dimensions.

The inequality (6) is now a purely group theoretical statement; *we shall see that* (6) *is true for any finite p-group G.*

According to our notation introduced in Section 1, let $\mathbf{Z}/p$ denote the cyclic group with p elements. The homology groups $H_i(G, \mathbf{Z}/p)$ are annihilated by p and may therefore be regarded as vector spaces over the field with p elements. Let us put

$$d_i^{(p)}G = \dim H_i(G, \mathbf{Z}/p).$$

LEMMA 8. *For any group G, there is a natural isomorphism* $H_1(G, \mathbf{Z}/p) = G/p$. *In particular,* $d_1^{(p)}G = d^{(p)}G$.

LEMMA 9. *For any finite group G, we have*

$$d^{(p)}H_2(G, \mathbf{Z}) = d_2^{(p)}G - d_1^{(p)}G.$$

Proofs. Consider the exact sequence

$$0 \to \mathbf{Z} \underset{p}{\to} \mathbf{Z} \to \mathbf{Z}/p \to 0$$

where $\underset{p}{\to}$ denotes the map "multiplication by p". Consider the corresponding

† Recall that the absence of ramification for an *infinite* prime means the corresponding local extension is trivial, i.e. of degree 1.

exact homology sequence

$$H_i(\mathbf{Z}) \underset{p}{\to} H_i(\mathbf{Z}) \to H_i(\mathbf{Z}/p) \to H_{i-1}(\mathbf{Z}) \underset{p}{\to} H_{i-1}(\mathbf{Z}).$$

(For brevity, we have written $H_i(\mathbf{Z})$ instead of $H_i(G, \mathbf{Z})$.)

In general, if A is any abelian group, let A_p be the kernel of the map $A \underset{p}{\to} A$; its cokernel is A/p. With this notation, we obtain the exact sequence

(7) $$0 \to H_i(\mathbf{Z})/p \to H_i(\mathbf{Z}/p) \to H_{i-1}(\mathbf{Z})_p \to 0.$$

First, take $i = 1$. We have $H_0(\mathbf{Z}) = \mathbf{Z}$ which has no p-torsion; it follows $H_0(\mathbf{Z})_p = 0$ and therefore

(8) $$H_1(\mathbf{Z})/p = H_1(\mathbf{Z}/p).$$

Here, $H_1(\mathbf{Z}) = H_1(G, \mathbf{Z}) = G^{ab}$ is the maximal abelian factor group of G. (See Chapter IV.) By definition of G/p, we have $G/p = G^{ab}/p$. This proves Lemma 8.

Secondly, take $i = 2$ in formula (7). Since G is finite, all groups occurring there are finite; hence they are finite dimensional vector spaces over the field with p elements. Comparing dimensions:

$$d_2^{(p)} G = d^{(p)} H_2(\mathbf{Z}) + \dim H_1(\mathbf{Z})_p.$$

In general, if A is any finite abelian group, we have

$$\dim A_p = \dim A/p$$

which is proved by decomposing A into cyclic direct factors. Applying this to $A = H_1(\mathbf{Z})$ and using formula (8) we obtain

$$\dim H_1(\mathbf{Z})_p = \dim H_1(\mathbf{Z}/p) = d_1^{(p)} G.$$

This proves Lemma 9.

Using Lemmas 8 and 9, we see that the inequality (6) to be proved is equivalent to the following.

THEOREM 10. *Let G be a finite p-group, p a prime number. Then*

$$d_2^{(p)} G > \tfrac{1}{4}(d_1^{(p)} G)^2,$$

where $d_i^{(p)} G = \dim H_i(G, \mathbf{Z}/p)$.

We use the following notations:

- $\Lambda = \mathbf{Z}(G)$ is the integral group ring of G;
- I is the augmentation ideal of Λ, defined to be the kernel of the augmentation map $\Lambda \to \mathbf{Z}$;
- Λ/p is the group ring of G over the field of p elements.

First we prove two preparatory lemmas.

LEMMA 11. *Let G be a finite p-group and A a G-module with $pA = 0$. Then the minimal number of generators of A as G-module equals*

$$\dim H_0(G, A) = \dim A/IA,$$

the dimension to be understood over the field with p elements.

More precisely: Let $a_i \in A$. Then the a_i generate A as a G-module if and only if their images a_i in A/IA generate A/IA as a vector space.

Proof. Assume the a_i generate A/IA. Let B be the G-submodule of A generated by the a_i. Then the natural map $B/IB \to A/IA$ is epimorphic, which is the same as the map $H_0(B) \to H_0(A)$. The exact sequence

$$0 \to B \to A \to A/B \to 0$$

yields the exact homology sequence

$$H_0(B) \to H_0(A) \to H_0(A/B) \to 0$$

from which we infer that $H_0(A/B) = 0$. Since A/B is annihilated by p and G a p-group, it follows $A/B = 0$, i.e. $A = B$. (See Chapter IV, § 9.) QED.

LEMMA 12. *Let G be a finite p-group and A a G-module with $pA = 0$. Then there exists a resolution*

$$\ldots \to Y_2 \to Y_1 \to Y_0 \to A \to 0$$

with the following properties:

(i) *Each Y_n is a free module over Λ/p.*
(ii) *The number of free module generators of Y_n over Λ/p equals* $\dim H_n(G, A)$.
(iii) *The image* $\mathrm{im}(Y_{n+1})$ *is contained in* $I.Y_n$.

Proof. Put $d = \dim H_0(G, A)$. By Lemma 11 there is a free Λ-module X on d generators and an epimorphism $X \to A$. Since $pA = 0$ we obtain by factorization an epimorphism $X/p \to A$. Put $Y = X/p$. Then Y is a free Λ/p-module on d generators. In particular,

$$H_i(Y) = 0 \textit{ for } i \geqq 1.$$

Let B be the kernel of $Y \to A$ so that

$$0 \to B \to Y \to A \to 0$$

is exact. The exact homology sequence

$$\ldots \to H_{i+1}(Y) \to H_{i+1}(A) \to H_i(B) - H_i(Y) \to \ldots$$

yields

$$H_i(B) = H_{i+1}(A) \tag{9}$$

for $i \geqq 1$. As to the case $i = 0$, we have the exact sequence

$$0 \to H_1(A) \to H_0(B) \to H_0(Y) \to H_0(A) \to 0.$$

By construction, Y and A have the same minimal number of generators as G-modules; hence $\dim H_0(Y) = \dim H_0(A)$ by Lemma 11 which shows that $H_0(Y) \to H_0(A)$ is an isomorphism. We conclude that (9) holds also in the case $i = 0$.

Since $H_0(Y) \to H_0(A)$ is an isomorphism, the map

$$B/IB = H_0(B) \to H_0(Y) = Y/IY$$

is zero; hence

$$B \subset I.Y. \tag{10}$$

Now put $Y = Y_0$. Then $Y_0 \to A \to 0$ is the first step in the resolution to be constructed. The second step is obtained by applying the same procedure to B. We obtain $Y_1 \to B \to 0$ with a kernel C such that

$$H_i(C) = H_{i+1}(B) = H_{i+2}(A)$$

for $i \geqq 0$, and

$$C \subset I.Y_1.$$

Y_1 is a free Λ/p-module on $\dim H_0(B) = \dim H_1(A)$ generators. If we define $Y_1 \to Y_0$ to be the composite map $Y_1 \to B \to Y_0$, then (10) says that $\mathrm{im}(Y_1) \subset I.Y_0$.

Continuing this process, we obtain Lemma 12 by induction. QED.

Let us apply Lemma 12 to the case $A = \mathbf{Z}/p$. Then $H_0(G, \mathbf{Z}/p) = \mathbf{Z}/p$ is of dimension 1. Hence Y_0 is free with one generator. By (iii), the kernel of $Y_0 \to \mathbf{Z}/p$ is contained in $I.Y_0$. Since $Y_0/I.Y_0$ is of dimension 1, this kernel is precisely $I.Y_0$. Hence $Y_1 \to I.Y_0 \to 0$ is exact. Changing notation, we obtain the

COROLLARY 13. *Let G be a finite p-group and put $d = d_1^{(p)}G$, $r = d_2^{(p)}G$. Then there is an exact sequence*

$$R \to D \to I.E \to 0 \text{ with } \mathrm{im}(R) \subset I.D$$

where E, D, R denote the free Λ/p-modules with 1, d, r generators respectively.

Proof of Theorem 10: We use the abbreviations of Corollary 13.

For any finite G-module A with $pA = 0$ we introduce the Poincaré polynomial

$$P_A(t) = \sum_{0 \leqq n} c_n(A).t^n \text{ with } c_n(A) = \dim I^n A/I^{n+1}A.$$

(Note that $c_n(A) = 0$ if n is sufficiently large.) We put

$$P(t) = P_E(t).$$

Since $c_0(E) = \dim E/IE = 1$ we have

$$P_{IE}(t) = \frac{P(t)-1}{t}.$$

Also, since $D = E^d$ is the d-fold direct product of E, we have $c_n(D) = d.c_n(E)$ and therefore

$$P_D(t) = d.P(t).$$

Similarly,

$$P_R(t) = r.P(t).$$

In general, if $0 < t < 1$ is a real variable, then

$$P_A(t)\frac{1}{1-t} = \sum_{0 \leqq n} s_n(A)t^n \text{ with } s_n(A) = \sum_{0 \leqq i \leqq n} c_i(A) = \dim A/I^{n+1}A.$$

Also,

$$P_A(t)\frac{t}{1-t} = \sum_{0 \leqq n} s_{n-1}(A)t^n$$

where we have to interpret $s_{-1}(A) = 0$.

From Corollary 13 we obtain an epimorphism $I^{n+1}D \to I^{n+2}E$. Hence, if R_{n+1} denotes the foreimage of $I^{n+1}D$ in R then the sequence

$$0 \to R/R_{n+1} \to D/I^{n+1}D \to IE/I^{n+2}E \to 0$$

is exact. This gives

$$s_n(D) = s_n(IE) + \dim R/R_{n+1}.$$

By Corollary 13, image$(R) \subset ID$, hence image $(I^nR) \subset I^{n+1}D$, $I^nR \subset R_{n+1}$. Therefore,

$$\dim R/R_{n+1} \leqq \dim R/I^nR = s_{n-1}(R).$$

This gives

$$s_n(D) \leqq s_n(IE) + s_{n-1}(R).$$

The numbers occuring in these inequalities are the coefficients of power series as given above. It follows that

$$P_D(t)\frac{1}{1-t} \leqq P_{IE}(t)\frac{1}{1-t} + P_R(t)\frac{t}{1-t},$$

or equivalently

$$d.P(t) \leqq \frac{P(t)-1}{t} + r.t.P(t) \text{ if } 0 < t < 1.$$

In other words:

$$1 \leqq P(t).(rt^2 - dt + 1) \text{ if } 0 < t < 1.$$

Since $P(t)$ has positive coefficients, we conclude that

$$0 < rt^2 - dt + 1 \text{ if } 0 < t < 1.$$

Substituting $t \to \dfrac{d}{2r}$ we get

$$r > \tfrac{1}{4}d^2$$

as contended. The substitution $t \to \dfrac{d}{2r}$ is permissible since we know from Lemma 9 that $d \leqq r < 2r$, hence $0 < \dfrac{d}{2r} < 1$. QED

Remark 14. Actually, Golod and Šafarevič have proved in their paper only $d_2^{(p)}G > \frac{1}{4}(d_1^{(p)}G-1)^2$. The inequality as given here has been obtained independently by Gaschütz and Vinberg.

Remark 15. Theorem 10 is important not only for the class field tower problem but also for various other problems in the theory of p-groups. This is due to the fact that the homological invariants $d_1^{(p)}G$ and $d_2^{(p)}G$ permit the following group theoretical interpretations if G is a finite p-group: $d_1^{(p)}G$ is the minimal number of generators of G (Burnside's basis theorem; see Chapter V, § 2.5) and $d_2^{(p)}$ is the minimal number of relations among these generators which define G as a p-group (see Serre, "Cohomologie Galoisienne").

3. Proof of Theorem 5 for Galois Extensions

Let $k/\mathbf{Q}$ be a Galois extension of finite degree n, and p a prime number. As said in Section 1, we are going to prove the inequality

$$d^{(p)}\,\mathrm{Cl}_k \geqq t_k^{(p)} - \left(\frac{r_k-1}{p-1} + w_p(n)\,.\,\delta_k^{(p)}\right). \tag{11}$$

Again, the proof will be divided into two parts. First, we shall reduce the proof to a group theoretical statement about the cohomology of finite groups. Secondly, we shall prove this group theoretical statement.

Let $K = k_1$ be the Hilbert class field of k;
G the Galois group of K/k;
G^* the Galois group of $K/\mathbf{Q}$;
$\mathfrak{g}$ the Galois group of $k/\mathbf{Q}$.

Then $\mathfrak{g} = G^*/G$ and we have the inflation–restriction sequence of cohomology groups

$$1 \to H^1(\mathfrak{g}, E_k) \to H^1(G^*, E_K) \to H^1(G, E_K)$$

where E_k as in Section 2 denotes the group of units in k. We conclude that

$$d^{(p)}H^1(G^*, E_K) \leqq d^{(p)}H^1(G, E_K) + d^{(p)}H^1(\mathfrak{g}, E_k).$$

Hence the inequality (11) to be proved is an immediate consequence of the following three statements:

$$H^1(G, E_K) = \mathrm{Cl}_k \tag{12}$$

$$d^{(p)}H^1(G^*, E_K) = t_k^{(p)} \tag{13}$$

$$d^{(p)}H^1(\mathfrak{g}, E_k) \leqq \frac{r_k-1}{p-1} + w_p(n)\,.\,\delta_k^{(p)}. \tag{14}$$

We are going to prove these three statements.

For any algebraic number field K of finite degree we consider the commutative and exact diagram:

$$\begin{array}{ccccccccc}
 & & 1 & & 1 & & 1 & & \\
 & & \downarrow & & \downarrow & & \downarrow & & \\
1 & \to & E_K & \to & U_K & \to & U_K/E_K & \to & 1 \\
 & & \downarrow & & \downarrow & & \downarrow & & \\
1 & \to & K^\times & \to & I_K & \to & C_K & \to & 1 \\
 & & \downarrow & & \downarrow & & \downarrow & & \\
1 & \to & P_K & \to & D_K & \to & \mathrm{Cl}_K & \to & 1 \\
 & & \downarrow & & \downarrow & & \downarrow & & \\
 & & 1 & & 1 & & & &
\end{array}$$

where $K^\times$ is the multiplicative group of K;

I_K the idèle group;
D_K the divisor group;
P_K the group of principal divisors;

and the other groups have the same meaning as before in Section 2. The arrows denote the natural maps. (In Section 2 we have used already the first row and the last column of this diagram.)

If K is a Galois extension of a subfield k with Galois group G then all groups and maps of this diagram are G-permissible and we obtain a corresponding commutative and exact cohomology diagram:

$$\begin{array}{ccccccccccc}
 & & 1 & & 1 & & 1 & & & & \\
 & & \downarrow & & \downarrow & & \downarrow & & & & \\
1 & \to & E_K & \to & U_k & \xrightarrow{\varepsilon} & (U_K/E_K)^G & \xrightarrow{\delta} & H^1(G,E_K) & \xrightarrow{\varphi} & H^1(G,U_K) \\
 & & \downarrow & & \zeta\downarrow & & \downarrow\gamma & & \downarrow & & \\
1 & \to & k^\times & \to & I_k & \xrightarrow{\eta} & C_k & \to & 1 & & \\
 & & \downarrow & & \xi\downarrow & & \downarrow\beta & & & & \\
1 & \to & P_K^G & \to & D_K^G & \xrightarrow{\alpha} & \mathrm{Cl}_K^G & & & & \\
 & & \downarrow & & \downarrow & & & & & & \\
 & & H^1(G,E_K) & \xrightarrow{\varphi} & H^1(G,U_K) & & & & & & \\
 & & \downarrow & & \downarrow & & & & & & \\
 & & 1 & & 1 & & & & & &
\end{array}$$

where we have twice used Hilbert's Theorem 90:

$$H^1(G,K^\times)=1$$

and also the corresponding local statement:

$$H^1(G,I_K)=1.$$

LEMMA 14. *Let K be an algebraic number field of finite degree which is a Galois extension of a subfield k with Galois group G.*

Assume $D_K^G \subset P_K$, i.e. that every invariant divisor is principal. Then there is a natural exact sequence

$$1 \to \mathrm{Cl}_k \to H^1(G,E_K) \xrightarrow{\varphi} H^1(G,U_K) \to 1.$$

Proof. We use the cohomology diagram as explained above. Observe that the natural map

$$\varphi : H^1(G, E_K) \to H^1(G, U_K)$$

occurs twice in this diagram. We have to show that, under the assumption of Lemma 14, φ is epimorphic and its kernel is Cl_k.

The assumption in Lemma 14 means $P_K^G = D_K^G$.

Looking at the left lower corner of our cohomology diagram we see therefore that φ is epimorphic.

On the other hand, $P_K^G = D_K^G$ shows that $\alpha = 1$. Hence $\alpha \circ \xi = \beta \circ \eta = 1$. Since η is epimorphic, $\beta = 1$. Hence γ is an isomorphism. Looking at the right upper corner of our diagram we see that

$$\text{kernel } (\varphi) = \text{image } (\delta) = (U_K/E_K)^G/\text{image } (\varepsilon);$$

the isomorphism γ shows that this equals

$$C_k/\text{image } (\gamma \circ \varepsilon) = C_k/\text{image } (\eta \circ \zeta) = I_k/k\,.\,U_k = \mathrm{Cl}_k. \quad \text{QED.}$$

Proof of (12): We use Lemma 14 in the case where (as in (12)) K is the Hilbert class field of k. Since K/k is unramified, we have $H^1(G, U_K) = 1$, as already observed in Section 2. In view of Lemma 14 it suffices therefore to show that the assumption of Lemma 14 is satisfied if K is the Hilbert class field of k.

Since $H^1(G, U_K) = 1$ we infer from our cohomology diagram above that $\xi : I_k \to D_K^G$ is epimorphic. On the other hand, its image is $I_k/U_k = D_k$. Hence $D_k = D_K^G$. Now, the principal divisor theorem for the Hilbert class field says that $D_k \subset P_K$. QED.

Proof of (13): We want to apply Lemma 14 to the Galois extension $K/\mathbf{Q}$, where K (as in (13)) is the Hilbert class field of k. First we have to show that the assumption of Lemma 14 is satisfied for $K/\mathbf{Q}$.

G^* is the group of $K/\mathbf{Q}$ and G the group of K/k. We have therefore $G \subset G^*$ and $D_K^{G^*} \subset D_K^G$. The foregoing proof shows $D_K^G \subset P_K$. Hence $D_K^{G^*} \subset P_K$.

Since $\mathrm{Cl}_{\mathbf{Q}} = 1$ we infer therefore from Lemma 14 an isomorphism

$$H^1(G^*, E_K) = H^1(G^*, U_K).$$

For any finite prime q of $\mathbf{Q}$ let $e_K(q)$ denote the ramification index of some extension $\mathfrak{Q}$ of q to K. (Since $K/\mathbf{Q}$ is Galois, this does not depend on the choice of $\mathfrak{Q}|q$.) Let $\mathbf{Z}/e_K(q)$ denote the cyclic group of order $e_K(q)$. Then

$$H^1(G^*, U_K) = \prod_q \mathbf{Z}/e_K(q).$$

(For the proof, decompose U_K into its local components and prove the similar fact for a local Galois extension and its unit group.)

Now K/k is unramified and therefore

$$e_K(q) = e_k(q)$$

for every q. Hence we obtain

$$H^1(G^*, E_K) = \prod_q \mathbf{Z}/e_k(q).$$

The p-rank of the direct product on the right-hand side is equal to the number of q with $p|e_K(q)$, i.e. to $t_k^{(p)}$. QED.

Proof of (14): The torsion group of E_k is the group W_k of roots of unity in k which is cyclic of p-rank $\delta_k^{(p)}$. Moreover, the unit theory says that E_k/W_k is a free abelian group on $r_k - 1$ generators. Hence (14) is an immediate consequence of the following group theoretical statement:

LEMMA 15. *Let G be a finite group of order n and p a prime number. Let A be a finitely generated G-module with torsion group tA, and let $\rho(A)$ be the number of free generators of A/tA as an abelian group. Then*

$$d^{(p)}H^1(G, A) \leqq \frac{\rho(A)}{p-1} + w_p(n).d^{(p)}tA.$$

Proof. Consider the restriction map

$$H^1(G, A) \to H^1(G^{(p)}, A)$$

of G to its p-Sylow subgroup $G^{(p)}$. This is a monomorphism of the p-primary components (Chapter IV, Prop. 8, Cor. 3). In particular,

$$d^{(p)}H^1(G, A) \leqq d^{(p)}H^1(G^{(p)}, A).$$

Hence we may assume in the following that $G = G^{(p)}$ is a p-group. (Observe that $w_p(n) = w_p(n^{(p)})$ where $n^{(p)}$ is the order of $G^{(p)}$.)

Now consider the exact sequence

$$0 \to tA \to A \to A/tA \to 0$$

and the corresponding exact cohomology sequence

$$H^1(G, tA) \to H^1(G, A) \to H^1(G, A/tA).$$

It follows that

$$d^{(p)}H^1(G, A) \leqq d^{(p)}H^1(G, tA) + d^{(p)}H^1(G, A/tA).$$

We shall show that

$$d^{(p)}H^1(G, tA) \leqq w_p(n).d^{(p)}tA$$

and

$$d^{(p)}H^1(G, A/tA) \leqq \frac{\rho(A)}{p-1}.$$

In other words: *We shall treat the following two cases separately:* (I) A is a torsion module; (II) A is torsion free.

(I) *The torsion case:* We have

$$d^{(p)}G = \dim G/p \leqq w_p(n)$$

and therefore it suffices to show:

(15) $$d^{(p)}H^1(A) \leqq d^{(p)}G . d^{(p)}A.$$

(For brevity, we omit the symbol G in the notation of the cohomology groups.) Let $Z^1(A)$ be the module of crossed homomorphisms $f: G \to A$. Let $g_1, \ldots, g_d$ be a minimal system of generators of G; Burnside's basis theorem for p-groups tells us that $d = d^{(p)}G$. Every crossed homomorphism f is uniquely determined by its values $f(g_i)$, $1 \leqq i \leqq d$. In other words: The map

$$f \to (f(g_1), \ldots, f(g_d))$$

is an injection of $Z^1(A)$ into the d-fold direct product A^d of A. It follows

$$d^{(p)}Z^1(A) \leqq d^{(p)}(A^d) = d.(d^{(p)}A) = d^{(p)}G . d^{(p)}A.$$

Since $H^1(A)$ is a factor module of $Z^1(A)$, we obtain (15).

Remark 16. In the proof just given, we have not made use of the fact that A is a torsion module. Hence the inequality (15) holds for *every* finitely generated G-module A. This means that we have proved instead of (14) the inequality

$$d^{(p)}H^1(\mathrm{g}, E_k) \leqq w_p(n)(r_k - 1 + \delta_k^{(p)})$$

and therefore instead of (11) the inequality

$$d^{(p)}\mathrm{Cl}_k \geqq t_k^{(p)} - w_p(n)(r_k - 1 + \delta_k^{(p)}).$$

This would suffice to obtain a function $c'(n)$ with

$$d^{(p)}\mathrm{Cl}_k \geqq t_k^{(p)} - c'(n),$$

as explained in Section 1. Namely, since $w_p(n) \leqq n-1$, we could take

$$c'(n) = (n-1).n.$$

The following proof, which permits to obtain a better estimate in the torsion free case, is needed only in order to obtain the better estimate $c'(n) = 2(n-1)$ as stated in Remark 6 of Section 1.

(II) *The torsion-free case:* We begin with

LEMMA 17 (Chevalley). *Let G be a group of order p and A a finitely generated G-module. Then*

$$d^{(p)}H^1(G, A) - d^{(p)}H^2(G, A) = \frac{\rho(A) - p.\rho(A^G)}{p-1}.$$

Proof. (i) Let us put

$$d_{1-2}(A) = d^{(p)}H^1(A) - d^{(p)}H^2(A).$$

Note that $p.H^i(A) = 0$ since G is of order p. Hence $d^{(p)}H^i(A)$ is the dimension of $H^i(A)$ over the field of p elements; the order $h^i(A)$ of $H^i(A)$ is therefore p to the power $d^{(p)}H^i(A)$. If we define the Herbrand quotient

$$h_{1/2}(A) = h^1(A)/h^2(A),$$

then it follows that

$$h_{1/2}(A) = p^{d_{1-2}(A)}.$$

We may therefore regard $d_{1-2}(A)$ as an additive analogue to the Herbrand quotient. The properties of the Herbrand quotient, as stated in Chapter IV, § 8, can therefore be applied *mutatis mutandis* to d_{1-2}. In particular, we have:

If $0 \to A \to B \to C \to 0$ is an exact sequence of G-modules, then

$$d_{1-2}(B) = d_{1-2}(A) + d_{1-2}(C).$$

We say therefore that d_{1-2} is an *additive function* of G-modules.

Let us say that two finitely generated G-modules A, B are *rationally equivalent* if $A \otimes \mathbf{Q}$ and $B \otimes \mathbf{Q}$ are isomorphic as $\mathbf{Q}(G)$-modules. (The tensor product is to be understood over $\mathbf{Z}$ and $\mathbf{Q}(G) = \mathbf{Z}(G) \otimes \mathbf{Q}$ is the group ring of G over $\mathbf{Q}$.) We may regard A/tA as a submodule of $A \otimes \mathbf{Q}$ and in fact as a G-invariant lattice of the rational representation space $A \otimes \mathbf{Q}$ of G. In view of Propositions 10 and 11, Section 8 of the cohomology course, we have:

If A and B are rationally equivalent, then $d_{1-2}(A) = d_{1-2}(B)$.

We say therefore that $d_{1-2}(A)$ is a *function of rational equivalence classes.*

(ii) For brevity, we define the function

$$\tau(A) = \frac{\rho(A) - p.\rho(A^G)}{p-1}.$$

We claim that $\tau(A)$ too is an additive function of rational equivalence classes, and have to show that both $\rho(A)$ and $\rho(A^G)$ are.

It follows from the definition of ρ that

$$\rho(A) = \dim_{\mathbf{Q}} A \otimes \mathbf{Q} \quad \text{and} \quad \rho(A^G) = \dim_{\mathbf{Q}} A^G \otimes \mathbf{Q}.$$

From the first relation we infer that $\rho(A)$ is a function of rational equivalence classes. From the second relation we infer the same for $\rho(A^G)$ since

$$A^G \otimes \mathbf{Q} = (A \otimes \mathbf{Q})^G.$$

If $0 \to A \to B \to C \to 0$ is exact then

$$0 \to A \otimes \mathbf{Q} \to B \otimes \mathbf{Q} \to C \otimes \mathbf{Q} \to 0$$

is exact too. This shows the additivity of $\rho(A)$. As to the additivity of $\rho(A^G)$, we have to use the fact that

$$0 \to (A \otimes \mathbf{Q})^G \to (B \otimes \mathbf{Q})^G \to (C \otimes \mathbf{Q})^G \to 0$$

is exact too, since $H^1(G, A \otimes \mathbf{Q}) = 0$ because $A \otimes \mathbf{Q}$ is uniquely divisible.

(iii) We have now seen that d_{1-2} and τ are both additive functions of rational equivalence classes. Furthermore, an easy computation shows

$$d_{1-2}(\mathbf{Z}) = \tau(\mathbf{Z}) = -1$$

$$d_{1-2}(\Lambda) = \tau(\Lambda) = 0$$

where we consider the integers $\mathbf{Z}$ and the group ring $\Lambda = \mathbf{Z}(G)$ as G-modules. Hence the contention of Lemma 17 follows from the following statement:

Every additive function f of rational equivalence classes of finitely generated G-modules A is uniquely determined by its values for the modules $\mathbf{Z}$ *and* Λ.

(iv) Proof of the statement in (iii): The exact sequence

$$0 \to I \to \Lambda \to \mathbf{Z} \to 0$$

shows $f(I) = f(\Lambda) - f(\mathbf{Z})$, so that $f(I)$ is determined by $f(\mathbf{Z})$ and $f(\Lambda)$. Hence it remains to be shown that every finitely generated G-module A is rationally equivalent to a direct sum of G-modules which are isomorphic either to $\mathbf{Z}$ or to I. In other words:

$$A \otimes \mathbf{Q} = \sum_i A_i \otimes \mathbf{Q}$$

where $A_i = \mathbf{Z}$ or $A_i = I$. Since $A \otimes \mathbf{Q}$ as a representation space of G over $\mathbf{Q}$ is a direct sum of *irreducible* representation spaces V_i, this amounts to showing that every irreducible representation space $V \neq 0$ of G over $\mathbf{Q}$ is either isomorphic to $\mathbf{Z} \otimes \mathbf{Q} = \mathbf{Q}$ or to $I \otimes \mathbf{Q}$.

Now every such V is isomorphic to a direct summand of $\mathbf{Q}(G) = \Lambda \otimes \mathbf{Q}$. Hence we have to determine the direct decomposition of $\mathbf{Q}(G)$. The exact augmentation sequence

$$0 \to I \otimes \mathbf{Q} \to \mathbf{Q}(G) \to \mathbf{Q} \to 0$$

splits; the corresponding map $\mathbf{Q} \to \mathbf{Q}(G)$ being given by

$$x \to x.e \qquad (x \in \mathbf{Q})$$

where e is the idempotent

$$e = \frac{1}{p} \sum_{g \in G} g.$$

We have therefore the direct decomposition

$$\mathbf{Q}(G) = (I \otimes \mathbf{Q}) \oplus \mathbf{Q}.e$$

and it remains to show that $I \otimes \mathbf{Q}$ is irreducible, i.e. that $I \otimes \mathbf{Q}$, as a $\mathbf{Q}$-algebra, is a field.

Let K denote the field of pth roots of unity. Let χ denote an isomorphism of G on to the group of pth roots of unity in K. By linearity, χ extends uniquely to an algebra homomorphism of $\mathbf{Q}(G)$ on to K. Its kernel contains e since the sum of all the pth roots of unity in K is 0. Hence χ defines an algebra homomorphism of $\mathbf{Q}(G)/e = I \otimes \mathbf{Q}$ on to K. Since

$$\dim_{\mathbf{Q}} K = p - 1 = \dim_{\mathbf{Q}} I \otimes \mathbf{Q}$$

it follows that this is an isomorphism of $I \otimes \mathbf{Q}$ on to K. QED.

LEMMA 18. *Let G be a finite p-group and A a finitely generated G-module which, as an abelian group, is torsion free. Then*

$$d^{(p)}H^1(G,A) \leqq \frac{\rho(A)-\rho(A^G)}{p-1}.$$

In particular, it follows that

$$d^{(p)}H^1(G,A) \leqq \frac{\rho(A)}{p-1}$$

which we wanted to prove.

Proof. First let G be of order p. Then Lemma 17 shows

$$d^{(p)}H^1(G,A) \leqq \frac{\rho(A)-p.\rho(A^G)}{p-1} + d^{(p)}H^2(G,A).$$

Since G is cyclic, $H^2(G,A) = \hat{H}^0(G,A)$ is a certain factor group of A^G and has therefore p-rank $\leqq d^{(p)}A^G = \rho(A^G)$, the latter equality holding since A^G is torsion free.

It follows

$$d^{(p)}H^1(G,A) \leqq \frac{\rho(A)-p.\rho(A^G)}{p-1} + \rho(A^G)$$

which proves our assertion if G has order p.

Now let G be of order $\geqq p^2$.

Let U be a proper normal subgroup. The inflation–restriction sequence

$$1 \to H^1(G/U, A^U) \to H^1(G,A) \to H^1(U,A)$$

shows

$$d^{(p)}H^1(G,A) \leqq d^{(p)}H^1(G/U,A^U) + d^{(p)}H^1(U,A).$$

Using induction, we may assume that

$$d^{(p)}H^1(G/U,A^U) \leqq \frac{\rho(A^U)-\rho(A^G)}{p-1}$$

and

$$d^{(p)}H^1(U,A) \leqq \frac{\rho(A)-\rho(A^U)}{p-1}.$$

Adding, we obtain our contention. QED.

REFERENCES

Brumer, A. (1965). Ramification and class towers of number fields. *Mich. math. J.* **12**, 129–131.

Brumer, A. and Rosen, M. (1963). Class number and ramification in number fields. *Nagoya math. J.* **23**, 97–101.

Fröhlich, A. (1954). On fields of class two. *Proc. Lond. math. Soc.* (3) **4**, 235–256.

Fröhlich, A. (1954). On the absolute class group of abelian fields. *J. Lond. math. Soc.* **29**, 211–217.

Fröhlich, A. (1954). A note on the class field tower. *Q. Jl. Math.* (2) **5,** 141–144.

Fröhlich, A. (1962). On non-ramified extensions with prescribed Galois group. *Mathematika,* **9,** 133–134.

Golod, E. S. and Šafarevič, I. R. (1964). On class field towers (Russian). *Izv. Akad. Nauk. SSSR,* **28,** 261–272. English translation in *Am. math. Soc. Transl.* (2) **48,** 91–102.

Hasse, H. (1926). Bericht über neuere Untersuchungen und Probleme der Theorie der algebraischen Zahlkörper, Teil 1. *Jber. dt. Matverein.* **35,** in particular p. 46.

Iwasawa, K. (1956). A note on the group of units of an algebraic number field. *J. Math. pures appl.* **35,** 189–192.

Koch, H. (1964). Über den 2—Klassenkörperturm eines quadratischen Zahlkörpers. *J. reine angew. Math.* **214/215,** 201–206.

Šafarevič, I. R. (1962). Algebraic number fields (Russian). *Proc. Int. Congr. Math. Stockholm,* 163–176. English translation by H. Alderson in *Am. math. Soc. Transl.* (2) **31,** 25–39.

Šafarevič, I. R. (1963). Extensions with prescribed ramification points (Russian with French summary). *Inst. Hautes Études Sci. Publ. Math.* **18,** 71–95.

Serre, J.-P. (1963). "Cohomologie galoisienne". (Lecture notes, Paris 1963, reprinted by Springer, Berlin.)

Scholz, A. (1929). Zwei Bemerkungen zum Klassenkörperturmproblem. *J. reine angew. Math.* **161,** 201–207.

Scholz, A. and Taussky, O. (1934). Die Hauptideale der kubischen Klassenkörper imaginärquadratischer Zahlkörper usw. *J. reine angew. Math.* **171,** 19–41.

CHAPTER X

Semi-Simple Algebraic Groups

M. KNESER

Introduction

Section 1 contains the basic definitions and statements of some fundamental results of an algebraic nature. Sections 2 and 3 are devoted to certain arithmetical questions relating to algebraic groups defined over local or global fields. Throughout, very few proofs are given, but references are given in the bibliography.

For more information on recent progress in the theory of algebraic groups, the reader is referred to the proceedings of the following conferences:

Colloque sur la Théorie des Groupes Algébriques, Bruxelles, 1962.
International Congress of Mathematicians, Stockholm, 1962.
Summer Institute on Algebraic Groups and Discontinuous Subgroups, Boulder, 1965.

References to the bibliography are at the end of this Chapter.

1. Algebraic Theory

Basic reference (Chevalley, 1956–58).

1. *Algebraic groups over an algebraically closed field* (Chevalley, 1956–58 and Rosenlicht, 1956)

Let k be an algebraically closed field. An *algebraic group* defined over k is an algebraic variety G defined over k, together with mappings $(x, y) \mapsto xy$ of $G \times G$ into G and $x \mapsto x^{-1}$ of G into G which are morphisms of algebraic varieties and satisfy the usual group axioms. From now on, the words group, subgroup, etc., shall mean algebraic group, algebraic subgroup (i.e. closed subgroup with respect to the Zariski topology), etc.

An algebraic group G is *linear* if it is affine as an algebraic variety. For example, $GL_n(k)$ is a linear algebraic group, since it can be represented as the set of points (x_{ij}, y) in k^{n^2+1} which satisfy the equation $y.\det(x_{ij}) = 1$. Hence any (closed) subgroup of $GL_n(k)$ is a linear algebraic group, and it is not difficult to show that conversely every linear algebraic group is of this form. The additive and multiplicative groups of k, considered as one-dimensional algebraic groups, are denoted by G_a and G_m respectively; they are both linear ($G_m = GL_1$). A *torus* is a product of copies of G_m. A linear algebraic group G is *unipotent* if every algebraic representation of G consists of unipotent matrices (i.e. matrices all of whose latent roots are 1). A connected algebraic group which is projective as an algebraic variety is an *abelian variety*. Every abelian variety is commutative. For example, any non-singular projective elliptic curve carries a structure of an abelian variety.

If G is any algebraic group, the connected component G_0 of the identity element of G is a normal subgroup of finite index. G_0 has a unique maximal connected linear subgroup G_1, which is normal, and G_0/G_1 is an abelian variety (Chevalley's theorem: proof in Rosenlicht, 1956). G_1 has a unique maximal connected linear solvable normal subgroup G_2, called the *radical* of G_1, and G_1/G_2 is *semi-simple*, i.e. it is connected and linear and its radical is (1). G_2 has a unique maximal connected unipotent subgroup G_3, which is normal in G_2, and G_2/G_3 is a torus. G_3 is called the *unipotent radical* of G_2.

Thus we have the following chain of subgroups of G:

$$\begin{array}{rcl} & G & \\ & | & \text{finite} \\ \text{connected} & G_0 & \\ & | & \text{abelian variety} \\ \text{linear} & G_1 & \\ & | & \text{semi-simple} \\ \text{solvable} & G_2 & \\ & | & \text{torus} \\ & G_3 & \\ & | & \text{unipotent} \\ & (1) & \end{array}$$

Example. $G = GL_n$. G is linear and connected, hence $G = G_1$. The radical G_2 is the centre of GL_n, consisting of the diagonal matrices ($\cong G_m$), and G/G_2 is *simple*.

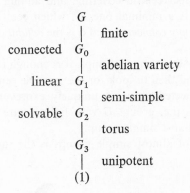

We shall concentrate our attention mainly on sem -simple groups.

2. *Semi-simple groups over an algebraically closed field* (Chevalley, 1956–58) Let k be an algebraically closed field, and G a semi-simple group defined over k. A *Cartan subgroup* of G is a maximal torus, and a *Borel subgroup* of G is a maximal connected solvable subgroup. For example, if G is the special linear group SL_n, then the group of diagonal matrices contained in G is a Cartan subgroup (it is clearly a torus, and it is maximal because it is equal to its centralizer), and the group of upper triangular matrices in G is a Borel subgroup.

A homomorphism $\varphi: G \to H$ is an *isogeny* if G, H are connected groups of the same dimension and the kernel of φ has dimension zero (i.e. is finite). It follows that φ is surjective, since $\varphi(G)$ is connected and of the same dimension as H. (For example, $SL_n \to PGL_n$ is an isogeny: its kernel is the group of nth roots of unity.) If the characteristic of k is zero, the kernel of φ is contained in the centre of G. In characteristic $p > 0$ there are unpleasant phenomena connected with the Frobenius automorphism. For example, let $G = H = SL_n$ and let φ be the mapping $x = (x_{ij}) \mapsto (x_{ij}^p)$, which is an isogeny. If the x_{ij} are in the field k and $\varphi(x) = 1$, then $x = 1$; φ is bijective but is not an isomorphism, since φ^{-1} is not algebraic. If we allow the x_{ij} to be, say, dual numbers (that is, elements of the k-algebra $k[\varepsilon]$, where $\varepsilon^2 = 0$), then $x = 1 + \varepsilon y$ is in the kernel of φ for every $y \in G$, but is not in the centre. We want to exclude this type of phenomenon, so we define a *central isogeny* to be an isogeny whose kernel is contained in the centre, for points with coordinates in any k-algebra. If $\varphi : G \to H$ is a central isogeny, G is said to be a *central covering* of H.

Among the groups which centrally cover G there is a maximal one, $\tilde{G}$, which admits no proper central covering, and among the groups centrally covered by G there is a minimal one, $\bar{G}$, which centrally covers no other group. $\tilde{G}$ is called *simply connected*, and $\bar{G}$ is the *adjoint group* of G. Example: $\tilde{G} = SL_n$, $\bar{G} = PGL_n$.

In order to classify semi-simple groups, it is enough to classify the simply-connected groups, and then to look for the possible central isogenies.

Every simply-connected group is uniquely expressible as a product of *almost simple* groups (i.e. groups G with finite centre C such that G/C is simple). SL_n is an almost simple group.

The classification of almost simple groups is the same as for simple Lie groups:

A_n: SL_{n+1}

C_n: Sp_{2n}

B_n, D_n: isogenous to orthogonal groups

E_6, E_7, E_8, F_4, G_2: exceptional groups.

3. *Semi-simple groups over perfect fields*

(For groups over non-perfect fields, see Demazure and Grothendieck, 1963–64)

Let k be a perfect field, with everything defined over k: this means that the coefficients of the defining equations lie in k. A *k-torus* is an algebraic group defined over k which over the algebraic closure $\bar{k}$ of k becomes a torus, i.e. is isomorphic to a product of groups $G_m = GL_1$; it is *split* over k if it is isomorphic to such a product over k. A semi-simple group is said to be *split* over k if it has a maximal k-torus which is split over k; it is *quasi-split* over k if it has a Borel subgroup defined over k. As this terminology indicates, a split group is quasi-split. For example, SL_n is split, and the group of elements of norm 1 in a quaternion division algebra over k is neither split nor quasi-split.

In the decomposition of a simply-connected semi-simple group $\tilde{G}$ as a product $G_1 \times \ldots \times G_r$ of almost simple groups, the factors G_i and the isomorphism $\tilde{G} \cong \prod G_i$ are defined over $\bar{k}$, not necessarily over k. The Galois group $\Gamma = \mathrm{Gal}(\bar{k}/k)$ permutes the G_i, and the product of the G_i belonging to a given transitivity class is a group defined over k. Thus we may assume that Γ permutes the G_i transitively. The isotropy group of G_1 is a subgroup of finite index in Γ, whose fixed field is a finite extension l of k, and G_1 is defined over l. $\tilde{G}$ is said to be obtained from G_1 by *restriction of the field of definition* from l to $k : \tilde{G} = R_{l/k}(G_1)$ (Weil, 1961). This procedure allows one to reduce many questions to the case of almost simple groups, so we shall assume from now on that $\tilde{G}$ is almost simple.

In view of the classification of almost simple groups over $\bar{k}$ mentioned in Section 2, it is natural to ask whether, for each of the types $A_n, \ldots, G_2$, there exists a group defined over k. In fact it is true that for each type there is a group G defined over k and split over k; and G is unique up to k-isomorphism if we require in addition that it should be simply-connected or adjoint (Chevalley, 1955; Demazure and Grothendieck, 1963–64). The classification of the various k-forms of G, i.e. of groups G' isomorphic to G over $\bar{k}$, is a problem of Galois cohomology.

2. Galois Cohomology

Basic reference (Serre, 1964).

1. *Non-commutative cohomology*

Let G be a group and let A be a *G-group*, i.e. a (not necessarily commutative) group on which G acts. (If G is profinite we require that the action of G should be continuous with respect to the discrete topology on A.) The action of $s \in G$ on $a \in A$ is denoted by ${}^s a$.

We define $H^0(G, A)$ to be the group A^G of G-invariant elements of A. Next we define a *cocycle* to be a function $s \mapsto a_s$ on G with values in A which satisfies

$$a_{st} = a_s . {}^s a_t \qquad (s, t \in G).$$

Two cocycles a_s, b_s are *equivalent* if there exists $c \in A$ such that

$$b_s = c^{-1} . a_s . {}^s c \qquad (s \in G).$$

The set of equivalence classes of cocycles is the *cohomology set* $H^1(G, A)$. This is a set with a distinguished element, namely the class of the identity cocycle. Both $H^0(G, A)$ and $H^1(G, A)$ are functorial in A.

If $1 \to A \to B \to C \to 1$ is an exact sequence of G-groups and G-homomorphisms, then one can define a coboundary map $H^0(G, C) \to H^1(G, A)$, and the sequence (of sets with distinguished elements)

$$1 \to H^0(G, A) \to H^0(G, B) \to H^0(G, C) \to H^1(G, A) \to H^1(G, B) \to H^1(G, C)$$

is exact. (Exactness is to be understood in the usual sense, the kernel of a map being defined as the inverse image of the distinguished element of the image set.) If A is contained in the centre of B (so that A is abelian and therefore $H^2(G, A)$ is defined) then one can define a coboundary map $H^1(G, C) \to H^2(G, A)$ which extends the exact sequence one stage further.

Let K be a perfect field and L a Galois extension of K, with Galois group G. Let A be an algebraic group defined over K, and A_L the group of points of A which are rational over L. Then A_L is a G-group, and we write $H^i(L/K, A)$ in place of $H^i(G, A_L)$. If $\bar{K}$ is the algebraic closure of K, we write $H^i(K, A)$ in place of $H^i(\bar{K}/K, A)$.

2. *K-forms*

Let V, V' be algebraic varieties with some additional algebraic structure (for example, algebraic groups, or vector spaces with a quadratic form, or algebras) all defined over a perfect field K. Suppose that $f: V \to V'$ is an isomorphism for the type of structure in question, defined over a Galois extension L of K. If s is any element of the Galois group G of L/K, then s transforms f into an isomorphism ${}^s f: V \to V'$, and $a_s = f^{-1} \circ {}^s f$ is a cocycle of G with values in Aut (V). It is easily seen that such a "K-form" V' of V is K-isomorphic to another K-form V'' of V if and only if the corresponding cocycles are equivalent, and therefore we have an injective mapping of the set of K-forms of V (modulo K-isomorphism) into the cohomology set $H^1(L/K, \text{Aut}(V))$. In many important cases (algebraic groups, vector spaces with a finite number of tensors) this mapping is *bijective*. In such cases the problem of classifying K-forms is solved by (i) classification over the algebraic closure $\bar{K}$ of K, and (ii) computation of $H^1(K, \text{Aut}(V))$.

Consider for example the classification of K-forms of simply-connected semi-simple linear algebraic groups. As we have seen in Section 1, it is enough to consider almost simple groups, and then the classification over

$\bar{K}$ is known. Let G be the split group of a given type; then the group of inner automorphisms of G is isomorphic to the adjoint group $\bar{G} \cong G/C$ where C is the centre of G, and the quotient $\text{Aut}(G)/\bar{G}$ is isomorphic to the group $\text{Sym}(G)$ of symmetries of the Dynkin diagram of G. So we have an exact sequence

$$1 \to \bar{G} \to \text{Aut}(G) \to \text{Sym}(G) \to 1$$

and the derived cohomology sequence:

$$H^0(K, \text{Sym}(G)) \to H^1(K, \bar{G}) \to H^1(K, \text{Aut}(G)) \xrightarrow{\varphi} H^1(K, \text{Sym}(G)).$$

The Galois group $\mathfrak{g}$ of $\bar{K}/K$ operates trivially on $\text{Sym}(G)$, so that a cocycle of $\mathfrak{g}$ with values in $\text{Sym}(G)$ is a homomorphism $\mathfrak{g} \to \text{Sym}(G)$, and therefore $H^1(K, \text{Sym}(G))$ is a quotient of the set $\text{Hom}(\mathfrak{g}, \text{Sym}(G))$. In fact φ is surjective, and for each $\alpha \in H^1(K, \text{Sym}(G))$ the fibre $\varphi^{-1}(\alpha)$ contains a quasi-split K-form G_α of G, which is unique up to K-isomorphism (Steinberg, 1959); and the elements of $\varphi^{-1}(\alpha)$ correspond to those K-forms G' of G such that there exists an isomorphism $f: G_\alpha \to G'$, defined over $\bar{K}$, for which $f^{-1} \circ {}^s f$ is an inner automorphism of G_α for all $s \in \mathfrak{g}$. By a twisting argument (cf. Serre, 1964, I–5.5) $\varphi^{-1}(\alpha)$ is seen to be a quotient of the cohomology set $H^1(K, \bar{G}_\alpha)$.

3. *Fields of dimension* $\leqslant 1$

A field K is of *dimension* $\leqslant 1$ if the Brauer group $\text{Br}(L)$ is zero for every algebraic extension L of K. Examples of such fields are all finite fields, and the maximal unramified extension K_{nr} of a field K which is complete with respect to a discrete valuation.

THEOREM 1 (Steinberg, 1965). *If K is a perfect field of dimension $\leqslant 1$, and if G is a connected linear algebraic group defined over K, then $H^1(K, G) = 1$.*

In the case where K is finite, this theorem was proved earlier by Lang.

From Steinberg's theorem and the results stated in Section 2, it follows that $\varphi^{-1}(\alpha)$ contains exactly one element, so that every K-form of G is quasi-split, and the K-forms are classified by $H^1(K, \text{Sym}(G))$.

4. $\mathfrak{p}$-*adic fields*

If K is a $\mathfrak{p}$-adic field (i.e. a completion of a global field with respect to a discrete absolute value) it is no longer true that $H^1(K, G) = 1$ for every connected group G. However, there is the following result:

THEOREM 2 (Kneser, 1965). *If K is a $\mathfrak{p}$-adic field and G is a simply-connected semi-simple linear algebraic group defined over K, then $H^1(K, G) = 1$.*

The proof in Kneser (1965) proceeds by reduction to the case of almost simple groups and then deals with each type $A_n, \ldots, G_2$ separately. For the classical groups the theorem is closely related to known results on the classification of quadratic, hermitian, etc., forms over a $\mathfrak{p}$-adic field. More recently Bruhat and Tits (1965) have indicated a uniform proof, based on results of Iwahori and Matsumoto (1965).

If G is the simply-connected covering group of an orthogonal group, Theorem 2 is essentially equivalent to the classification of quadratic forms over a $\mathfrak{p}$-adic field. Let q be a non-degenerate quadratic form in $n \geqslant 3$ variables over a $\mathfrak{p}$-adic field K of characteristic $\neq 2$, let O be the orthogonal group of q, and SO the special orthogonal group of q. All non-degenerate quadratic forms in n variables are equivalent over the algebraic closure $\bar{K}$ of K, so the classification over K of non-degenerate quadratic forms in n variables is equivalent to the determination of $H^1(K, O)$.

We have an exact sequence

$$1 \to SO \to O \to \mu_2 \to 1$$

where $\mu_2 = \{\pm 1\}$; now the map $H^0(K, O) \to H^0(K, \mu_2)$, i.e. $O_K \to \mu_2$, is surjective, hence we have an exact sequence (of sets)

$$1 \to H^1(K, SO) \xrightarrow{\alpha} H^1(K, O) \xrightarrow{d} H^1(K, \mu_2). \tag{1}$$

By a twisting technique it may be shown that α is injective. To compute $H^1(K, \mu_2)$ we use the exact sequence

$$1 \to \mu_2 \to \bar{K}^* \xrightarrow{2} \bar{K}^* \to 1$$

where $\bar{K}^* \xrightarrow{2} \bar{K}^*$ is the map $x \mapsto x^2$. This exact sequence gives rise to a cohomology exact sequence (of groups)

$$K^* \xrightarrow{2} K^* \to H^1(K, \mu_2) \to 1 \to 1 \to H^2(K, \mu_2) \to \mathrm{Br}(K) \xrightarrow{2} \mathrm{Br}(K)$$

(since $H^1(K, \bar{K}^*) = 1$ by Hilbert's Satz 90). We deduce that

$$H^1(K, \mu_2) \cong K^*/K^{*2}, \qquad H^2(K, \mu_2) \cong \mathrm{Br}(K)_2$$

where $\mathrm{Br}(K)_2$ denotes the group of elements of order 2 in the Brauer group $\mathrm{Br}(K)$. (Since $\mathrm{Br}(K) = \mathbf{Q}/\mathbf{Z}$, we have $\mathrm{Br}(K)_2 = \mu_2$.) The exact sequence (1) now becomes

$$1 \to H^1(K, SO) \xrightarrow{\alpha} H^1(K, O) \xrightarrow{d} K^*/K^{*2}.$$

Here d is essentially the *discriminant*: more precisely, if $\xi \in H^1(K, O)$, $d(\xi)$ is the discriminant (modulo squares) of the quadratic form defined by ξ divided by that of q (and therefore d is surjective). The quadratic forms defined over K which have the same discriminant (modulo squares) as q are classified by $H^1(K, SO)$.

The simply-connected covering of SO is the spin group: *Spin*. We have an exact sequence

$$1 \to \mu_2 \to Spin \to SO \to 1$$

and hence a cohomology exact sequence (of sets)

$$Spin_K \to SO_K \xrightarrow{\delta} K^*/K^{*2} \to H^1(K, Spin) \to H^1(K, SO) \xrightarrow{\Delta} \mathrm{Br}(K)_2.$$

Here δ is the *spinor norm* and Δ is closely related to the Witt invariant of a quadratic form. From Theorem 2 we have $H^1(K, Spin) = 1$; hence

(i) the spinor norm $\delta : SO_K \to K^*/K^{*2}$ is surjective;

(ii) every quadratic form with the same discriminant d and the same Witt invariant as q is K-isomorphic to q.

Conversely, (i) and (ii) imply that $H^1(K, Spin) = 1$.

5. *Number fields*

Let K be an algebraic number field, G a linear algebraic group defined over K. If v is any prime of K and if K_v denotes the completion of K at v, we have mappings

$$H^1(K, G) \to H^1(K_v, G)$$

obtained by restriction together with the embedding $G_K \to G_{K_v}$, hence a mapping

$$\theta: H^1(K, G) \to \prod_v H^1(K_v, G). \qquad (1)$$

The theorem of Minkowski–Hasse states that two quadratic forms defined over K are isomorphic over K if and only if they are isomorphic over K_v for all v (discrete and archimedean). In terms of Galois cohomology, this theorem is equivalent to the injectivity of the map

$$\theta: H^1(K, O) \to \prod_v H^1(K_v, O)$$

where O is the orthogonal group of a quadratic form.

The map θ defined by (1) is not always injective, even if G is connected and semi-simple (Serre, 1964). However, if G is simply-connected, the following theorem seems to hold:

THEOREM 3. *Let K be an algebraic number field, G a simply-connected semi-simple linear algebraic group defined over K. Then*

$$\theta: H^1(K, G) \to \prod_v H^1(K_v, G)$$

is bijective.

In fact, $H^1(K_v, G)$ is trivial for all discrete v (Theorem 2), so that Theorem 3 is equivalent to

THEOREM 3′. *The mapping*

$$H^1(K, G) \to \prod_{v \in \infty} \mathrm{H}^1(K_v, G)$$

is bijective, where ∞ denotes the set of archimedean primes of K.

The proof of Theorem 3 proceeds by reduction to the case of almost-simple groups, and then by examination of each type $A_n, \ldots, G_2$ separately. For the classical groups it is related to known results on quadratic, hermitian, etc., forms. For the exceptional groups other than E_8 see Harder (1965). The case E_8 is still open.

3. Tamagawa Numbers

Basic reference (Weil, 1961).

Introduction

Let K be an algebraic number field, A the adèle ring of K. The letter v will denote a prime (discrete or archimedean) of K; K_v denotes the completion of K at v, and $\mathfrak{o}_v$ the ring of integers of K_v if v is discrete.

Let G be a connected linear algebraic group defined over K. G is isomorphic to a subgroup of a general linear group GL_n, and we may therefore regard G as a closed subset of affine m-space ($m = n^2+1$, see Chapter 1, Section 1) when convenient. The *adèle group* G_A of G is the set of all points in A^m which satisfy the equations of G. We give G_A the topology induced by the product topology on A^m, and G_A is then a locally compact topological group. G_A may also be defined as the restricted direct product of the groups G_{K_v} with respect to their compact subgroups $G_{\mathfrak{o}_v}$, where G_{K_v} (resp. $G_{\mathfrak{o}_v}$) is the set of points of G with coordinates in K_v (resp. $\mathfrak{o}_v$). At first sight, G_A appears to depend on the embedding of G in affine space. But it is not difficult to show that if we change the embedding we change $G_{\mathfrak{o}_v}$ at only a finite set of primes v, and hence G_A is unaltered.

Examples. If $G = G_a$, then $G_A = A$. If $G = G_m$, then G_A is the idèle group of K.

Since K is a discrete subgroup of A, it follows that G_K is a discrete subgroup of G_A. Since G_A is locally compact, it has a left-invariant Haar measure, unique up to a constant factor. The product formula shows that right multiplication by an element of G_K does not change the measure on G_A, and therefore we have an induced left-invariant measure on the homogeneous space G_A/G_K.

There is a canonical choice of the Haar measure on G_A, called the *Tamagawa measure* τ (Section 1). Once this is defined there is the problem of computing the *Tamagawa number* $\tau(G) = \tau(G_A/G_K)$ (Section 2). This, applied to the case where G is an orthogonal group, is equivalent to the classical arithmetical results of Minkowski and Siegel on quadratic forms (Section 3).

1. *The Tamagawa measure*

Let V be an algebraic variety of dimension n, defined over K. Let x^0 be a simple point of V and let $x_1, \ldots, x_n$ be local coordinates on V at x^0 (not necessarily zero at x^0). A *differential n-form* on V is defined in a neighbourhood of x^0 in V by an expression

$$\omega = f(x)\, dx_1 \ldots dx_n$$

where f is a rational function on V which is defined at x^0. The form ω is said to be defined over K if f and the coordinate functions x_i are defined over K. The rule for transforming ω under change of coordinates is the usual one. If $\varphi : W \to V$ is a morphism of algebraic varieties, a differential form ω on V pulls back to a differential form $\varphi^*(\omega)$ on W.

Suppose now that V is a connected linear algebraic group G. The left translation $\lambda_a : x \mapsto ax$ $(a \in G)$ is a morphism $V \to V$ and therefore transforms a differential form ω on G into a differential form $\lambda_a^*(\omega)$. Thus we can define left-invariant differential forms on G, and the basic fact is that there exists a non-zero left-invariant differential n-form ω on G, defined over K, and ω is unique up to a constant factor $c \in K^*$.

Examples.

$$G = G_a, \quad \omega = dx; \qquad G = G_m, \quad \omega = dx/x;$$
$$G = GL_n, \quad \omega = (\textstyle\prod dx_{ij})/(\det x_{ij})^n.$$

We shall use ω to construct measures ω_v on the local groups G_{K_v}. For this purpose we need to fix Haar measures μ_v on the additive groups K_v^+. When $K = \mathbf{Q}$ we fix μ_p (p a finite prime) by $\mu_p(\mathbf{Z}_p) = 1$, and μ_∞ we take to be ordinary Lebesgue measure on $\mathbf{R}$. When K is an arbitrary number field, there are various possible normalizations: all we require is that

(i) $\mu_v(\mathfrak{o}_v) = 1$ for almost all discrete v, and
(ii) if $\mu = \prod \mu_v$ is the product measure on A, then $\mu(A_K/K) = 1$.

(One such normalization is to take $\mu_v(\mathfrak{o}_v) = 1$ for all discrete v, and μ_v to be c_v times Lebesgue measure for archimedean v, where the c_v are positive real numbers such that

$$\prod_{v \in \infty} c_v = 2^{r_2} |d_K|^{-\frac{1}{2}},$$

where ∞ denotes the set of infinite primes of K, r_2 is the number of complex infinite primes, and d_K is the discriminant of K.)

To define ω_v, we proceed as follows. The rational function f can be written as a formal power series in $t_i = x_i - x_i^0$ with coefficients in K. If the x_i^0 are in K_v, then f is a power series in the x_i with coefficients in K_v, which converges in some neighbourhood of the origin in K_v^n. Hence there is a neighbourhood U of x^0 in G_{K_v} such that $\varphi : x \mapsto (t_1, \ldots, t_n)$ is a homeomorphism of U onto a neighbourhood U' of the origin in K_v^n, and such that the above power series converges in U'. In U' we have the positive measure $|f(t)|_v\, dt_1 \ldots dt_n$ (where $dt_1 \ldots dt_n$ is the product measure $\mu_v \times \ldots \times \mu_v$ on K_v^n); pull this back to U by means of φ and we have a positive measure ω_v on U. Explicitly, if g is a continuous real-valued function on G_{K_v} with compact support, then

$$\int_U g\omega_v = \int_{U'} g(\varphi^{-1}(t))|f(t)|_v\, dt_1 \ldots dt_n.$$

The measure ω_v is in fact independent of the choice of local coordinates x_i. In the archimedean case this follows from the Jacobian formula for change of variables in a multiple integral, and in the discrete case from its $\mathfrak{p}$-adic analogue.

If the product

$$\prod_{v \notin \infty} \omega_v(G_{\mathfrak{o}_v})$$

converges absolutely, we define the *Tamagawa measure* by

$$\tau = \prod_v \omega_v.$$

Explicitly, if S is a finite set of primes such that $\infty \subseteq S$ and if, for each $v \in S$, U_v is an open set in G_{K_v} with compact closure, then τ is the unique Haar measure on G_A for which

$$\tau\Big(\prod_{v \in S} U_v \times \prod_{v \notin S} G_{\mathfrak{o}_v}\Big) = \prod_{v \in S} \omega_v(U_v) \times \prod_{v \notin S} \omega_v(G_{\mathfrak{o}_v}).$$

If the product

$$\prod_{v \notin \infty} \omega_v(G_{\mathfrak{o}_v})$$

does not converge absolutely, we have to introduce factors to make it converge. A family (λ_v) of strictly positive real numbers, indexed by the primes v of K, is a *set of convergence-factors* if the product

$$\prod_{v \notin \infty} \lambda_v^{-1} \omega_v(G_{\mathfrak{o}_v})$$

is absolutely convergent. The Tamagawa measure τ (relative to the λ_v) is then

$$\tau = \prod_v \lambda_v^{-1} \omega_v.$$

In either case, τ does not depend on the choice of the form ω. For if we replace ω by $c\omega$ ($c \in K^*$) then $(c\omega)_v = |c|_v \omega_v$, and $\prod_v |c|_v = 1$ by the product formula.

Let $k(v)$ denote the residue field at v (v discrete) and let $G^{(v)}$ denote the algebraic group defined over the finite field $k(v)$ obtained by reducing the equations of G modulo the maximal ideal $\mathfrak{p}_v$ of $\mathfrak{o}_v$. Then it can be shown by a generalization of Hensel's lemma that for almost all v we have

$$\omega_v(G_{\mathfrak{o}_v}) = (Nv)^{-n} \operatorname{card}(G^{(v)}_{k(v)}), \tag{1}$$

where Nv is the number of elements in $k(v)$, and $G^{(v)}_{k(v)}$ is the group of points of $G^{(v)}$ rational over $k(v)$.

Examples. If $G = G_a$,

$$\omega_v(G_{\mathfrak{o}_v}) = 1.$$

If $G = G_m$,

$$\omega_v(G_{\mathfrak{o}_v}) = 1 - \frac{1}{Nv};$$

if $G = GL_m$ then

$$\omega_v(G_{\mathfrak{o}_v}) = \left(1 - \frac{1}{Nv}\right) \cdots \left(1 - \frac{1}{(Nv)^m}\right);$$

if $G = SL_m$ then

$$\omega_v(G_{\mathfrak{o}_v}) = \left(1 - \frac{1}{(Nv)^2}\right) \cdots \left(1 - \frac{1}{(Nv)^m}\right).$$

Since

$$\prod_v \left(1 - \frac{1}{(Nv)^s}\right) = \zeta_K(s)^{-1}$$

is convergent for $\mathrm{Re}\,(s) > 1$ but not for $s = 1$, it follows that the product $\prod_v \omega_v(G_{\mathfrak{o}_v})$ converges when $G = SL_m$ but not when $G = GL_m$. In the latter case we may take

$$\lambda_v = 1 - \frac{1}{Nv}$$

as convergence-factors.

PROPOSITION. *If G is semi-simple, the product $\prod_v \omega_v(G_{\mathfrak{o}_v})$ is absolutely convergent (and so convergence-factors are not needed).*

In outline, the proof is as follows (for details, see Ono (1965)). From (1) we have to prove that the product

$$\prod_v \{(Nv)^{-n} \operatorname{card}(G^{(v)}_{k(v)})\} \tag{2}$$

is absolutely convergent. Using the theorem (due to Lang) that isogenous groups over a finite field have the same number of rational points we can reduce to the case where G is simple over the algebraic closure $\bar{K}$ of K i.e. has no non-trivial algebraic normal subgroups defined over $\bar{K}$. For such a group the order of $G^{(v)}_{k(v)}$ can be explicitly determined and is of the form

$$(Nv)^n\{1 + O((Nv)^{-2})\}.$$

The convergence of (2) now follows from the convergence of the zeta-function $\zeta_K(s)$ for $\mathrm{Re}\,(s) > 1$.

2. *The Tamagawa number*

The *Tamagawa number* $\tau(G)$ is defined to be $\tau(G_A/G_K)$.

THEOREM 1 (Borel and Harish-Chandra, 1962). *If G is semi-simple, $\tau(G)$ is finite.*

For another proof of this theorem see Godement (1962–63).

THEOREM 2 (Ono, 1965). *Let G be a semi-simple group, $\tilde{G}$ its universal (i.e. simply-connected) covering, C the (finite) kernel of the covering map $\tilde{G} \to G$, and let $\hat{C}$ denote the character group* Hom (C, G_m). *Then*

$$\frac{\tau(G)}{\tau(\tilde{G})} = \frac{h^0(\hat{C})}{i^1(\hat{C})},$$

where $h^0(\hat{C}) = \text{Card}\, H^0(K, \hat{C})$ and $i^1(\hat{C})$ is the number of elements in the kernel of the map $H^1(K, \hat{C}) \to \prod_v H^1(K_v, \hat{C})$.

Hence it is enough to compute one Tamagawa number in each isogeny class, for example $\tau(\tilde{G})$. In this direction, there is Weil's

CONJECTURE. $\tau(\tilde{G}) = 1$.

This conjecture is proved for many of the classical groups [(Weil, 1961, 1964, 1965) for all groups of types B_n and C_n, and some of types A_n and D_n; and (Mars, 196?; Weil, 1961) for some exceptional groups]. Langlands gave a non-enumerative proof for all split semi-simple groups (Bruhat-Tits (1965)).

Example. $G = SO_n$ $(n \geqslant 3)$. Here C has order 2, and it can be shown that $h^0(\hat{C})/i^1(\hat{C}) = 2$. So in this case $\tau(\tilde{G}) = 1$ is equivalent to $\tau(G) = 2$. As we shall see (Section 3), $\tau(G) = 2$ is equivalent to the theorems of Minkowski–Siegel on quadratic forms.

3. *The theorem of Minkowski and Siegel*

Let K be an algebraic number field, V an n-dimensional vector space over K $(n \geqslant 3)$, q a non-degenerate quadratic form on V defined over K, $G = SO(q)$ the group of all automorphisms of the vector space V which preserve q and have determinant 1. We regard G as acting on V on the *right*. We shall identify V with K^n by choosing a fixed basis of V; then the elements of G are $n \times n$ matrices.

A *lattice M* in V is a finitely generated $\mathfrak{o}$-submodule of V of rank n, where $\mathfrak{o}$ is the ring of integers of K. In particular $L = \mathfrak{o}^n$ is a lattice, called the *standard* lattice (with respect to the chosen basis of V). Two lattices M, M' are *isomorphic* if $M' = Mx$ for some $x \in G_K$. For each finite prime v, let $M_v = \mathfrak{o}_v \otimes M$, which is a lattice in K_v^n. It can be shown that M is uniquely determined by the M_v [namely $M = \bigcap_v (M_v \cap V)$]; that $M_v = \mathfrak{o}_v^n$ for almost all v; and that, conversely, if M_v is a lattice in K_v^n for each finite v, such that $M_v = \mathfrak{o}_v^n$ for almost all v, then there is a unique lattice M in K^n whose local components are the M_v.

The adèle group G_A operates on the set of lattices in K^n as follows: if M is a lattice and $x \in G_A$, then $(Mx)_v = M_v x_v$ (observe that, since $M_v = \mathfrak{o}_v^n$ for almost all v, and $x_v \in G_{\mathfrak{o}_v}$ for almost all v, we have $(Mx)_v = \mathfrak{o}_v^n$ for almost all v). The orbit of M under G_A is the *genus* of M, which therefore consists of the lattices in V which are locally isomorphic to M at all finite primes. The *class* of M is the orbit of M under G_K, i.e. the set of all lattices globally isomorphic to M.

The stabilizer of the standard lattice L in G_A is the open subgroup

$$G_{A_\infty} = \Big(\prod_{v \notin \infty} G_{\mathfrak{o}_v}\Big) \times \Big(\prod_{v \in \infty} G_{K_v}\Big) = G_{\mathfrak{o}} \times G_\infty \quad \text{say,}$$

where ∞ denotes the set of archimedean primes of K. Hence the lattices in the genus of L are in one–one correspondence with the cosets $G_{A_\infty} x$ in G_A, and the classes in the genus with the double cosets $G_{A_\infty} x G_K$ in G_A. For any semi-simple group, the number of double cosets $G_{A_\infty} x G_K$ in G_A is finite (Borel and Harish-Chandra, 1962). In our special case $G = SO(q)$, this is the well-known finiteness of the number of classes in a genus. Let h denote this number.

We have

$$\begin{aligned}\tau(G) = \tau(G_A/G_K) &= \sum_{i=1}^{h} \tau(G_{A_\infty} x_i G_K/G_K) \\ &= \sum_{i=1}^{h} \tau(x_i^{-1} G_{A_\infty} x_i G_K/G_K) \qquad (1)\end{aligned}$$

since τ is left-invariant. The group $x_i^{-1} G_{A_\infty} x_i$ is the stabilizer of Lx_i in G_A. Hence we need consider only one term in this sum, say $\tau(G_{A_\infty} G_K/G_K)$. We have $G_{A_\infty} G_K/G_K \cong G_{A_\infty}/G_{\mathfrak{o}}$ (since $G_{A_\infty} \cap G_K = G_{\mathfrak{o}}$). Hence

$$\tau(G_{A_\infty} G_K/G_K) = \tau(G_{A_\infty}/G_{\mathfrak{o}}) = \tau(F)$$

where F is a fundamental domain for $G_{\mathfrak{o}}$ in G_{A_∞}, i.e. a Borel set in G_{A_∞} which meets each coset $xG_{\mathfrak{o}}$ exactly once. The projection $G_{A_\infty} = G_{\mathfrak{o}} \times G_\infty \to G_\infty$, restricted to $G_{\mathfrak{o}}$, embeds $G_{\mathfrak{o}}$ injectively in G_∞, and we may take F to be a set of the form $G_{\mathfrak{o}} \times F_\infty$, where F_∞ is a fundamental domain for $G_{\mathfrak{o}}$ in G_∞. Hence we have

$$\begin{aligned}\tau(G_{A_\infty} G_K/G_K) &= \tau(G_{\mathfrak{o}} \times F_\infty) \\ &= \prod_{v \notin \infty} \omega_v(G_{\mathfrak{o}_v}) \times \omega_\infty(G_\infty/G_{\mathfrak{o}})\end{aligned}$$

where

$$\omega_\infty = \prod_{v \in \infty} \omega_v.$$

If we replace L by Lx_i, $G_{\mathfrak{o}_v}$ is replaced by $x_{i,v}^{-1} G_{\mathfrak{o}_v} x_{i,v}$ and therefore the term

$\omega_v(G_{\mathfrak{o}_v})$ is unaltered (since ω is right-invariant as well as left-invariant, for any semi-simple group); and $G_\mathfrak{o} = G_K \cap G_{A_\infty}$ is replaced by

$$G_\mathfrak{o}(x_i) = G_K \cap x_i^{-1} G_{A_\infty} x_i.$$

Hence

$$\tau(x_i^{-1} G_{A_\infty} x_i G_K / G_K) = \prod_{v \notin \infty} \omega_v(G_{\mathfrak{o}_v}) \times \omega_\infty(G_\infty / G_\mathfrak{o}(x_i)) \tag{2}$$

and therefore, from (1) and (2),

$$2 = \tau(G) = \prod_{v \notin \infty} \omega_v(G_{\mathfrak{o}_v}) \times \sum_{i=1}^{h} \omega_\infty(G_\infty / G_\mathfrak{o}(x_i)),$$

that is,

$$\sum_{i=1}^{h} \omega_\infty(G_\infty / G_\mathfrak{o}(x_i)) = 2 \prod_{v \notin \infty} \omega_v(G_{\mathfrak{o}_v})^{-1}. \tag{3}$$

Suppose now that the form q is *totally definite*, i.e. that each archimedean v is real and that q is definite at each archimedean completion K_v. Then

$$G_\infty = \prod_{v \in \infty} G_{k_v}$$

is a product of real orthogonal groups and is therefore compact, and $G_\mathfrak{o}(x_i)$ is the *group of units* $E(Lx_i)$ of the lattice Lx_i, i.e. the group of all integer matrices which transform Lx_i onto itself, and is finite. (If S_i is the matrix of q with respect to a basis of Lx_i, then $E(Lx_i)$ is the group of all integer matrices X such that $X'S_i X = S_i$; since S_i is definite, $E(Lx_i)$ is clearly finite.) Hence (3) now takes the form

$$\sum_{i=1}^{h} \frac{1}{\text{Card}\,(E(Lx_i))} = \frac{2}{\omega_\infty(G_\infty)} \prod_{v \notin \infty} \frac{1}{\omega_v(G_{\mathfrak{o}_v})} = \frac{2}{\tau(G_{A_\infty})}. \tag{4}$$

When $K = \mathbf{Q}$, this is equivalent to Minkowski's formula for the weight of a genus of definite quadratic forms.

Similarly, we can recover Siegel's theorem (1935–37) on the number of representations of one quadratic form (in n variables, say) by another (in m variables), by considering an m-dimensional vector space V endowed with a non-degenerate quadratic form q, an n-dimensional subspace W and the Tamagawa number of the group G of all q-orthogonal transformations which induce the identity on W. For details see Kneser (1961) and Weil (1962).

REFERENCES

Borel, A. and Harish-Chandra (1962). Arithmetic subgroups of algebraic groups. *Ann. Math.* **75**, 485–535.

Bruhat, F. and Tits, J. (1965). A.M.S. Summer Institute on Algebraic Groups and Discontinuous Subgroups, Boulder. (To appear.)

Chevalley, C. (1955). Sur certains groupes simples. *Tohoku math. J.* **7**, 14–66.

Chevalley, C. (1956–58). Classification des groupes de Lie algébriques. *Séminaire E.N.S.*

Demazure, M. and Grothendieck, A. (1963–64). Schémes en groupes. *Séminaire de Géometrie Algébrique I.H.E.S.*

Godement, R. (1962–63). Domaines fondamentaux des groupes arithmétiques. *Séminaire Bourbaki*, No. 257.

Harder, G. (1965), Über die Galoiskohomologie halbeinfacher Matrizengruppen, I. *Math. Z.* **90,** 404–428; and II, (1966), **92,** 396–415.

Iwahori, N. and Matsumoto, H. (1965). On some Bruhat decomposition and the structure of the Hecke rings of $\mathfrak{p}$-adic Chevalley groups. *Publs. math. ht. Etud. scient.*, No. 25.

Kneser, M. (1961). Darstellungsmaße indefiniter quadratischer Formen. *Math. Z.* **77,** 188–194.

Kneser, M. (1965). Galois–Kohomologie halbeinfacher algebraischer Gruppen über $\mathfrak{p}$-adischen Körpern. *Math. Z.* **88,** 40–47; and **89,** 250–272.

Mars, J. M. G. (196?). Les nombres de Tamagawa de certains groupes exceptionnels. (To appear.)

Ono, T. (1965). On the relative theory of Tamagawa numbers. *Ann. Math.* **82,** 88–111.

Rosenlicht, M. (1956). Some basic theorems on algebraic groups. *Am. J. Math.* **78,** 401–443.

Serre, J.-P. (1964). "Cohomologie Galoisienne", Lecture notes, Collège de France, 1962–63, 2nd edition, Springer-Verlag.

Siegel, C. L. Über die analytische Theorie der quadratischen Formen. *Ann. Math.* (1935), **36,** 527–606; (1936), **37,** 230–263; (1937), **38,** 212–291.

Steinberg, R. (1959). Variations on a theme of Chevalley. *Pacif. J. Math.* **9,** 875–891.

Steinberg, R. (1965). Regular elements of semi-simple algebraic groups. *Publs. math. Inst. ht. Etud. scient.*, No. 25.

Weil, A. (1961). "Adeles and Algebraic Groups", Lecture notes, Princeton.

Weil, A. (1962). Sur la théorie des formes quadratiques. Colloque sur la Théorie des Groupes Algébriques, Bruxelles, 9–22.

Weil, A. (1964). Sur certains groupes d'opérateurs unitaires. *Acta Math. Stockh.* **111,** 143–211.

Weil, A. (1965). Sur la formula de Siegel dans la théorie des groupes classiques. *Acta Math. Stockh.* **113,** 1–87.

CHAPTER XI

History of Class Field Theory

HELMUT HASSE

1. The notion of *class field* is generally attributed to Hilbert. In truth this notion was already present in the mind of Kronecker and the term was coined by Weber, before Hilbert's fundamental papers appeared.

Kronecker, in his large treatise "*Grundzüge einer arithmetischen Theorie der algebraischen Grössen*" of 1882, discusses at length the "*zu assoziierenden Gattungen*" (species to be associated). What he means by this is, in modern terminology, an algebraic extension K of a given algebraic number field k such that all divisors† in k become principal divisors in K. By his investigations he had found that for imaginary quadratic fields k the "singular moduli" generate such extensions K. By this notion Kronecker anticipates the *principal divisor theorem* of class field theory, stated and in special cases proved by Hilbert.

Weber (1891, 1897*a*, *b*, 1898, 1908), however, did not define the notion of class field on this basis, a basis which, as we know today, is unsuitable for building the theory. What he postulated is part of the *law of decomposition.* Whereas Hilbert in his later definition considered only the case of absolute divisor classes, Weber gave his definition in full generality, viz.

Let k be an algebraic number field and A/H a congruence divisor class group in k. An algebraic extension K/k is called class field to A/H, if exactly those prime divisors in k of first degree which belong to the principal class H split completely in K.

In order to define Weber's notion of a *congruence divisor class group A/H* in k, consider integer *divisor moduli* $\mathfrak{m}$ in k, i.e. formal finite products composed of finite prime spots (prime divisors) of k with positive integer exponents and real infinite prime spots of k with exponents 1. Call a number or a divisor in k prime to $\mathfrak{m}$ if it is prime to all prime divisors contained in $\mathfrak{m}$, and understand congruence mod $\mathfrak{m}$ as congruence modulo all prime divisor powers contained in $\mathfrak{m}$ and equality of sign for all real prime spots contained

† I use throughout the term "divisor" instead of the classical term "ideal", because valuation theory, derived from the Kronecker–Hensel notion of divisor, has been nowadays adopted widely as a more suitable foundation of algebraic number theory than Dedekind's ideal theory.

in $\mathfrak{m}$. Further consider quotient groups $A_{\mathfrak{m}}/H_{\mathfrak{m}}$ where $A_{\mathfrak{m}}$ is the group of all divisors in k prime to $\mathfrak{m}$ for a given integer divisor modulus $\mathfrak{m}$ and $H_{\mathfrak{m}}$ is a subgroup containing all numbers $a \equiv 1 \bmod \mathfrak{m}$ in k (considered as principal divisors in k). Call two such quotient groups $A_{\mathfrak{m}_1}/H_{\mathfrak{m}_1}$ and $A_{\mathfrak{m}_2}/H_{\mathfrak{m}_2}$ "equal" to each other if for the least common multiple $\mathfrak{m} = [\mathfrak{m}_1, \mathfrak{m}_2]$ (and hence for every common multiple of $\mathfrak{m}_1$ and $\mathfrak{m}_2$) there holds the equality $H_{\mathfrak{m}_1} \cap A_{\mathfrak{m}} = H_{\mathfrak{m}_2} \cap A_{\mathfrak{m}}$, which implies the isomorphy $A_{\mathfrak{m}_1}/H_{\mathfrak{m}_1} \cong A_{\mathfrak{m}_2}/H_{\mathfrak{m}_2}$. Each set of quotient groups $A_{\mathfrak{m}_1}/H_{\mathfrak{m}_1}, A_{\mathfrak{m}_2}/H_{\mathfrak{m}_2}, \ldots$ that are all "equal" to each other defines a congruence divisor class group A/H in Weber's sense. The single quotient groups $A_{\mathfrak{m}_1}/H_{\mathfrak{m}_1}, A_{\mathfrak{m}_2}/H_{\mathfrak{m}_2}, \ldots$ are called the *interpretations* (Erklärungen) mod $\mathfrak{m}_1$, mod $\mathfrak{m}_2, \ldots$ of A/H. The lowest possible *interpretation modulus* (Erklärungsmodul) $\mathfrak{f}$, which turns out to be the greatest common divisor of all possible $\mathfrak{m}_1, \mathfrak{m}_2, \ldots$ is called the *conductor* (Führer) of A/H. Occasionally the single *interpretations* are also called congruence divisor class groups.

Besides the theorems on class fields proved by Weber which will be adduced presently, in the cases he treated he further observed also the fundamental *isomorphy theorem*:

The Galois group $\mathfrak{G}(K/k)$ *is isomorphic to the class group* A/H, *and hence is surely abelian.*

Already Kronecker (1853, 1877) knew that the cyclotomic fields are class fields in the above sense. He stated his famous *completeness theorem:*

Every abelian field over the rational number field is a cyclotomic field, and hence is a class field.

This was first proved completely by Weber (1886, 1887) and later more simply by Hilbert (1896, 1897); further proofs were given by Weber (1909), Speiser (1919) and Delaunay (1923).

Further Kronecker (1883–1890), by his investigations on modular functions and elliptic functions with "singular moduli", had ascertained that their transformation and division equations generate relatively abelian fields K over imaginary quadratic fields k. It was his "*liebster Jugendtraum*" (1880) (dearest dream of his youth) to prove also in this case the *completeness theorem, that every relatively abelian field K over an imaginary quadratic field k is obtained by such transformation and division equations.* This was proved later, first partially by Weber (1908) and Fueter (1914), then completely by Takagi (1920) and once more by Fueter (with Gut) (1927).

Weber (1897, 1898) conceived his notion of class field from those examples. By making use of Dirichlet's analytic means (L-series) he deduced from his class field definition the *first*† *fundamental inequality* of class field theory:

$$[A:H] = h \leqslant n = [K:k],$$

† In modern terminology: second.

further the *uniqueness theorem:*

$$H = H' \Leftrightarrow K = K',$$

the *ordering theorem:*

$$H \supseteq H' \Leftrightarrow K \subseteq K',$$

and the following presupposition for the isomorphy theorem:

$$K/k \text{ is normal.}$$

From the introduction to Weber (1897, 1898) it is safe to conclude that he was convinced of the validity of the general *existence theorem:*

To every congruence divisor class group A/H in k there exists a class field K/k.

He points out that from the existence of a class field K/k follows the existence of an infinity of prime divisors in the single classes of A/H, i.e. a far-reaching generalization of Dirichlet's famous theorem on primes in prime residue classes. He did not know, however, other examples for the existence of class fields than those from the theory of cyclotomic, modular and elliptic functions.

2. The preceding references to Weber's share in the origin of class field theory are not meant to detract from the great merit of Hilbert in the development of this theory, but only to put it in the right light. Hilbert himself had a high opinion of Weber; he has repeatedly quoted and duly acknowledged his ideas and results on class fields.

The publications of Hilbert (1898, 1899*a*, *b*, 1900*a*, *b*, 1902) on class field theory are apparently concerned only with the special case of *absolute* divisor classes, i.e. where the principal class H contains all principal divisors (without or with sign conditions). Moreover, he had carried through the proofs only for the *relatively quadratic* number fields—i.e. $n = 2$—with *class number* $h = 2$. Before his mind's eye, however, he had throughout the most general case. For instance, in his lecture (1899*a*) before the DMV (German Mathematical Association) meeting at Braunschweig (Brunswick) in 1897 he declared (in free translation):

> "In this lecture we have restricted ourselves to the investigation of relatively abelian fields of *second* degree. This restriction however is only a provisional one, and since all conclusions in the proofs of the theorems are capable of generalization, it is to be hoped that the difficulties of establishing a theory of relatively abelian fields will not be insurmountable."

In this sense he had in mind in full generality the main theorems of class field theory already mentioned (*existence theorem, uniqueness theorem, ordering theorem, isomorphy theorem* and *decomposition law*).

For Hilbert class field theory was not only, as it was for Kronecker and

Weber, a means towards proving the completeness theorem and towards generalizing Dirichlet's prime number theorem. As clearly stated in utterances like that quoted above and in the headline to his note (1898, 1902) in the *Göttinger Nachrichten,* he rather regarded it as a "Theory of relatively abelian fields". A further aim of his was the problem of the *higher reciprocity laws,* handed down from Gauss, Jacobi, Eisenstein and Kummer, and appearing in his famous Paris lecture of 1900 as Problem 9. Indeed, one of Hilbert's most profound achievements is the conception of the reciprocity law as a *product formula* for his *norm residue symbol*

$$\prod_{\mathfrak{p}} \left(\frac{a, b}{\mathfrak{p}}\right)_n = 1.$$

Here k is assumed to contain the nth roots of uinty and $\mathfrak{p}$ runs through all prime divisors of k, including what we call today the infinite prime spots, introduced by him as symbols 1, 1′, 1″,.... He pointed out the analogy of this formula (given by him only in special cases) to the residue theorem for algebraic functions—the prime spots $\mathfrak{p}$ with norm residue symbol $\neq 1$ corresponding to the ramification points of the Riemann surface.† This analogy was later splendidly justified by the subsummation of the product formula in algebraic function fields with finite constant field under the residue theorem by Schmid (1936) and Witt (1937). Moreover, Hilbert stated (again only in special cases) the *norm theorem:*

$$\left(\frac{a, b}{\mathfrak{p}}\right)_n = 1 \textit{ for all } \mathfrak{p} \Leftrightarrow a \textit{ is relative norm from } k(\sqrt[n]{b}),$$

so important for the further development of the theory. This theorem was proved later in full generality by me (1930*c*).

Due to the restriction to the *absolute divisor class group* A/H, Hilbert's list of class field theorems contains, in addition to those already mentioned, the *discriminant theorem:*

$$K/k \textit{ has relative discriminant } \mathfrak{d} = 1.$$

He further stated the *principal divisor theorem,* already touched upon earlier in this Chapter:

All divisors from k become principal divisors in K.

Moreover, he asserted:

The class number of K is not divisible by 2,

and this not only under his original restriction, that k has class number $h = 2$, but also for $h = 4$.

† From today's standpoint this is not quite correct. In number theory the norm residue symbol may be different from 1 also without ramification, namely by inertia. In algebraic function fields over the complex number field this does not occur, so that for them only ramification comes into question.

Excepting only this latter assertion, which is true for $h = 2$ but not necessarily for $h = 4$, all Hilbert's assertions on class fields have proved true in the general case. For the principal divisor theorem, however, things turned out to be much more complicated than Hilbert apparently thought. One cannot help feeling the greatest admiration for his keen-mindedness and penetration, which enabled him to conceive with such accuracy general laws from rather special cases.

3. As to the *reciprocity law*, in 1899 the "*Königliche Gesellschaft der Wissenschaften zu Göttingen*", presumably on Hilbert's suggestion, had set as prize-subject for 1901 the detailed treatment of this law for prime exponents $l \neq 2$. This problem was solved by Furtwängler. In the prize-treatise (1902, 1904) itself he gave the solution only for fields k with class number not divisible by l, and without distinguishing between the $l-1$ different non-residue classes. In further papers (1909, 1912, 1913, 1928), however, he proved the law of reciprocity for prime exponents l (including 2) in full generality. Not only did he prove it in the classical shape:

$$\left(\frac{a}{b}\right)_l = \left(\frac{b}{a}\right)_l, \textit{ if } a \textit{ and } b \textit{ are primary (and in case } l = 2\textit{, totally positive)},$$

but also in the shape of Hilbert's product formula for the norm residue symbol. According to a very beautiful idea of his, the law in the classical shape—by passing to the extension field $\bar{k} = k(\sqrt[l]{(ab^{-1})})$ over which $\bar{k}(\sqrt[l]{a}) = \bar{k}(\sqrt[l]{b})$ is unramified and hence contained in the absolute class field $\bar{K}$—comes back to the *decomposition law* in $\bar{K}/\bar{k}$. In other words, that $\left(\frac{a}{\mathfrak{p}}\right)_l = \left(\frac{b}{\mathfrak{p}}\right)_l$ over $\bar{k}$ depends only on the absolute class in $\bar{k}$ to which $\mathfrak{p}$ belongs. This decomposition law was at his disposal since he had previously proved the existence theorem for the absolute class field (1907).

4. A decisive step forward was taken by Takagi (1920, 1922) in two highly important papers on class field theory and the law of reciprocity. Takagi had been studying Hilbert's papers on the theory of numbers at the turn of the century and had investigated the relatively abelian fields over the Gaussian number field. This resulted in his solution (1903) of Kronecker's famous completeness problem over this field by means of the division theory of elliptic functions in the lemniscatic case (i.e. where the period parallelogram is a square).

In his big class field paper of 1920 Takagi gave class field theory the decisive new turn by starting from a new definition of the notion of "class field". His new definition was more suitable than Weber's because it allows one to envisage the important completeness theorem right from the beginning.

For an arbitrary relative field K/k he makes correspond to each integer divisor modulus $\mathfrak{m}$ in k a congruence divisor class group *interpretated* (erklärt) mod $\mathfrak{m}$, viz. the smallest quotient group $A_{\mathfrak{m}}/H_{\mathfrak{m}}$ whose principal class $H_{\mathfrak{m}}$ contains all relative norms $N(\mathfrak{A})$ of divisors $\mathfrak{A}$ in K prime to $\mathfrak{m}$ and hence consists of all divisors $\mathfrak{a}$ in k prime to $\mathfrak{m}$ with

$$\mathfrak{a} \sim N(\mathfrak{A}) \bmod \mathfrak{m}, \text{ i.e., } \frac{\mathfrak{a}}{N(\mathfrak{A})} \cong a \equiv 1 \bmod \mathfrak{m} \ (a \in k).$$

For $\mathfrak{m}$ sufficiently high, more precisely for all multiples $\mathfrak{m}$ of a lowest $\mathfrak{f}$ (the conductor of K/k) the class groups $A_{\mathfrak{m}}/H_{\mathfrak{m}}$ turn out to be "equal" and hence constitute a congruence divisor class group A/H in Weber's sense with conductor $\mathfrak{f}$. According to Weber there holds the already mentioned first fundamental inequality

$$[A:H] = h \leqslant n = [K:k],$$

proved by analytic means. Takagi's class field definition then runs:

K/k is called class field to the congruence divisor class group A/H, if and only if the equality $h = n$ holds.

The main theorems of class field theory proved by Takagi, and based on this definition, may be summarized as follows:

The class field relation establishes a one–one correspondence between all relatively abelian fields K/k and all congruence divisor class groups A/H in k.

This statement comprises the existence theorem, uniqueness theorem, completeness theorem in the older terminology, and also the *limitation theorem:*

$$h < n \textit{ if } K/k \textit{ is not relatively abelian,}$$

which was added later.

For "partners" in the said one–one correspondence there hold the following further facts:

$$K \subseteq K' \Leftrightarrow H \supseteq H' \quad \textit{(ordering theorem)},$$

$$\mathfrak{G}(K/k) \cong A/H \qquad \textit{(isomorphy theorem)},$$

$\mathfrak{p}$ splits in K into prime divisors of relative degree f and relative order e if and only if $\mathfrak{p}^f$ is the least power of $\mathfrak{p}$ in $H_{\mathfrak{p}}$, where $A/H_{\mathfrak{p}}$ is the maximal factor group of A/H with conductor prime to $\mathfrak{p}$, and where $e = [H_{\mathfrak{p}} : H]$ (decomposition law).

Hence

$$\mathfrak{p} | \mathfrak{d} \Leftrightarrow \mathfrak{p} | \mathfrak{f},$$

an assertion which was later supplemented by me (1926, 1927, 1930*a*, 1930*d*) to

$$\mathfrak{d} = \prod_{\chi} \mathfrak{f}_{\chi}, \qquad \mathfrak{f} = \underset{\chi}{\mathrm{M}}\, \mathfrak{f}_{\chi},$$

(*conductor-discriminant theorem*) where χ runs through the characters of A/H and $\mathfrak{f}_\chi$ denotes their conductors, while $\underset{\chi}{\mathsf{M}}$ denotes the least common multiple taken over all χ.

Whereas the existence theorem is obtained from the uniqueness theorem and completeness theorem by a suitable enumeration, the proof of the completeness theorem comes back to the *second*† *fundamental inequality:*

$$h \geqslant n.$$

This is obtained by a far-reaching generalization of the classical theory of genera from Gauss' *Disquisitiones Arithmeticae.* Nowadays the theory of cohomology has permitted one to systematize the rather complicated chain of conclusions that leads to this inequality.

5. As to the reciprocity law, the above mentioned further paper of Takagi's (1922) already gave considerable simplifications of Furtwängler's rather complicated argument (only 40 instead of 80 pages!). These simplifications were possible because of the availability of the full class field theory instead of that only for the *absolute* class field. It was not before Artin, however, that an entirely new idea of fundamental importance was brought to bear on this law. He found the key to its conceptual (as opposed to formal) significance in explicitly giving a *canonical isomorphism of the class group* A/H *onto the Galois group* $\mathfrak{G}(K/k)$.

Artin (1927) showed that such an isomorphism is obtained by making correspond to each prime divisor $\mathfrak{p} \nmid \mathfrak{d}$, or rather to its class in A/H, the so-called Frobenius automorphism $F_\mathfrak{p}$ of K/k with respect to $\mathfrak{p}$. This automorphism is defined by

$$\mathsf{A}^{F_\mathfrak{p}} \equiv \mathsf{A}^{\mathfrak{N}(\mathfrak{p})} \bmod \mathfrak{p}, \text{ for all integers } \mathsf{A} \in K,$$

where $\mathfrak{N}(\mathfrak{p})$ is the absolute norm of $\mathfrak{p}$. Today one writes

$$F_\mathfrak{p} = \left(\frac{K/k}{\mathfrak{p}}\right),$$

and one defines from this the *Artin symbol* $\left(\frac{K/k}{\mathfrak{a}}\right)$ as a multiplicative function on the group $A_\mathfrak{f}$ of all divisors $\mathfrak{a}$ in k prime to $\mathfrak{d}$ or, what is the same, to $\mathfrak{f}$. The isomorphy between A/H and $\mathfrak{G}(K/k)$ may then be expressed by *Artin's reciprocity law:*

$$\left(\frac{K/k}{\mathfrak{a}}\right) = 1 \Leftrightarrow \mathfrak{a} \in H_\mathfrak{f}.$$

Artin (1924) had conceived this reciprocity law four years earlier, and had proved it in simple special cases. However, it was not until he came to know

† In modern terminology: first.

Tchebotarev's method of crossing the classes of A/H with the congruence classes corresponding to a relatively cyclotomic field, that he succeeded in giving a general proof. Tchebotarev (1926) had invented this method in order to improve on a theorem of Frobenius (1896), viz.: The prime divisors $\mathfrak{P}$ of a normal K/k with Frobenius automorphism $F_{\mathfrak{P}}$ in a given *division* (Abteilung) $S^{-1}F_{\mathfrak{P}}^{\nu}S$ (ν prime to the order of $F_{\mathfrak{P}}$, S running through $\mathfrak{G}(K/k)$) have a density, namely the relative frequency of the division in the whole group $\mathfrak{G}(K/k)$. The method in question enabled Tchebotarev to generalize this theorem to a single *conjugacy class* $S^{-1}F_{\mathfrak{P}}S$.

For a Kummer field $K = k(\sqrt[n]{b})$ (where k contains the nth roots of unity) the Frobenius automorphism $\left(\frac{K/k}{\mathfrak{p}}\right)$ changes $\sqrt[n]{b}$ into $\left(\frac{b}{\mathfrak{p}}\right)_n \sqrt[n]{b}$, as is clear from the definition of the power residue symbol $\left(\frac{b}{\mathfrak{p}}\right)_n$ by Euler's criterion. Hence Artin's reciprocity law yields the assertion:

$\left(\frac{b}{\mathfrak{p}}\right)_n$ *depends only on the class to which* $\mathfrak{p}$ *belongs in the congruence class group mod* $\mathfrak{f}_b$ *corresponding to* $k(\sqrt[n]{b})$.

Here $\mathfrak{f}_b$ denotes the conductor of $k(\sqrt[n]{b})$.

On the other hand, from the definition $\left(\frac{b}{\mathfrak{p}}\right)_n$ depends only on the residue class to which b belongs mod $\mathfrak{p}$. From this it is easy to deduce the reciprocity in its classical shape and also in the shape of Hilbert's product formula. Thus it becomes understandable and justified that Artin called the above isomorphy assertion the "general law of reciprocity".

With the help of this law, Artin (1930) could also reduce the *principal divisor theorem*, enunciated by Hilbert and not yet proved by Takagi, to a pure group-theoretical proposition, which then was proved by Furtwängler (1930). Further proofs of this proposition were given by Magnus (1934), Iyanaga (1934), Witt (1936, 1954) and Schumann and Franz (1938), whereas Taussky and Scholz (1932, 1934) investigated more closely the process of "capitulation", i.e. of becoming a principal divisor in the subfields of the absolute class field. Exhaustive results concerning this latter problem, however, have not been achieved up to now.

6. Analogously to the process of basing the power residue symbol $\left(\frac{b}{\mathfrak{a}}\right)_n$ on the more general Artin symbol $\left(\frac{K/k}{\mathfrak{a}}\right)$, I succeeded (1926, 1927 and 1930*a*, *b*) in basing the Hilbert norm residue symbol $\left(\frac{a, b}{\mathfrak{p}}\right)_n$ (where k contains the nth roots of unity) on a symbol $\left(\frac{a, K/k}{\mathfrak{p}}\right)$ over an arbitrary k (which need not contain the nth roots of unity). At first, for all prime spots $\mathfrak{p}$ of k, my definition followed the round-about way Hilbert was forced to take for the prime divisors $\mathfrak{p}|n$. As a consequence of this, the connection of the symbol with the norm residues became apparent only on the strength of Artin's reciprocity law. Shortly afterwards, however, I was able to give (1933) a new definition from which this connection was immediately clear. My new definition proceeded on a conceptual basis from the theory of algebras.

I had shown previously (1931*b*) that every central simple algebra of degree n over a local field $k_\mathfrak{p}$ with prime element π possesses an unramified (and hence cyclic) splitting field $Z_\mathfrak{p}$. Consequently such an algebra has a canonical generation

$$u_\mathfrak{p}^n = \pi^{\nu_\mathfrak{p}}, \qquad u_\mathfrak{p}^{-1} Z_\mathfrak{p} u_\mathfrak{p} = Z_\mathfrak{p}^{F_\mathfrak{p}}$$

($F_\mathfrak{p}$ the Frobenius automorphism). On the strength of this, the residue class $\frac{\nu_\mathfrak{p}}{n} \bmod^+ 1$ is invariantly associated with the algebra. For a global relatively cyclic field K/k I put then

$$\left(\frac{a, K/k}{\mathfrak{p}}\right) = S^{-\nu_\mathfrak{p}},$$

when the cyclic algebra over k, generated by

$$u^n = a, \qquad u^{-1} K u = K^S,$$

after extension to the completion $k_\mathfrak{p}$, has the invariant $\frac{\nu_\mathfrak{p}}{n} \bmod^+ 1$. In particular, for a Kummer field $K = k(\sqrt[n]{b})$ (where k contains the nth roots of unity) the automorphism $\left(\frac{a, K/k}{\mathfrak{p}}\right)$ changes $\sqrt[n]{b}$. into $\left(\frac{a, b}{\mathfrak{p}}\right)_n \sqrt[n]{b}$.

From this definition one infers immediately the *local* property:

$$\left(\frac{a, K/k}{\mathfrak{p}}\right) = 1 \Leftrightarrow a \textit{ norm from } K^\mathfrak{p}/k_\mathfrak{p},$$

where $K^\mathfrak{p}$ denotes the isomorphy type of the completions $K_\mathfrak{P}$ for the prime divisors $\mathfrak{P}|\mathfrak{p}$. Hence the symbol $\left(\frac{a, K/k}{\mathfrak{p}}\right)$ is now called simply the *norm symbol*. *Globally* I could prove (1926, 1927, 1930*a*, 1930*c*) the *norm theorem:*

$$\left(\frac{a, K/k}{\mathfrak{p}}\right) = 1 \textit{ for all } \mathfrak{p} \Leftrightarrow a \textit{ norm from } K/k,$$

anticipated by Hilbert for his symbol, as mentioned before. So Hilbert's product formula for his symbol became the *product formula for the norm symbol:*

$$\prod_{\mathfrak{p}} \left(\frac{a, K/k}{\mathfrak{p}}\right) = 1.$$

This is equivalent to my *sum theorem for central simple algebras* (1933):

$$\sum_{\mathfrak{p}} \frac{\nu_{\mathfrak{p}}}{n} \equiv 0 \mod^{+} 1.$$

Whereas the definition of the norm symbol generalizes from relatively cyclic to arbitrary relatively abelian fields K/k by formal composition, I showed (1931*a*) that the norm theorem does not remain true in this generality.

In connection with the local property of the norm symbol I was led (1930*c*) to establish the main theorems of a *class field theory over local fields* $k_{\mathfrak{p}}$. Here one has a one–one correspondence between all relatively abelian fields $K^{\mathfrak{p}}/k_{\mathfrak{p}}$ and all congruence number class groups $A_{\mathfrak{p}}/H_{\mathfrak{p}}$ in $k_{\mathfrak{p}}$, such that $\left(\frac{a, K^{\mathfrak{p}}/k_{\mathfrak{p}}}{\mathfrak{p}}\right)$ gives a canonical isomorphism of $A_{\mathfrak{p}}/H_{\mathfrak{p}}$ onto $\mathfrak{G}(K^{\mathfrak{p}}/k_{\mathfrak{p}})$. The connection with class field theory over global fields k is given by the relations:

(i) $K^{\mathfrak{p}}/k_{\mathfrak{p}}$ represents the isomorphy type of the completion of K/k for the $\mathfrak{P}|\mathfrak{p}$;

(ii) $\mathfrak{G}(K^{\mathfrak{p}}/k_{\mathfrak{p}})$ is the decomposition group of K/k for the $\mathfrak{P}|\mathfrak{p}$.

Subsequently, Schmidt (1930) and Chevalley (1933*a*) gave a systematic development of local class field theory without making reference, as I had done, to that connection with global class field theory. Here I should also mention the essential contributions made by Herbrand (1931 and 1932) to the group theoretical mechanism of certain proofs in local as well as global class field theory, and to the higher ramification theory of normal extensions.

7. In Takagi's class field theory the characterization of the relatively abelian fields K/k by means of the corresponding congruence divisor class groups A/H in k has a disadvantageous fault of beauty. This fault arises from the approximations $A_{\mathfrak{m}}/H_{\mathfrak{m}}$ to A/H by a kind of limit process with ascending divisor moduli $\mathfrak{m}$. After $\mathfrak{p}$-adic concepts and methods had been brought to bear on class field theory in the manner described before, Chevalley (1933*b*) had further the happy idea of replacing also the Weber–Takagi characterization in terms of the congruence divisor class groups A/H by a smoother $\mathfrak{p}$-adic characterization. In this he succeeded by introducing his *ideal elements*, or briefly *idèles*, namely vectors

$$\mathfrak{a} = (\ldots, a_{\mathfrak{p}}, \ldots)$$

with components $a_{\mathfrak{p}}$ from the single completions $k_{\mathfrak{p}}$ satisfying a suitable finiteness condition, viz.,

$$a_{\mathfrak{p}} \cong 1 \quad \text{for almost all } \mathfrak{p}.$$

He replaced the Weber–Takagi congruence divisor class groups A/H by factor groups **A/H** of the *absolute idèle class group* $\mathbf{A}/k^*$, where k^* denotes the group of principal idèles $(\ldots, a, \ldots)$ corresponding to the numbers $a \neq 0$ from k. He proved that the symbol

$$\left(\frac{K/k}{\mathbf{a}}\right) = \prod_{\mathfrak{p}} \left(\frac{a_{\mathfrak{p}}, K^{\mathfrak{p}}/k_{\mathfrak{p}}}{\mathfrak{p}}\right),$$

named after him the *Chevalley symbol*, gives an isomorphism between an idèle class group **A/H** and the Galois group $\mathfrak{G}(K/k)$. Here, the principal class **H** consists of all those absolute idèle classes in k that contain idèle norms from K. In Chevalley's class field theory this idèle class group takes the role of Takagi's congruence divisor class group A/H. To the set of all relatively abelian fields K/k corresponds in this way the set of all idèle class groups **A/H** with open principal class **H** in a suitable topology of **A**, namely that in which the idèle units $\equiv 1 \bmod \mathfrak{m}$ for all divisor moduli $\mathfrak{m}$ form a complete system of neighbourhoods of 1.

Thus one can say that by Chevalley's ideas (not to say: idèles) the *local–global principle* has taken root in class field theory.

There is a further fault of beauty in Takagi's class field theory that was obviated by Chevalley (1940). This is the recourse to analytic means (Dirichlet's L-series) for the proof of the first fundamental inequality $h \leqslant n$. Chevalley succeeded in proving this inequality in a purely arithmetical manner.

8. There still remains much to be said about further developments arising from the class field theory delineated up to this point. For instance, what lies particularly close to my heart, the *explicit reciprocity formulae* (determination of the norm symbol $\left(\frac{a, b}{\mathfrak{p}}\right)_n$ for prime divisors $\mathfrak{p}|n$); further *inclusion of infinite algebraic extensions* K/k, *class field theory over congruence function fields* (algebraic function fields with finite constant field), *Artin's L-series and conductors*, and so on. I must, however, refrain from talking about those subjects here, because that would exceed the frame of this lecture.

I cannot touch either on the further development of class field theory after the war, but suppose I must conclude my survey of the historical development at this point.

If I have understood rightly, it was my task here to delineate for the mathematicians of the post-war generation a vivid and lively picture of the great and beautiful edifice of class field theory erected by the pre-war generations. For the sharply profiled lines and individual features of this magnificent edifice seem to me to have lost somewhat of their original splendour and plasticity by the penetration of class field theory with cohomological concepts and methods, which set in so powerfully after the war.

I should like to think that I have succeeded to some extent in this task.

REFERENCES†

Artin, E. (1924). Über eine neue Art von L-Reihen. *Abh. Math. Semin. Univ. Hamburg*, **3**, 89–108. (Collected Papers (1965), 105–124. Addison Wesley.)

Artin, E. (1927). Beweis des allgemeinen Reziprozitätsgesetzes. *Abh. Math. Semin. Univ. Hamburg*, **5**, 353–363. (Collected Papers (1965), 131–141. Addison Wesley.)

Artin, E. (1930). Idealklassen in Oberkörpern und allgemeines Reziprozitätsgesetz. *Abh. Math. Semin. Univ. Hamburg*, **7**, 46–51. (Collected Papers (1965), 159–164. Addison Wesley.)

Chevalley, C. (1933*a*). La théorie du symbole de restes normiques. *J. reine angew. Math.* **169**, 140–157.

Chevalley, C. (1933*b*). Sur la théorie du corps de classes dans les corps finis et les corps locaux. *J. Fac. Sci. Tokyo Univ.* **2**, 365–476.

Chevalley, C. (1940). La théorie du corps de classes. *Ann. Math.* **41**, 394–417.

Delaunay, B. (1923). Zur Bestimmung algebraischer Zahlkörper durch Kongruenzen; eine Anwendung auf die Abelschen Gleichungen. *J. reine angew. Math.* **152**, 120–123.

Frobenius, G. (1896). Über die Beziehungen zwischen den Primidealen eines algebraischen Körpers und den Substitutionen seiner Gruppe. *Sber. preuss. Akad. Wiss.*, 689–703.

Fueter, R. (1914). Abel'sche Gleichungen in quadratisch-imaginären Zahlkörpern. *Math. Annln.* **75**, 177–255.

Fueter, R. (1927). "Vorlesungen über die singulären Moduln und die komplexe Multiplikation der elliptischen Funktionen II" (unter Mitwirkung von M. Gut). Leipzig-Berlin.

Furtwängler, Ph. (1902). Über die Reziprozitätsgesetze zwischen l^{ten} Potenzresten in algebraischen Zahlkörpern, wenn l eine ungerade Primzahl bedeutet. *Abh. K. Ges. Wiss. Göttingen.* (*Neue Folge*), **2**, Nr. 3, 1–82.=*Math. Annln.* **58** (1904), 1–50.

Furtwängler, Ph. (1907). Allgemeiner Existenzbeweis für den Klassenkörper eines beliebigen algebraischen Zahlkörpers. *Math. Annln.* **63**, 1–37.

Furtwängler, Ph. Reziprozitätsgesetze für Potenzreste mit Primzahlexponenten in algebraischen Zahlkörpern I, II, III. *Math. Annln.* (1909), **67**, 1–31; (1912), **72**, 346–386; (1913), **74**, 413–429.

Furtwängler, Ph. (1928). Über die Reziprozitätsgesetze für ungerade Primzahlexponenten. *Math. Annln.* **98**, 539–543.

Furtwängler, Ph. (1930). Beweis des Hauptidealsatzes für Klassenkörper algebraischer Zahlkörper. *Abh. Math. Semin. Univ. Hamburg*, **7**, 14–36.

† This list of publications from the years 1853–1940 (with one exception from 1954) does not pretend to be a complete list of publications about class field theory and related subjects for this period. It contains only those publications which appeared important as references for what has been said in the lecture.

Hasse, H. Bericht über neuere Untersuchungen und Probleme aus der Theorie der algebraischen Zahlkörper I, Ia, II. *Jber. dt. MatVerein.* (1926), **35,** 1–55; (1927), **36,** 233–311; *Exg. Bd.* (1930*a*), **6,** 1–204.

Hasse, H. (1930*b*). Neue Begründung und Verallgemeinerung der Theorie des Normenrestsymbols. *J. reine angew. Math.* **162,** 134–144.

Hasse, H. (1930*c*). Die Normenresttheorie relativ-Abelscher Zahlkörper als Klassenkörpertheorie im Kleinen. *J. reine angew. Math.* **162,** 145–154.

Hasse, H. (1930*d*). Führer, Diskriminante und Verzweigungskörper relativ-Abelscher Zahlkörper. *J. reine angew. Math.* **162,** 169–184.

Hasse, H. (1931*a*). Beweis eines Satzes und Widerlegung einer Vermutung über das allgemeine Normenrestsymbol. *Nachr. Ges. Wiss. Göttingen,* 64–69.

Hasse, H. (1931*b*). Über *p*-adische Schiefkörper und ihre Bedeutung für die Arithmetik hyperkomplexer Zahlsysteme. *Math. Annln.* **104,** 495–534.

Hasse, H. (1933). Die Struktur der R. Brauerschen Algebrenklassengruppe über einem algebraischen Zahlkörper. *Math. Annln.* **107,** 731–760.

Herbrand, J. (1931). Sur la théorie des groupes de décomposition, d'inertie et de ramification. *J. Math. pures appl.* **10,** 481–498.

Herbrand, J. (1932). Sur les théorèmes du genre principal et des idéaux principaux. *Abh. Math. Semin. Univ. Hamburg,* **9,** 84–92.

Hilbert, D. (1896). Neuer Beweis des Kronecker'schen Fundamentalsatzes über Abel'sche Zahlkörper. *Nachr. Ges. Wiss. Göttingen,* 29–39.

Hilbert, D. (1897). Bericht: Die Theorie der algebraischen Zahlkörper. *Jber. dt. MatVerein.* **4,** 175–546.

Hilbert, D. (1898). Über die Theorie der relativ-Abel'schen Zahlkörper. *Nachr. Ges. Wiss. Göttingen,* 377–399= *Acta math. Stockh.* (1902), **26,** 99–132.

Hilbert, D. (1899*a*). Über die Theorie der relativquadratischen Zahlkörper. *Jber. dt. MatVerein.* **6,** 88–94.

Hilbert, D. (1899*b*). Über die Theorie des relativquadratischen Zahlkörpers. *Math. Annln.* **51,** 1–127.

Hilbert, D. (1900*a*). Theorie der algebraischen Zahlkörper. *Enzykl. math. Wiss.* I C 4a, 675–698.

Hilbert, D. (1900*b*). Theorie des Kreiskörpers. *Enzykl. math. Wiss.* I C 4b, 699–732.

Hilbert, D. (1900*c*). Mathematische Probleme. Vortrag auf internat. Math. Kongr. Paris 1900. *Nachr. Ges. Wiss. Göttingen,* 253–297 (reprinted in "A Collection of Modern Mathematical Classics, Analysis" (ed. R. Bellman), Dover, 1961).

Iyanaga, S. (1934). Zum Beweis des Hauptidealsatzes. *Abh. Math. Semin. Univ. Hamburg,* **10,** 349–357.

Kronecker, L. (1853). Über die algebraisch auflösbaren Gleichungen I. *Sber. preuss. Akad. Wiss.* 365–374= Werke IV, 1–11.

Kronecker, L. (1877). Über Abel'sche Gleichungen. *Sber. preuss. Akad. Wiss.* 845–851= Werke IV, 63–72.

Kronecker, L. (1882). Grundzüge einer arithmetischen Theorie der algebraischen Grössen. *J. reine angew. Math.* **92,** 1–122=Werke II, 237–388. See there § 19, 65–68= 321–324.

Kronecker, L. (1883–90). Zur Theorie der elliptischen Funktionen I–XXII. *Sber. preuss. Akad. Wiss.*=Werke IV, 345–496= V, 1–132.

Kronecker, L. Auszug aus Brief an R. Dedekind vom 15 März 1880. Werke V, 453–458. See also my detailed "*Zusatz*", ibid., 510–515.

Magnus, W. (1934). Über den Beweis des Hauptidealsatzes. *J. reine angew. Math.* **170,** 235–240.

Schmid, H. L. (1936). Zyklische algebraische Funktionenkorper vom Grade p^n über endlichem Konstantenkörper der Charakteristik *p*. *J. reine angew. Math.* **175**, 108–123.

Schmidt, F. K. (1930). Zur Klassenkörpertheorie im Kleinen. *J. reine angew. Math.* **162**, 155–168.

Schumann, H. G. (1938). Zum Beweis des Hauptidealsatzes (unter Mitwirkung von W. Franz). *Abh. Math. Semin. Univ. Hamburg*, **12**, 42–47.

Speiser, A. (1919). Die Zerlegungsgruppe. *J. reine angew. Math.* **149**, 174–188.

Takagi, T. (1903). Über die im Bereich der rationalen komplexen Zahlen Abel'schen Zahlkörper. *J. Coll. Sci. imp. Univ. Tokyo*, **19**, Nr. 5, 1–42.

Takagi, T. (1920). Über eine Theorie des relativ-Abel'schen Zahlkörpers. *J. Coll. Sci. imp. Univ. Tokyo*, **41**, Nr. 9, 1–133.

Takagi, T. (1922). Über das Reziprozitätsgesetz in einem beliebigen algebraischen Zahlkörper. *J. Coll. Sci. imp. Univ. Tokyo*, **44**, Nr. 5, 1–50.

Taussky, O. (1932). Über eine Verschärfung des Hauptidealsatzes für algebraische Zahlkörper. *J. reine angew. Math.* **168**, 193–210.

Taussky, O. and Scholz, A. (1934). Die Hauptideale der kubischen Klassenkörper imaginärquadratischer Zahlkörper: ihre rechnerische Bestimmung und ihr Einfluß auf den Klassenkörperturm. *J. reine angew. Math.* **171**, 19–41.

Tchebotarev, N. (1926). Bestimmung der Dichtigkeit einer Menge von Primzahlen, welche zu einer gegebenen Substitutionsklasse gehören. *Math. Annln.* **95**, 191–228.

Weber, H. Theorie der Abel'schen Zahlkörper I, II. *Acta math. Stockh.* (1886), **8**, 193–263; (1887), **9**, 105–130.

Weber, H. Über Zahlengruppen in algebraischen Körpen I, II, III. *Math. Annln.* (1897), **48**, 433–473; (1897), **49**, 83–100; (1898), **50**, 1–26.

Weber, H. (1891). "Elliptische Funktionen und algebraische Zahlen". Braunschweig.

Weber, H. (1908). "Lehrbuch der Algebra III".† Braunschweig.

Weber, H. (1909). Zur Theorie der zyklischen Zahlkörper. *Math. Annln.* **67**, 32–60.

Witt, E. (1936). Bemerkungen zum Beweis des Hauptidealsatzes von S. Iyanaga. *Abh. Math. Semin. Univ. Hamburg*, **11**, 221.

Witt, E. (1937). Zyklische Körper und Algebren der Charakteristik *p* vom Grade p^n. *J. reine angew. Math.* **176**, 126–140.

Witt, E. (1954). Verlagerung von Gruppen und Hauptidealsatz. Proc. Internat. Math. Congress II, Amsterdam 1954, 71–73.

† Second edition of "Elliptische Funktionen und Algebraische Zahlen".

CHAPTER XII

An Application of Computing to Class Field Theory

H. P. F. SWINNERTON-DYER

Let G be a connected algebraic group. Chevalley has shown that G contains a normal subgroup R such that R is a connected linear group and G/R is an Abelian variety†; and these properties determine R uniquely. The general theory of algebraic groups therefore depends on theories for linear groups and for Abelian varieties. In Chapter X of this book Kneser has described the known number-theoretical properties of linear groups, and the same thing will be done here for Abelian varieties. But there is a fundamental difference between these two topics. Kneser has expounded a theory which is reasonably complete and satisfactory—the major results have been or are on the point of being proved, and there is no reason to think that there are important theorems as yet undiscovered. For Abelian varieties, on the other hand, very few number-theoretical theorems have yet been proved. The most interesting results are conjectures, based on numerical computation of special cases, and the fact that one has no idea how to attack these conjectures suggests that there must be important theorems which have not yet even been stated.

The original calculations are largely due to Birch and Swinnerton-Dyer; and their results can be expressed in respectable language through the efforts of Cassels and of Tate. One object of this chapter is to describe the numerical evidence, to show how far the conjectures are directly based on it, and to explain why it seems right to state the conjectures in very general terms although all the evidence refers to cases of one particular kind.

With the advent of electronic computers, calculations which would previously have been out of the question are now quite practicable, provided that they are sufficiently repetitive. There must be many topics in number theory in which intelligently directed calculation would yield valuable results. (At the moment, most number-theoretical calculations merely pile up lists of integers in the manner of a magpie; they are neither designed to produce valuable results nor capable of doing so.) The second object of this chapter

† An Abelian variety is a connected algebraic group which is also a *complete* algebraic variety; the group operation on an Abelian variety must necessarily be commutative. The simplest example of an Abelian variety is an non-singular cubic curve in the projective plane, together with a point on it which is the identity for the group operation.

is to show what can reasonably be done on a computer, and what the number-theorist must consider before he can ask someone to do his calculations for him.

When a modern algebraist defines something, he usually begins by taking the quotient of one very infinite object by another. A process of this kind can seldom be carried out on a computer even in theory; and it never can in practice. Thus an object which can only be defined in this sort of way is not effectively computable. Conversely, if something has to be computed it must be defined in a way which is more down-to-earth, even if less canonical. This applies not only to the final result of the calculation, but to anything which turns up in the course of it. This may be difficult or even impossible: for example the Tate-Šafarevič group (defined below) has at the moment no constructive definition.

Once a number-theorist has phrased his problem in computable terms, he can estimate how much machine time it will take. This depends on the number of operations involved—an operation for this purpose being an addition, subtraction, multiplication or division. (This is a crude method of estimation, and ignores for example the time spent in organizational parts of the program; but it will give the right order of magnitude.) A calculation which takes 10^6 operations is trivial, and is worth doing even if its results will probably be useless. A calculation which takes 10^9 operations is substantial but not unreasonable. It is worth doing in pursuit of any serious idea, but not just in the hope that something may turn up; moreover, the method of calculation should now be reasonably efficient, whereas for a smaller problem one chooses the simplest possible method in order to minimize the effort of writing the program. Finally, a calculation which takes 10^{12} operations is close to the limit of what is physically possible; it can only be justified by a major scientific advance such as landing a man on the moon.

When a calculation is complete, one must still ask whether the results are reliable. A typical program, in machine-coded form, is a string of several thousand symbols; and a slip of the pen in any one of them will change the calculation being carried out by the computer. Most errors have disastrous results, and can therefore be detected and removed; but some errors are analogous to mistakes in a formula, and will merely cause the production of wrong answers. Some calculations are self-checking: one example is given below, in which an integer is obtained as the value of a complicated analytic expression—if this had been wrongly evaluated, the result would not always have come out to be approximately an integer. There are other calculations in which once the answer has been found it can be checked with relatively little effort: for example in searching for a solution of a diophantine equation. But in general it is desirable either to work out some typical results by hand, for comparison with those obtained from the machine, or to have the whole calculation repeated *ab initio* by a different programmer on a different machine.

If Γ is a curve defined over **Q**, the field of rationals, under what conditions can we say that Γ contains rational points? This problem is completely solved for curves of genus 0, for Γ is then birationally equivalent over **Q** to a straight line or a conic; so it is natural to consider the case when Γ has genus 1. This is equivalent to saying that if $P_1, \ldots, P_n, Q_1, \ldots, Q_{n-1}$ are any points on Γ then there is a unique Q_n such that the P_i are the poles and the Q_i the zeros of some function on Γ. It follows that for any given point O on Γ we can give Γ the structure of a group with O as the identity; for if P_1, P_2 are any points on Γ we define $Q = P_1 + P_2$ by the property that P_1, P_2 are the poles and O, Q the zeros of some function on Γ. Moreover if O and Γ are defined over **Q**, then so is the group law; thus the set of rational points on Γ form a group, which we call Γ_Q.

We can associate with Γ another curve J, the Jacobian of Γ, as follows. On $\Gamma \times \Gamma$ we define an equivalence relation by writing $P_1 \times Q_1 \sim P_2 \times Q_2$ if and only if P_1, Q_2 are the poles and P_2, Q_1 the zeros of a function on Γ. J is defined (up to birational equivalence) as the curve, each point of which corresponds to an equivalence class on $\Gamma \times \Gamma$. J is defined over **Q** and certainly contains a rational point, corresponding to the class of points $P \times P$ on $\Gamma \times \Gamma$; and we can write the equation of J in the form

$$y^2z = x^3 - Axz^2 - Bz^3. \tag{1}$$

We say that Γ is a *principal homogeneous space* for J. Clearly Γ is birationally equivalent to J over **Q** if and only if it contains a rational point; and because J has a canonical rational point it has a canonical group structure.

The problem of rational points on Γ now breaks up into two parts: (i) is there a rational point on Γ, and (ii) what is the structure of the group of rational points on J? Of these, the second is more attractive because there is more structure associated with it. Mordell in 1922 proved the following theorem.

MORDELL'S THEOREM. *The group of rational points on J is finitely generated.*

It is easy to find the elements of finite order in this group, in any particular case. Thus it is natural to ask for a means of finding g, the number of independent generators of infinite order, and if possible for an actual set of generators. Mordell's argument is semi-constructive, in that it gives in any numerical case an upper bound for g which is not absurdly large; and by using the ideas underlying his proof one can usually find g and an actual set of generators. But the process can be very laborious and there is no guarantee that it will always work. Moreover g is not connected with anything else in the theory. What should it be connected with?

We can regard a solution of the equation (1) as the result of fitting together a compatible set of solutions of the congruences

$$y^2z \equiv x^3 - Axz^2 - Bz^3 \pmod{p^n}. \tag{2}$$

One can hope that if these congruences have a lot of solutions it will be relatively easy to find compatible sets, and so (1) will have a lot of solutions and g will be large. Hence we look for a measure of the density of solutions of the congruences (2). Let N_{p^n} be the number of essentially distinct primitive solutions of (2). Except at finitely many bad primes p it follows from Hensel's Lemma that

$$N_{p^n} = p^{n-1}N_p$$

and we are therefore led to consider the infinite product

$$\prod (N_p/p). \tag{3}$$

We can also define N_p as the number of points on (1) considered as a curve over the finite field of p elements. For finitely many primes we expect that the factor in (3) is wrong, but it is not yet clear what to put in its place.

There is a more respectable reason for considering the product (3), though in the end it will turn out to be misleading. We have

$$N_p = p - \alpha_p - \bar{\alpha}_p + 1$$

where $|\alpha_p| = p^{1/2}$; and the local zeta-function of Γ is defined as

$$\zeta_{\Gamma,p}(s) = \frac{(1-\alpha_p p^{-s})(1-\bar{\alpha}_p p^{-s})}{(1-p^{-s})(1-p^{1-s})}.$$

The numerator of the right-hand side has the value N_p/p at $s = 1$; if we write

$$L_\Gamma(s) = \prod [(1-\alpha_p p^{-s})(1-\bar{\alpha}_p p^{-s})]^{-1} \tag{4}$$

then

$$\zeta_\Gamma(s) = \prod \zeta_{\Gamma,p}(s) = \frac{\zeta(s)\zeta(s-1)}{L_\Gamma(s)}$$

and formally

$$[L_\Gamma(1)]^{-1} = \prod (N_p/p).$$

The product (4) is only known to converge in $\mathscr{R}s > 3/2$, though it is conjectured (and in special cases known) that $L_\Gamma(s)$ can be analytically continued over the whole plane. Moreover one can at best hope that the product (3) is finitely oscillatory, because one expects that $L_\Gamma(s)$ will have complex zeros on $\mathscr{R}s = 1$. However, it is easy to calculate the finite products

$$f(P) = \prod (N_p/p)$$

taken over all $p \leq P$ for values of P up to several thousand†. To a sympathetic eye, the results suggested that $f(P)$ oscillates finitely when $g = 0$, and tends to infinity when $g > 0$; and this led to the linked pair of conjectures

$$f(P) \textit{ lies between constant multiples of } (\log P)^g,$$

$$L_\Gamma(s) \textit{ has a zero of order } g \textit{ at } s = 1.$$

(Of course the constants in the first conjecture depend on Γ.) By looking at the behaviour of $f(P)$, Birch and Swinnerton-Dyer were able to predict the value of g for individual curves, and the predictions were right in about 90% of the cases tried; these were curves for which $g = 0, 1, 2$ or 3. But there seems to be no objective numerical method for estimating g accurately in this way.

To do better than this, we have to know more about $L_\Gamma(s)$. It is therefore natural to consider curves J which admit complex multiplication, since there is then an explicit formula for N_p and $L_\Gamma(s)$ is a product of Hecke L-series. The simplest such curves have the form

$$y^2 z = x^3 - Dxz^2, \tag{5}$$

in which we can assume that D is an integer and is fourth-power-free; and if we write $(..)_4$ for the biquadratic residue symbol in $\mathbf{Q}(i)$ we have the following formulae.

THEOREM (DAVENPORT-HASSE). *For the curve* $y^2 z = x^3 - Dxz^2$,

$$N_p = \begin{cases} p+1 & \textit{for } p \equiv 3 \bmod 4, \\ p+1-\pi\left(\dfrac{D}{\bar{\pi}}\right)_4 - \bar{\pi}\left(\dfrac{D}{\pi}\right)_4 & \textit{for } p \equiv 1 \bmod 4, \end{cases}$$

where in the second case $p = \pi\bar{\pi}$ *in* $\mathbf{Q}(i)$ *with* $\pi, \bar{\pi} \equiv 1 \bmod (2+2i)$.

There is no easy proof of the full theorem. That α_p/π is a power of i goes back to Jacobsthal, who gave an elementary proof which makes it look like a piece of good luck. The reason why such formulae exist in this case is that $\mathbf{Q}(i)$ is here the ring of endomorphisms of J in characteristic 0. Thus if $p \equiv 1 \bmod 4$, $\mathbf{Q}(i)$ must be the whole ring of endomorphisms of J in characteristic p; for the known structure theorems rule out any strictly larger ring. Hence α_p, being the image of the Frobenius endomorphism, must lie in $\mathbf{Q}(i)$; and since $\alpha_p \bar{\alpha}_p = p$ we find that α_p/π is a unit in $\mathbf{Q}(i)$.

† The naïve way of calculating N_p is to set $z = 1$ in (1) and test all possible pairs x, y; this would have taken $O(p^2)$ operations, and used more machine time than was justifiable. But because (1) can be written as

$$y^2 = w = x^3 - Ax - B$$

it is only necessary to tabulate for each value of w the number of ways in which it is a square; for each value of x one can then read off the number of solutions. In this way, N_p can be found after only $O(p)$ operations.

Using the values above for the N_p we have

$$L_\Gamma(s) = L_D(s) = \prod_{p \equiv 3 \bmod 4} (1+p^{1-2s})^{-1} \prod_{p \equiv 1 \bmod 4} \left[1 - \pi p^{-s}\left(\frac{D}{\bar{\pi}}\right)_4\right]^{-1} \left[1 - \bar{\pi} p\left(\frac{D}{\pi}\right)_4\right]^{-1}$$

$$= \prod\left[1 - \left(\frac{D}{\pi}\right)_4 \bar{\pi}(N\pi)^{-s}\right]^{-1} = \sum\left(\frac{D}{\sigma}\right)_4 \bar{\sigma}(N\sigma)^{-s}$$

where the product is taken over all Gaussian primes $\pi \equiv 1 \bmod (2 + 2i)$, the sum is over all Gaussian integers $\sigma \equiv 1 \bmod (2 + 2i)$ and N is the norm for $\mathbf{Q}(i)/\mathbf{Q}$. Writing $\sigma = 16D\lambda + \mu$, where λ runs over all Gaussian integers and μ over a suitably chosen finite set of values, we have

$$L_D(s) = \sum_\mu \left(\frac{D}{\mu}\right)_4 \sum_\lambda \bar{\sigma}(N\sigma)^{-s}.$$

We cannot yet write $s = 1$, for the inner series would not converge; thus we write

$$\psi(\alpha, s) = \frac{\bar{\alpha}}{|\alpha|^{2s}} + \sum_{\nu \neq 0} \left\{\frac{\bar{\alpha}+\bar{\nu}}{|\alpha+\nu|^{2s}} - \frac{\bar{\nu}}{|\nu|^{2s}}\left[1 - \frac{s\alpha}{\nu} + \frac{\bar{\alpha}(1-s)}{\bar{\nu}}\right]\right\},$$

which converges for $\mathcal{R}s > \frac{1}{2}$, and after some reduction we obtain

$$L_D(s) = (16D)^{1-2s}\left[\sum_\mu \left(\frac{D}{\mu}\right)_4 \psi\left(\frac{\mu}{16D}, s\right) + 4(1-s)\zeta_{\mathbf{Q}(i)}(s) \sum_\mu \frac{\bar{\mu}}{16D}\left(\frac{D}{\mu}\right)_4\right].$$

Here we can at last let s tend to 1; and since $\psi(\alpha, 1) = \xi(\alpha)$, the Weierstrass zeta function, we obtain

$$L_D(1) = \frac{1}{16D}\sum\left(\frac{D}{\mu}\right)_4 \xi\left(\frac{\mu}{16D}\right) - \frac{\pi}{(16D)^2}\sum \bar{\mu}\left(\frac{D}{\mu}\right)_4. \tag{6}$$

This is an explicit finite formula from which the value of $L_D(1)$ can be computed.

In the interests of simplicity, I have derived a relatively clumsy formula for $L_D(1)$. In fact, if Δ is the product of the distinct odd primes dividing D, then $L_D(1)$ can be expressed as a sum of $O(\Delta^2)$ terms instead of the $O(D^2)$ given above, and can therefore be calculated in $O(\Delta^2)$ operations. The constant implied in this formula is quite large because each term is complicated; but it was possible to evaluate $L_D(1)$ for all $|\Delta| < 108$, which gave some very large values of D. Moreover, provided that $|\Delta| > 1$ the second term in (6) vanishes for a suitable choice of the μ and $L_D(1)$ can be written as a sum of terms involving Weierstrass $\wp$-functions. In this way it can be shown that

$D^{1/4}L_D(1)/\omega$ *is a rational integer if* $D > 0$

where ω is the real period of the Weierstrass $\wp$-function defined by

$$\wp'^2 = 4\wp^3 - 4\wp.$$

The proof is in two parts: $2^{3/4}\Delta L_D(1)/\omega$ is an algebraic integer, because of the addition formula for $\wp$; and $D^{1/4} L_D(1)/\omega$ is rational, because of the Kronecker Jugendtraum. There is a similar result for $D < 0$. From this, and the approximate calculations of $L_D(1)$, which are accurate to one part in 10^5, we can obtain the exact values of $L_D(1)$ for a large number of particular curves; and all these support the conjecture that

$$L_D(1) = 0 \textit{ if and only if } g > 0.$$

However, the numerical results still leave something to be explained away or fitted into the theory, to wit, the rational integer $D^{1/4}L_D(1)/\omega$ when $g = 0$. The possible non-trivial factors from which this can be built up are (i) $\eta(D)$, the number of rational points of finite order on J; (ii) Ш (D), the order of the Tate–Šafarevič group of J; (iii) "fudge factors" corresponding to the finitely many "bad" primes. For the curve (5), $\eta(D)$ is 4 if D is a square and 2 otherwise. "Bad" primes are those for which J has a bad reduction modulo p; that is, those which divide $2D$. One has also the right to deem "infinity" to be "bad" if this is expedient.

We have next to define the Tate–Šafarevič group. There is an equivalence relation among the principal homogeneous spaces Γ for a fixed Jacobian J, defined by birational equivalence over **Q**. The equivalence classes under this relation form the Weil-Châtelet group,† which is a commutative torsion group of infinite order. Those Γ which contain points defined over each p-adic field and over the reals, fill a certain number of equivalence classes; and these classes form the Tate-Šafarevič group. It is conjectured that this group is always finite, though there is no case in which this has yet been proved; however Cassels has shown that when it is finite its order is a perfect square. The whole group is not constructively defined, and is not computable; but it is theoretically possible to compute those of its elements which have any given order (of which there can only be finitely many), and for the curve (5) it is practicable to find the elements of orders 2 and 4 at least.

Fudge factors must be purely local, and there are now two plausible alternatives: (i) fill in the missing factors of $L_\Gamma(s)$ by means of the functional equation—this is possible whenever there is complex multiplication; (ii) supply the missing factors of the product $\prod(N_p/p)$ by considering the Tamagawa measure of the curve J.

† This can also be defined as the cohomology group $H^1(\mathbf{Q},J)$—see Chapter X for the details of a parallel case. The group law can be defined geometrically as follows. There is a map $\Gamma \times \Gamma \to J$ which can be written $P \times Q \to (P - Q)$ in an obvious notation. On $\Gamma_1 \times \Gamma_2$ we define an equivalence relation by writing $P_1 \times P_2 \sim Q_1 \times Q_2$ if and only if $P_1 - Q_1 = Q_2 - P_2$. Now $\Gamma_1 + \Gamma_2$ is defined as Γ_3, the curve whose points are in one–one correspondence with the equivalence classes on $\Gamma_1 \times \Gamma_2$.

It must be emphasized that these two alternatives do lead to numerical different results, and that the second one appears to work while the first definitely does not. To define the Tamagawa measure, let ω be a differential of the first kind on J; this induces a measure ω_p on J over each p-adic field, and the Tamagawa measure of J is defined to be

$$\prod \int_J \omega_p$$

taken over all primes including infinity. Here ω is defined up to multiplication by an arbitrary constant, and the contributions of this constant to the infinite product evidently cancel out.

LEMMA. *If p is a "good" finite prime then* $\int_J \omega_p = N_p/p$.

Here "good" means that both J and ω have a good reduction mod p. We can take ω to be

$$\frac{dx}{2y} = \frac{dy}{3x^2 - D} \tag{8}$$

possibly multiplied by a p-adic unit. Let (x_0, y_0) be any solution of

$$y^2 \equiv x^3 - Dx \bmod p$$

with $y_0 \not\equiv 0 \bmod p$. By Hensel's Lemma, to each p-adic $x \equiv x_0 \bmod p$ there corresponds just one $y \equiv y_0 \bmod p$ satisfying $y^2 = x^3 - Dx$; all these solutions together contribute to $\int \omega_p$ an amount equal to the p-adic measure of the set of $x \equiv x_0 \bmod p$, which is p^{-1}. A similar argument works for the solutions with $y_0 = 0$ or ∞. This proves the Lemma.

If we define ω to be (8), which is in fact the canonical form for the differential on J, then the bad primes are just those which divide $2D\,\infty$. It can be shown that

$$\int \omega_\infty = 2\omega D^{-\frac{1}{4}} \text{ if } D > 0$$

with a similar result for $D < 0$. Thus the Tamagawa measure of J, defined by (7), is formally equal to

$$2\omega D^{-\frac{1}{4}} [L_D(1)]^{-1} \prod \int \omega_p = \tau(D), \text{ say,} \tag{9}$$

where the product is taken over the finite bad primes p. This is a rational number. The contributions from the bad primes can be found by arguments similar to those of the Lemma, though more tedius; and it can be shown that $\int \omega_p$ for a bad prime p is just the number of components into which J decomposes under reduction modulo p in the sense of Néron (Modèles minimaux .., Publ. IHES, 21).

The numerical results lead to the conjecture that the Tamagawa measure (9) is equal to

$$[\eta(D)]^2/\text{Ш}(D). \tag{10}$$

They cannot be said to support this conjecture directly since Ш(D) cannot be calculated; but if we write

$$\gamma(D) = [\eta(D)]^2/\tau(D),$$

the conjectural value of Ш(D), it has the following properties in every case in which it has been calculated. (i) $\gamma(D)$ is a perfect square, and usually contains no prime factor other than 2; in most cases $\gamma(D) = 1$. (ii) Whenever the exact power of 2 which divides Ш(D) has been calculated, this is also the exact power of 2 which divides $\gamma(D)$. In the outstanding cases, Ш(D) must be and $\gamma(D)$ is divisible by a substantial power of 2. Moreover, a comparison of the conjectures for the isogenous curves $y^2 = x^3 - Dx$ and $y^2 = x^3 + 4Dx$ yields an explicit formula for Ш$(-4D)$/Ш(D); this has subsequently been proved by Cassels.

The surprising part of this conjecture is the presence of a square in (10). We expect to measure a union of representatives of the elements of the Tate–Šafarevič group modulo the group of rational points on this union; and the measure turns out to be $\eta(D)$ rather than a constant.

To describe what happens for $g > 0$, or for more general curves Γ, it is convenient to define the modified L-series

$$L_\Gamma^*(s) = L_\Gamma(s)/\prod \int \omega_p \tag{11}$$

in which the product is taken over all bad primes including infinity, and $L_\Gamma(s)$ is defined by (4) in which the product is taken over all good primes. If J admits complex multiplication, we can give explicit formulae for the coefficients of the power series expansion of $L_\Gamma(s)$ about $s = 1$ by arguments similar to those above; the only change is that instead of Weierstrass zeta functions the formulae involve series which converge but have no interesting theoretical properties.

Nelson Stephens, a student of Birch, has carried out these calculations for curves of the form

$$J: y^3 = x^3 - Dz^3, \tag{12}$$

which also admit complex multiplication. His results are consistent with the formula

$$L_\Gamma^*(s) \approx 2^g(s-1)^g \kappa\, Ш(J)/[\eta(J)]^2 \tag{13}$$

in which g is the number of independent generators of J_Q of infinite order, $\eta(J)$ is the order of the torsion subgroup of J_Q, Ш(J) is the order of the Tate-Šafarevič group of J, and κ measures the size of the generators of infinite order for J_Q in the following way. Let $P = (x, y, z)$ be a rational point on J, where x, y, z are integers with no common factor, and write

$$R(P) = \log [\mathrm{Max}\,(|x|, |y|, |z|)].$$

Tate has defined the canonical height of P to be

$$R^*(P) = \lim n^{-2} R(nP);$$

he has shown that this limit exists and behaves like a quadratic form on the additive group J_Q. In particular it gives rise to the bilinear form

$$<P_1, P_2> = \tfrac{1}{2}[R^*(P_1+P_2) - R^*(P_1) - R^*(P_2)].$$

If $P_1, \ldots, P_g$ are the elements of infinite order in a base for J_Q, then

$$\kappa = \det(<P_i, P_j>)$$

which clearly does not depend on the particular base chosen.

The conjecture (13) is meaningful for any elliptic curve, although all the evidence so far given for it relates to curves with complex multiplication. Shimura has shown that $L_\Gamma(s)$ can be analytically continued for those elliptic curves which can be parametized by modular functions, and has suggested that it should be possible to verify the conjecture for some of them. The few such curves that appear in the literature all have $g = 0$ and can be easily shown to have $L_\Gamma(1) \neq 0$. Birch has been able to calculate $L^*_\Gamma(1)$ for one of them, and to show that it has the value which the conjecture demands. But we have not yet been able to mechanize the process of finding such curves—though they appear to be extremely common—nor that of calculating $L^*_\Gamma(1)$.

It is natural to generalize these conjectures to apply to other varieties. Assuming the Weil conjectures, let V be a complete non-singular variety of dimension n; then its local zeta-function has the form

$$\zeta_{V,p}(s) = \frac{L_{p,0}(s)L_{p,2}(s)\ldots L_{p,2n}(s)}{L_{p,1}(s)\ldots L_{p,2n-1}(s)}$$

where

$$L_{p,m}(s) = \prod (1 - \alpha_{mj} p^{-s})^{-1}. \tag{19}$$

Here $|\alpha_{mj}| = p^{m/2}$, and the product (14) has B_m factors, where B_m is the mth Betti number of V. Moreover, we can write

$$L_m(s) = \prod L_{p,m}(s)$$

where the product is taken over all primes for which V has a good reduction modulo p. In general we do not know how to define the factors corresponding to the bad primes, and so cannot go on to obtain $L^*_m(s)$; the one exceptional case is when V is an Abelian variety A and $m = 1$ or $2n - 1$. In this case we can proceed as we did for J; the only novelty is we must now distinguish between A and its dual $\hat{A}$, whereas for an elliptic curve $J = \hat{J}$. Since the proper generalization of (13) should follow from (13) when A is a product of elliptic curves, it ought to be

$$L^*_{2n-1}(s+n-1) = L^*_1(s) \approx 2^g(s-1)^g \kappa Ш(A)/\eta(A)\eta(\hat{A}). \tag{15}$$

The form of the denominator on the right has been obtained from the role which duality plays in the proof of Cassels' relation between $Ш(J_1)$ and $Ш(J_2)$ for two isogenous elliptic curves J_1 and J_2.

Except in this special case, we can only try to generalize the weaker conjecture that $L_\Gamma(s)$ has a zero of order g at $s = 1$. In these terms, there is a natural analogue of (15) for general V:

$L_{2n-1}(s)$ has a zero of order g at $s = n$, where g is the rank of the group of rational points on the Picard variety of V.

But the extra generality is spurious, for one believes that $L_{2n-1}(s)$ depends only on the Picard variety of V and not on V itself.

For even suffices, Tate in his Wood's Hole talk† produced a remarkable new conjecture:

$L_{2r}(s)$ has a pole of order υ at $s = r + 1$, where υ is the rank of the group of r-cycles on V defined over $\mathbf{Q}$, modulo algebraic equivalence.

Note that $L_{2r}(s)$ converges in $\mathscr{R}s > r + 1$, so that this conjecture can be given a meaning even if $L_{2r}(s)$ cannot be analytically continued; by contrast, all the previous conjectures have refered to a point which is a distance $\frac{1}{2}$ from the region of known convergence. Tate's conjecture is known to hold for rational surfaces, and he has proved it for other varieties of certain special types. Moreover, by applying it to the n-fold product of an elliptic curve Γ with itself, he has been able to state the distribution of the characteristic roots α_p and $\bar{\alpha}_p$ of Γ as p varies; and these predictions have been verified numerically.

Is there a comparable conjecture for $L_{2r-1}(s)$? One expects to associate $L_{2r}(s)$ with r-cycles modulo algebraic equivalence, and $L_{2r-1}(s)$ with $(r-1)$-cycles algebraically equivalent to zero. Moreover, any conjecture must generalize the one stated above for $L_{2n-1}(s)$, and must take into account the duality between $L_m(s)$ and $L_{2n-m}(s)$. Bearing these facts in mind, there is one plausible form that such a conjecture could take. Let $\mathfrak{a}_1$ and $\mathfrak{a}_2$ be two algebraically equivalent r-cycles on V; this means that there is a non-singular variety W whose points correspond to r-cycles on V, and there are points P_1 and P_2 on W which correspond to $\mathfrak{a}_1$ and $\mathfrak{a}_2$ respectively. We shall say that $\mathfrak{a}_1$ and $\mathfrak{a}_2$ are *Abelian equivalent* if it is possible to choose W, P_1 and P_2 in such a way that the image of $P_1 \times P_2$ in the Albanese variety of W is the identity. It is known that this gives an equivalence relation, though it is one about which very little has been proved. The most natural conjecture now is as follows:

$L_{2r-1}(s)$ has a zero of order at least v at $s = r$, where v is the rank of the group of $(r-1)$ – cycles on V defined over $\mathbf{Q}$ and algebraically equivalent to zero, modulo Abelian equivalence.

† Published paradoxically in " Arithmetical Algebraic Geometry. Proceedings of a Conference held in Purdue University, December 5–7, 1963." (Ed. O. F. G. Schilling.) Harper & Row.

This is supported by unpublished results of Bombieri and Swinnerton-Dyer for the cubic threefold, and for the intersection of two quadrics in $2n + 1$ dimensions. In both these cases the conjecture appears to hold with actual equality. However, numerical calculations show that for the n-fold product of an elliptic curve with itself we can have either inequality or equality, depending on the particular curve.

CHAPTER XIII

Complex Multiplication

J.-P. SERRE

Introduction

A central problem of algebraic number theory is to give an explicit construction for the abelian extensions of a given field K. For instance, if K is $\mathbf{Q}$, the field of rationals, the theorem of Kronecker-Weber tells us that the maximal abelian extension $\mathbf{Q}^{ab}$ of $\mathbf{Q}$ is precisely $\mathbf{Q}^{cycl}$, the union of all cyclotomic extensions. There is a canonical isomorphism

$$\operatorname{Gal}(\mathbf{Q}^{cycl}/\mathbf{Q}) \cong \prod_p U_p,$$

so we have an explicit class-field theory over $\mathbf{Q}$ (Chapter VII, § 5.7).

If K is an imaginary quadratic field, complex multiplication does essentially the same. We get the extensions $K^{ab} \supset \tilde{K} \supset K$ ($\tilde{K}$ is the absolute class field the maximum unramified abelian extension) essentially by adjoining points of finite order on an elliptic curve with the right complex multiplication.

1. The Theorems

Let E be an elliptic curve over $\mathbf{C}$ (the complex field); in normal form, its equation may be taken as $y^2 = 4x^3 - g_2 x - g_3$. We know that $E \cong \mathbf{C}/\Gamma$ where Γ is a lattice in $\mathbf{C}$. An endomorphism of E is a multiplication by an element $z \in \mathbf{C}$ with $z\Gamma \subset \Gamma$. In general, $\operatorname{End}(E) = \mathbf{Z}$; if $\operatorname{End}(E)$ is larger, then $\operatorname{End}(E) \otimes \mathbf{Q} = K$ must be an imaginary quadratic field.

Let R be the ring of integers of such a field K; then $\operatorname{End}(E)$ is a subring of R of finite index. Every such subring of R has the form $R_f = \mathbf{Z} + fR$ ($f \geqslant 1$ is the "conductor"); so, if E has complex multiplication, there is a complex quadratic field K with integers R, and an integer f, such that $\operatorname{End}(E) \cong R_f$. Conversely, given R_f, there are corresponding elliptic curves.

THEOREM. *The elliptic curves with given endomorphism ring R_f correspond one–one (up to isomorphism) with the class group* $\operatorname{Cl}(R_f)$.

[$\mathrm{Cl}(R_f)$ is the same as $\tilde{K}_0(R_f)$, the group of projective modules of rank 1 over R_f. If $f = 1$, it is simply the group of ideal classes of R.]

Sketch of Proof. Such a curve E determines a lattice Γ by $E \cong \mathbf{C}/\Gamma$ (so essentially Γ is $\pi_1(E)$). Γ is an R_f-module of rank 1, whose endomorphism ring is exactly R_f; this implies that Γ is an R_f-projective module of rank 1. Conversely, given such a Γ, $\mathbf{C}/\Gamma$ is an elliptic curve with $\mathrm{End}(\mathbf{C}/\Gamma) = R_f$.

COROLLARY. *Up to isomorphism, there are only finitely many curves E with* $\mathrm{End}(E) = R_f$; *in fact, there are precisely* $h_f = \mathrm{Card}(\mathrm{Cl}(R_f))$.

To each E, associate its invariant $j(E)$; so there are h_f such numbers associated with R_f. For simplicity, take $f = 1$.

THEOREM (Weber-Fueter). (i) *The $j(E)$ are algebraic integers.*

(ii) *Let $\alpha = j(E)$ be one of them. The field $K(\alpha)$ is the absolute class field of K.*

(iii) $\mathrm{Gal}(K(\alpha)/K)$ *permutes the $j(E)$'s associated with R transitively.*

There are analogous results for $f > 1$; in particular, the $j(E)$ are still algebraic integers. In fact, we can be more explicit. Call $\mathrm{Ell}(R_f)$ the set of elliptic curves with endomorphism ring R_f; if $E \cong \mathbf{C}/\Gamma \in \mathrm{Ell}(R_f)$, write $j(\Gamma)$ for its invariant; Γ is an inversible ideal of R_f, and $j(\Gamma)$ depends only on its class. Hasse (1927, 1931) has proved the following theorem.

THEOREM. *Let $\mathfrak{p}$ be a good prime of K, with $(\mathfrak{p}, f) = (1)$; let $\mathfrak{p}_f = \mathfrak{p} \cap R_f$ be the corresponding ideal of R_f. Then the Frobenius element $F(\mathfrak{p})$ acts on $j(\Gamma)$ by*

$$(j(\Gamma))^{F(\mathfrak{p})} = j(\Gamma \cdot \mathfrak{p}_f^{-1}).$$

COROLLARY ($f = 1$). *If $E \leftrightarrow e \in \mathrm{Cl}(R)$, and the Artin map takes $c \in \mathrm{Cl}(R)$ to $\sigma_c \in \mathrm{Gal}(K(\alpha)/K)$, then $\sigma_c(e) = e - c$.*

Briefly, $\mathrm{Cl}(R)$ acts on $\mathrm{Ell}(R)$ by translation with a minus sign.

2. The Proofs

We describe Deuring's algebraic proof of these theorems (Deuring, 1949, 1952); for generalizations, see the tract of Shimura and Taniyama (1961).

First, we must make sure that everything we are using is algebraically defined. So, as before, let K be a complex quadratic field with integers R. A curve E defined over an algebraic closure $\bar{K}$ by $y^2 = 4x^3 - g_2 x - g_3$ has an invariant $j = 1728 g_2^3/\Delta$ where $\Delta = g_2^3 - 27 g_3^2$; and $\mathrm{End}(E)$ is well-defined algebraically. We consider the set $\mathrm{Ell}(R_f)$ of (classes of) curves with endomorphism ring R_f.

Our correspondence $\mathrm{Ell}(R_f) \leftrightarrow \mathrm{Cl}(R_f)$ was obtained using the topology of $\mathbf{C}$; so it must be replaced by something algebraic. We assert that $\mathrm{Ell}(R_f)$ is an affine space over $\mathrm{Cl}(R_f)$ (in other words, given $x \in \mathrm{Ell}$ and $y \in \mathrm{Cl}$ we can define $x - y \in \mathrm{Ell}$). In fact, if E is a curve and M is a projective module of rank 1 over R_f, we may define $M*E = \mathrm{Hom}(M, E)$. More explicitly, take a resolution

$$R_f^m \xrightarrow{\phi} R_f^n \to M \to 0;$$

then $\mathrm{Hom}(R_f, E) = E$, so $\mathrm{Hom}(M, E)$ is the kernel of ${}^t\phi : E^n \to E^m$.

Proof of the Theorem. Certainly $j(E)$ is an algebraic number; for if it were transcendental, there would be infinitely many curves with complex multiplication by R_f, but $\mathrm{Cl}(R_f)$ is finite. In fact, the $j(E)$ are algebraic *integers*, but we will not prove this (one needs other methods; for instance, show there is a model of E over a finite extension of K with a "good reduction" everywhere).

$G = \mathrm{Gal}(\bar{K}/K)$ operates on the set $\mathrm{Ell}(R_f)$ and preserves its structure of $\mathrm{Cl}(R_f)$-affine space; hence G acts by translations. This means that there is a homomorphism $\phi : G \to \mathrm{Cl}(R_f)$ such that the action of $\sigma \in G$ on $\mathrm{Ell}(R_f)$ is translation by $\phi(\sigma)$.

We make the following assertions.

(i) ϕ is onto.

If $\mathfrak{p}$ is a good prime, let $F_\mathfrak{p} \in \mathrm{Cl}(R_f)$ be the image of the Frobenius element by ϕ.

(ii) $F_\mathfrak{p} = \mathrm{Cl}(\mathfrak{p})$.

Clearly, (ii) implies (i); for, given (ii), $\mathrm{Cl}(\mathfrak{p}) \in \phi(G)$ for all good $\mathfrak{p}$ and trivially $\mathrm{Cl}(R_f)$ is generated by the $\mathrm{Cl}(\mathfrak{p})$'s. The assertion (i) tells us that the Galois group permutes the $j(E)$ transitively, and (i) and (ii) taken together tell us that $K(j(E))$ is the absolute class field (for $f = 1$). Note that it is actually enough to know (ii) for almost all primes $\mathfrak{p}$ of first degree; class field theory takes care of the others.

Proof of (ii). Let E be an elliptic curve defined over L, where L/K is abelian. If $\mathfrak{P}$ is a prime of L, not in a finite set S' of bad primes, E has a good reduction $\tilde{E}_\mathfrak{P}$ modulo $\mathfrak{P}$. Suppose that $\mathfrak{P}|\mathfrak{p}, \mathfrak{p}$ a prime of K. If $N\mathfrak{p}$ is the absolute norm of $\mathfrak{p}$, $(\tilde{E}_\mathfrak{P})^{N\mathfrak{p}}$ is got by raising all coefficients to the $N\mathfrak{p}$-th power. We assert

(iii) $(\tilde{E}_\mathfrak{P})^{N\mathfrak{p}} \cong \mathfrak{p}*\tilde{E}_\mathfrak{P} \cong \widetilde{(\mathfrak{p}*E)}_\mathfrak{P}$.

Now (iii) implies (ii), for by (iii), $j(E)^{N\mathfrak{p}} \equiv j(\mathfrak{p}*E)$ (modulo $\mathfrak{P}$), so the Frobenius map $j(E) \mapsto j(E)^{N\mathfrak{p}}$ is the translation $j(E) \mapsto j(\mathfrak{p}*E)$.

Proof of (iii). The inclusion map $\mathfrak{p} \to R_f$ induces $\mathfrak{p}*E \leftarrow R_f*E = E$. This map $E \to \mathfrak{p}*E$ is an isogeny of elliptic curves, and we see easily that its degree is $N\mathfrak{p}$. Taking reductions modulo $\mathfrak{P}$, we have an isogeny $\tilde{E} \to \widetilde{\mathfrak{p}*E}$.

Case 1. $\mathfrak{p}$ of degree 1, $N\mathfrak{p} = p$. The map $\tilde{E} \to \widetilde{\mathfrak{p}*E}$ has degree p, and may be seen to be inseparable (look at the tangent space). Hence, it can only be the map $x \mapsto x^p$ of $\tilde{E} \to \tilde{E}^p$. For our application, this is actually enough. But we had better sort out the other case:

Case 2. $\mathfrak{p}$ of degree 2, so $N\mathfrak{p} = p^2$ where p is inert in $K/\mathbf{Q}$. Then one can show that $\tilde{E}$ has Hasse invariant zero; that is, it has no point of order p. The map $\widetilde{E \to \mathfrak{p}*E}$ accordingly has trivial kernel, so again it is purely inseparable, so it is $\tilde{E} \to \tilde{E}^{p^2}$.

Example. There are either 13 or 14 complex quadratic R_f's with class number 1, namely $\mathbf{Q}(\sqrt{-d})$ with $f = 1$ for $d = 1,2,3,7,11,19,43,67,163$, and possibly ?, and also $\mathbf{Q}(\sqrt{-1})$, $\mathbf{Q}(\sqrt{-3})$ and $\mathbf{Q}(\sqrt{-7})$ with $f = 2$ and $\mathbf{Q}(\sqrt{-3})$ with $f = 3$. Hence there are 13 or 14 curves with complex multiplication with $j \in \mathbf{Q}$. Their invariants are: (see end of chapter)

$$j = 2^6 3^3,\ 2^6 5^3,\ 0,\ -3^3 5^3,\ -2^{15},\ -2^{15} 3^3,\ -2^{18} 3^3 5^3,$$
$$-2^{15} 3^3 5^3 11^3,\ -2^{18} 3^3 5^3 23^3 29^3,\ -(??)^3,$$
$$2^3 3^3 11^3,\ 2^4 3^3 5^3,\ 3^3 5^3 17^3,\ -3^1 2^{15} 5^3.$$

3. Maximal Abelian Extension

We want the *maximal abelian extension* K^{ab} of K. As a first shot, try $K^?$, the union of the fields given by the j's of the elliptic curves of $\mathrm{Ell}(R_f)$, for $f = 1, 2, \ldots$; this field is generated by the $j(\tau)$'s where $\mathrm{Im}(\tau) > 0$ and $\tau \in K$. Now enlarge $K^?$ by adding the roots of unity; we get a field $K^{??} = \mathbf{Q}^{\mathrm{cycl}}.K^?$ which is very near K^{ab}. The following theorem states this result more precisely:

THEOREM. *$\mathrm{Gal}(K^{ab}/K^{??})$ is a product of groups of order* 2.

This follows easily from class field theory and the results of Section 2.

Let now $\tilde{K}$ be the absolute class field of K, and let E be an elliptic curve defined over $\tilde{K}$, with $\mathrm{End}(E) = R$. Let L_E be the extension of $\tilde{K}$ generated by the coordinates of the points of finite order of E. This is an abelian extension of $\tilde{K}$, whose Galois group is embedded in a natural way in the group $U(K) = \prod U_v(K)$, where $U_v(K)$ means the group of units of K at the finite prime v. By class field theory, L_E is then described by a homomorphism

$$\theta_E : I_{\tilde{K}} \to U(K)$$

where $I_{\tilde{K}}$ is the idele group of $\tilde{K}$. Let U be the group of (global) units of K, so that $U = \{\pm 1\}$ unless K is $\mathbf{Q}(\sqrt{-1})$ or $\mathbf{Q}(\sqrt{-3})$. One can prove without much difficulty that the restriction of θ_E to the group $U(\tilde{K})$ is:

$$\theta_E(x) = N_{\tilde{K}/K}(x^{-1}).\rho_E(x)$$

where ρ_E is an homomorphism of $U(\tilde{K})$ into U.

The extension L_E, and the homomorphism ρ_E, depend on the choice of E. To get rid of this, let $X = E/U$ be the quotient of E by U (X is a projective line), and let L be the extension of $\tilde{K}$ generated by the coordinates of the images in X of the points of finite order of E. This extension is independent of the choice of E.

THEOREM. *L is the maximal abelian extension of K.*

This follows by class field theory from the properties of θ_E given above.

Remark. If U is of order 2 (resp. 4, 6) the map $E \to X$ is given by the coordinate x (resp. by x^2, x^3). Hence K^{ab} is generated by $j(E)$ and the coordinates x (resp. x^2, x^3) of the points of finite order on E; this has an obvious translation in analytical terms, using the j and $\wp$ functions.

[For further and deeper results, analogous to those of Kummer in the cyclotomic case, see a recent paper of Ramachandra (1964).]

REFERENCES

Deuring, M. (1949). Algebraische Begründung der komplexen Multiplikation. *Abh. Math. Sem. Univ. Hamburg*, **16**, 32–47.

Deuring, M. (1952). Die Struktur der elliptischen Funktionenkörper und die Klassenkörper der imaginären quadratischen Zahlkörper. *Math. Ann.* **124**, 393–426.

Deuring, M. Die Zetafunktion einer algebraischen Kurve vom Geschlechte Eins. *Nachr. Akad. Wiss. Göttingen, Math-Phys. Kl.* (1953) 85–94; (1955) 13–42; (1956) 37–76; (1957) 55–80.

Deuring, M. Die Klassenkörper der komplexen Multiplikation. *Enz. Math. Wiss.* Band I_2, Heft 10, Teil II (60 pp.).

Fueter, R. "Vorlesungen über die singulären Moduln und die komplexe Multiplikation der elliptischen Funktionen", (1924) Vol. I; (1927) Vol. II (Teubner).

Hasse, H. Neue Begründung der komplexen Multiplikation. *J. reine angew. Math.* (1927) **157**, 115–139; (1931) **165**, 64–88.

Ramachandra, K. (1964). Some applications of Kronecker's limit formulas. *Ann. Math.* **80**, 104–148.

Shimura, G. and Taniyama, Y. (1961). Complex multiplication of abelian varieties *Publ. Math. Soc. Japan*, **6**.

Weber, H. (1908). "Algebra", Vol. III (2nd edition). Braunschweig.

Weil, A. (1955). On the theory of complex multiplication. *Proc. Int. Symp. Algebraic Number Theory, Tokyo-Nikko*, pp. 9–22.

STOP PRESS

H. M. Stark has shown (*Proc. Nat. Acad. Sci. U.S.A.* **57** (1967), 216–221) that there is no tenth imaginary quadratic field with class-number 1 (the ? of the Example at the end of §2). Practically simultaneously A. Baker (*Mathematika*, **13** (1966), 204–216) proved an important general theorem which reduces the problem of its existence to a finite amount of computation.

CHAPTER XIV

l-Extensions

K. HOECHSMANN

Introduction

Let l be a rational prime, Ω a group of order l (multiplicative). For a profinite group G, we shall denote by $H^i(G)$ the cohomology group $H^i(G, \Omega)$, G operating trivially on Ω. If G is the Galois group of a field extension K/k, we shall sometimes write $H^i(K/k)$. We shall be interested in these groups particularly for $i = 1, 2$ in the case where k is a local or global field and K its maximal l-extension, i.e. the maximal normal extension whose Galois group is a pro-l-group.

1. Two Lemmas

LEMMA 1. *Consider a family* (φ_v) *of morphisms of exact sequences of pro-l-groups:*

$$\begin{array}{ccccccccc} 1 & \to & R & \to & F & \to & G & \to & 1 \\ & \varphi_v\uparrow & & & \uparrow & & \uparrow & & \\ 1 & \to & R_v & \to & F_v & \to & G_v & \to & 1 \end{array}$$

where (a) F, F_v *are free*† $(H^2(F) = H^2(F_v) = 1)$.

(b) F, F_v *are built from a* minimal *system of generators.*

G, G_v *resp.* $(H^1(G) \to H^1(F)$, *etc., are surjective).*

Then R *is generated (as a closed normal subgroup of* F*) by the totality of images* $\varphi_v(R_v) \Leftrightarrow$ *the map*

$$H^2(G) \to \prod_v H^2(G_v)$$

is injective.

Proof. In analogy to Prop. 26 of Serre (1964) we have: R generated by the $\varphi_v(R_v) \Leftrightarrow H^1(R)^G \to \prod_v H^1(R_v)$ injective. On the other hand, the trans-

† Cf. Serre (1964) for the meaning of freedom, etc., in this context.

gressions (Tg) in the diagram

$$\begin{array}{ccc} H^1(R)^G & \xrightarrow{\text{Tg}} & H^2(G) \\ \downarrow & & \downarrow \\ H^1(R_v)^{G_v} & \xrightarrow{\text{Tg}} & H^2(G_v) \end{array}$$

are isomorphisms by the exactness of the Hochschild–Serre sequence and our hypotheses (a) and (b).

LEMMA 2. *Given field extensions as shown in the diagram (everything Galois over k), where K/k and K'/k' are l-extensions, $E = \text{Gal}(k'/k)$ is finite with order prime to l, consider the obvious map θ*: $\text{Gal}(K'/k') \to \text{Gal}(K/k)$. *Suppose*

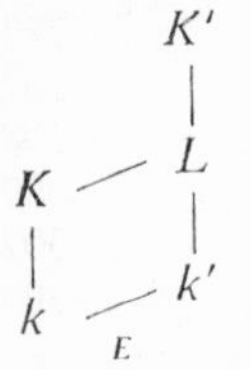

(a) $H^1(K'/K) = 1$ *and*

(b) Res: $H^2(K'/k) \to H^2(K'/L)$ *to be trivial.*

Then θ induces an isomorphism

$$\theta^*: H^2(K/k) \to H^2(K'/k')^E.$$

Proof. θ^* is the composition of

$$\text{Inf}: H^2(K/k) \to H^2(K'/k)$$

and

$$\text{Res}: H^2(K'/k) \to H^2(K'/k')^E.$$

The bijectivity of Res follows from the fact that l is prime to the order of E. To see it, one could use dimension-shifting on finite subextensions and the Hochschild–Serre sequence. Hypothesis (a) yields the exactness of the pertinent Inf–Res sequence in dimension 2, hence the injectivity of Inf. Its surjectivity then follows from hypothesis (b) and the injectivity of the restriction from (K'/K) to (K'/L).

2. Local Fields

Let k be a finite extension of the rational p-adic field $\mathbf{Q}_p$, K the maximal l-extension of k, and $G = \text{Gal}(K/k)$.

Put δ = rank of l-torsion part of k^*,

$$n = \begin{cases} [k:\mathbf{Q}_p] & \text{if } l = p \\ 0 & \text{otherwise.} \end{cases}$$

We are interested in the numbers d^1 and d^2 of generators and defining relations for G: i.e. the ranks of $H^1(G)$ and $H^2(G)$.

THEOREM 1.

$$d^1 = n+\delta+1, \qquad d^2 = \delta.$$

Proof. By the Burnside Basis Theorem, it suffices to count generators of $G/G^l[G, G]$, which by local class field theory amounts to looking at k^*/k^{*l}.

The 1 in the formula for d^1 comes from the infinite cyclic group generated by a prime element, the $n+\delta$ from the group U of units. For U is the direct product of a finite cyclic group and a free $\mathbf{Z}_p$-module of rank $[k:\mathbf{Q}_p]$ (cf. Hasse (1962) II. 15. 5). So much for d^1.

To find d^2, we distinguish two cases.

(1) $\delta = 1$. Inject Ω into K obtaining an exact sequence

$$1 \to \Omega \xrightarrow{i} K^* \xrightarrow{l} K^* \to 1,$$

where l means raising to the lth power. Because of Hilbert 90, we have an isomorphism

$$i: H^2(G) \to H^2(G, K^*)_l,$$

lower l meaning l-torsion part. These are the Brauer classes of order l, by local class field theory a group of order l.

(2) $\delta = 0$. Adjoin lth roots of unity obtaining a field k' and, by construction of its maximal l-extension K', a diagram as in Lemma 2. The hypotheses of Lemma 2 are readily verified.

(a) $H^1(K'/K) = \text{Hom}(\text{Gal}(K'/K), \Omega) = 1$, since a nontrivial element would yield a proper l-extension of K.

(b) Already the restriction from $H^2(K'/k')$ to $H^2(K'/L)$ is trivial, since elements of these groups can, as in (1), be identified with Brauer classes of order l; these die in the vastness of L/k'.

By Lemma 2,

$$H^2(G) \simeq H^2(K'/k')^E.$$

E is cyclic; let ε be a generator. Our injection

$$i: \Omega \to K'^*$$

is not an ε-map. Indeed, for $\omega \in \Omega$, we have

$$i(\varepsilon\omega) = i(\omega) = [\varepsilon i(\omega)]^m,$$

where $m \in \mathbf{Z}$ such that $\varepsilon^{-1}\zeta = \zeta^m$ for lth roots ζ of unity. Accordingly, we get a commutative diagram

$$\begin{array}{ccc} H^2(K'/k') & \xrightarrow{i} & Br(k') \\ \varepsilon \downarrow & & \downarrow \varepsilon.m \\ H^2(K'/k') & \xrightarrow{i} & Br(k') \end{array}$$

i.e. for $\alpha \in H^2(K'/k')$ we have:

$$\text{inv}[i(\alpha^\varepsilon)] = m.\text{inv}[(i\alpha)^\varepsilon] = m.\text{inv}[i\alpha],$$

which shows that, for $\alpha \in H^2(K'/k')^E$, $i\alpha = 1$ and hence $\alpha = 1$.

Remark. The invariants d^1 and d^2 and the exponent l^s of the l-torsion part of k^* determine G completely except in the case $\delta = 1$, $l^s = 2$. If

$\delta = 0$, we are dealing with a free group, and the remark is trivial. If $\delta = 1$, G has the properties:

(1) $H^2(G) \simeq \Omega$.
(2) The pairing $H^1(G) \times H^1(G) \to \Omega$ defined by cup-product and (1) is non-degenerate.

(Via the Kummer isomorphism $H^1(G) \simeq k^*/k^{*l}$, this pairing corresponds to Hilbert's l-power residue symbol.) Pro-l-groups having a finite number d of generators and satisfying (1) and (2) are called *Demuškin groups*. If G is any Demuškin group such that the exponent l^s of the torsion part of $G/[G, G]$ is greater than 2, generators $x_1, \ldots, x_d$ of G can be found such that the relation defining G takes on the form

$$x_1^{l^s}[x_1, x_2] \ldots [x_{d-1}, x_d] = 1,$$

square brackets denoting commutators, If $l^s = 2$, there are several group types depending on a more subtle invariant. For details, see Labute (1965) and Serre (1964).

In the present context, all this machinery is necessary only if $l = p$. If $l \neq p$, the cardinality q of the residue class field of k must be $\equiv 1 \pmod{l}$ in order for δ to be $=1$. Let $l^s | q-1$, s maximal; ζ be a primitive l^s-th root of unity in k. Then G has two generators σ and τ obtained by arbitrary extension to K of the norm residue symbols for π (prime element) and ζ. Every finite subextension L/k is metabelian with the unramified part T/k left fixed by τ. Therefore $\tau = (\xi, L/T)$, where $\xi \in T$ may be chosen to be a root of unity. Hence $\sigma\tau\sigma^{-1} = (\sigma\xi, L/T) = (\xi^q, L/T) = \tau^q$, this relation holding on every finite L/k and hence on K/k.

3. Global Fields

Let k be a finite extension of $\mathbf{Q}$, and K the maximal l-extension of k with Galois group G.

For each prime v of k consider the completion k_v and its maximal l-extension K_v (here we deviate from standard notation!) with Galois group G_v.

We fix an extension w of v to K, obtaining an injection

$$\varphi_v : G_v \to G$$

whose image is the decomposition group of w.

Let δ, δ_v be the l-torsion rank of k^*, k_v^* resp.

THEOREM 2. *The φ_v induce a monomorphism*

$$\varphi^* : H^2(G) \to \coprod_v H^2(G_v)$$

whose cokernel has rank δ.

Proof. We proceed as in the proof of Theorem 1.

(1) $\delta = 1$. An injection $i: \Omega \to K^*$ yields corresponding injections $i_v: \Omega \to K_v^*$ to make commutative diagrams

$$\begin{array}{ccc} H^2(G) & \to & H^2(G,K^*)_l \\ \downarrow & & \downarrow \\ H^2(G_v) & \to & H^2(G_v,K_v^*)_l \end{array}$$

bijectivity of the horizontal arrows being furnished by Hilbert (Theorem 90) via the exact sequence

$$1 \to \Omega \xrightarrow{i} K^* \xrightarrow{l} K^* \to 1$$

and its local counterpart. We use the right-hand sides of these diagrams and Hasse's characterization of Brauer classes by their local invariants to obtain the exact sequence

$$1 \to H^2(G) \xrightarrow{\varphi^*} \coprod_v H^2(G_v) \xrightarrow{\chi} \Omega \to 1.$$

where χ denotes the sum of invariants written multiplicatively.

(2) $\delta = 0$. Again we adjoin lth roots of unity obtaining a field k'. We extend each place v' of k' to a place w' of the maximal l-extension K', so that w' agrees with the already chosen w on K. We now have a diagram as in Lemma 2 for the global fields and, for each v', a similar local one, showing K_v/k_v and $K'_{v'}/k'_{v'}$ with Galois groups G_v and $G'_{v'}$ resp. The commutation rule: $\varphi_v \circ \theta_{v'} = \theta \circ \varphi_{v'}$ $(v'|v)$ yields a commutative diagram

$$\begin{array}{ccc} H^2(G') & \xrightarrow{\varphi^*_{v'}} & H^2(G'_{v'}) \\ \theta^*\downarrow & & \downarrow\theta^*_{v'} \\ H^2(G) & \xrightarrow{\varphi^*_v} & H^2(G_v) \end{array}$$

for each v'.

Taking all these diagrams together and noting the injectivity of θ^* (since $H^1(K'/K) = 1$, again by maximality of K), we deduce the injectivity of $\varphi^* = \prod_v \varphi_v^*$ from that of $\prod_{v'} \varphi_{v'}^*$, which was established in (1).

To prove surjectivity, we note that, by Lemma 2, the image of θ^* is $H^2(G')^E$, hypothesis (b) being verified as before by identifying $H^2(K'/k')$, $H^2(K'/L)$ with the l-torsion of Brauer groups over k' and L resp. and watching the former die (locally everywhere) as we restrict them to L. Next we observe that $H^2(G_v) \neq 1 \Leftrightarrow \delta_v = 1 \Leftrightarrow v$ splits completely in k', and that we can limit our attention to the set S_0 of these places. We now have a diagram

$$\begin{array}{ccc} H^2(G')^E & \to & \coprod_{v'} H^2(G'_{v'}) \\ \theta^*\uparrow & & \uparrow \\ H^2(G) & \xrightarrow{\varphi^*} & \coprod_{v \in S_0} H^2(G_v) \end{array}$$

where θ^* is a bijection, and propose to prove the surjectivity of φ^* by showing that the map

$$H^2(G) \to \coprod_{v \in S_0 \setminus b} H^2(G_v)$$

is no longer injective, if we leave out any $b \in S_0$ from the product on the right. This amounts to finding a non-trivial $\alpha \in H^2(G')^E$ such that $\varphi_{v'}^*(\alpha) = 1$ for all v' not lying over b.

Arguing as at the end of the proof of Theorem 1 and using the notation introduced there, we find

$$\mathrm{inv}_{\varepsilon v'}[i(\alpha^\varepsilon)] = m.\mathrm{inv}_{v'}[i\alpha]$$

(N.B. this time ε operates on the places, too.) Therefore

$$\alpha \in H^2(G')^E \Leftrightarrow \mathrm{inv}_{\varepsilon v'}[i\alpha] = m.\mathrm{inv}_{v'}[i\alpha].$$

We define the desired α by prescribing the invariants of $i\alpha$:

$$\mathrm{nv}_{v'}[i\alpha] = \begin{cases} 0 & \text{if } v' \not| b \\ \dfrac{m^j}{l} & \text{if } v' = \varepsilon^j b' \quad (j = 0, \ldots, r-1) \end{cases}$$

where b' is a fixed place above b, and $r = [k' : k]$. Since

$$\sum_{j=0}^{r-1} m^j \equiv 0 \pmod{l},$$

this does define a Brauer class $i\alpha$ of order l.

Remark. By Lemma 1, this result can be translated into a theorem of H. Koch (1965) about relations defining the group G. If we present G, G_v as factor groups of free groups F, F_v and extend φ_v to a morphism of the corresponding exact sequences as in Lemma 1, it follows from Theorem 2 that R is generated by the images $\varphi_v(R_v)$. Now, R_v is generated by a single relation r_v, which is trivial if $\delta_v = 0$ (cf. Theorem 1). Theorem 2 also asserts that the $\varphi_v(r_v)$ form a minimal system of relations if $\delta = 0$ and that, if $\delta = 1$, a minimal system is obtained by leaving one of them out.

APPENDIX

Restricted Ramification

Let S be a set of places on the field k considered in the preceding paragraph, and let $K(S)$ be the maximal l-extension of k unramified outside of S. So far, we have been dealing with the case S = all places; the other extreme, $S = \emptyset$, is the topic of Roquette's Chapter IX. We wish to conclude with some remarks about the general situation.

In Koch (1965), $G(S) = \mathrm{Gal}\,(K(S)/k)$ is studied as a factor group of G. Generators of G are obtained from the norm residue symbols for generators of I/k^*I^l (I = idèles of k). More precisely, one considers the exact sequence

$$1 \to U/k^*I^l \cap U \to I/k^*I^l \to \mathrm{Cl}/\mathrm{Cl}^l \to 1$$

(U = idèle units; Cl = ideal classes), and chooses for generators: (1) pre-images of a basis of the finite cokernel and (2) for each place v a basis B_v of U_v/U_v^l. The natural map

$$G \to G(S)$$

is then given by setting $\tau = 1$ whenever $\tau \in B_v$, $v \notin S$ (the elements of B_v lie in the inertia group of v).

If we had a description of G in terms of these generators and some defining relations, we should get a corresponding description of $G(S)$ by simply crossing out the unwanted τ's everywhere. But Theorem 2, gives relations for G only if we start with a minimal system of generators; and our system is not minimal! Indeed, a certain finite number of elements of $\bigcup_v B_v$ has to be eliminated to make it minimal, and the outlined procedure works only if S is large enough to include the v's corresponding to these elements. In general this approach is still strong enough, to yield a fundamental inequality of Šafarevič (1963, Theorem 5), and in favourable special cases it leads to a satisfactory description of $G(S)$. For details, see (Koch, 1965).

In Brumer (196?), the methods used by us to prove Theorem 2 (case (1)) are directly applied to the more general problem. It is assumed that $\delta_k = 1$ and that S contains all primes lying above l. Then the extraction of lth roots of S-units leads to extensions unramified outside of S and thus to an exact sequence

$$1 \to \Omega \xrightarrow{i} E(S) \xrightarrow{l} E(S) \to 1.$$

where $E(S)$ denotes S-units of $K(S)$. Passing to cohomology, we have

$$1 \to {}_lH^1(G(S), E(S)) \to H^2(G(S)) \xrightarrow{i} H^2(G(S), E(S))_l \to 1.$$

where, for abelian groups X, ${}_lX$ means X/X^l. It is not difficult, to identify the last term with a subgroup of Br $(k)_l$, more precisely: with those Brauer classes of order l whose localizations are trivial outside of S. Furthermore, $H^1(G(S), E(S))$ turns out to be isomorphic to ideal classes of k modulo classes containing elements of S; we shall call this group $A(S)$. We obtain an exact sequence

$$1 \to {}_lA(S) \to H^2(G(S)) \to \coprod_{v \in S} H^2(G_v) \xrightarrow{\chi} \Omega \to 1$$

analogous to the one in the proof of Theorem 1 (part (1)).

The more difficult case ($\delta = 0$) has not yet been successfully dealt with by this method.

REFERENCES

Brumer, A. (196?). Galois groups of extensions of algebraic number fields with given ramification. (Unpublished.)

Hasse, H. (1962). "Zahlentheorie", Akademie-Verlag, Berlin.

Koch, H. (1965). *l*-Erweiterungen mit vorgegebenen Verzweigungsstellen. *J. reine angew. Math.* **219**, 30–61.

Labute, J. (1965). Classification des groupes de Demuškin. *Comptes rendues*, **260**, 1043–1046.

Serre, J.-P. (1963). Structure de certains pro-*p*-groupes. *Séminaire Bourbaki*, exp. **252**.

Serre, J.-P. (1964). Cohomologie galoisienne. Lecture notes in Mathematics, **5**. Springer-Verlag.

Šafarevič, I. R. (1963). Extensions with given ramification. *Publs. math. Inst. ht. Etud. scient.* **18**, 71–95. (Russian with French summary.)

CHAPTER XV

Fourier Analysis in Number Fields and Hecke's Zeta-Functions†

J. T. TATE

ABSTRACT

We lay the foundations for abstract analysis in the groups of valuation vectors and idèles associated with a number field. This allows us to replace the classical notion of ζ-function, as the sum over integral ideals of a certain type of ideal character, by the corresponding notion for idèles, namely, the integral over the idèle group of a rather general weight function times an idèle character which is trivial on field elements. The role of Hecke's complicated theta-formulas for theta functions formed over a lattice in the n-dimensional space of classical number theory can be played by a simple Poisson formula

† This is an unaltered reproduction of Tate's doctoral thesis (Princeton, May 1950). The editors were urged by several of the participants of the Conference to include this thesis in the published proceedings because although it has been widely quoted it has never been published. The editors are very grateful to Tate for his permission to do this and for the comments on recent literature (p. 346).

for general functions of valuation vectors, summed over the discrete subgroup of field elements. With this Poisson formula, which is of great importance in itself, inasmuch as it is the number theoretic analogue of the Riemann–Roch theorem, an analytic continuation can be given at one stroke for all of the generalized ζ-functions, and an elegant functional equation can be established for them. Translating these results back into classical terms one obtains the Hecke functional equation, together with an interpretation of the complicated factor in it as a product of certain local factors coming from the archimedean primes and the primes of the conductor. The notion of local ζ-function has been introduced to give local definition of these factors, and a table of them has been computed.

1. Introduction

1.1. *Relevant History*

Hecke was the first to prove that the Dedekind ζ-function of *any* algebraic number field has an analytic continuation over the whole plane and satisfies a simple functional equation. He soon realized that his method would work, not only for the Dedekind ζ-function and L-series, but also for a ζ-function formed with a new type of ideal character which, for principal ideals depends not only on the residue class of the number modulo the "conductor", but also on the position of the conjugates of the number in the complex field. Overcoming rather extraordinary technical complications, he showed (1918 and 1920) that these "Hecke" ζ-functions satisfied the same type of functional equation as the Dedekind ζ-function, but with a much more complicated factor.

In a work (Chevalley, 1940) the main purpose of which was to take analysis *out* of class field theory, Chevalley introduced the excellent notion of the idèle group, as a refinement of the ideal group. In idèles Chevalley had not only found the best approach to class field theory, but to algebraic number theory generally. This is shown by Artin and Whaples (1945). They defined valuation vectors as the additive counterpart of idèles, and used these notions to derive from simple axioms all of the basic statements of algebraic number theory.

Matchett, a student of Artin's, made a first attempt (1946) to continue this program and do analytic number theory by means of idèles and vectors. She succeeded in redefining the classical ζ-functions in terms of integrals over the idèle group, and in interpreting the characters of Hecke as exactly those characters of the ideal group which can be derived from idèle characters. But in proving the functional equation she followed Hecke.

1.2. *This Thesis*

Artin suggested to me the possibility of generalizing the notion of ζ-function, and simplifying the proof of the analytic continuation and functional equation for it, by making fuller use of analysis in the spaces of valuation vectors and idèles themselves than Matchett had done. This thesis is the result of my work on his suggestion. I replace the classical notion of ζ-function, as the sum over integral ideals of a certain type of ideal character, by the corresponding notion for idèles, namely, the integral over the idèle group of a rather general weight function times an idèle character which is trivial on field elements. The role of Hecke's complicated theta-formulas for theta functions formed over a lattice in the n-dimensional space of classical number theory can be played by a simple Poisson Formula for general functions of valuation vectors, summed over the discrete subgroup of field elements. With this Poisson Formula, which is of great importance in itself, inasmuch as it is the number theoretic analogue of the Riemann–Roch theorem, an analytic continuation can be given at one stroke for all of the generalized ζ-functions, and an elegant functional equation can be established for them. Translating these results back into classical terms one obtains the Hecke functional equation, together with an interpretation of the complicated factor in it as a product of certain local factors coming from the archimedean primes and the primes of the conductor. The notion of local ζ-function has been introduced to give a local definition of these factors, and a table of them has been computed.

I wish to express to Artin my great appreciation for his suggestion of this topic and for the continued encouragement he has given me in my work.

1.3. "*Prerequisites*"

In number theory we assume only the knowledge of the classical algebraic number theory, and its relation to the local theory. No knowledge of the idèle and valuation vector point of view is required, because, in order to introduce abstract analysis on the idèle and vector groups we redefine them and discuss their structure in detail.

Concerning analysis, we assume only the most elementary facts and definitions in the theory of analytic functions of a complex variable. No knowledge whatsoever of classical analytic number theory is required. Instead, the reader must know the basic facts of abstract Fourier analysis in a locally compact abelian group G: (1) The existence and uniqueness of a Haar measure on such a group, and its equivalence with a positive invariant functional on the space $L(G)$ of continuous functions on G which vanish outside a compact. (2) The duality between G and its character group, $\hat{G}$, and between subgroups of G and factor groups of $\hat{G}$. (3) The definition of the Fourier transform, $\hat{f}$, of a function $f \in L_1(G)$, together with the fact that, if we choose in $\hat{G}$ the measure which is dual to the measure in G, the Fourier Inversion Formula holds (in the naïve sense) for all functions for which it could be expected to hold; namely, for functions $f \in L_1(G)$

such that f is continuous and $\hat{f} \in L_1(\hat{G})$. (This class of functions we denote by $\mathfrak{B}_1(G)$.) An elegant account of this theory can be found for example in Cartan and Godement (1947).

2. The Local Theory

2.1. *Introduction*

Throughout this section, k denotes the completion of an algebraic number field at a prime divisor $\mathfrak{p}$. Accordingly, k is either the real or complex field if $\mathfrak{p}$ is archimedean, while k is a "$\mathfrak{p}$-adic" field if $\mathfrak{p}$ is discrete. In the latter case k contains a ring of integers $\mathfrak{o}$ having a single prime ideal $\mathfrak{p}$ with a finite residue class field $\mathfrak{o}/\mathfrak{p}$ of $N\mathfrak{p}$ elements. In both cases k is a complete topological field in the topology associated with the prime divisor $\mathfrak{p}$.

From the infinity of equivalent valuations of k belonging to $\mathfrak{p}$ we select the normed valuation defined by:

$|\alpha| =$ ordinary absolute value if k is real.
$|\alpha| =$ square of ordinary absolute value if k is complex.
$|\alpha| = (N\mathfrak{p})^{-\nu}$, where ν is the ordinal number of α, if k is $\mathfrak{p}$-adic.

We know that k is locally compact. The more exact statement which one can prove is: a subset $B \subset k$ is relatively compact (has a compact closure) if and only if it is bounded in absolute value. Indeed, this is a well known fact for subsets of the line or plane if k is the real or complex field; and one can prove it in a similar manner in case k is $\mathfrak{p}$-adic by using a "Schubfachschluss" involving the finiteness of the residue class field.

2.2. *Additive Characters and Measure*

Denote by k^+ the additive group of k, as a locally compact commutative group, and by ξ its general element. We wish to determine the character group of k^+, and are happy to see that this task is essentially accomplished by the following:

LEMMA 2.2.1. *If $\xi \to \mathrm{X}(\xi)$ is one non-trivial character of k^+, then for each $\eta \in k^+$, $\xi \to \mathrm{X}(\eta\xi)$ is also a character. The correspondence $\eta \leftrightarrow \mathrm{X}(\eta\xi)$ is an isomorphism, both topological and algebraic, between k^+ and its character group.*

Proof. (1) $\mathrm{X}(\eta\xi)$ is a character for any fixed η because the map $\xi \to \eta\xi$ is a continuous homomorphism of k^+ into itself.

(2) $\mathrm{X}((\eta_1+\eta_2)\xi) = \mathrm{X}(\eta_1\xi+\eta_2\xi) = \mathrm{X}(\eta_1\xi)\mathrm{X}(\eta_2\xi)$ shows that the map $\eta \to \mathrm{X}(\eta\xi)$ is an algebraic homomorphism of k^+ into its character group.

(3) $\mathrm{X}(\eta\xi) = 1$, all $\xi \Rightarrow \eta k^+ \neq k^+ \Rightarrow \eta = 0$. Hence it is an algebraic isomorphism into.

(4) $\mathrm{X}(\eta\xi) = 1$, all $\eta \Rightarrow k^+\xi \neq k^+ \Rightarrow \xi = 0$. Therefore the characters of the form $\mathrm{X}(\eta\xi)$ are everywhere dense in the character group.

(5) Denote by B the (compact) set of all $\xi \in k^+$ with $|\xi| \leqslant M$ for a large M. Then: η close to 0 in $k^+ \Rightarrow \eta B$ close to 0 in $k^+ \Rightarrow \mathrm{X}(\eta B)$ close to 1 in complex plane $\Rightarrow \mathrm{X}(\eta\xi)$ close to the identity character in the character group. On the other hand, if ξ_0 is a fixed element with $\mathrm{X}(\xi_0) \neq 1$, then: $\mathrm{X}(\eta\xi)$ close to identity character $\Rightarrow \mathrm{X}(\eta B)$ close to 1, closer, say, than $\mathrm{X}(\xi_0) \Rightarrow \xi_0 \notin \eta B \Rightarrow \eta$ close to 0 in k^+. Therefore the correspondence $\eta \leftrightarrow \mathrm{X}(\eta\xi)$ is bicontinuous.

(6) Hence the characters of the form $\mathrm{X}(\eta\xi)$ comprise a locally compact subgroup of the character group. Local compactness implies completeness and therefore closure, which together with (4) shows that the mapping is onto.

To fix the identification of k^+ with its character group promised by the preceding lemma, we must construct a special non-trivial character. Let p be the rational prime divisor which $\mathfrak{p}$ divides, and R the completion of the rational field at p. Define a map $x \to \lambda(x)$ of R into the reals mod 1 as follows:

Case 1. p archimedean, and therefore R the real numbers.

$$\lambda(x) = -x \pmod 1$$

(Note the minus sign!)

Case 2. p discrete, R the field of p-adic numbers. $\lambda(x)$ shall be determined by the properties:

(a) $\lambda(x)$ is a rational number with only a p-power in the denominator.
(b) $\lambda(x) - x$ is a p-adic integer.

(To find such a $\lambda(x)$, let $p^\nu x$ be integral, and choose an ordinary integer n such that $n \equiv p^\nu x \pmod{p^\nu}$. Then put $\lambda(x) = n/p^\nu$; $\lambda(x)$ is obviously uniquely determined modulo 1.)

LEMMA 2.2.2. *$x \to \lambda(x)$ is a non-trivial, continuous additive map of R into the group of reals* (*mod* 1).

Proof. In case 1 this is trivial. In case 2 we check that the number $\lambda(x)+\lambda(y)$ satisfies properties (a) and (b) for $x+y$, so the map is additive. It is continuous at 0, yet non-trivial because of the obvious property: $\lambda(x) = 0 \Leftrightarrow x$ is p-adic integer.

Define now for $\xi \in k^+$, $\Lambda(\xi) = \lambda(S_{k/R}\,\xi)$. Recalling that $S_{k/R}$ is an additive continuous map of k onto R, we see that $\xi \to e^{2\pi i \Lambda(\xi)}$ is a non-trivial character of k^+. We have proved:

THEOREM 2.2.1. *k^+ is naturally its own character group if we identify the character $\xi \to e^{2\pi i \Lambda(\eta\xi)}$ with the element $\eta \in k^+$.*

LEMMA 2.2.3. *In case $\mathfrak{p}$ is discrete, the character $e^{2\pi i \Lambda(\eta\xi)}$ associated with η is trivial on $\mathfrak{o}$ if and only if $\eta \in \mathfrak{d}^{-1}$, $\mathfrak{d}$ denoting the absolute different of k.*

Proof.

$$\Lambda(\eta\mathfrak{o}) = 0 \Leftrightarrow \lambda(S_{k/R}(\eta\mathfrak{o})) = 0 \Leftrightarrow S_{k/R}(\eta\mathfrak{o}) \subset \mathfrak{o}_R \Leftrightarrow \eta \in \mathfrak{d}^{-1}.$$

Let now μ be a Haar measure for k^+.

LEMMA 2.2.4. *If we define $\mu_1(M) = \mu(\alpha M)$ for $\alpha \neq 0 \in k$, and M a measurable set in k^+, then μ_1 is a Haar measure, and consequently there exists a number $\varphi(\alpha) > 0$ such that $\mu_1 = \varphi(\alpha)\mu$.*

Proof. $\xi \to \alpha\xi$ is an automorphism of k^+, both topological and algebraic. Haar measure is determined, up to a positive constant, by the topological and algebraic structure of k^+.

LEMMA 2.2.5. *The constant $\varphi(\alpha)$ of the preceding lemma is $|\alpha|$, i.e. we have $\mu(\alpha M) = |\alpha|\mu(M)$.*

Proof. If k is the real field, this is obvious. If k is complex, it is just as obvious since in that case we chose $|\alpha|$ to be the square of the ordinary absolute value. If k is $\mathfrak{p}$-adic, we notice that since $\mathfrak{o}$ is both compact and open, $0 < \mu(\mathfrak{o}) < \infty$, and it therefore suffices to compare the size of $\mathfrak{o}$ with that of $\alpha\mathfrak{o}$. For α integral, there are $\mathcal{N}(\alpha\mathfrak{o})$ cosets of $\alpha\mathfrak{o}$ in $\mathfrak{o}$, hence $\mu(\alpha\mathfrak{o}) = (N(\alpha\mathfrak{o}))^{-1}\mu(\mathfrak{o}) = |\alpha|\mu(\mathfrak{o})$. For non-integral α, replace α by α^{-1}.

We have now another reason for calling the normed valuation the natural one. $|\alpha|$ may be interpreted as the factor by which the additive group k^+ is "stretched" under the transformation $\xi \to \alpha\xi$.

For the integral, the meaning of the preceding lemma is clearly:

$$d\mu(\alpha\xi) = |\alpha|\, d\mu(\xi);$$

or more fully:

$$\int f(\xi)\, d\mu(\xi) = |\alpha| \int f(\alpha\xi)\, d\mu(\xi).$$

So much for a general Haar measure μ. Let us now select a fixed Haar measure for our additive group k^+. Theorem 2.2.1 enables us to do this in an invariant way by selecting the measure which is its own Fourier transform under the interpretation of k^+ as its own character group established in that theorem. We state the choice of measure which does this, writing $d\xi$ instead of $d\mu(\xi)$, for simplicity:

$d\xi$ = ordinary Lebesgue measure on real line if k is real.
$d\xi$ = twice ordinary Lebesgue measure in the plane if k is complex.
$d\xi$ = that measure for which $\mathfrak{o}$ gets measure $(N\mathfrak{d})^{-\frac{1}{2}}$ if k is $\mathfrak{p}$-adic.

THEOREM 2.2.2. *If we define the Fourier transform $\hat{f}$ of a function $f \in L_1(k^+)$ by:*

$$\hat{f}(\eta) = \int f(\xi)\, e^{-2\pi i\Lambda(\eta\xi)}\, d\xi,$$

then with our choice of measure, the inversion formula

$$f(\xi) = \int \hat{f}(\eta)\, e^{2\pi i\Lambda(\xi\eta)}\, d\eta = \hat{\hat{f}}(-\xi)$$

holds for $f \in \mathfrak{B}_1(k^+)$.

Proof. We need only establish the inversion formula for one non-trivial function, since from abstract Fourier analysis we know it is true, save possibly for a constant factor. For k real we can take $f(\xi) = e^{-\pi|\xi|^2}$, for k complex, $f(\xi) = e^{-2\pi|\xi|}$; and for k $\mathfrak{p}$-adic, $f(\xi) =$ the characteristic function of $\mathfrak{o}$, for instance. For the details of the computations, the reader is referred to Section 2.6 below.

2.3. *Multiplicative Characters and Measure*

Our first insight into the structure of the multiplicative group k^* of k is given by the continuous homomorphism $\alpha \to |\alpha|$ of k^* into the multiplicative group of positive real numbers. The kernel of this homomorphism, the subgroup of all α with $|\alpha| = 1$ will obviously play an important role. Let us denote it by u. u is compact in all cases, and in case k is $\mathfrak{p}$-adic, u is also open.

Concerning the characters of k^*, the situation is different from that of k^+. First of all, we are interested in all continuous multiplicative maps $\alpha \to c(\alpha)$ of k^* into the complex numbers, not only in the bounded ones, and shall call such a map a quasi-character, reserving the word "character" for the conventional character of absolute value 1. Secondly, we shall find no model for the group of quasi-characters, or even for the group of characters, though such a model would be of the utmost importance.

We call a quasi-character unramified if it is trivial on u, and first determine the unramified quasi-characters.

LEMMA 2.3.1. *The unramified quasi-characters are the maps of the form* $c(\alpha) = |\alpha|^s \equiv e^{s \log |\alpha|}$, *where s is any complex number, s is determined by c if $\mathfrak{p}$ is archimedean, while for discrete $\mathfrak{p}$, s is determined only* $\operatorname{mod} 2\pi i/\log \mathcal{N}\mathfrak{p}$.

Proof. For any s, $|\alpha|^s$ is obviously an unramified quasi-character. On the other hand, any unramified quasi-character will depend only on $|\alpha|$, and as function of $|\alpha|$ will be a quasi-character of the value group of k. This value group is the multiplicative group of all positive real numbers, or of all powers of $\mathcal{N}\mathfrak{p}$, according to whether $\mathfrak{p}$ is archimedean or discrete; it is well known that the quasi-characters of these groups are those described.

If $\mathfrak{p}$ is archimedean, we may write the general element $\alpha \in k^*$ uniquely in the form $\alpha = \tilde{\alpha}\rho$, with $\tilde{\alpha} \in u$, $\rho > 0$. For discrete $\mathfrak{p}$, we must select a fixed element π of ordinal number 1 in order to write, again uniquely, $\alpha = \tilde{\alpha}\rho$, with $\tilde{\alpha} \in u$ and, this time, ρ a power of π. In either case the map $\alpha \to \tilde{\alpha}$ is a continuous homomorphism of k^* onto u which is identity on u.

THEOREM 2.3.1. *The quasi-characters of k^* are the maps of the form* $\alpha \to c(\alpha) = \tilde{c}(\tilde{\alpha})|\alpha|^s$, *where $\tilde{c}$ is any character of u. $\tilde{c}$ is uniquely determined by c. s is determined as in the preceding lemma.*

Proof. A map of the given type is obviously a quasi-character. Conversely, if c is a given quasi-character and we define $\tilde{c}$ to be the restriction of c to u, then $\tilde{c}$ is a quasi-character of u and is therefore a character of u since u is compact. $\alpha \to c(\alpha)/\tilde{c}(\tilde{\alpha})$ is an unramified quasi-character, and therefore is of the form $|\alpha|^s$ according to the preceding lemma.

The problem of quasi-characters c of k^* therefore boils down to that of the characters $\tilde{c}$ of u. If k is the real field, $u = \{1, -1\}$ and the characters are $\tilde{c}(\tilde{\alpha}) = \tilde{\alpha}^n$, $n = 0, 1$. If k is complex, u is the unit-circle, and the characters are $\tilde{c}(\tilde{\alpha}) = \tilde{\alpha}^n$, n any integer. In case k is $\mathfrak{p}$-adic, the subgroups $1+\mathfrak{p}^\nu$, $\nu > 0$, of u form a fundamental system of neighborhoods of 1 in u. We must have therefore $\tilde{c}(1+\mathfrak{p}^\nu) = 1$ for sufficiently large ν. Selecting ν minimal ($\nu = 0$ if $\tilde{c} = 1$), we call the ideal $\mathfrak{f} = \mathfrak{p}^\nu$ the conductor of $\tilde{c}$. Then $\tilde{c}$ is a character of the finite factor group $u/(1+\mathfrak{f})$ and may be described by a finite table of data.

From the expression $c(\alpha) = \tilde{c}(\tilde{\alpha})|\alpha|^s$ for the general quasi-character given in Theorem 2.3.1, we see that $|c(\alpha)| = |\alpha|^\sigma$, where $\sigma = \operatorname{Re}(s)$ is uniquely determined by $c(\alpha)$. It will be convenient to call σ the exponent of c. A quasi-character is a character if and only if its exponent is 0.

We will be able to select a Haar measure $d\alpha$ on k^* by relating it to the measure $d\xi$ on k^+. If $g(\alpha) \in L(k^*)$, then $g(\xi)|\xi|^{-1} \in L(k^+ - 0)$. So we may define on $L(k^*)$ a functional

$$\Phi(g) = \int_{k^+-0} g(\xi)|\xi|^{-1}\, d\xi.$$

If $h(\alpha) = g(\beta\alpha)$ ($\beta \in k^*$, fixed) is a multiplicative translation of $g(\alpha)$, then

$$\Phi(h) = \int_{k^+-0} g(\beta\xi)|\xi|^{-1}\, d\xi = \Phi(g),$$

as we see by the substitution $\xi \to \beta^{-1}\xi$; $d\xi \to |\beta|^{-1}\, d\xi$ discussed in Lemma 2.2.5. Therefore our functional Φ which is obviously non-trivial and positive, is also invariant under translation. It must therefore come from a Haar measure on k^*. Denoting this measure by $\mathrm{d}_1\alpha$, we may write

$$\int g(\alpha)\mathrm{d}_1\alpha = \int_{k^+-0} g(\xi)|\xi|^{-1}\, d\xi.$$

Obviously, the correspondence $g(\alpha) \leftrightarrow g(\xi)|\xi|^{-1}$ is a 1–1 correspondence between $L(k^*)$ and $L(k^+ - 0)$. Viewing the functions of $L_1(k^*)$ and $L_1(k^+ - 0$ as limits of these basic functions we obtain:

Lemma 2.3.2. *$g(\alpha) \in L_1(k^*) \Leftrightarrow g(\xi)|\xi|^{-1} \in L_1(k^+ - 0)$, and for these functions*

$$\int g(\alpha)\mathrm{d}_1\alpha = \int_{k^+-0} g(\xi)|\xi|^{-1}\, d\xi.$$

For later use, we need a multiplicative measure which will in general give the subgroup u the measure 1. To this effect we choose as our standard

Haar measure on k^*:

$$d\alpha = d_1\alpha = \frac{d\alpha}{|\alpha|}, \qquad \text{if } \mathfrak{p} \text{ is archimedean.}$$

$$d\alpha = \frac{N\mathfrak{p}}{N\mathfrak{p}-1}\, d_1\alpha = \frac{N\mathfrak{p}}{N\mathfrak{p}-1}\frac{d\alpha}{|\alpha|}, \qquad \text{if } \mathfrak{p} \text{ is discrete.}$$

LEMMA 2.3.3. *In case* $\mathfrak{p}$ *is discrete,*

$$\int_u d\alpha = (\mathcal{N}\mathfrak{d})^{-\frac{1}{2}}.$$

Proof.

$$\int_u d_1\alpha = \int_u |\xi|^{-1}\, d\xi = \int_u d\xi = \frac{N\mathfrak{p}-1}{N\mathfrak{p}}\int_\mathfrak{o} d\xi.$$

Therefore

$$\int_u d\alpha = \frac{N\mathfrak{p}}{N\mathfrak{p}-1}\int_u d_1\alpha = \int_\mathfrak{o} d\xi = (\mathcal{N}\mathfrak{d})^{-\frac{1}{2}}.$$

2.4. *The Local* ζ*-function; Functional Equation*

In this section $f(\xi)$ will denote a complex valued function defined on k^+; $f(\alpha)$ its restriction to k^*. We let $\mathfrak{z}$ denote the class of all these functions which satisfy the two conditions:

$\mathfrak{z}_1$) $f(\xi)$, and $\hat{f}(\xi)$ continuous, $\in L_1(k^+)$; i.e. $f(\xi) \in \mathfrak{B}_1(k^+)$

$\mathfrak{z}_2$) $f(\alpha)|\alpha|^\sigma$ and $\hat{f}(\alpha)|\alpha|^\sigma \in L_1(k^*)$ for $\sigma > 0$.

A ζ-function of k will be what one might call a multiplicative quasi-Fourier transform of a function $f \in \mathfrak{z}$. Precisely what we mean is stated in

DEFINITION 2.4.1. *Corresponding to each* $f \in \mathfrak{z}$, *we introduce a function* $\zeta(f, c)$ *of quasi-characters* c, *defined for all quasi-characters of exponent greater than* 0 *by*

$$\zeta(f, c) = \int f(\alpha)c(\alpha)d\alpha,$$

and call such a function a ζ*-function of* k.

Let us call two quasi-characters equivalent if their quotient is an unramified quasi-character. According to Lemma 2.3.1, an equivalence class of quasi-characters consists of all quasi-characters of the form $c(\alpha) = c_0(\alpha)|\alpha|^s$, where $c_0(\alpha)$ is a fixed representative of the class, s a complex variable. It is apparent that by introducing the complex parameter s we may view an equivalence class of quasi-characters as a Riemann surface. In case $\mathfrak{p}$ is archimedean, s is uniquely determined by c, and the surface will be isomorphic to the complex plane. In case $\mathfrak{p}$ is discrete, s is determined only mod $2\pi i/\log \mathcal{N}\mathfrak{p}$, so the surface is isomorphic to a complex plane in which points differing by an integral multiple of $2\pi i/\log \mathcal{N}\mathfrak{p}$ are identified—the type of surface on which singly periodic functions are really defined. Looking at the set of all quasi-characters as a collection of Riemann surfaces, it becomes clear what we mean when we talk of the regularity of a function of quasi-characters at a point or in a region, or of singularities. We may also consider the question of analytic continuation of such a function, though this must of course be carried out on each surface (equivalence class of quasi-characters) separately.

LEMMA 2.4.1. *A ζ-function is regular in the "domain" of all quasi-characters of exponent greater than* 0.

Proof. We must show that for each c of exponent > 0 the integral $\int f(\alpha)c(\alpha)|\alpha|^s \mathrm{d}\alpha$ represents a regular function of s for s near 0. Using the fact that the integral is absolutely convergent for s near 0 to make estimates, it is a routine matter to show that the function has a derivative for s near 0. The derivative can in fact be computed by "differentiating under the integral sign".

It is our aim to show that the ζ-functions have a single-valued meromorphic analytic continuation to the domain of all quasi-characters by means of a simple functional equation. We start out from

LEMMA 2.4.2. *For c in the domain* $0 <$ *exponent* $c < 1$ *and* $\hat{c}(\alpha) = |\alpha| c^{-1}(\alpha)$ *we have*

$$\zeta(f, c)\zeta(\hat{g}, \hat{c}) = \zeta(\hat{f}, \hat{c})\zeta(g, c)$$

for any two functions $f, g \in \mathfrak{z}$.

Proof. $\zeta(f, c)\zeta(\hat{g}, \hat{c}) = \int f(\alpha)c(\alpha)\,\mathrm{d}\alpha . \int \hat{g}(\beta)c^{-1}(\beta)|\beta|\,\mathrm{d}\beta$ with both integrals absolutely convergent for c in the region we are considering. We may write this as an absolutely convergent "double integral" over the direct product, $k^* \times k^*$, of k^* with itself:

$$\iint f(\alpha)\hat{g}(\beta)c(\alpha\beta^{-1})|\beta|\mathrm{d}(\alpha, \beta).$$

Subjecting $k^* \times k^*$ to the "shearing" automorphism $(\alpha, \beta) \to (\alpha, \alpha\beta)$, under which the measure $\mathrm{d}(\alpha, \beta)$ is invariant we obtain

$$\iint f(\alpha)\hat{g}(\alpha\beta)c(\beta^{-1})|\alpha\beta|\mathrm{d}(\alpha, \beta).$$

According to Fubini this is equal to the repeated integral

$$\int \left(\int f(\alpha)\hat{g}(\alpha\beta)|\alpha|\mathrm{d}\alpha\right)c(\beta^{-1})|\beta|\mathrm{d}\beta.$$

To prove our contention it suffices to show that the inner integral $\int f(\alpha)\hat{g}(\alpha\beta)|\alpha|\,\mathrm{d}\alpha$ is symmetric in f and g. This we do by writing down the obviously symmetric additive double integral

$$\iint f(\xi)g(\eta)\, e^{-2\pi i\Lambda(\xi\beta\eta)}\, d(\xi, \eta),$$

changing it with the Fubini theorem into

$$\int f(\xi)\Big(\int g(\eta)\, e^{-2\pi i\Lambda(\xi\beta\eta)}\, d\eta\Big)\, d\xi = \int f(\xi)\hat{g}(\xi\beta)\, d\xi,$$

and observing that according to Lemma 2.3.2 this last expression is equal to the multiplicative integral

$$\int f(\alpha)\hat{g}(\alpha\beta)|\alpha|\mathsf{d}_1\alpha = \text{constant}.\int f(\alpha)\hat{g}(\alpha\beta)|\alpha|\mathsf{d}\alpha.$$

We can now announce the *Main Theorem* of the local theory.

THEOREM 2.4.1. *A ζ-function has an analytic continuation to the domain of all quasi-characters given by a functional equation of the type*

$$\zeta(f, c) = \rho(c)\zeta(\hat{f}, \hat{c}).$$

The factor $\rho(c)$, which is independent of the function f, is a meromorphic function of quasi-characters defined in the domain $0 <$ exponent $c < 1$ by the functional equation itself, and for all quasi-characters by analytic continuation.

Proof. In the next section we will exhibit for each equivalence class C of quasi-characters an explicit function $f_C \in \mathfrak{z}$ such that the function

$$\rho(c) = \zeta(f_C, c)/\zeta(\hat{f}_C, \hat{c})$$

is defined (i.e. has denominator not identically 0) for c in the strip $0 <$ exponent $c < 1$ on C. The function $\rho(c)$ defined in this manner will turn out to be a familiar meromorphic function of the parameter s with which we describe the surface C, and therefore will have an analytic continuation over all of C.

From these facts, which will be proved in § 2.5, the theorem follows directly. For since C was in any equivalence class, $\rho(c)$ is defined for all quasi-characters. And if $f(\xi)$ is any function of $\mathfrak{z}$ we have according to the preceding lemma

$$\zeta(f, c)\zeta(\hat{f}_C, \hat{c}) = \zeta(\hat{f}, \hat{c})\zeta(f_C, c),$$

therefore

$$\zeta(f, c) = \rho(c)\zeta(\hat{f}, \hat{c}),$$

if c is any quasi-character in the domain of $0 <$ exponent $c < 1$, where $\zeta(f, c)$ and $\zeta(\hat{f}, \hat{c})$ are originally both defined, and C is the equivalence class of c.

Before going on to the computations of the next section which will put this theory on a sound basis, we can prove some simple properties of the factor $\rho(c)$ in the functional equation which follow directly from the functional equation itself.

LEMMA 2.4.3.

(1) $\rho(\hat{c}) = \dfrac{c(-1)}{\rho(c)}$.

(2) $\rho(\bar{c}) = c(-1)\overline{\rho(c)}$.

Proof.

(1) $\zeta(f, c) = \rho(c)\zeta(\hat{f}, \hat{c}) = \rho(c)\rho(\hat{c})\zeta(\hat{\hat{f}}, \hat{\hat{c}}) = c(-1)\zeta(f, c)$

because $\hat{\hat{f}}(\alpha) = f(-\alpha)$ and $\hat{\hat{c}}(\alpha) = c(\alpha)$. Therefore $\rho(c)\rho(\hat{c}) = c(-1)$.

(2) $\overline{\zeta(f, c)} = \zeta(\bar{f}, \bar{c}) = \rho(\bar{c})\zeta(\hat{\bar{f}}, \hat{\bar{c}})$

$$= \rho(\bar{c})c(-1)\zeta(\bar{\hat{f}}, \bar{\hat{c}}) = \rho(\bar{c})c(-1)\overline{\zeta(\hat{f}, \hat{c})}$$

because $\hat{\bar{f}}(\alpha) = \bar{\hat{f}}(-\alpha)$ and $\hat{\bar{c}}(\alpha) = \bar{\hat{c}}(\alpha)$. On the other hand,

$$\overline{\zeta(f, c)} = \overline{\rho(c)}\ \overline{\zeta(\hat{f}, \hat{c})}.$$

Therefore $\rho(\bar{c}) = c(-1)\overline{\rho(c)}$.

COROLLARY 2.4.1. $|\rho(c)| = 1$ for c of exponent $\frac{1}{2}$.

Proof. (exponent c) $= \frac{1}{2} \Rightarrow c(\alpha)\bar{c}(\alpha) = |c(\alpha)|^2 = |\alpha| = c(\alpha)\hat{c}(\alpha) \Rightarrow \bar{c}(\alpha) = \hat{c}(\alpha)$. Equating the two expressions for $\rho(\bar{c})$ and $\rho(\hat{c})$ given in the preceding lemma yields $\rho(c)\overline{\rho(c)} = 1$.

2.5. *Computation of $\rho(c)$ by Special ζ-functions*

This section contains the computations promised in the proof of theorem 2.4.1. For each equivalence class C of quasi-characters we give an especially simple function $f_C \in \mathfrak{z}$ with which it is easy to compute $\rho(c)$ on the surface C. Carrying out this computation we obtain a table which gives the analytic expression for $\rho(c)$ in terms of the parameters on each surface C. It will be necessary to treat the cases k real; k complex; and k $\mathfrak{p}$-adic separately.

k Real

ξ is a real variable. α is a non-zero real variable.

$\Lambda(\xi) = -\xi$. $|\alpha|$ is the ordinary absolute value.

$d\xi$ means ordinary Lebesgue measure. $\mathrm{d}\alpha = \dfrac{d\alpha}{|\alpha|}$.

The Equivalence Classes of Quasi-Characters. The quasi-characters of the form $|\alpha|^s$, which we denote simply by $|\,|^s$, comprise one equivalence class. Those of the form (sign α)$|\alpha|^s$, which we denote by $\pm|\,|^s$, comprise the other.

The Corresponding Functions of $\mathfrak{z}$. We put

$$f(\xi) = e^{-\pi\xi^2} \quad \text{and} \quad f_\pm(\xi) = \xi\, e^{-\pi\xi^2}.$$

Their Fourier Transforms. We contend

$$\hat{f}(\xi) = f(\xi) \quad \text{and} \quad \hat{f}_\pm(\xi) = if_\pm(\xi).$$

Indeed, these are simply the two identities

$$\int_{-\infty}^{\infty} e^{-\pi\eta^2 + 2\pi i\xi\eta}\, d\eta = e^{-\pi\xi^2} \quad \text{and} \quad \int_{-\infty}^{\infty} \eta\, e^{-\pi\eta^2 + 2\pi i\xi\eta}\, d\eta = i\xi\, e^{-\pi\xi^2}$$

familiar from classical Fourier analysis. The first of these can be established directly by completing the square in the exponent, making the complex substitution $\eta \to \eta + i\xi$, which is allowed by Cauchy's integral theorem, and replacing the definite integral $\int_{-\infty}^{\infty} e^{-\pi\xi^2}\,d\xi$ by its well-known value 1. The second identity is obtained by applying the operation $\frac{1}{2\pi i}\frac{d}{d\xi}$ to the first.

The ζ-functions. We readily compute:

$$\zeta(f, |\,|^s) = \int f(\alpha)|\alpha|^s\,d\alpha = \int_{-\infty}^{\infty} e^{-\pi\alpha^2}|\alpha|^s \frac{d\alpha}{|\alpha|}$$

$$= 2\int_0^{\infty} e^{-\pi\alpha^2}\alpha^{s-1}\,d\alpha = \pi^{-\frac{s}{2}}\Gamma\left(\frac{s}{2}\right),$$

$$\zeta(f_\pm, \pm|\,|^s) = \int f_\pm(\alpha)(\pm|\alpha|^s)\,d\alpha = \int_{-\infty}^{0} \alpha\, e^{-\pi\alpha^2}(-1)|\alpha|^s\frac{d\alpha}{|\alpha|} + \int_0^{\infty} \alpha\, e^{-\pi\alpha^2}|\alpha|^s\frac{d\alpha}{|\alpha|}$$

$$= 2\int_0^{\infty} e^{-\pi\alpha^2}\alpha^s\,d\alpha = \pi^{-\frac{s+1}{2}}\Gamma\left(\frac{s+1}{2}\right),$$

$$\zeta(\hat{f}, \widehat{|\,|^s}) = \zeta(f, |\,|^{1-s}) = \pi^{-\frac{1-s}{2}}\Gamma\left(\frac{1-s}{2}\right),$$

$$\zeta(\hat{f}_\pm, \widehat{\pm|\,|^s}) = \zeta(if_\pm, \pm|\,|^{1-s}) = i\pi^{-\frac{(1-s)+1}{2}}\Gamma\left(\frac{(1-s)+1}{2}\right).$$

Explicit Expressions for ρ(c):

$$\rho(|\,|^s) = \frac{\pi^{-\frac{s}{2}}\Gamma\left(\frac{s}{2}\right)}{\pi^{-\frac{1-s}{2}}\Gamma\left(\frac{1-s}{2}\right)} = 2^{1-s}\pi^{-s}\cos\left(\frac{\pi s}{2}\right)\Gamma(s)$$

$$\rho(\pm|\,|^s) = i\frac{\pi^{-\frac{s+1}{2}}\Gamma\left(\frac{s+1}{2}\right)}{\pi^{-\frac{(1-s)+1}{2}}\Gamma\left(\frac{(1-s)+1}{2}\right)} = -i2^{1-s}\pi^{-s}\sin\left(\frac{\pi s}{2}\right)\Gamma(s).$$

Here the quotient expressions for ρ come directly from the definition of ρ as quotient of suitable ζ-functions; the second form follows from elementary Γ-function identities.

k Complex

$\xi = x+iy$ is a complex variable.

$\Lambda(\xi) = -2\ \mathrm{Re}\,(\xi) = -2x.$

$d\xi = 2|dx\,dy|$ is twice the ordinary Lebesgue measure.

$\alpha = re^{i\theta}$ is a non-zero complex variable.

$|\alpha| = r^2$ is the square of the ordinary absolute value.

$$d\alpha = \frac{d\alpha}{|\alpha|} = \frac{2r|dr\,d\theta|}{r^2} = \frac{2}{r}\,|dr\,d\theta|.$$

Equivalence Classes of Quasi-Characters. The characters $c_n(\alpha)$ defined by $c_n(re^{i\theta}) = e^{in\theta}$, n any integer, represent the different equivalence classes. The nth class consists of the characters $c_n(\alpha)|\alpha|^s$, which we denote by $c_n|\,|^s$.

The Corresponding Functions of $\mathfrak{z}$. We put

$$f_n(\xi) = \begin{cases} (x-iy)^{|n|}\,e^{-2\pi(x^2+y^2)}, & n \geq 0 \\ (x+iy)^{|n|}\,e^{-2\pi(x^2+y^2)}, & n \leq 0. \end{cases}$$

Their Fourier Transforms. We contend

$$\hat{f}_n(\xi) = i^{|n|}f_{-n}(\xi), \quad \text{for all } n.$$

Let us first establish this formula for $n \geq 0$ by induction. For $n = 0$, the contention is simply that $f_0(\xi) = e^{-2\pi(x^2+y^2)}$ is its own Fourier transform. This can be shown by breaking up the Fourier integral over the complex plane into a product of two reals and using again the classical formula

$$\int_{-\infty}^{+\infty} e^{-\pi u^2+2\pi ixu}\,du = e^{-\pi x^2}.$$

(The factor 2 in the exponent of our function $f_0(\xi)$ just compensates the factor 2 in $d\xi$ and in $\Lambda(\xi)$.)

Assume now we have proved the contention for some $n \geq 0$. This means we have established the formula

$$\int f_n(\eta)\,e^{-2\pi i\Lambda(\xi\eta)}\,d\eta = i^n f_{-n}(\xi),$$

which, written out, becomes

$$\int_{-\infty}^{\infty}\int_{-\infty}^{\infty} (u-iv)^n\,e^{-2\pi(u^2+v^2)+4\pi i(xu-yv)}\,2du\,dv = i^n(x+iy)^n e^{-2\pi(x^2+y^2)}.$$

Applying the operator

$$D = \frac{1}{4\pi i}\left(\frac{\partial}{\partial x} + i\frac{\partial}{\partial y}\right)$$

to both sides (a simple task in view of the fact that since z^n is analytic,

$D(x+iy)^n = 0)$, we obtain

$$\int_{-\infty}^{\infty}\int_{-\infty}^{\infty} (u+iv)^{n+1}\, e^{-2\pi(u^2+v^2)+4\pi i(xu-yv)}\, 2du\, dv = i^{n+1}(x+iy)^{n+1}\, e^{-2\pi(x^2+y^2)}.$$

This is the contention for $n+1$. The induction step is carried out.

To handle the case $n < 0$, put a roof on the formula $\hat{f}_{-n}(\xi) = i^{|n|} f_n(\xi)$ which we have already proved, and remember that

$$\hat{\hat{f}}_{-n}(\xi) = f_{-n}(-\xi) = (-1)^{|n|} f_{-n}(\xi).$$

The ζ-Functions. For $\alpha = r\, e^{i\theta}$ we have

$$f_n(\alpha) = r^{|n|}\, e^{-in\theta}\, e^{-2\pi r^2} \qquad |\alpha|^s = r^{2s}$$

$$c_n(\alpha) = e^{in\theta} \qquad d\alpha = \frac{2r\, dr\, d\theta}{r^2}.$$

Therefore

$$\zeta(f_n, c_n|\,|^s) = \int f_n(\alpha) c_n(\alpha) |\alpha|^s\, d\alpha = \int_0^{\infty}\int_0^{2\pi} r^{2(s-1)+|n|}\, e^{-2\pi r^2}\, 2r\, dr\, d\theta$$

$$= 2\pi \int_0^{\infty} (r^2)^{(s-1)+\frac{|n|}{2}}\, e^{-2\pi r^2}\, d(r^2) = (2\pi)^{(1-s)+\frac{|n|}{2}}\, \Gamma\left(s+\frac{|n|}{2}\right),$$

and

$$\zeta(\hat{f}_n, \widehat{c_n|\,|^s}) = \zeta(i^{|n|} f_{-n}, c_{-n}|\,|^{1-s}) = i^{|n|}(2\pi)^{s+\frac{|n|}{2}}\, \Gamma\left(1-s+\frac{|n|}{2}\right).$$

Explicit Expressions for $\rho(c)$.

$$\rho(c_n|\,|^s) = (-i)^{|n|}\, \frac{(2\pi)^{1-s}\, \Gamma\left(s+\frac{|n|}{2}\right)}{(2\pi)^s\, \Gamma\left((1-s)+\frac{|n|}{2}\right)}.$$

k $\mathfrak{p}$-adic

ξ = a $\mathfrak{p}$-adic variable.

$\Lambda(\xi) = \lambda(S(\xi))$.

$d\xi$ is chosen so that $\mathfrak{o}$ gets measure $(\mathcal{N}\mathfrak{d})^{-\frac{1}{2}}$.

$\alpha = \tilde{\alpha}\pi^\nu$, non-zero $\mathfrak{p}$-adic variable, π a fixed element of ordinal number 1, ν an integer.

$|\alpha| = (\mathcal{N}\mathfrak{p})^{-\nu}$.

$d\alpha = \dfrac{\mathcal{N}\mathfrak{p}}{\mathcal{N}\mathfrak{p}-1} \cdot \dfrac{d\alpha}{|\alpha|}$, so that u gets multiplicative measure $(\mathcal{N}\mathfrak{d})^{-\frac{1}{2}}$.

The Equivalence Classes of Quasi-Characters. $c_n(\alpha)$, for $n \geq 0$ shall denote any *character* of k^* with conductor exactly $\mathfrak{p}^n$, such that $c_n(\pi) = 1$. These characters represent the different equivalence classes of quasi-characters.

The Corresponding Functions of $\mathfrak{z}$. We put

$$f_n(\xi) = \begin{cases} e^{2\pi i \Lambda(\xi)}, & \text{for } \xi \in \mathfrak{d}^{-1}\mathfrak{p}^{-n} \\ 0, & \text{for } \xi \notin \mathfrak{d}^{-1}\mathfrak{p}^{-n}. \end{cases}$$

Their Fourier Transforms. We contend

$$\hat{f}_n(\xi) = \begin{cases} (\mathcal{N}\mathfrak{d})^{\frac{1}{2}}(\mathcal{N}\mathfrak{p})^n, & \text{for } \xi \equiv 1 (\text{mod } \mathfrak{p}^n) \\ 0, & \text{for } \xi \not\equiv 1 (\text{mod } \mathfrak{p}^n). \end{cases}$$

Proof.

$$\hat{f}_n(\xi) = \int f_n(\eta)\, e^{-2\pi i \Lambda(\xi\eta)}\, d\eta = \int_{\mathfrak{d}^{-1}\mathfrak{p}^{-n}} e^{-2\pi i \Lambda((\xi-1)\eta)}\, d\eta.$$

This is the integral, over the compact subgroup $\mathfrak{d}^{-1}\mathfrak{p}^{-n} \subset k^+$, of the additive character $\eta \to e^{-2\pi i \Lambda((\xi-1)\eta)}$. If $\xi \equiv 1$ (mod $\mathfrak{p}^n$), this character is trivial on the subgroup, and the integral is simply the measure of the subgroup: $(\mathcal{N}\mathfrak{d})^{\frac{1}{2}}(\mathcal{N}\mathfrak{p})^n$. In case $\xi \not\equiv 1$ (mod $\mathfrak{p}^n$), this character is not trivial on the subgroup and the integral is 0.

The ζ-Functions. First we treat the unramified case: $n = 0$. The only character of type c_0 is the identity character, and f_0 is the characteristic function of the set $\mathfrak{d}^{-1}$. We shall therefore compute

$$\zeta(f_0, |\,|^s) = \int_{\mathfrak{d}^{-1}} |\alpha|^s\, d\alpha.$$

Denote by A_v the "annulus" of elements of order v, and let $\mathfrak{d} = \mathfrak{p}^d$. Then $\mathfrak{d}^{-1} = \bigcup_{v=-d}^{\infty} A_v$, a disjoint union, and

$$\begin{aligned} \zeta(f_0, |\,|^s) &= \sum_{v=-d}^{\infty} \int_{A_v} |\alpha|^s\, d\alpha = \sum_{v=-d}^{\infty} \mathcal{N}\mathfrak{p}^{-vs} \int_{A} d\alpha \\ &= \left(\sum_{v=-d}^{\infty} \mathcal{N}\mathfrak{p}^{-vs}\right) \mathcal{N}\mathfrak{d}^{-\frac{1}{2}} = \frac{\mathcal{N}\mathfrak{p}^{ds}}{1-\mathcal{N}\mathfrak{p}^{-s}} \mathcal{N}\mathfrak{d}^{-\frac{1}{2}} \\ &= \frac{\mathcal{N}\mathfrak{d}^{s-\frac{1}{2}}}{1-\mathcal{N}\mathfrak{p}^{-s}}. \end{aligned}$$

$\hat{f}_0$ is $\mathcal{N}\mathfrak{d}^{\frac{1}{2}}$ times the characteristic function of $\mathfrak{o}$, so we have, similarly,

$$\begin{aligned} \zeta(\hat{f}_0, \widehat{|\,|^s}) &= \zeta(\hat{f}_0, |\,|^{1-s}) = \mathcal{N}\mathfrak{d}^{\frac{1}{2}} . \int_{\mathfrak{o}} |\alpha|^{1-s}\, d\alpha \\ &= \sum_{v=0}^{\infty} \mathcal{N}\mathfrak{p}^{-v(1-s)} = \frac{1}{1-\mathcal{N}\mathfrak{p}^{s-1}}. \end{aligned}$$

In the ramified case, $n > 0$,

$$\zeta(f_n, c_n|\,|^s) = \int_{\mathfrak{d}^{-1}\mathfrak{p}^{-n}} e^{2\pi i\Lambda(\alpha)} c_n(\alpha)|\alpha|^s \, d\alpha$$

$$= \sum_{\nu=-d-n}^{\infty} \mathcal{N}\mathfrak{p}^{-\nu s} \int_{A_\nu} e^{2\pi i\Lambda(\alpha)} c_n(\alpha) \, d\alpha.$$

We assert that all terms in this sum after the first are 0. In other words that

$$\int_{A_\nu} e^{2\pi i\Lambda(\alpha)} c_n(\alpha) \, d\alpha = 0 \quad \text{for } \nu > -d-n.$$

Proof. Case 1. $\nu \geq -d$. Then $A_\nu \subset \mathfrak{d}^{-1}$, so $e^{2\pi i\Lambda(\alpha)} = 1$ on A_ν, and the integral is

$$\int_{A_\nu} c_n(\alpha) \, d\alpha = \int_u c_n(\alpha\pi^\nu) \, d\alpha = \int_u c_n(\alpha) \, d\alpha = 0$$

since $c_n(\alpha)$ is ramified and therefore non-trivial on the subgroup u.

Case 2. $-d > \nu > -d-n$. (Occurs only if there is "higher ramification"; i.e. if $n > 1$.) To handle this case we break up A_ν into disjoint sets of the type $\alpha_0 + \mathfrak{d}^{-1} = \alpha_0 + \mathfrak{p}^{-d} = \alpha_0(1 + \mathfrak{p}^{-d-\nu})$. On such a set, Λ is constant $= \Lambda(\alpha_0)$ and

$$\int_{\alpha_0 + \mathfrak{d}^{-1}} e^{2\pi i\Lambda(\alpha)} c_n(\alpha) \, d\alpha = e^{2\pi i\Lambda(\alpha_0)} \int_{\alpha_0 + \mathfrak{d}^{-1}} c_n(\alpha) \, d\alpha.$$

This is 0 because

$$\int_{\alpha_0 + \mathfrak{d}^{-1}} c_n(\alpha) \, d\alpha = \int_{\alpha_0(1 + \mathfrak{p}^{-d-\nu})} c_n(\alpha) \, d\alpha = \int_{1 + \mathfrak{p}^{-d-\nu}} c_n(\alpha\alpha_0) \, d\alpha$$

$$= c_n(\alpha_0) \int_{1 + \mathfrak{p}^{-d-\nu}} c_n(\alpha) \, d\alpha,$$

and this last integral is the integral over a multiplicative subgroup $1 + \mathfrak{p}^{-d-\nu}$ of a character $c_n(\alpha)$ which is not trivial on the subgroup. Namely, $-d > \nu \Rightarrow \mathfrak{p} | \mathfrak{p}^{-d-\nu} \Rightarrow 1 + \mathfrak{p}^{-d-\nu}$ is a subgroup of k^*, and $\nu > -d-n \Rightarrow$ the conductor $\mathfrak{p}^n \nmid \mathfrak{p}^{-d-\nu} \Rightarrow c_n(\alpha)$ not trivial on it.

We have now shown

$$\zeta(f_n, c_n|\,|^s) = \mathcal{N}\mathfrak{p}^{(d+n)s} \int_{A_{-d-n}} e^{2\pi i\Lambda(\alpha)} c_n(\alpha) \, d\alpha.$$

To write this in a better form, let $\{\varepsilon\}$ be a set of representatives of the elements of the factor group $u/(1 + \mathfrak{p}^n)$, so that $u = \bigcup_\varepsilon \varepsilon(1 + \mathfrak{p}^n)$, a disjoint union. Then

$$A_{-d-n} = u\pi^{-d-n} = \bigcup_\varepsilon \varepsilon\pi^{-d-n}(1 + \mathfrak{p}^n) = \bigcup_\varepsilon (\varepsilon\pi^{-d-n} + \mathfrak{d}^{-1}).$$

On each of these sets into which we have dissected A_{-d-n}, c_n is constant

$= c_n(\varepsilon\pi^{-d-n}) = c_n(\varepsilon)$, and Λ is constant $= \Lambda(\varepsilon\pi^{-d-n})$. We therefore have

$$\zeta(f_n, c_n||^s) = \mathcal{N}\mathfrak{p}^{(d+n)s}\Big(\sum_{\varepsilon} c_n(\varepsilon)\, e^{2\pi i\Lambda(\varepsilon/\pi^{d+n})}\Big) \int_{1+\mathfrak{p}^n} d\alpha,$$

a form which will be convenient enough.

The pay-off comes in computing

$$\zeta(\hat{f}_n, \widehat{c_n||^s}) = \zeta(\hat{f}_n, c_n^{-1}||^{1-s}).$$

For $\hat{f}_n$ is $\mathcal{N}\mathfrak{d}^{\frac{1}{2}}\mathcal{N}\mathfrak{p}^n$ times the characteristic function of the set $1+\mathfrak{p}^n$, a set on which $c_n^{-1}(\alpha)|\alpha|^{1-s} = 1$. Therefore

$$\zeta(\hat{f}_n, \widehat{c_n||^s}) = \mathcal{N}\mathfrak{d}^{\frac{1}{2}}\mathcal{N}\mathfrak{p}^n \int_{1+\mathfrak{p}^n} d\alpha, \text{ a constant!}$$

Explicit Expressions for $\rho(c)$

$$\rho(||^s) = \mathcal{N}\mathfrak{d}^{s-\frac{1}{2}}\frac{1-\mathcal{N}\mathfrak{p}^{s-1}}{1-\mathcal{N}\mathfrak{p}^{-s}}$$

$\rho(c||^s) = \mathcal{N}(\mathfrak{d}\mathfrak{f})^{s-\frac{1}{2}}\rho_0(c)$, if c is a ramified character with conductor $\mathfrak{f}$, such that $c(\pi) = 1$.

$$\rho_0(c) = \mathcal{N}\mathfrak{f}^{-\frac{1}{2}}\sum_{\varepsilon} c(\varepsilon)\, e^{2\pi i\Lambda(\varepsilon/\pi^{\operatorname{ord}\mathfrak{d}\mathfrak{f}})}$$

is a so-called **root number** and has absolute value 1. $\{\varepsilon\}$ is a set of representatives of the cosets of $1+\mathfrak{f}$ in u.

Taking the quotients of the ζ-functions we have worked out yields these expressions directly if we remember that $\mathfrak{d} = \mathfrak{p}^d$ and, in the ramified case, that the conductor of c_n was $\mathfrak{f} = \mathfrak{p}^n$. The fact that constant $\rho_0(c)$ has absolute value 1 follows from Corollary 2.4.1. Namely, since c is a character, $c||^{\frac{1}{2}}$ has exponent $\frac{1}{2}$, so we must have $|\rho(c||^{\frac{1}{2}})| = |\rho_0(c)| = 1$.

3. Abstract Restricted Direct Product

3.1. *Introduction.* Let $\{\mathfrak{p}\}$ be a set of indices. Suppose we are given for each $\mathfrak{p}$ a locally compact abelian group $G_{\mathfrak{p}}$, and for almost all $\mathfrak{p}$ (meaning for all but a finite number of $\mathfrak{p}$), a fixed subgroup $H_{\mathfrak{p}} \subset G_{\mathfrak{p}}$ which is *open* and *compact.*

We may then form a new abstract group G whose elements $\mathfrak{a} = (\ldots, \mathfrak{a}_{\mathfrak{p}}, \ldots)$ are "vectors" having one component $\mathfrak{a}_{\mathfrak{p}} \in G_{\mathfrak{p}}$ for each $\mathfrak{p}$, with $\mathfrak{a}_{\mathfrak{p}} \in H_{\mathfrak{p}}$ for almost all $\mathfrak{p}$. Multiplication is defined component-wise.

Let S be a finite set of indices $\mathfrak{p}$, including at least all those $\mathfrak{p}$ for which $H_{\mathfrak{p}}$ is not defined. The elements $\mathfrak{a} \in G$ such that $\mathfrak{a}_{\mathfrak{p}} \in H_{\mathfrak{p}}$ for $\mathfrak{p} \notin S$ comprise a subgroup of G which we denote by G_S. G_S is naturally isomorphic to a direct product $\prod_{\mathfrak{p}\in S} G_{\mathfrak{p}} \times \prod_{\mathfrak{p}\notin S} H_{\mathfrak{p}}$ of locally compact groups, almost all of which are compact, and is therefore a locally compact group in the product topology. We define a topology in G by taking as a fundamental system of neighborhoods of 1 in G, the set of neighborhoods of 1 in G_S. The resulting topology in G does not depend on the set of indices, S, which we selected. This can be seen from

LEMMA 3.1.1. *The totality of all "parallelotopes" of the form* $N = \prod_{\mathfrak{p}} N_{\mathfrak{p}}$, *where* $N_{\mathfrak{p}}$ *is a neighborhood of* 1 *in* $G_{\mathfrak{p}}$ *for all* $\mathfrak{p}$, *and* $N_{\mathfrak{p}} = H_{\mathfrak{p}}$ *for almost all* $\mathfrak{p}$*—remember the* $H_{\mathfrak{p}}$ *are open by hypothesis—is a fundamental system of neighborhoods of* 1 *in* G.

Proof. By the definition of product topology a neighborhood of 1 in G_S contains a parallelotope of the type described. On the other hand, since $N_{\mathfrak{p}} = H_{\mathfrak{p}}$ for almost all $\mathfrak{p}$, the intersection

$$\left(\prod_{\mathfrak{p}} N_{\mathfrak{p}}\right) \cap G_S = \prod_{\mathfrak{p} \in S} N_{\mathfrak{p}} \times \prod_{\mathfrak{p} \notin S} (N_{\mathfrak{p}} \cap H_{\mathfrak{p}})$$

is a neighborhood of 1 in G_S.

It is obvious that G_S is open in G and that the topology induced in G_S as a subspace of G is the same as the product topology we imposed on G_S to begin with. Therefore a compact neighborhood of 1 in G_S is a compact neighborhood of 1 in G. It follows that G is locally compact.

DEFINITION 3.1.1. *We call* G *(as locally compact abelian group) the restricted direct product of the groups* $G_{\mathfrak{p}}$ *relative to the subgroups* $H_{\mathfrak{p}}$.

It will, of course, be convenient to identify the basic group $G_{\mathfrak{p}}$ with the subgroup of G consisting of the elements $\mathfrak{a}_{\mathfrak{p}} = (1, 1, \ldots, \mathfrak{a}_{\mathfrak{p}}, \ldots)$ having all components but the $\mathfrak{p}$-th equal to 1. For that subgroup of G is naturally isomorphic, both topologically and algebraically to $G_{\mathfrak{p}}$.

Since the components, $\mathfrak{a}_{\mathfrak{p}}$, of any element $\mathfrak{a}$ of G lie in $H_{\mathfrak{p}}$ for almost all $\mathfrak{p}$, G is the union of the subgroups of the type G_S. This fact will allow us to reduce our investigations of G to a study of the subgroups G_S.

These G_S in turn may be effectively analyzed by introducing the subgroup $G^S \subset G_S$ consisting of all elements $\mathfrak{a} \in G$ such that $\mathfrak{a}_{\mathfrak{p}} = 1$ for $\mathfrak{p} \in S$; $\mathfrak{a}_{\mathfrak{p}} \in H_{\mathfrak{p}}$, $\mathfrak{p} \notin S$. G^S is compact since it is naturally isomorphic to a direct product $\prod_{\mathfrak{p} \notin S} H_{\mathfrak{p}}$ of compact groups. G_S can be considered as the direct product $G_S = \left(\prod_{\mathfrak{p} \in S} G_{\mathfrak{p}}\right) \times G^S$ of a finite number of our basic groups $G_{\mathfrak{p}}$ and the compact group G^S.

We close our introduction of the restricted direct product with

LEMMA 3.1.2. *A subset* $C \subset G$ *is relatively compact (has a compact closure) if, and only if, it is contained in a parallelotope of the type* $\prod_{\mathfrak{p}} B_{\mathfrak{p}}$, *where* $B_{\mathfrak{p}}$ *is a compact subset of* $G_{\mathfrak{p}}$ *for all* $\mathfrak{p}$, *and* $B_{\mathfrak{p}} = H_{\mathfrak{p}}$ *for almost all* $\mathfrak{p}$.

Proof. Any compact subset of G is contained in some G_S, because the G_S are open sets covering G, and the union of a finite number of subgroups G_S is again a G_S. Any compact subset of a G_S is contained in a parallelotope of the type described, for it is contained in the cartesian product of its "projections" onto the component groups $G_\mathfrak{p}$. These projections are compact since they are continuous images, and are contained in $H_\mathfrak{p}$ for $\mathfrak{p} \notin S$.

On the other hand, any parallelotope $\prod_\mathfrak{p} B_\mathfrak{p}$ is obviously a compact subset of some G_S; therefore of G.

3.2. *Characters*

Let $c(\mathfrak{a})$ be a quasi-character of G, i.e. a continuous multiplicative mapping of G into the complex numbers. We denote by $c_\mathfrak{p}$ the restriction of c to $G_\mathfrak{p}$: $(c_\mathfrak{p}(\mathfrak{a}_\mathfrak{p}) = c(\mathfrak{a}_\mathfrak{p}) = c(1, 1, \ldots, \mathfrak{a}_\mathfrak{p}, \ldots)$ for $\mathfrak{a}_\mathfrak{p} \in G_\mathfrak{p})$. $c_\mathfrak{p}$ is obviously a quasi-character of $G_\mathfrak{p}$.

LEMMA 3.2.1. *$c_\mathfrak{p}$ is trivial on $H_\mathfrak{p}$, for almost all $\mathfrak{p}$, and we have for any $\mathfrak{a} \in G$*

$$c(\mathfrak{a}) = \prod_\mathfrak{p} c_\mathfrak{p}(\mathfrak{a}_\mathfrak{p})$$

almost all factors of the product being 1.

Proof. Let U be a neighbourhood of 1 in the complex numbers containing no multiplicative subgroup except $\{1\}$. Let $N = \prod_\mathfrak{p} N_\mathfrak{p}$ be a neighborhood of 1 in G such that $c(N) \subset U$. Select an S containing all $\mathfrak{p}$ for which $N_\mathfrak{p} \neq H_\mathfrak{p}$. Then $G^S \subset N \Rightarrow c(G^S) \subset U \Rightarrow c(G^S) = 1 \Rightarrow c(H_\mathfrak{p}) = 1$ for $\mathfrak{p} \notin S$. If $\mathfrak{a}$ is a fixed element of G we impose on S the further condition that $\mathfrak{a} \in G_S$ and write $\mathfrak{a} = \prod_{\mathfrak{p} \in S} \mathfrak{a}_\mathfrak{p} . \mathfrak{a}^S$ with $\mathfrak{a}^S \in G^S$. Then

$$c(\mathfrak{a}) = \prod_{\mathfrak{p} \in S} c(\mathfrak{a}_\mathfrak{p}) . c(\mathfrak{a}^S) = \prod_{\mathfrak{p} \in S} c_\mathfrak{p}(\mathfrak{a}_\mathfrak{p}) = \prod_\mathfrak{p} c_\mathfrak{p}(\mathfrak{a}_\mathfrak{p}),$$

since for $\mathfrak{p} \notin S$, $c_\mathfrak{p}(\mathfrak{a}_\mathfrak{p}) = 1$.

LEMMA 3.2.2. *Let $c_\mathfrak{p}$ be a given quasi-character of $G_\mathfrak{p}$ for each $\mathfrak{p}$, with $c_\mathfrak{p}$ trivial on $H_\mathfrak{p}$ for almost all $\mathfrak{p}$. Then if we define $c(\mathfrak{a}) = \prod_\mathfrak{p} c_\mathfrak{p}(\mathfrak{a}_\mathfrak{p})$ we obtain a quasi-character of G.*

Proof. $c(\mathfrak{a})$ is obviously multiplicative. To see that it is continuous select an S containing all $\mathfrak{p}$ for which $c_\mathfrak{p}(H_\mathfrak{p}) \neq 1$. Let s be the number of $\mathfrak{p}$ in S. Given a neighborhood, U, of 1 in the complex numbers, choose a neighborhood V such that $V^s \subset U$. Let $N_\mathfrak{p}$ be a neighbourhood of 1 in $G_\mathfrak{p}$ such that $c_\mathfrak{p}(N_\mathfrak{p}) \subset V$ for $\mathfrak{p} \in S$, and let $N_\mathfrak{p} = H_\mathfrak{p}$ for $\mathfrak{p} \notin S$. Then

$$c\Big(\prod_\mathfrak{p} N_\mathfrak{p}\Big) \subset V^s \subset U.$$

Restricting our consideration to characters, we notice first of all that $c(\mathfrak{a}) = \prod_\mathfrak{p} c_\mathfrak{p}(\mathfrak{a}_\mathfrak{p})$ is a character if, and only if, all $c_\mathfrak{p}$ are characters. Denote by $\hat{G}_\mathfrak{p}$ the character group of $G_\mathfrak{p}$, for all $\mathfrak{p}$; for the $\mathfrak{p}$ where $H_\mathfrak{p}$ is defined let $H_\mathfrak{p}^* \subset \hat{G}_\mathfrak{p}$ be the subgroup of all $c_\mathfrak{p} \in \hat{G}_\mathfrak{p}$ which are trivial on $H_\mathfrak{p}$. Then

$H_\mathfrak{p}$ compact $\Rightarrow \hat{H}_\mathfrak{p} \cong \hat{G}_\mathfrak{p}/H_\mathfrak{p}^*$ discrete $\Rightarrow H_\mathfrak{p}^*$ open, and $H_\mathfrak{p}$ open $\Rightarrow G_\mathfrak{p}/H_\mathfrak{p}$ discrete $\Rightarrow \widehat{G_\mathfrak{p}/H_\mathfrak{p}} \cong H_\mathfrak{p}^*$ compact.

THEOREM 3.2.1. *The restricted direct product of the groups $\hat{G}_\mathfrak{p}$ relative to the subgroups $H_\mathfrak{p}^*$ is naturally isomorphic, both topologically and algebraically, to the character group $\hat{G}$ of G.*

Proof. Of course we mean to identify $c = (\ldots, c_\mathfrak{p}, \ldots)$ with the character $c(\mathfrak{a}) = \prod_\mathfrak{p} c_\mathfrak{p}(\mathfrak{a}_\mathfrak{p})$. The two preceding lemmas, applied to characters, show that this is an algebraic isomorphism between the two groups. We have only to check that the topology is the same. To this effect we reason as follows: $c = (\ldots, c_\mathfrak{p}, \ldots)$ is close to 1 as a character $\Leftrightarrow c(B)$ close to 1 for a large compact $B \subset G \Leftrightarrow c\left(\prod_\mathfrak{p} B_\mathfrak{p}\right)$ close to 1 for $B_\mathfrak{p} \subset G_\mathfrak{p}$, compact, $B_\mathfrak{p} = H_\mathfrak{p}$ for almost all $\mathfrak{p} \Leftrightarrow c_\mathfrak{p}(B_\mathfrak{p})$ close to 1 wherever $B_\mathfrak{p} \neq H_\mathfrak{p}$ and $c_\mathfrak{p}(B_\mathfrak{p}) = c_\mathfrak{p}(H_\mathfrak{p}) = 1$ at the remaining $\mathfrak{p}$ (since $H_\mathfrak{p}$ is a subgroup, $c_\mathfrak{p}(H_\mathfrak{p})$ can be close to 1 only if $c_\mathfrak{p}(H_\mathfrak{p}) = 1) \Leftrightarrow c_\mathfrak{p}$ close to 1 in $\hat{G}_\mathfrak{p}$ for a finite number of $\mathfrak{p}$ and $c_\mathfrak{p} \in H_\mathfrak{p}^*$ at the other $\mathfrak{p} \Leftrightarrow c$ close to 1 in the restricted direct product of the $\hat{G}_\mathfrak{p}$.

3.3. *Measure*

Assume now that we have chosen a Haar measure $d\mathfrak{a}_\mathfrak{p}$ on each $G_\mathfrak{p}$ such that $\int_{H_\mathfrak{p}} d\mathfrak{a}_\mathfrak{p} = 1$ for almost all $\mathfrak{p}$. We wish to define a Haar measure $d\mathfrak{a}$ on G for which, in some sense, $d\mathfrak{a} = \prod_\mathfrak{p} d\mathfrak{a}_\mathfrak{p}$. To do this, we select an S; then consider G_S as the finite direct product $G_S = \left(\prod_{\mathfrak{p}\in S} G_\mathfrak{p}\right) \times G^S$, in order to define on G_S a measure $d\mathfrak{a}_S = \left(\prod_{\mathfrak{p}\in S} d\mathfrak{a}_\mathfrak{p}\right) . d\mathfrak{a}^S$, where $d\mathfrak{a}^S$ is that measure on the compact group G^S for which $\int_{G^S} d\mathfrak{a}^S = \prod_{\mathfrak{p}\notin S}\left(\int_{H_\mathfrak{p}} d\mathfrak{a}_\mathfrak{p}\right)$. Since G_S is an open subgroup of G, a Haar measure $d\mathfrak{a}$ on G is now determined by the requirement that $d\mathfrak{a} = d\mathfrak{a}_S$ on G_S. To see that the $d\mathfrak{a}$ we have just chosen is really independent of the set S, let $T \supset S$ be a larger set of indices. Then $G_S \subset G_T$, and we have only to check that the $d\mathfrak{a}_T$ constructed with T coincides on G_S with the $d\mathfrak{a}_S$ constructed with S. Now one sees from the decomposition $G^S = \left(\prod_{\mathfrak{p}\in T-S} H_\mathfrak{p}\right) \times G^T$ that $d\mathfrak{a}^S = \left(\prod_{\mathfrak{p}\in T-S} d\mathfrak{a}_\mathfrak{p}\right). \; d\mathfrak{a}^T$; for the measure on the right-hand side gives to the compact group G^S the required measure. Therefore

$$d\mathfrak{a}_S = \prod_{\mathfrak{p}\in S} d\mathfrak{a}_\mathfrak{p} . d\mathfrak{a}^S = \prod_{\mathfrak{p}\in S} d\mathfrak{a}_\mathfrak{p} . \prod_{\mathfrak{p}\in T-S} d\mathfrak{a}_\mathfrak{p} . d\mathfrak{a}^T = d\mathfrak{a}_T.$$

We have therefore determined a unique Haar measure $d\mathfrak{a}$ on G which we may denote symbolically by $d\mathfrak{a} = \prod_\mathfrak{p} d\mathfrak{a}_\mathfrak{p}$.

If $\varphi(S)$ is any function of the finite sets of indices S, with values in a topological space, we shall mean by the expression $\lim_S \varphi(S) = \varphi_0$ the statement: "given any neighborhood V of φ_0, there exists a set $S(V)$ such that $S \supset S(V) \Rightarrow \varphi(S) \in V$". Intuitively, $\lim_S \varphi(S)$ means the limit of $\varphi(S)$ as S becomes larger and larger.

LEMMA 3.3.1. *If $f(\mathfrak{a})$ is a function on G,*

$$\int f(\mathfrak{a})\,d\mathfrak{a} = \lim_S \int_{G_S} f(\mathfrak{a})\,d\mathfrak{a},$$

if either (1) $f(\mathfrak{a})$ measurable, $f(\mathfrak{a}) \geq 0$, in which case $+\infty$ is allowed as value of the integrals; or (2) $f(\mathfrak{a}) \in L_1(G)$, in which case the values of the integrals are complex numbers.

Proof. In either case (1) or (2) $\int f(\mathfrak{a})\,d\mathfrak{a}$ is the limit of $\int_B f(\mathfrak{a})\,d\mathfrak{a}$ for larger and larger compacts $B \subset G$. Since any compact, B, is contained in some G_S, the statement follows.

LEMMA 3.3.2. *Assume we are given for each $\mathfrak{p}$ a continuous function $f_\mathfrak{p} \in L_1(G_\mathfrak{p})$ such that $f_\mathfrak{p}(\mathfrak{a}_\mathfrak{p}) = 1$ on $H_\mathfrak{p}$ for almost all $\mathfrak{p}$. We define on G the function $f(\mathfrak{a}) = \prod_\mathfrak{p} f_\mathfrak{p}(\mathfrak{a}_\mathfrak{p})$, (this is really a finite product), and contend:*

(1) *$f(\mathfrak{a})$ is continuous on G.*

(2) *For any set S containing at least those $\mathfrak{p}$ for which either $f_\mathfrak{p}(H_\mathfrak{p}) \neq 1$, or $\int_{H_\mathfrak{p}} d\mathfrak{a}_\mathfrak{p} \neq 1$, we have*

$$\int_{G_S} f(\mathfrak{a})\,d\mathfrak{a} = \prod_{\mathfrak{p} \in S} \left[\int_{G_\mathfrak{p}} f_\mathfrak{p}(\mathfrak{a}_\mathfrak{p})\,d\mathfrak{a}_\mathfrak{p} \right].$$

Proof. (1) $f(\mathfrak{a})$ is obviously continuous on any G_S; therefore on G.

(2) For $\mathfrak{a} \in G_S$, $f(\mathfrak{a}) = \prod_{\mathfrak{p} \in S} f_\mathfrak{p}(\mathfrak{a}_\mathfrak{p})$. Hence

$$\int_{G_S} f(\mathfrak{a})\,d\mathfrak{a} = \int_{G_S} f(\mathfrak{a})\,d\mathfrak{a}_S = \int_{G_S} \Big(\prod_{\mathfrak{p} \in S} f_\mathfrak{p}(\mathfrak{a}_\mathfrak{p})\Big)\Big(\prod_{\mathfrak{p} \in S} d\mathfrak{a}_\mathfrak{p} \,.\, d\mathfrak{a}^S\Big)$$

$$= \prod_{\mathfrak{p} \in S} \left[\int f_\mathfrak{p}(\mathfrak{a}_\mathfrak{p})\,d\mathfrak{a}_\mathfrak{p}\right] \cdot \int_{G^S} d\mathfrak{a}^S = \prod_{\mathfrak{p} \in S} \left[\int f_\mathfrak{p}(\mathfrak{a}_\mathfrak{p})\,d\mathfrak{a}_\mathfrak{p}\right].$$

THEOREM 3.3.1. *If $f_\mathfrak{p}(\mathfrak{a}_\mathfrak{p})$ and $f(\mathfrak{a})$ are the functions of the preceding lemma and if furthermore*

$$\prod_\mathfrak{p} \left[\int |f_\mathfrak{p}(\mathfrak{a}_\mathfrak{p})|\,d\mathfrak{a}_\mathfrak{p}\right] \quad \Big(= \lim_S \Big\{\prod_{\mathfrak{p} \in S} \Big[\int |f_\mathfrak{p}(\mathfrak{a}_\mathfrak{p})|\,d\mathfrak{a}_\mathfrak{p}\Big]\Big\}\Big) < \infty$$

then $f(\mathfrak{a}) \in L_1(G)$ and,

$$\int f(\mathfrak{a})\,d\mathfrak{a} = \prod_\mathfrak{p} \left[\int f_\mathfrak{p}(\mathfrak{a}_\mathfrak{p})\,d\mathfrak{a}_\mathfrak{p}\right].$$

Proof. Combine the two preceding lemmas; first for the function $|f(\mathfrak{a})| = \prod_{\mathfrak{p}} |f_{\mathfrak{p}}(\mathfrak{a}_{\mathfrak{p}})|$ to see that $f(\mathfrak{a}) \in L_1(G)$, then for $f(\mathfrak{a})$ itself to evaluate $\int f(\mathfrak{a})\, d\mathfrak{a}$.

We close this chapter with some remarks about Fourier analysis in a restricted direct product. As we have seen $\hat{G}$ the character group of G is the direct product of the character groups $\hat{G}_{\mathfrak{p}}$ of $G_{\mathfrak{p}}$, relative to the subgroups $H_{\mathfrak{p}}^*$ orthogonal to $H_{\mathfrak{p}}$. Denote by $c = (\ldots, c_{\mathfrak{p}}, \ldots)$ the general element of $\hat{G}$. (In this paragraph, c, and $c_{\mathfrak{p}}$ are characters, not quasi-characters). Let $dc_{\mathfrak{p}}$ be the measure in $\hat{G}_{\mathfrak{p}}$ dual to the measure $d\mathfrak{a}_{\mathfrak{p}}$ in $G_{\mathfrak{p}}$. Notice that if $f_{\mathfrak{p}}(\mathfrak{a}_{\mathfrak{p}})$ is the characteristic function of $H_{\mathfrak{p}}$, its Fourier transform $\hat{f}_{\mathfrak{p}}(c_{\mathfrak{p}}) = \int f_{\mathfrak{p}}(\mathfrak{a}_{\mathfrak{p}})\overline{c_{\mathfrak{p}}(\mathfrak{a}_{\mathfrak{p}})}\, d\mathfrak{a}_{\mathfrak{p}}$ is $\int_{H_{\mathfrak{p}}} d\mathfrak{a}_{\mathfrak{p}}$ times the characteristic function of $H_{\mathfrak{p}}^*$. A consequence of this fact and the inversion formula is that

$$\Big(\int_{H_{\mathfrak{p}}} d\mathfrak{a}_{\mathfrak{p}}\Big)\Big(\int_{H_{\mathfrak{p}}^*} dc_{\mathfrak{p}}\Big) = 1.$$

Therefore $\int_{H_{\mathfrak{p}}^*} dc_{\mathfrak{p}} = 1$ for almost all $\mathfrak{p}$, and we may put $dc = \prod_{\mathfrak{p}} dc_{\mathfrak{p}}$.

LEMMA 3.3.3. *If $f_{\mathfrak{p}}(\mathfrak{a}_{\mathfrak{p}}) \in \mathfrak{B}_1(G_{\mathfrak{p}})$ for all $\mathfrak{p}$ and $f_{\mathfrak{p}}(\mathfrak{a}_{\mathfrak{p}})$ is the characteristic function of $H_{\mathfrak{p}}$ for almost all $\mathfrak{p}$, then the function $f(\mathfrak{a}) = \prod_{\mathfrak{p}} f_{\mathfrak{p}}(\mathfrak{a}_{\mathfrak{p}})$ has the Fourier transform $\hat{f}(c) = \prod_{\mathfrak{p}} \hat{f}_{\mathfrak{p}}(c_{\mathfrak{p}})$, and $f(\mathfrak{a}) \in \mathfrak{B}_1(G)$.*

Proof. Apply Theorem 3.3.1 to the function $f(\mathfrak{a})\overline{c(\mathfrak{a})} = \prod_{\mathfrak{p}} f_{\mathfrak{p}}(\mathfrak{a}_{\mathfrak{p}})\overline{c_{\mathfrak{p}}(\mathfrak{a}_{\mathfrak{p}})}$ to see that the Fourier transform of the product is the product of the Fourier transforms. Since $f_{\mathfrak{p}}(\mathfrak{a}_{\mathfrak{p}}) \in \mathfrak{B}_1(G_{\mathfrak{p}})$, we have $\hat{f}_{\mathfrak{p}}(c_{\mathfrak{p}}) \in L_1(\hat{G}_{\mathfrak{p}})$ for all $\mathfrak{p}$. For almost all $\mathfrak{p}$, $\hat{f}_{\mathfrak{p}}(c_{\mathfrak{p}})$ is the characteristic function of $H_{\mathfrak{p}}^*$ according to the remark above. From this we see that $\hat{f}(c) \in L_1(\hat{G})$, hence $f(\mathfrak{a}) \in \mathfrak{B}_1(G)$.

COROLLARY 3.3.1. *The measure $dc = \prod_{\mathfrak{p}} dc_{\mathfrak{p}}$ is dual to $d\mathfrak{a} = \prod_{\mathfrak{p}} d\mathfrak{a}_{\mathfrak{p}}$.*

Proof. Applying the preceding lemma to the group $\hat{G}$ with the measure dc, we obtain for our "product" functions the inversion formula

$$f(\mathfrak{a}) = \int \hat{f}(c)c(\mathfrak{a})\, dc$$

from the component-wise inversion formulas.

4. The Theory in the Large

4.1. *Additive Theory*

In this chapter, k denotes a finite algebraic number field, $\mathfrak{p}$ is the generic prime divisor of k. The completion of k at the prime divisor $\mathfrak{p}$ shall from now on be denoted by $k_{\mathfrak{p}}$, and all the symbols $\mathfrak{o}$, Λ, $\mathfrak{d}$, $||$, c, etc., defined in Chapter 2 for this local field $k_{\mathfrak{p}}$ shall also receive the subscript $\mathfrak{p}$: $\mathfrak{o}_{\mathfrak{p}}$, $\Lambda_{\mathfrak{p}}$, $\mathfrak{d}_{\mathfrak{p}}$, $||_{\mathfrak{p}}$, $c_{\mathfrak{p}}, \ldots$, etc.

DEFINITION 4.1.1. *The additive group V of valuation vectors of k is the restricted direct sum, over all prime divisors $\mathfrak{p}$, of the groups $k_{\mathfrak{p}}^{+}$ relative to the subgroups $\mathfrak{o}_{\mathfrak{p}}$.*

We shall denote the generic element of V (= valuation vector) by $\mathfrak{x} = (\ldots, \mathfrak{x}_{\mathfrak{p}}, \ldots)$. From Theorems 3.2.1. and 2.2.1 and Lemma 2.2.3 we see that the character group of V is naturally the restricted direct sum of the groups $k_{\mathfrak{p}}^{+}$ relative to the subgroups $\mathfrak{d}_{\mathfrak{p}}^{-1}$. Since $\mathfrak{d}_{\mathfrak{p}} = \mathfrak{o}_{\mathfrak{p}}$ for almost all $\mathfrak{p}$ this sum is simply V again! Looking more closely at the identifications set up in these theorems we see that the element $\mathfrak{y} = (\ldots, \mathfrak{y}_{\mathfrak{p}}, \ldots) \in V$ is to be identified with the character

$$\mathfrak{x} = (\ldots, \mathfrak{x}_{\mathfrak{p}}, \ldots) \to \prod_{\mathfrak{p}} \exp(2\pi i \Lambda_{\mathfrak{p}}(\mathfrak{y}_{\mathfrak{p}}\mathfrak{x}_{\mathfrak{p}}) = \exp\left[2\pi i \sum_{\mathfrak{p}} \Lambda_{\mathfrak{p}}(\mathfrak{y}_{\mathfrak{p}}\mathfrak{x}_{\mathfrak{p}})\right]$$

of V. This suggests that we define the additive function

$$\Lambda(\mathfrak{x}) = \sum_{\mathfrak{p}} \Lambda_{\mathfrak{p}}(\mathfrak{x}_{\mathfrak{p}})$$

on V, and introduce component-wise multiplication

$$\mathfrak{y}\mathfrak{x} = (\ldots, \mathfrak{y}_{\mathfrak{p}}, \ldots)(\ldots, \mathfrak{x}_{\mathfrak{p}}, \ldots) = (\ldots, \mathfrak{y}_{\mathfrak{p}}\mathfrak{x}_{\mathfrak{p}}, \ldots)$$

of elements of V in order to be able to assert neatly:

THEOREM 4.1.1. *V is naturally its own character group if we identify the element $\mathfrak{y} \in V$ with the character $\mathfrak{x} \to e^{2\pi i \Lambda(\mathfrak{y}\mathfrak{x})}$ of V.*

On V we shall, of course, take the measure $d\mathfrak{x} = \prod_{\mathfrak{p}} d\mathfrak{x}_{\mathfrak{p}}$ described in Section 3.3, $d\mathfrak{x}_{\mathfrak{p}}$ being the local additive measure defined in Section 2.2. Since these local measures $d\mathfrak{x}_{\mathfrak{p}}$ were chosen to be self-dual, the same is true of $d\mathfrak{x}$, according to Corollary 3.3.1. We state this fact formally in

THEOREM 4.1.2. *If for a function $f(\mathfrak{x}) \in L_1(V)$ we define the Fourier transform*

$$\hat{f}(\mathfrak{y}) = \int f(\mathfrak{x})\, e^{-2\pi i \Lambda(\mathfrak{y}\mathfrak{x})}\, d\mathfrak{x},$$

then for $f(\mathfrak{x}) \in \mathfrak{B}_1(V)$ the inversion formula

$$f(\mathfrak{x}) = \int \hat{f}(\mathfrak{y})\, e^{2\pi i \Lambda(\mathfrak{x}\mathfrak{y})}\, d\mathfrak{y}$$

holds.

What is the analogue in the large of the local Lemma 2.2.4 and 2.2.5, that is, of the statement $d(\alpha\xi) = |\alpha|\, d\xi$ for $\alpha \in k^{*}$? In that local consideration, α played the role of an automorphism of $k_{\mathfrak{p}}^{+}$, namely the automorphism $\xi \to \alpha\xi$. This leads us to investigate the question: for what $\mathfrak{a} \in V$ is $\mathfrak{x} \to \mathfrak{a}\mathfrak{x}$ an automorphism of V? We first observe that for any $\mathfrak{a} \in V$, $\mathfrak{x} \to \mathfrak{a}\mathfrak{x}$ is a continuous homomorphism of V into V. A necessary condition for it to be an automorphism is the existence of a $\mathfrak{b} \in V$ such that $\mathfrak{a}\mathfrak{b} = 1 = (1, 1, \ldots)$. But this is also sufficient, for with this $\mathfrak{b}$ we obtain an inverse map $\mathfrak{x} \to \mathfrak{b}\mathfrak{x}$ of the same form. Now for such a $\mathfrak{b}$ to exist at all as an "unrestricted" vector, we need $\mathfrak{a}_{\mathfrak{p}} \neq 0$ for all $\mathfrak{p}$, and then $\mathfrak{b}_{\mathfrak{p}} = \mathfrak{a}_{\mathfrak{p}}^{-1}$. The further condition

$\mathfrak{b} \in V$ means $\mathfrak{a}_{\mathfrak{p}}^{-1} \in \mathfrak{o}_{\mathfrak{p}}$ for almost all $\mathfrak{p}$, therefore $|\mathfrak{a}_{\mathfrak{p}}|_{\mathfrak{p}} = 1$ for almost all $\mathfrak{x}$. These two conditions mean simply that $\mathfrak{a}$ is an idèle in the sense of Chevalley. We have proved

LEMMA 4.1.1. *The map $\mathfrak{x} \to \mathfrak{a}\mathfrak{x}$ is an automorphism of V if and only if $\mathfrak{a}$ is an idèle.*

At present we shall consider idèles only in this role. Later we shall study the multiplicative group of idèles as a group in its own right, with its own topology, as the restricted direct product of the groups $k_{\mathfrak{p}}^*$ relative to the subgroups $u_{\mathfrak{p}}$.

To answer the original question concerning the transformation of the measure under these automorphisms we state

LEMMA 4.1.2. *For an idèle, $\mathfrak{a}$,*

$$d(\mathfrak{a}\mathfrak{x}) = |\mathfrak{a}|\, d\mathfrak{x},$$

where

$$|\mathfrak{a}| = \prod_{\mathfrak{p}} |\mathfrak{a}_{\mathfrak{p}}|_{\mathfrak{p}}$$

(really a finite product).

Proof. If $N = \prod_{\mathfrak{p}} N_{\mathfrak{p}}$ is a compact neighborhood of 0 in V, then by Theorem 3.3.1 and Lemma 2.2.5

$$\int_N d\mathfrak{x} = \prod_{\mathfrak{p}} \int_{N\mathfrak{p}} d\mathfrak{x}_{\mathfrak{p}}, \quad \text{and} \quad \int_{\mathfrak{a}N} d\mathfrak{x} = \prod_{\mathfrak{p}} \int_{\mathfrak{a}\mathfrak{p}N\mathfrak{p}} d\mathfrak{x}_{\mathfrak{p}} = \prod_{\mathfrak{p}} |\mathfrak{a}_{\mathfrak{p}}|_{\mathfrak{p}} \int_{N\mathfrak{p}} d\mathfrak{x}_{\mathfrak{p}}.$$

The last, and most important thing we must do in our preliminary discussion of V is to see how the field k is imbedded in V. We identify the element $\xi \in k$ with the valuation vector $\xi = (\xi, \xi, \ldots, \xi, \ldots)$ having all components equal to ξ, and view k as subgroup of V. What kind of subgroup is it?

LEMMA 4.1.3. *If S_∞ denotes the set of archimedean primes of k, then* (1) *$k \cap V_{S_\infty} = \mathfrak{o}$, the ring of algebraic integers in k, and* (2) *$k + V_{S_\infty} = V$.*

Proof. (1) This is simply the statement that an element $\xi \in k$ is an algebraic integer if and only if it is an integer at all finite primes.

(2) $k + V_{S_\infty} = V$ means: given any $\mathfrak{x} \in V$, there exists a $\xi \in k$ approximating it in the sense that $\xi - \mathfrak{x}_{\mathfrak{p}} \in \mathfrak{o}_{\mathfrak{p}}$ for all finite $\mathfrak{p}$. Such a ξ can be found by solving simultaneous congruences in $\mathfrak{o}$. The existence of a solution is guaranteed by the Chinese Remainder theorem.

Let now $\overset{\infty}{V}$ denote the "infinite part" of V, i.e. the cartesian product $\prod_{\mathfrak{p} \in S_\infty} k_{\mathfrak{p}}$ of the archimedean completions of k. If a generating equation for k over the rational field has r_1 real roots and r_2 pairs of conjugate complex roots, then $\overset{\infty}{V}$ is the product of r_1 real lines and r_2 complex planes. As such it is naturally a vector space over the real numbers of dimension $n = r_1 + 2r_2$ = absolute degree of k. For any $\mathfrak{x} \in V$ denote by $\overset{\infty}{\mathfrak{x}}$ the projection $\overset{\infty}{\mathfrak{x}} = (\ldots, \mathfrak{x}_\mathfrak{p}, \ldots)_{\mathfrak{p} \in S_\infty}$ of $\mathfrak{x}$ on $\overset{\infty}{V}$.

LEMMA 4.1.4. *If $\{\omega_1, \omega_2, \ldots, \omega_n\}$ is a minimal basis for the ring of integers $\mathfrak{o}$ of k over the rational integers, then $\left\{\overset{\infty}{\omega}_1, \overset{\infty}{\omega}_2, \ldots, \overset{\infty}{\omega}_n\right\}$ is a basis for the vector space $\overset{\infty}{V}$ over the real numbers. The parallelotope $\overset{\infty}{D}$ spanned by this basis ($\overset{\infty}{D}$ = set of all $\overset{\infty}{\mathfrak{x}} \equiv \sum_{\nu=1}^{n} x_\nu \overset{\infty}{\omega}_\nu$ with $0 \leq x_\nu < 1$) has the volume $\sqrt{|d|}$ (where $d = (\det(\omega_i^{(j)}))^2$ = absolute discriminant of k) if measured in the measure $d\overset{\infty}{\mathfrak{x}} = \prod_{\mathfrak{p} \in S_\infty} d\mathfrak{x}_\mathfrak{p}$ which is natural in our set-up.*

Proof. The projection $\xi \to \overset{\infty}{\xi}$ of k into $\overset{\infty}{V}$ is just the classical imbedding of a number field into n-space. The reader will remember the classical argument which runs:

$$k \text{ separable} \Rightarrow d = (\det(\omega_i^{(j)}))^2 \neq 0 \Rightarrow \{\overset{\infty}{\omega}_1, \overset{\infty}{\omega}_2, \ldots, \overset{\infty}{\omega}_n\}$$

linearly independent, and (with a simple determinant computation) $\overset{\infty}{D}$ has volume $2^{-r_2}\sqrt{|d|}$. For us the volume is 2^{r_2} times as much because we have chosen for complex $\mathfrak{p}$ a measure which is twice the ordinary measure in the complex plane.

DEFINITION 4.1.2. *The additive fundamental domain $D \subset V$ is the set of all $\mathfrak{x}$ such that $\mathfrak{x} \in V_{S_\infty}$ and $\overset{\infty}{\mathfrak{x}} \in \overset{\infty}{D}$.*

THEOREM 4.1.3. (1) *D deserves its name because any vector $\mathfrak{x} \in V$ is congruent to one and only one vector of D modulo the field elements ξ. In other words, $V = \bigcup_{\xi \in k} (\xi + D)$, a disjoint union.*

(2) *D has measure* 1.

Proof. (1) Starting with an arbitrary $\mathfrak{x} \in V$ we can bring it into V_{S_∞} by the addition of a field element which is unique mod $\mathfrak{o}$ (Lemma 4.1.3). Once in V_{S_∞} we can find a unique element of $\mathfrak{o}$, by the addition of which we can stay in V_{S_∞} and adjust the infinite components so that they lie in $\overset{\infty}{D}$ (Lemma 4.1.4).

(2) To compute the measure of D, notice that $D \subset V_{S_\infty}$ and $D = \overset{\infty}{D} \times V^{S_\infty}$. Therefore

$$\int_D d\mathfrak{x} = \int_D d\mathfrak{x}_{S_\infty} = \int_{\overset{\infty}{D} \times V^{S_\infty}} d\overset{\infty}{\mathfrak{x}}\, d\mathfrak{x}^{S_\infty} = \int_{\overset{\infty}{D}} d\overset{\infty}{\mathfrak{x}} \cdot \int_{V^{S_\infty}} d\mathfrak{x}^{S_\infty} = \sqrt{|d|} \prod_{\mathfrak{p} \notin S} (\mathcal{N}_\mathfrak{p} \mathfrak{d}_\mathfrak{p})^{-\frac{1}{2}}.$$

Now since the discriminant d (as ideal) is the norm of the absolute different $\mathfrak{b}$ of k, and since $\mathfrak{d}$ is the product of the local differents $\mathfrak{d}_\mathfrak{p}$, we have $|d| = \prod_{\mathfrak{p} \in S_\infty} (\mathcal{N}_\mathfrak{p} \mathfrak{d}_\mathfrak{p})$. Therefore the measure which we have computed is 1.

COROLLARY 4.1.1. *k is a discrete subgroup of V. The factor group V mod k is compact.*

Proof. k is discrete, since D has an interior. V mod k is compact, since D is relatively compact.

LEMMA 4.1.5. *$\Lambda(\xi) = 0$ for all $\xi \in k$.*

Proof.

$$\Lambda(\xi) = \sum_{\mathfrak{p}} \Lambda_\mathfrak{p}(\xi) = \sum_{\mathfrak{p}} \lambda_p(S_\mathfrak{p}(\xi)) = \sum_{p} \lambda_p \Big(\sum_{\mathfrak{p}|p} S_\mathfrak{p}(\xi)\Big) = \sum_{\mathfrak{p}} \lambda_p(S(\xi))$$

because "the trace is the sum of the local traces". Since $S(\xi)$ is a rational number, the problem is reduced to proving that $\sum_p \lambda_p(x) \equiv 0 \pmod 1$ for rational x. This we do by observing that the rational number $\sum_p \lambda_p(x)$ is integral with respect to each fixed rational prime q. Namely

$$\sum_p \lambda_p(x) = \Big(\sum_{p \neq q,\, p_\infty} \lambda_p(x)\Big) + \lambda_q(x) + \lambda_{p_\infty}(x) = \Big(\sum_{p \neq q,\, p_\infty} \lambda_p(x)\Big) + (\lambda_q(x) - x)$$

expresses $\lambda(x)$ as sum of q-adic integers.

THEOREM† 4.1.4. *$k^* = k$, that is $\Lambda(\mathfrak{x}\xi) = 0$ for all $\xi \Leftrightarrow \mathfrak{x} \in k$.*

Proof. Since k^* is the character group of the compact factor group V mod k, k^* is discrete. k^* contains k according to the preceding lemma, and therefore we may consider the factor group k^* mod k. As discrete subgroup of the compact group V mod k, k^* mod k is a finite group. But since it is *a priori* clear that k^* is a vector space over k, and since k is not a finite field, the index $(k^* : k)$ cannot be finite unless it is 1.

4.2. *Riemann–Roch Theorem*

We shall call a function $\varphi(\mathfrak{x})$ periodic if $\varphi(\mathfrak{x}+\xi) = \varphi(\mathfrak{x})$ for all $\xi \in k$. The periodic functions represent in a natural way all functions on the compact factor group V mod k. $\varphi(\mathfrak{x})$ represents a continuous function on V mod k if and only if it is itself continuous on V.

LEMMA 4.2.1. *If $\varphi(\mathfrak{x})$ is continuous and periodic, then $\int_D \varphi(\mathfrak{x})\, d\mathfrak{x}$ is equal to:*

the integral over the factor group V mod k of the function on that group which $\varphi(\mathfrak{x})$ represents with respect to that Haar measure on V mod k which gives the whole group V mod k the measure 1.

Proof. Define $I(\varphi) = \int_D \varphi(\mathfrak{x})\, d\mathfrak{x}$ and consider it as functional on $L(V \bmod k)$. Observe that it has the properties characterizing the Haar integral. (To

† Here k^* is the dual of k, not the multiplicative group of k (!).

check invariance under translation merely requires breaking D up into a disjoint sum of its intersections with a translation of itself.) The functional is normed to 1 because $\int_D d\mathfrak{x} = 1$.

k is naturally the character group of V mod k in view of Theorem 4.1.4. The Fourier transform, $\phi(\xi)$, of the continuous function on V mod k which is represented by $\varphi(\mathfrak{x})$ is

$$\phi(\xi) = \int_D \varphi(\mathfrak{x})\, e^{-2\pi i\Lambda(\xi\mathfrak{x})}\, d\mathfrak{x}.$$

LEMMA 4.2.2. *If $\varphi(\mathfrak{x})$ is continuous and periodic and $\sum_{\xi\in k} |\phi(\xi)| < \infty$, then*

$$\varphi(\mathfrak{x}) = \sum_{\xi\in k} \phi(\xi)\, e^{2\pi i\Lambda(\mathfrak{x}\xi)}.$$

Proof. The hypothesis $\sum_{\xi\in k} |\phi(\xi)| < \infty$ means that the Fourier transform $\phi(\xi)$ is summable on k, guaranteeing that the inversion formula holds. The asserted equality is simply the inversion formula explicitly written out.

LEMMA 4.2.3. *If $f(\mathfrak{x})$ is continuous, $\in L_1(V)$, and $\sum_{\eta\in k} f(\mathfrak{x}+\eta)$ is uniformly convergent for $\mathfrak{x}\in D$ (convergence means absolute convergence because k is not ordered in any way), then for the resulting continuous periodic function $\varphi(\mathfrak{x}) = \sum_{\eta\in k} f(\mathfrak{x}+\eta)$ we have $\phi(\xi) = \hat{f}(\xi)$.*

Proof.

$$\begin{aligned}\phi(\xi) &= \int_D \varphi(\mathfrak{x})\, e^{-2\pi i\Lambda(\xi\mathfrak{x})}\, d\mathfrak{x}\\ &= \int_D \Big(\sum_{\eta\in k} f(\mathfrak{x}+\eta)\, e^{-2\pi i\Lambda(\mathfrak{x}\xi)}\Big) d\mathfrak{x}\\ &= \sum_{\eta\in k} \int_D f(\mathfrak{x}+\eta)\, e^{-2\pi i\Lambda(\mathfrak{x}\xi)}\, d\mathfrak{x}\end{aligned}$$

(The interchange is justified because we assumed the convergence to be uniform on D, and D has finite measure.)

$$\begin{aligned}&= \sum_{\eta\in k} \int_{\eta+D} f(\mathfrak{x})\, e^{-2\pi i\Lambda(\mathfrak{x}\xi-\eta\xi)}\, d\mathfrak{x}\\ &= \sum_{\eta\in k} \int_{\eta+D} f(\mathfrak{x})\, e^{-2\pi i\Lambda(\mathfrak{x}\xi)}\, d\mathfrak{x}\end{aligned}$$

(since $\Lambda(\eta\xi) = 0$)

$$\begin{aligned}&= \int f(\mathfrak{x})\, e^{-2\pi i\Lambda(\mathfrak{x}\xi)}\, d\mathfrak{x}\\ &= \hat{f}(\xi).\end{aligned}$$

Combining the last two Lemmas 4.2.2. and 4.2.3, and putting $\mathfrak{x} = 0$ in the assertion of Lemma 4.2.2 we obtain

LEMMA 4.2.4. (Poisson Formula.) *If* $f(\mathfrak{x})$ *satisfies the conditions:*

(1) $f(\mathfrak{x})$ *continuous*, $\in L_1(V)$;

(2) $\sum_{\xi \in k} f(\mathfrak{x}+\xi)$ *uniformly convergent for* $\mathfrak{x} \in D$;

(3) $\sum_{\xi \in k} |\hat{f}(\xi)|$ *convergent*;

then

$$\sum_{\xi \in k} \hat{f}(\xi) = \sum_{\xi \in k} f(\xi).$$

If we replace $f(\mathfrak{x})$ by $f(\mathfrak{a}\mathfrak{x})$ ($\mathfrak{a}$ an idèle) we obtain a theorem which may be looked upon as the number theoretic analogue of the Riemann–Roch theorem.

THEOREM 4.2.1. (Riemann–Roch Theorem.) *If* $f(\mathfrak{x})$ *satisfies the conditions:*

(1) $f(\mathfrak{x})$ *continuous*, $\in L_1(V)$;

(2) $\sum_{\xi \in k} f(\mathfrak{a}(\mathfrak{x}+\xi))$ *convergent for all idèles* $\mathfrak{a}$ *and valuation vectors* $\mathfrak{x}$, *uniformly for* $\mathfrak{x} \in D$;

(3) $\sum_{\xi \in k} |\hat{f}(\mathfrak{a}\xi)|$ *convergent for all idèles* $\mathfrak{a}$

then

$$\frac{1}{|\mathfrak{a}|} \sum_{\xi \in k} \hat{f}(\xi/\mathfrak{a}) = \sum_{\xi \in k} f(\mathfrak{a}\xi).$$

Proof. The function $g(\mathfrak{x}) = f(\mathfrak{a}\mathfrak{x})$ satisfies the conditions of the preceding lemma because

$$\hat{g}(\mathfrak{x}) = \int f(\mathfrak{a}\mathfrak{y})\, e^{-2\pi i \Lambda(\mathfrak{x}\mathfrak{y})}\, d\mathfrak{y}$$

$$= \frac{1}{|\mathfrak{a}|} \int f(\mathfrak{y})\, e^{-2\pi i \Lambda(\mathfrak{x}\mathfrak{y}/\mathfrak{a})}\, d\mathfrak{y}.$$

(Under the transformation $\mathfrak{y} \to \mathfrak{y}/\mathfrak{a}$, $d\mathfrak{y} \to (1/|\mathfrak{a}|)\, d\mathfrak{y}$.)

$$= \frac{1}{|\mathfrak{a}|} \hat{f}(\mathfrak{x}/\mathfrak{a}).$$

We may therefore conclude

$$\sum_{\xi \in k} \hat{g}(\xi) = \sum_{\xi \in k} g(\xi);$$

that is,

$$\frac{1}{|\mathfrak{a}|} \sum_{\xi \in k} \hat{f}(\xi/\mathfrak{a}) = \sum_{\xi \in k} f(\mathfrak{a}\xi).$$

It is amusing to remark that, had we never bothered to compute the exact measure of D, we would now know it is 1. For we could have carried out all the arguments of this section with an unknown measure, say $\mu(D)$, of D.

The only change would be that in order to have the inversion formula of Lemma 4.2.2 we would have to have given each element of k the weight $1/\mu(D)$. The Poisson Formula would then have read,

$$\frac{1}{\mu(D)}\sum_{\xi \in k} \hat{f}(\xi) = \sum_{\xi \in k} f(\xi).$$

Iteration of this would yield $(\mu(D))^2 = 1$, therefore $\mu(D) = 1$!

4.3. *Multiplicative Theory*

In this section we shall discuss the basic features of the multiplicative group of idèles.

DEFINITION 4.3.1. *The multiplicative group, I, of idèles is the restricted direct product of the groups $k_{\mathfrak{p}}^*$ relative to the subgroups $u_{\mathfrak{p}}$.*

We shall denote the generic idèle by $\mathfrak{a} = (\ldots, \mathfrak{a}_{\mathfrak{p}}, \ldots)$. The name idèle is explained (at least partly explained!) by the fact that the idèle group may be considered as a refinement of the ideal group of k. For if we associate with an idèle $\mathfrak{a}$ the ideal $\varphi(\mathfrak{a}) = \prod_{\mathfrak{p} \notin S_\infty} \mathfrak{p}^{\text{ord}_{\mathfrak{p}} \mathfrak{a}_{\mathfrak{p}}}$, then the map $\mathfrak{a} \to \varphi(\mathfrak{a})$ is obviously a continuous homomorphism of the idèle group onto the discrete group of ideals of k. Since the kernel of this homomorphism is I_{S_∞}, we may say that an idèle is a refinement of an ideal in two ways. First, the archimedean primes figure in its make-up, and second, it takes into account the units at the discrete primes.

Concerning quasi-characters of I, we can only state, according to Section 3.2, that the general quasi-character $c(\mathfrak{a})$ is of the form $c(\mathfrak{a}) = \prod_{\mathfrak{p}} c_{\mathfrak{p}}(\mathfrak{a}_{\mathfrak{p}})$, where $c_{\mathfrak{p}}(\mathfrak{a}_{\mathfrak{p}})$ is a local quasi-character (described in Section 2.3) and $c_{\mathfrak{p}}(\mathfrak{a}_{\mathfrak{p}})$ is unramified at almost all $\mathfrak{p}$.

For a measure, $d\mathfrak{a}$, on I we shall of course choose $d\mathfrak{a} = \prod_{\mathfrak{p}} d\mathfrak{a}_{\mathfrak{p}}$, the $d\mathfrak{a}_{\mathfrak{p}}$ being the local multiplicative measure defined in Section 2.3.

We can do nothing really significant with the idèle group until we imbed the multiplicative group k^* of k in it, by identifying the element $\alpha \in k^*$ with the idèle $\alpha = (\alpha, \alpha, \ldots, \alpha, \ldots)$. Throughout the remainder of this section our discussion will center about the structure of I relative to the subgroup k^*. The first fact to notice is that the ideal $\varphi(\alpha)$ associated with an idèle $\alpha \in k^*$ is the principal ideal $\alpha\mathfrak{o}$ generated by α, as it should be. Next we have the "product formula" for elements $\alpha \in k^*$. Though this is well known, we state it formally in a theorem in order to present an amusing proof.

THEOREM 4.3.1. $|\alpha| \left(= \prod_{\mathfrak{p}} |\alpha|_{\mathfrak{p}}\right) = 1$ *for* $\alpha \in k^*$.

Proof. According to Lemma 4.1.2 the (additive) measure of αD is $|\alpha|$ times the measure of D. Since $\alpha k^+ = k^+$, αD would serve as additive fundamental domain just as well as D. From this it is intuitively clear that αD has the same measure as D and therefore $|\alpha| = 1$. To make a formal proof one has simply to chop up D and αD into congruent pieces of the form $D \cap (\xi + \alpha D)$ and $(-\xi + D) \cap \alpha D$ respectively, ξ running through k.

This theorem reminds us to mention explicitly the continuous homomorphism $\mathfrak{a} \to |\mathfrak{a}| = \prod_{\mathfrak{p}} |\mathfrak{a}|_{\mathfrak{p}}$ of I onto the multiplicative group of positive real numbers. The kernel is a closed subgroup of I which will play an important role. We denote this subgroup by J, and its generic element (idèle of absolute value 1) by $\mathfrak{b}$.

It will be convenient (although it is aesthetically disturbing and not really necessary) to select arbitrarily a subgroup T of I with which we can write $I = T \times J$ (direct product). To this effect we choose at random one of the archimedean primes of k—call it $\mathfrak{p}_0$—and let T be the subgroup of all idèles $\mathfrak{a}$ such that $\mathfrak{a}_{\mathfrak{p}_0} > 0$ and $\mathfrak{a}_{\mathfrak{p}} = 1$ for $\mathfrak{p} \neq \mathfrak{p}_0$. Such an idèle is obviously uniquely determined by its absolute value; indeed the map $\mathfrak{a} \to |\mathfrak{a}|$, restricted to T, is an isomorphism between T and the multiplicative group of positive real numbers, and it will cause no confusion if we denote an idèle of T simply by the real number which is its absolute value. Thus a real number $t > 0$ also stands either for the idèle $(t, 1, 1, \ldots)$ or for the idèle $(\sqrt{t}, 1, 1, \ldots)$, according to whether $\mathfrak{p}_0$ is real or complex, if we write the $\mathfrak{p}_0$-component first. Since we can write any idèle $\mathfrak{a}$ uniquely in the form $\mathfrak{a} = |\mathfrak{a}|.\mathfrak{b}$ with $|\mathfrak{a}| \in T$ and $\mathfrak{b} = \mathfrak{a}|\mathfrak{a}|^{-1} \in J$, it is clear that $I = T \times J$ (direct product).

In order to select a fixed measure $d\mathfrak{b}$ on J we take on T the measure $\mathrm{d}t = dt/t$ and require $d\mathfrak{a} = \mathrm{d}t.d\mathfrak{b}$. Then for computational purposes we have (in the sense of Fubini) the formulas

$$\int_I f(\mathfrak{a})\, d\mathfrak{a} = \int_0^\infty \left[\int_J f(t\mathfrak{b})\, d\mathfrak{b} \right] \frac{dt}{t} = \int_J \left[\int_0^\infty f(t\mathfrak{b}) \frac{dt}{t} \right] d\mathfrak{b}$$

for a summable idèle function $f(\mathfrak{a})$.

The product formula means that $k^* \subset J$, and we wish now to describe a "fundamental domain" for J mod k^*. The mapping of idèles onto ideals allows us to descend to the subgroup $J_{S_\infty} = J \cap I_{S_\infty}$. To study J_{S_∞} we map the idèles $\mathfrak{b} \in J_{S_\infty}$ onto vectors $l(\mathfrak{b}) = (\ldots, \log |\mathfrak{b}|_{\mathfrak{p}}, \ldots)_{\mathfrak{p} \in S'_\infty}$ having one component, $\log |\mathfrak{b}|_{\mathfrak{p}}$ for each archimedean prime except $\mathfrak{p}_0$. (This set of $r = r_1 + r_2 - 1$ primes is denoted by S'_∞.) It is obvious that the map $\mathfrak{b} \to l(\mathfrak{b})$ is a continuous homomorphism of J_{S_∞} onto the additive group of the Euclidean r-space. The onto-ness results from the fact that although the infinite components of an idèle $\mathfrak{b} \in J_{S_\infty}$ are constrained by the condition $\prod_{\mathfrak{p}} |\mathfrak{b}|_{\mathfrak{p}} = \prod_{\mathfrak{p} \in S_\infty} |\mathfrak{b}|_{\mathfrak{p}} = 1$, they are completely free in the set S'_∞ since we can adjust the $\mathfrak{p}_0$ component.

$k^* \cap J_{S_\infty}$ is the group of all elements $\varepsilon \in k^*$ which are units at all finite primes; that is, which are units of the ring $\mathfrak{o}$. The units ζ for which $l(\zeta) = 0$ are the roots of unity in k and form a finite cyclic group. It is proved classically that the group of units ε, modulo the group of roots of unity ζ, is a free abelian group on r generators. This proof is effected by showing that the images $l(\varepsilon)$ of units form a lattice of highest dimension in the r-space.

If, therefore, $\{\varepsilon_i\}_{1 \leq i \leq r}$ is a basis for the group of units modulo roots of unity, the vectors $l(\varepsilon_i)$ are a basis for the r-space over the real numbers and we may write for any $\mathfrak{b} \in J_{S_\infty}$,

$$l(\mathfrak{b}) = \sum_{\nu=1}^{r} x_\nu l(\varepsilon_\nu),$$

with unique real numbers x_ν. Call P the parallelotope in the R-space spanned by the vectors $l(\varepsilon_i)$; that is, the set of all vectors $\sum_{\nu=1}^{r} x_\nu l(\varepsilon_\nu)$ with $0 \leq x_\nu < 1$. Call Q the "unit cube" in the r-space; that is the set of all vectors $(\ldots, x_\mathfrak{p}, \ldots)_{\mathfrak{p} \in S'_\infty}$ with $0 \leq x_\mathfrak{p} < 1$.

LEMMA 4.3.1.

$$\int_{l^{-1}(P)} d\mathfrak{b} = \frac{2^{r_1}(2\pi)^{r_2}}{\sqrt{|d|}} R,$$

where $l^{-1}(P)$ is the set of all $\mathfrak{b} \in J_{S_\infty}$ such that $l(\mathfrak{b}) \in P$, and

$$R = \pm \det (\log |\varepsilon_i|_\mathfrak{p})_{\substack{1 \leq i \leq r \\ \mathfrak{p} \in S'_\infty}}$$

is the regulator of k.

Proof. Because l is a homomorphism,

$$\frac{\text{measure of } l^{-1}(P)}{\text{measure of } l^{-1}(Q)} = \frac{\text{volume of } P}{\text{volume of } Q} = \pm \det (\log |\varepsilon_i|_\mathfrak{p}) = R,$$

and we have only to show

$$\int_{l^{-1}(Q)} d\mathfrak{b} = \frac{2^{r_1}(2\pi)^{r_2}}{\sqrt{|d|}}.$$

$l^{-1}(Q)$ is the set of all $\mathfrak{b} \in J_{S_\infty}$ with $1 \leq |\mathfrak{b}|_\mathfrak{p} < e$ for $\mathfrak{p} \in S'_\infty$. Let Q^* be the set of all $\mathfrak{a} \in I_{S_\infty}$ with $1 \leq |\mathfrak{a}|_\mathfrak{p} < e$ for $\mathfrak{p} \in S_\infty$. Then

$$\int_{Q^*} d\mathfrak{a} = \int_J \left[\int_{t\mathfrak{b} \in Q^*} \frac{dt}{t} \right] d\mathfrak{b} = \int_{l^{-}(Q)} \left[\int_{|\mathfrak{b}|_{\mathfrak{p}_0}^{-1}}^{e|\mathfrak{b}|_{\mathfrak{p}_0}^{-1}} \frac{dt}{t} \right] d\mathfrak{b} = \int_{l^{-1}(Q)} d\mathfrak{b},$$

because $t\mathfrak{b} \in Q^* \Leftrightarrow \mathfrak{b} \in l^{-1}(Q)$ and $1 \leq |t\mathfrak{b}|_{\mathfrak{p}_0} < e$. We have therefore only to show that

$$\int_{Q^*} d\mathfrak{a} = \frac{2^{r_1}(2\pi)^{r_2}}{\sqrt{|d|}}.$$

Write Q^* as the cartesian product $Q^* = \prod_{\mathfrak{p} \in S_\infty} Q_\mathfrak{p}^* \times I^{S_\infty}$, where $Q_\mathfrak{p}^*$ is the set of all $\mathfrak{a}_\mathfrak{p} \in k_\mathfrak{p}^*$ such that $1 \leq |\mathfrak{a}_\mathfrak{p}|_\mathfrak{p} < e$, for $\mathfrak{p} \in S_\infty$. Then

$$\int_{Q^*} d\mathfrak{a} = \prod_{\mathfrak{p} \in S_\infty} \int_{Q_\mathfrak{p}^*} d\mathfrak{a}_\mathfrak{p} \cdot \int_{I^{S_\infty}} d\mathfrak{a}^{S_\infty} = \frac{2^{r_1}(2\pi)^{r_2}}{\sqrt{|d|}},$$

because for $\mathfrak{p}$ real,

$$\int_{Q^*} d\mathfrak{a}_\mathfrak{p} = \left[\int_{-e}^{-1} + \int_{1}^{e}\right] \frac{dx}{|x|} = 2\int_1^e \frac{dx}{x} = 2,$$

for $\mathfrak{p}$ complex,

$$\int_{Q_\mathfrak{p}^*} d\mathfrak{a}_\mathfrak{p} = \int_0^{2\pi} \int_1^{\sqrt{e}} \frac{2\,dr\,d\theta}{r} = 2\pi,$$

and

$$\int_{I^{S_\infty}} d\mathfrak{a}^{S_\infty} = \prod_{\mathfrak{p} \notin S_\infty} \int_{\mathfrak{u}_\mathfrak{p}} d\mathfrak{a}_\mathfrak{p} = \prod_{\mathfrak{p} \notin S_\infty} (\mathcal{N}_\mathfrak{p} \mathfrak{d}_\mathfrak{p})^{-\frac{1}{2}} = \frac{1}{\sqrt{|d|}}.$$

DEFINITION 4.3.2. *Let h be the class number of k, and select idèles $\mathfrak{b}^{(1)}, \ldots, \mathfrak{b}^{(h)} \in J$ such that the corresponding ideals $\varphi(\mathfrak{b}^{(1)}), \ldots, \varphi(\mathfrak{b}^{(h)})$ represent the different ideal classes. Let w be the number of roots of unity in k. Let E_0 be the subset of all $\mathfrak{b} \in l^{-1}(P)$ (see preceding lemma) such that $0 \leq \arg \mathfrak{b}_{\mathfrak{p}_0} < \dfrac{2\pi}{w}$. We define the multiplicative fundamental domain, E, for $J \bmod k^*$ to be*

$$E = E_0\mathfrak{b}^{(1)} \cup E_0\mathfrak{b}^{(2)} \cup \ldots \cup E_0\mathfrak{b}^{(h)}.$$

THEOREM 4.3.2. (1) $J = \bigcup_\alpha \alpha E$, *a disjoint union.*

(2) $\displaystyle\int_E d\mathfrak{b} = \frac{2^{r_1}(2\pi)^{r_2} hR}{\sqrt{|d|}\, w}$.

Proof. (1) Starting with any idèle $\mathfrak{b} \in J$ we can change it into an idèle which represents a principal ideal by dividing it by a uniquely determined $\mathfrak{b}^{(i)}$. If this principal ideal is $\alpha\mathfrak{o}$ (α uniquely determined modulo units), multiplication by α^{-1} brings us to an idèle of J representing the ideal $\mathfrak{o}$—therefore into J_{S_∞}. Once in J_{S_∞} we can find a unique power product of the fundamental units ε_i which lands us in $l^{-1}(P)$, with only a root of unity, ζ, at our disposal. This ζ is exactly what we need to adjust the argument of the $\mathfrak{p}_0$ component to be in the interval $\left(0, \dfrac{2\pi}{w}\right)$. Lo and behold we are in E_0! For our original idèle $\mathfrak{b}$ we have found a unique $\beta \in k^*$ and a unique $\mathfrak{b}^{(i)}$ such that $\mathfrak{b} \in \beta\mathfrak{b}^{(i)}E_0$.

(2) (measure E) $= h$. (measure E_0) $= \frac{h}{w}$. (measure $l^{-1}(P)$) $= \frac{2^{r_1}(2\pi)^{r_2}hR}{\sqrt{|d|}w}$

according to the two disjoint decompositions

$$E = \bigcup_{\nu=1}^{h} \mathfrak{b}^{(\nu)}E_0, \qquad l^{-1}(P) = \bigcup_{\zeta} \zeta E_0$$

and the preceding lemma.

COROLLARY 4.3.1. *k^* is a discrete subgroup of J (therefore of I). J mod k^* is compact.*

Proof. One sees easily that E has an interior in J. On the other hand, E is contained in a compact.

We shall really be interested not in all quasi-characters of I, but only in those which are trivial on k^*. From now on when we use the word quasi-character we mean one of this type. Let us close our introduction to the idèle group with a few remarks about these quasi-characters.

The first thing to notice is that on the subgroup J, a quasi-character is a character; i.e. $|c(\mathfrak{b})| = 1$ for all $\mathfrak{b} \in J$, because J mod k^* is compact.

Next we mention that the quasi-characters which are trivial on J are exactly those of the form $c(\mathfrak{a}) = |\mathfrak{a}|^s$, where s is a complex number uniquely determined by $c(\mathfrak{a})$. For if $c(\mathfrak{a})$ is trivial on J, then $c(\mathfrak{a})$ depends only on $|\mathfrak{a}|$, and in this dependence is a continuous multiplicative map of the positive real numbers into the complex numbers. Such a map is of the form $t \to t^s$ as is well known.

To each quasi-character $c(\mathfrak{a})$ there exists a unique real number σ such that $|c(\mathfrak{a})| = |\mathfrak{a}|^\sigma$. Namely, $|c(\mathfrak{a})|$ is a quasi-character which is trivial on J. Therefore $|c(\mathfrak{a})| = |\mathfrak{a}|^s$, for some complex s. Since $|c(\mathfrak{a})| > 0$, s is real. We call σ the exponent of c. A quasi-character is a character if and only if its exponent is 0.

4.4. *The ζ-Functions; Functional Equation*

In this section $f(\mathfrak{x})$ will denote a complex-valued function of valuation vectors; $f(\mathfrak{a})$ its restriction to idèles. We let $\mathfrak{z}$ denote the class of all functions $f(\mathfrak{x})$ satisfying the three conditions:

($\mathfrak{z}_1$) $f(\mathfrak{x})$, and $\hat{f}(\mathfrak{x})$ are continuous, $\in L_1(V)$; i.e. $f(\mathfrak{x}) \in \mathfrak{B}_1(V)$.

($\mathfrak{z}_2$) $\sum_{\xi \in k} f(\mathfrak{a}(\mathfrak{x}+\xi))$ and $\sum_{\xi \in k} \hat{f}(\mathfrak{a}(\mathfrak{x}+\xi))$ are both convergent for each idèle $\mathfrak{a}$ and vector $\mathfrak{x}$, the convergence being uniform in the pair $(\mathfrak{a}, \mathfrak{x})$ for $\mathfrak{x}$ ranging over D and $\mathfrak{a}$ ranging over any fixed compact subset of I.

($\mathfrak{z}_3$) $f(\mathfrak{a}).|\mathfrak{a}|^\sigma$ and $\hat{f}(\mathfrak{a})|\mathfrak{a}|^\sigma \in L_1(I)$ for $\sigma > 1$.

(Notice that if $f(\mathfrak{x})$ is continuous on V, then, *a fortiori*, $f(\mathfrak{a})$ is continuous on I, since the topology we have adopted in I is stronger than that which I would get as subspace of V.)

In view of $(\mathfrak{z}_1)$ and $(\mathfrak{z}_2)$, the Riemann–Roch theorem is valid for functions of $\mathfrak{z}$. The purpose of $(\mathfrak{z}_3)$ is to enable us to define ζ-functions with them:

DEFINITION 4.4.1. *We associate with each $f \in \mathfrak{z}$ a function $\zeta(f, c)$ of quasi-characters, defined for all quasi-characters c of exponent greater than* 1 *by*

$$\zeta(f, c) = \int f(\mathfrak{a})c(\mathfrak{a})\, d\mathfrak{a}.$$

We call such a function a ζ-function of k.

Remember that we are now considering only those quasi-characters which are trivial on k^*. These were discussed at the end of the preceding section, where the notion "exponent" is explained. If we call two quasi-characters which coincide on J equivalent, then an equivalence class of quasi-characters consists of all quasi-characters of the form $c(\mathfrak{a}) = c_0(\mathfrak{a})|\mathfrak{a}|^s$, where $c_0(\mathfrak{a})$ is a fixed representative of the class and s is a complex number uniquely determined by c. Such a parametrization by the complex variable s allows us to view an equivalence class of quasi-characters as a Riemann surface, just as we did in the local theory (cf. Section 2.4). It is obvious from their definition as an integral that the ζ-functions are regular in the domain of all quasi-characters of exponent greater than 1 (see the corresponding local lemma). What about analytic continuation???

MAIN THEOREM 4.4.1. (Analytic Continuation and Functional Equation of the ζ-Functions.) *By analytic continuation we may extend the definition of any ζ-function $\zeta(f, c)$ to the domain of all quasi-characters. The extended function is single valued and regular, except at $c(\mathfrak{a}) = 1$ and $c(\mathfrak{a}) = |\mathfrak{a}|$ where it has simple poles with residues $-\kappa f(0)$ and $+\kappa \hat{f}(0)$, respectively ($\kappa = 2^{r_1}(2\pi)^{r_2}hR/(\sqrt{|d|}w)$ = volume of the multiplicative fundamental domain). $\zeta(f, c)$ satisfies the functional equation*

$$\zeta(f, c) = \zeta(\hat{f}, \hat{c}),$$

where $\hat{c}(\mathfrak{a}) = |\mathfrak{a}|c^{-1}(\mathfrak{a})$ as in the local theory.

Proof. For c of exponent greater than 1 we have

$$\zeta(f, c) = \int f(\mathfrak{a})c(\mathfrak{a})\, d\mathfrak{a} = \int_0^\infty \left[\int_J f(t\mathfrak{b})c(t\mathfrak{b})\, d\mathfrak{b}\right] \frac{dt}{t} = \int_0^\infty \zeta_t(f, c)\frac{dt}{t}, \quad \text{say.}$$

Here

$$\zeta_t(f, c) = \int_J f(t\mathfrak{b})c(t\mathfrak{b})\, d\mathfrak{b}$$

is absolutely convergent for c of any exponent, at least for almost all t, because it is convergent for some c, and $|c(t\mathfrak{b})| = t$ exponent c is constant for $\mathfrak{b} \in J$. The essential step in our proof consists in using the Riemann–Roch theorem to establish a functional equation for $\zeta_t(f, c)$:

LEMMA A. *For all quasi-characters c we have*

$$\zeta_t(f, c)+f(0)\int_E c(t\mathfrak{b})\,d\mathfrak{b} = \zeta_{1/t}(\hat{f}, \hat{c})+\hat{f}(0)\int_E \hat{c}\left(\frac{1}{t}\mathfrak{b}\right)d\mathfrak{b}.$$

Proof.

$$\zeta_t(f, c)+f(0)\int_E c(t\mathfrak{b})\,d\mathfrak{b} = \sum_{\alpha\in k^*}\int_{\alpha E} f(t\mathfrak{b})c(t\mathfrak{b})\,d\mathfrak{b}+f(0)\int_E c(t\mathfrak{b})\,d\mathfrak{b}$$

(Because $J = \cup_\alpha \alpha E$, a disjoint union)

$$= \sum_{\alpha\in k^*}\int_{E} f(\alpha t\mathfrak{b})c(t\mathfrak{b})\,d\mathfrak{b}+f(0)\int_E c(t\mathfrak{b})\,d\mathfrak{b}$$

($d(\alpha\mathfrak{b}) = d\mathfrak{b}$; $c(\alpha t\mathfrak{b}) = c(t\mathfrak{b})$)

$$= \int_E \Big[\sum_{\alpha\in k^*} f(\alpha t\mathfrak{b})\Big]c(t\mathfrak{b})\,d\mathfrak{b} + \int_E f(0)c(t\mathfrak{b})\,d\mathfrak{b}.$$

(By hypothesis ($\mathfrak{z}_2$) for f, the sum is uniformly convergent for $\mathfrak{b}$ in the relatively compact subset E)

$$= \int_E \Big[\sum_{\xi\in k} f(\xi t\mathfrak{b})\Big]c(t\mathfrak{b})\,d\mathfrak{b}$$

$$= \int_E \Big[\sum_{\xi\in k} \hat{f}\left(\frac{\xi}{t\mathfrak{b}}\right)\Big]\frac{1}{|t\mathfrak{b}|}\,c(t\mathfrak{b})\,d\mathfrak{b}$$

(Riemann–Roch theorem 4.2.1)

$$= \int_E \Big[\sum_{\xi\in k} \hat{f}\left(\xi\frac{1}{t}\mathfrak{b}\right)\Big]\hat{c}\left(\frac{1}{t}\mathfrak{b}\right)d\mathfrak{b}$$

($\mathfrak{b}\to 1/\mathfrak{b}$; $d\mathfrak{b}\to d\mathfrak{b}$).

Reversing the steps completes the proof.

LEMMA B.

$$\int_E c(t\mathfrak{b})\,d\mathfrak{b} = \begin{cases}\kappa t^s, & \text{if } c(\mathfrak{a}) = |\mathfrak{a}|^s\\ 0, & \text{if } c(\mathfrak{a}) \text{ is non trivial on } J.\end{cases}$$

Proof.

$$\int_E c(t\mathfrak{b})\,d\mathfrak{b} = c(t)\int_E c(\mathfrak{b})\,d\mathfrak{b}.$$

Here $\int_E c(\mathfrak{b})\,d\mathfrak{b}$ is the integral over the factor group J mod k^* of the character of this group which $c(\mathfrak{b})$ represents. Therefore it is either κ (= measure of E), or 0, according to whether $c(\mathfrak{a})$ is trivial on J or not. In the former case we must notice that $c(t) = |t|^s = t^s$.

To prove the theorem write, for c of exponent greater than 1,

$$\zeta(f, c) = \int_0^\infty \zeta_t(f, c)\frac{dt}{t} = \int_0^1 \zeta_t(f, c)\frac{dt}{t} + \int_1^\infty \zeta_t(f, c)\frac{dt}{t}.$$

The $\int_1^\infty$ is no problem. For it is equal to the integral of $f(\mathfrak{a})\,c(\mathfrak{a})\,d\mathfrak{a}$ over that half of I where $|\mathfrak{a}| \geq 1$. Therefore it converges the better, the less the exponent of c is; and since it converges for c of exponent greater than 1, it must converge for all c. Now, the point is that we can use Lemma A (and the auxiliary Lemma B) to transform the $\int_0^1$ into an $\int_1^\infty$, thereby obtaining an analytic expression for $\zeta(f, c)$ which will be good for all c. Namely:

$$\int_0^1 \zeta_t(f, c)\frac{dt}{t} = \int_0^1 \zeta_{1/t}(\hat{f}, \hat{c})\frac{dt}{t} + \left\{\left\{\int_0^1 \kappa\hat{f}(0)\left(\frac{1}{t}\right)^{1-s}\frac{dt}{t} - \int_0^1 \kappa f(0)t^s\frac{dt}{t}\right\}\right\},$$

where the expression $\{\{\ldots\}\}$ is to be included only if c is trivial on J, in which case we assume $c(\mathfrak{a}) = |\mathfrak{a}|^s$. We are still looking only at c of exponent greater than 1. If $c(\mathfrak{a}) = |\mathfrak{a}|^s$ this means $\operatorname{Re}(s) > 1$, which is just what is needed for the auxiliary integrals under the double bracket to make sense. Evaluating them and making the substitution $t \to 1/t$ in the main part of the expression we obtain

$$\int_0^1 \zeta_t(f, c)\frac{dt}{t} = \int_1^\infty \zeta_t(\hat{f}, \hat{c})\frac{dt}{t} + \left\{\left\{\frac{\kappa\hat{f}(0)}{s-1} - \frac{\kappa f(0)}{s}\right\}\right\},$$

and therefore

$$\zeta(f, c) = \int_1^\infty \zeta_t(f, c)\frac{dt}{t} + \int_1^\infty \zeta_t(\hat{f}, \hat{c})\frac{dt}{t} + \left\{\left\{\frac{\kappa\hat{f}(0)}{s-1} - \frac{\kappa f(0)}{s}\right\}\right\}.$$

The two integrals are analytic for all c. This expression gives therefore the analytic continuation of $\zeta(f, c)$ to the domain of all quasi-characters. From it we can read off the poles and residues directly. Noticing that for $c(\mathfrak{a}) = |\mathfrak{a}|^s$, $\hat{c}(\mathfrak{a}) = |\mathfrak{a}|^{1-s}$, we see that even the form of the expression is unchanged by the substitution $(f, c) \to (\hat{f}, \hat{c})$. Therefore the functional equation

$$\zeta(f, c) = \zeta(\hat{f}, \hat{c})$$

holds. The Main Theorem is proved!

4.5. *Comparison with the Classical Theory*

We will now show that our theory is not without content, inasmuch as there do exist non-trivial ζ-functions. In fact we shall exhibit for each equivalence class C of quasi-characters an explicit function $f \in \mathfrak{z}$ such that the corresponding ζ-function $\zeta(f, c)$ is non-trivial on C. These special ζ-functions will turn out to be, essentially, the classical ζ-functions and L-series. The analytic continuation and the functional equation for our ζ-functions will yield the same for the classical functions.

We can pattern our discussion after the computation of the special local ζ-functions in Section 2.5. There we treated the cases k real, k complex, and k $\mathfrak{p}$-adic. Now we treat the case

k in the large!

The Equivalence Classes of Quasi-Characters. According to a remark at the end of Section 4.3, each class of quasi-characters can be represented by a character. To describe the characters in detail, we will take an arbitrary, but fixed, finite set of primes, S (containing at least all archimedean primes) and discuss the characters which are unramified outside S. A character of this type is nothing more nor less than a product

$$c(\mathfrak{a}) = \prod_{\mathfrak{p}} c_{\mathfrak{p}}(\mathfrak{a}_{\mathfrak{p}})$$

of local characters, $c_{\mathfrak{p}}$, satisfying the two conditions

(1) $c_{\mathfrak{p}}$ unramified outside S.
(2) $\prod_{\mathfrak{p}} c_{\mathfrak{p}}(\alpha) = 1$, for $\alpha \in k^*$.

To construct such characters and express them in more concrete terms, we write for $\mathfrak{p} \in S$:

$$c_{\mathfrak{p}}(\mathfrak{a}_{\mathfrak{p}}) = \tilde{c}_{\mathfrak{p}}(\tilde{\mathfrak{a}}_{\mathfrak{p}})|\mathfrak{a}_{\mathfrak{p}}|_{\mathfrak{p}}^{it_{\mathfrak{p}}},$$

$\tilde{c}_{\mathfrak{p}}$ being a character of $u_{\mathfrak{p}}$, $t_{\mathfrak{p}}$ a real number (cf. Theorem 2.3.1). For $\mathfrak{p} \notin S$, we throw all the local characters together into a single character, say

$$c^*(\mathfrak{a}) = \prod_{\mathfrak{p} \notin S} c_{\mathfrak{p}}(\mathfrak{a}_{\mathfrak{p}}),$$

and interpret c^* as coming from an ideal character. Namely: The map

$$\mathfrak{a} \to \varphi_S(\mathfrak{a}) = \prod_{\mathfrak{p} \notin S} \mathfrak{p}^{\operatorname{ord}_{\mathfrak{p}}\mathfrak{a}}$$

is a homomorphism of the idèle group onto the multiplicative group of ideals prime to S. Its kernel is I_S. $c^*(\mathfrak{a})$ is identity on I_S. We have therefore

$$c^*(\mathfrak{a}) = \chi(\varphi_S(\mathfrak{a})),$$

where χ is some character of the group of ideals prime to S. Our character $c(\mathfrak{a})$ is now written in the form

$$c(\mathfrak{a}) = \prod_{\mathfrak{p} \in S} \tilde{c}_{\mathfrak{p}}(\tilde{\mathfrak{a}}_{\mathfrak{p}}) \cdot \prod_{\mathfrak{p} \in S} |\mathfrak{a}|_{\mathfrak{p}}^{it_{\mathfrak{p}}} \cdot \chi(\varphi_S(\mathfrak{a})).$$

To construct such characters we must select our $\tilde{c}_{\mathfrak{p}}$, $t_{\mathfrak{p}}$ and χ such that $c(\alpha) = 1$, for $\alpha \in k^*$. For this purpose we first look at the S-units, ε, of k, i.e. the elements of $k^* \cap I_S$, for which $\varphi_S(\varepsilon) = \mathfrak{o}$. Assume S contains $m+1$ primes; let ε_0 be a primitive root of unity in k, and let $\{\varepsilon_1, \varepsilon_2, \ldots, \varepsilon_m\}$ be a basis for the free abelian group of S-units modulo roots of unity. For $c(\mathfrak{a})$ to be trivial on the S-units it is then necessary and sufficient that $c(\varepsilon_\nu) = 1$, $0 \leq \nu \leq m$. The requirement $c(\varepsilon_0) = 1$ is simply a condition on the $\tilde{c}_\mathfrak{p}$:

$$\text{(A)} \qquad \prod_{\mathfrak{p} \in S} \tilde{c}_\mathfrak{p}(\varepsilon_0) = 1.$$

We therefore first select a set of $\tilde{c}_\mathfrak{p}$, for $\mathfrak{p} \in S$, which satisfies A. The requirements $c(\varepsilon_\nu) = 1$, $1 \leq \nu \leq m$, give conditions on the $t_\mathfrak{p}$:

$$\prod_{\mathfrak{p} \in S} |\varepsilon_\nu|_\mathfrak{p}^{it_\mathfrak{p}} = \prod_{\mathfrak{p} \in S} \tilde{c}_\mathfrak{p}^{-1}(\tilde{\varepsilon}_{\nu\mathfrak{p}}), \qquad 1 \leq \nu \leq m$$

which will be satisfied if and only if the numbers $t_\mathfrak{p}$ solve the real linear equations

$$\text{(B)} \qquad \sum_{\mathfrak{p} \in S} t_\mathfrak{p} \log |\varepsilon_\nu|_\mathfrak{p} = i \log \Big(\prod_{\mathfrak{p} \in S} \tilde{c}_\mathfrak{p}(\tilde{\varepsilon}_{\nu\mathfrak{p}}) \Big), \qquad 1 \leq \nu \leq m$$

for *some* value of the logarithms on the right-hand side. We now select a set of values for those logarithms and a set of numbers $t_\mathfrak{p}$ solving the resulting equations B. Since, as is well known, the rank of the matrix $(\log |\varepsilon_\nu|_\mathfrak{p})$ is m, there always exist solutions $t_\mathfrak{p}$. And since $\sum_{\mathfrak{p} \in S} \log |\varepsilon_\nu|_\mathfrak{p} = 0$ for all ν, the most general solution is then $t_\mathfrak{p} = t_\mathfrak{p} + t$, for any t. While we are on the subject of existence and uniqueness of the $t_\mathfrak{p}$ we may remind the reader that if $\mathfrak{p}$ is archimedean, different $t_\mathfrak{p}$ give different local characters $c_\mathfrak{p} = \tilde{c}_\mathfrak{p} ||_\mathfrak{p}^{it_\mathfrak{p}}$; but if $\mathfrak{p}$ is discrete, those $t_\mathfrak{p}$ which are congruent mod $2\pi/\log \mathcal{N}\mathfrak{p}$ give the same local $c_\mathfrak{p}$.

Having selected the $\tilde{c}_\mathfrak{p}$ and $t_\mathfrak{p}$, how much freedom is left for the ideal character χ? Not much. The requirement $c(\alpha) = 1$ for all $\alpha \in k^*$ means that χ must satisfy the condition

$$\text{(C)} \qquad \chi(\varphi_S(\alpha)) = \prod_{\mathfrak{p} \in S} \tilde{c}^{-1}(\tilde{\alpha}_\mathfrak{p}) |\alpha|_\mathfrak{p}^{-it_\mathfrak{p}}$$

for all ideals of the form $\varphi_S(\alpha)$, the ideals obtained from principal ideals by cancelling the powers of primes in S from their factorization. These ideals form a subgroup of finite index h_S (less than or equal to the class number h; $h_S = 1$ if S is large enough) in the group of all ideals prime to S. Since the multiplicative function of α on the right-hand side of condition (C) has been fixed up to be trivial on the S-units, it amounts to a character of this subgroup of ideals of the form $\varphi_S(\alpha)$. We must select χ to be one of the finite number h_S of extensions of this character to the group of all ideals prime to S.

The Corresponding Functions of $\mathfrak{z}$. Having selected a character

$$c(\mathfrak{a}) = \prod_{\mathfrak{p}} c_\mathfrak{p}(\mathfrak{a}_\mathfrak{p}) = \prod_{\mathfrak{p} \in S} \tilde{c}_\mathfrak{p}(\tilde{\mathfrak{a}}_\mathfrak{p}) |\mathfrak{a}|_\mathfrak{p}^{it_\mathfrak{p}} . \chi(\varphi_S(\mathfrak{a})),$$

unramified outside S, we wish to find a simple function $f(\mathfrak{x}) \in \mathfrak{z}$ whose ζ-function is non-trivial on the surface on which $c(\mathfrak{a})$ lies. To this effect we choose for each $\mathfrak{p} \in S$ some function $f_{\mathfrak{p}}(\mathfrak{x}_{\mathfrak{p}}) \in \mathfrak{z}_{\mathfrak{p}}$ whose (local) ζ-function is non-trivial on the surface on which $c_{\mathfrak{p}}$ lies (for instance select f to be the function used to compute $\rho_{\mathfrak{p}}(c_{\mathfrak{p}} \| \|_{\mathfrak{p}}^{s})$ in Section 2.5). For $\mathfrak{p} \notin S$, we let $f_{\mathfrak{p}}(\mathfrak{x}_{\mathfrak{p}})$ be the characteristic function of the set $\mathfrak{o}_{\mathfrak{p}}$. We then put

$$f(\mathfrak{x}) = \prod_{\mathfrak{p}} f_{\mathfrak{p}}(\mathfrak{x}_{\mathfrak{p}}).$$

(We will show in the course of our computations that the $f(\mathfrak{x})$ is in the class $\mathfrak{z}$.)

Their Fourier Transforms. According to Lemma 3.3.3,

$$\hat{f}(\mathfrak{x}) = \prod_{\mathfrak{p}} \hat{f}_{\mathfrak{p}}(\mathfrak{x}_{\mathfrak{p}}),$$

and moreover, $f \in \mathfrak{B}_1(V)$, i.e. f satisfies axiom ($\mathfrak{z}_1$). Notice that $\hat{f}(\mathfrak{x})$ is the same type of function as $f(\mathfrak{x})$, except for the fact that at those $\mathfrak{x} \notin S$ where $\mathfrak{d}_{\mathfrak{p}} \neq 1$, $f_{\mathfrak{p}}(\mathfrak{x}_{\mathfrak{p}})$ equals $N\mathfrak{d}_{\mathfrak{p}}^{-\frac{1}{2}}$ times the characteristic function of $\mathfrak{d}_{\mathfrak{p}}^{-1}$, rather than the characteristic function of $\mathfrak{o}_{\mathfrak{p}}$.

The ζ-Functions. Since $|f(\mathfrak{a})|\,|\mathfrak{a}|^{\sigma} = \prod_{\mathfrak{p}} |f_{\mathfrak{p}}(\mathfrak{a}_{\mathfrak{p}})|\,|\mathfrak{a}|_{\mathfrak{p}}^{\sigma}$ is a product of local functions, almost all of which are 1 on $u_{\mathfrak{p}}$, we may use Theorem 3.3.1 to check the summability of $|f(\mathfrak{a})|\,|\mathfrak{a}|^{\sigma}$ for $\sigma > 1$. A simple computation shows, for $\mathfrak{p} \notin S$,

$$\int_{k_{\mathfrak{p}}^{*}} |f_{\mathfrak{p}}(\mathfrak{a}_{\mathfrak{p}})|\,|\mathfrak{a}_{\mathfrak{p}}|_{\mathfrak{p}}^{\sigma}\, d\mathfrak{a}_{\mathfrak{p}} = \frac{\mathcal{N}\mathfrak{d}_{\mathfrak{p}}^{-\frac{1}{2}}}{1 - \mathcal{N}\mathfrak{p}^{-\sigma}}.$$

The summability follows therefore from the well-known fact that the product

$$\prod_{\mathfrak{p} \notin S_{\infty}} \frac{1}{1 - \mathcal{N}\mathfrak{p}^{-\sigma}}$$

is convergent for $\sigma > 1$. Well known as this fact is, it should be stressed that it is a keystone of the whole theory. The existence of our ζ-functions just as that of the classical functions, depends on it. It is proved by descending directly to the basic field of rational numbers (see, for example, E. Landau, "Algebraische Zahlen", 2nd edition, pages 55 and 56). Because $\hat{f}(\mathfrak{x})$ is the same type of function as $f(\mathfrak{x})$, we see that $|\hat{f}(\mathfrak{a})|\,|\mathfrak{a}|^{\sigma}$ is also summable for $\sigma > 1$. Therefore $f(\mathfrak{x})$ satisfies axiom ($\mathfrak{z}_3$).

Having established the summability, we can also use Theorem 3.3.1 to express the ζ-function as a product of local ζ-functions. Namely

$$\zeta(f, c) = \prod_{\mathfrak{p}} \zeta_{\mathfrak{p}}(f_{\mathfrak{p}}, c_{\mathfrak{p}})$$

for any quasi-character $c = \prod_{\mathfrak{p}} c_{\mathfrak{p}}$ of exponent greater than 1. If c now denotes our special character,

$$c(\mathfrak{a}) = \prod_{\mathfrak{p}} c_{\mathfrak{p}}(\mathfrak{a}_{\mathfrak{p}}) = \prod_{\mathfrak{p} \in S} c_{\mathfrak{p}}(\mathfrak{a}_{\mathfrak{p}}) \cdot \chi(\varphi_S(\mathfrak{a})),$$

we can compute explicitly the local factors of $\zeta(f, c\|^s)$ for $\mathfrak{p} \notin S$. Indeed

$$\zeta_{\mathfrak{p}}(f_{\mathfrak{p}}, c_{\mathfrak{p}}\|_{\mathfrak{p}}^{s}) = \int_{\mathfrak{o}_{\mathfrak{p}}} c_{\mathfrak{p}}(\mathfrak{a}_{\mathfrak{p}})|\mathfrak{a}_{\mathfrak{p}}|_{\mathfrak{p}}^{s}\, d\mathfrak{a}_{\mathfrak{p}}$$

$$= \sum_{\nu=0}^{\infty} \chi(\mathfrak{p}^{\nu})\mathcal{N}_{\mathfrak{p}}^{-\nu s}.\mathcal{N}\mathfrak{d}_{\mathfrak{p}}^{-\frac{1}{2}}$$

$$= \frac{\mathcal{N}\mathfrak{d}_{\mathfrak{p}}^{-\frac{1}{2}}}{1-\chi(\mathfrak{p})\mathcal{N}_{\mathfrak{p}}^{-s}},$$

because, for $\mathfrak{p} \notin S$, $c_{\mathfrak{p}}(\mathfrak{a}_{\mathfrak{p}}) = \chi(\mathfrak{p}^{\mathrm{ord}_{\mathfrak{p}}\mathfrak{a}_{\mathfrak{p}}})$. If therefore we introduce the classical ζ-function $\zeta(s, \chi)$, defined for Re $(s) > 1$ by the Euler product

$$\zeta(s, \chi) = \prod_{\mathfrak{p} \notin S} \frac{1}{1-\chi(\mathfrak{p})\mathcal{N}_{\mathfrak{p}}^{-s}},$$

we can write

$$\zeta(f, c\|^s) = \prod_{\mathfrak{p} \in S} \zeta_{\mathfrak{p}}(f_{\mathfrak{p}}, c_{\mathfrak{p}}\|_{\mathfrak{p}}^{s}) \cdot \prod_{\mathfrak{p} \notin S} \mathcal{N}\mathfrak{d}_{\mathfrak{p}}^{-\frac{1}{2}}.\zeta(s, \chi).$$

We see that our $\zeta(f, c\|^s)$ is, essentially, the classical function $\zeta(s, \chi)$. It may be remarked here that we could have obtained directly the additive expression for $\zeta(s, \chi)$,

$$\zeta(s, \chi) = \sum_{\substack{\mathfrak{a} \text{ integral ideal} \\ \text{prime to } S}} \frac{\chi(\mathfrak{a})}{\mathcal{N}\mathfrak{a}^{s}},$$

had we computed $\zeta(f, c\|^s)$ by breaking up I into the cosets of I_S, integrating over each coset, and summing the results, rather than by using Theorem 3.3.1 to express the ζ-function integral as a product of local integrals.

Treating the ζ-function of $\hat{f}$ in the same way we find

$$\zeta(\hat{f}, \widehat{c\|^s}) = \prod_{\mathfrak{p} \in S} \zeta(\hat{f}_{\mathfrak{p}}, \widehat{c_{\mathfrak{p}}\|_{\mathfrak{p}}^{s}}) \cdot \prod_{\mathfrak{p} \notin S} \chi(\mathfrak{d}_{\mathfrak{p}})\mathcal{N}\mathfrak{d}_{\mathfrak{p}}^{-s}.\zeta(1-s, \chi^{-1}),$$

for Re $(s) < 0$.

Before discussing the resulting analytic continuation and functional equation for $\zeta(s, \chi)$, we should set our minds completely at rest by checking that our $f(\mathfrak{x})$ satisfies axiom $(\mathfrak{z}_2)$; that is, that the sum

$$\sum_{\xi \in k} f(\mathfrak{a}(\mathfrak{x}+\xi))$$

is uniformly convergent for $\mathfrak{a}$ in a compact subset of I and $\mathfrak{x} \in D$. We can do this easily under the assumption that, for $\mathfrak{p} \in S$, the local functions $f_{\mathfrak{p}}$ we chose in constructing f do not differ too much from the standard local functions which we wrote down in Section 2.5. Namely, we assume for discrete $\mathfrak{p} \in S$, that $f_{\mathfrak{p}}$ vanishes outside a compact; and for archimedean $\mathfrak{p}$, that $f_{\mathfrak{p}}(\mathfrak{x}_{\mathfrak{p}})$ goes exponentially to zero as $\mathfrak{x}_{\mathfrak{p}}$ tends to infinity. Under these assumptions one sees first that there is an ideal, $\mathfrak{a}$, of k such that $f(\mathfrak{a}(\mathfrak{x}+\xi)) = 0$ if $\xi \notin \mathfrak{a}$, for all $\mathfrak{a}$ in the compact and $\mathfrak{x}$ in D. The sum may then be viewed as a sum over a lattice in the n-dimensional space which is the infinite part of V, of the values of a function which goes exponentially to zero with the distance from the origin. The lattice depends on $\mathfrak{a}$ and $\mathfrak{x}$, to be sure, but the restriction of $\mathfrak{a}$ to a compact means that a certain fixed small cube will always fit into the fundamental parallelotope of the lattice. The uniform convergence of the sum is then obvious.

Analytic Continuation and Functional Equation for $\zeta(s, \chi)$. The analytic continuation which we have established for our ζ-functions, both in the large and locally, now gives directly the analytic continuation of $\zeta(s, \chi)$ into the whole plane. Our functional equations

$$\zeta(\hat{f}, \hat{c}) = \zeta(f, c) \quad \text{and} \quad \zeta_{\mathfrak{p}}(f_{\mathfrak{p}}, c_{\mathfrak{p}}) = \rho_{\mathfrak{p}}(c_{\mathfrak{p}})\zeta_{\mathfrak{p}}(\hat{f}_{\mathfrak{p}}, \hat{c}_{\mathfrak{p}})$$

yield for $\zeta(s, \chi)$ the functional equation

$$\zeta(1-s, \chi^{-1}) = \prod_{\mathfrak{p} \in S} \rho_{\mathfrak{p}}(\tilde{c}_{\mathfrak{p}}\|_{\mathfrak{p}}^{s+it_{\mathfrak{p}}}) . \prod_{\mathfrak{p} \notin S} \mathcal{N}\mathfrak{d}_{\mathfrak{p}}^{s-\frac{1}{2}}\chi^{-1}(\mathfrak{d}_{\mathfrak{p}}) . \zeta(s, \chi).$$

The explicit expressions for the local functions $\rho_{\mathfrak{p}}$ are tabulated in Section 2.5. The meaning of the $\hat{c}_{\mathfrak{p}}$ and $t_{\mathfrak{p}}$, and their relationship to the ideal character χ, is discussed in the first paragraph of this section.

These ideal characters, χ, which we have constructed out of idèle characters, are exactly the characters which Hecke introduced in order to define his "new type of ζ-function". $\zeta(s, \chi)$ is that ζ-function; and the functional equation we have just written down is the functional equation Hecke proved for it.

A Few Comments on Recent Related Literature

[Added January 1967]

In Lang's book *Algebraic Numbers* (Addison-Wesley, 1964) there is a review of the theory above, in which the global results are renormalized in a way which corresponds more closely to the classical theory and which is more suitable for applications. The applications to prime densities, the Brauer-Siegel theorem, and the "explicit formulas" are also treated there. Lang has urged me to point out that in the main theorem on equidistribution of primes (Theorem 6, p. 130 *loc. cit.*) one must assume that $\sigma(J_k^0) = G$, not only that $\sigma(J_k) = G$; thus the first application following that theorem, concerning the equidistribution of $\log p$, is not valid.

For a reinterpretation of the proof of the functional equation given above, see Weil, *Fonction zêta et distributions*, Séminaire Bourbaki, No. 312, June 1966.

Siegel's work on quadratic forms has inspired much adèlic (adèle is the modern term for valuation-vector) analysis in recent years. For some crucial results and bibliography in that direction, see Weil's papers in *Acta Mathematica*, 1964 and 1965.

REFERENCES

Artin, E. and Whaples, G. (1945). Axiomatic characterization of fields by the product formula for valuations. *Bull. Am. math. Soc.* **51,** 469–492.

Cartan, H. and Godement, R. (1947). Théorie de la dualité et analyse harmonique dans les groupes abéliens localement compacts. *Annls. scient. Ec. norm. sup., Paris* (3), **64,** 79–99.

Chevalley, C. (1940). La théorie du corps de classes. *Ann. Math.* **41,** 394–418.

Hecke, E. Über eine neue Art von Zetafunktionen und ihre Beziehungen zur Verteilung der Primzahlen. *Math. Z.* **1** (1918), 357–376; **4** (1920), 11–21. Reprinted in "Mathematische Werke", Vandenhoeck und Ruprecht, Göttingen, 1959.

Matchett, M. *Thesis*, Indiana University (1946), unpublished.

Exercises†

Exercise 1: The Power Residue Symbol (Legendre, Gauss, et al.)

This exercise is based on Chapter VII, § 3, plus Kummer theory (Chapter III, § 2). Let m be a fixed natural number and K a fixed global field containing the group μ_m of mth roots of unity. Let S denote the set of primes of K consisting of the archimedean ones and those dividing m. If $a_1, \ldots, a_r$ are elements of K^*, we let $S(a_1, \ldots, a_r)$ denote the set of primes in S, together with the primes v such that $|a_i|_v \neq 1$ for some i. For $a \in K^*$ and $\mathfrak{b} \in I^{S(a)}$ the symbol $\left(\frac{a}{\mathfrak{b}}\right)$ is defined by the equation

$$(\sqrt[m]{a})^{F_{L/K}(\mathfrak{b})} = \left(\frac{a}{\mathfrak{b}}\right) \sqrt[m]{a},$$

where L is the field $K(\sqrt[m]{a})$.

EXERCISE 1.1. Show $\left(\frac{a}{\mathfrak{b}}\right)$ is an mth root of 1, independent of the choice of $\sqrt[m]{a}$.

EXERCISE 1.2. Working in the field $L' = K(\sqrt[m]{a}, \sqrt[m]{a'})$ and using Chapter VII, § 3.2 with $K' = K$ and $L = K(\sqrt[m]{a})$, show

$$\left(\frac{aa'}{\mathfrak{b}}\right) = \left(\frac{a}{\mathfrak{b}}\right)\left(\frac{a'}{\mathfrak{b}}\right) \qquad \text{if } \mathfrak{b} \in I^{S(a,a')}.$$

EXERCISE 1.3. Show

$$\left(\frac{a}{\mathfrak{b}\mathfrak{b}'}\right) = \left(\frac{a}{\mathfrak{b}}\right)\left(\frac{a}{\mathfrak{b}'}\right) \qquad \text{if } \mathfrak{b} \in I^{S(a)}.$$

† These "exercises" refer primarily to Chapter VII, "Global class field theory", and were prepared after the Conference by Tate with the connivance of Serre. They adumbrate some of the important results and interesting applications for which unfortunately there was not enough time in the Conference itself.

Hence,

$$\left(\frac{a}{\mathfrak{b}}\right) = \prod_{v \notin S(a)} \left(\frac{a}{v}\right)^{n_v} \qquad \text{if } \mathfrak{b} = \sum n_v v.$$

EXERCISE 1.4. (*Generalized Euler criterion.*) If $v \notin S(a)$ then $m|(Nv-1)$, where $Nv = [k(v)]$, and $\left(\frac{a}{v}\right)$ is the unique mth root of 1 such that

$$\left(\frac{a}{v}\right) \equiv a^{\frac{Nv-1}{m}} \pmod{\mathfrak{p}_v}.$$

EXERCISE 1.5. (*Explanation of the name "power residue symbol".*) For $v \notin S(a)$ the following statements are equivalent:

(i) $\left(\frac{a}{v}\right) = 1.$

(ii) The congruence $x^m \equiv a \pmod{\mathfrak{p}_v}$ is solvable with $x \in \mathfrak{o}_v$.

(iii) The equation $x^m = a$ is solvable with $x \in K_v$.

(Use the fact that $k(v)^*$ is cyclic of order $(Nv-1)$, and Hensel's lemma, Chapter II, App. C.)

EXERCISE 1.6. If $\mathfrak{b}$ is an integral ideal prime to m, then

$$\left(\frac{\zeta}{\mathfrak{b}}\right) = \zeta^{\frac{N\mathfrak{b}-1}{m}} \qquad \text{for } \zeta \in \mu_m.$$

(Do this first, using Exercise 1.4, in case $\mathfrak{b} = v$ is prime. Then for general $\mathfrak{b} = \sum n_v v$, note that, putting $Nv = 1+mr_v$, we have

$$N\mathfrak{b} = \prod (1+mr_v)^{n_v} \equiv 1+m\sum n_v r_v \pmod{m^2}.)$$

EXERCISE 1.7. If a and $\mathfrak{b} \in I^{S(a)}$ are integral, and if $a' \equiv a \pmod{\mathfrak{b}}$, then $\left(\frac{a'}{\mathfrak{b}}\right) = \left(\frac{a}{\mathfrak{b}}\right)$.

EXERCISE 1.8. Show that Artin's reciprocity law (Chapter VII, § 3.3) for a simple Kummer extension $L = K(\sqrt[m]{a})$ implies the following statement: *If $\mathfrak{b}$ and $\mathfrak{b}' \in I^{S(a)}$, and $\mathfrak{b}'\mathfrak{b}^{-1} = (c)$ is the principal ideal of an element $c \in K^*$ such that $c \in (K_v^*)^m$ for all $v \in S(a)$, then* $\left(\frac{a}{\mathfrak{b}'}\right) = \left(\frac{a}{\mathfrak{b}}\right)$. Note that for $v \notin S$, the condition $c \in (K_v^*)^m$ will certainly be satisfied if $c \equiv 1 \pmod{\mathfrak{p}_v}$.

EXERCISE 1.9. Specialize now to the case $K = \mathbf{Q}$, $m = 2$. Let $a, b, \ldots$ denote arbitrary non-zero rational integers, and let $P, Q, \ldots$ denote *positive*, *odd* rational integers. For $(a, P) = 1$, the symbol $\left(\frac{a}{P}\right) = \left(\frac{a}{(P)}\right) = \pm 1$ is defined, is multiplicative in each argument separately, and satisfies

$$\left(\frac{a}{P}\right) = \left(\frac{b}{P}\right) \quad \text{if } a \equiv b \pmod{P}.$$

Artin's reciprocity law for $\mathbf{Q}(\sqrt{a})/\mathbf{Q}$ implies

(*) $$\left(\frac{a}{P}\right) = \left(\frac{a}{Q}\right) \quad \text{if } P \equiv Q \pmod{8a_0},$$

where a_0 denotes the "odd part of a", i.e. $a = 2^v a_0$, with a_0 odd. (Use the fact that numbers $\equiv 1 \pmod 8$ are 2-adic squares.)

EXERCISE 1.10. From Exercise 1.9 it is easy to derive the classical law of quadratic reciprocity, namely

$$\left(\frac{-1}{P}\right) = (-1)^{\frac{P-1}{2}}, \quad \left(\frac{2}{P}\right) = (-1)^{\frac{P^2-1}{8}}, \quad \text{and} \quad \left(\frac{P}{Q}\right)\left(\frac{Q}{P}\right) = (-1)^{\frac{P-1}{2}\cdot\frac{Q-1}{2}}$$

Indeed the formula (*) above allows one to calculate $\left(\frac{a}{P}\right)$ as function of P for any fixed a in a finite number of steps, and taking $a = -1$ and 2 one proves the first two assertions easily. For the last, define

$$\langle P, Q\rangle = \left(\frac{P}{Q}\right)\left(\frac{Q}{P}\right), \quad \text{for } (P, Q) = 1.$$

Then check first that if $P \equiv Q \pmod 8$ we have

$$\langle P, Q\rangle = \left(\frac{-1}{Q}\right)$$

and the given formula is correct. (Writing $Q = P+8a$ one finds using Exercise 1.9 that, indeed,

$$\left(\frac{Q}{P}\right) = \left(\frac{8a}{P}\right) = \left(\frac{8a}{Q}\right) = \left(\frac{-P}{Q}\right).)$$

Now, given arbitrary relatively prime P and Q, one can find R such that $RP \equiv Q \pmod 8$ and $(R, Q) = 1$ (even $R \equiv 1 \pmod{Q}$), and then, by what we have seen,

$$\langle P, Q\rangle\langle R, Q\rangle = \langle PR, Q\rangle = \left(\frac{-1}{Q}\right).$$

Fixing R and varying P, keeping $(P, Q) = 1$, we see that $\langle P, Q\rangle$ depends only on $P \pmod 8$. By symmetry (and the fact that the odd residue classes (mod 8) can be represented by numbers prime to any given number), we see that $\langle P, Q\rangle$ depends only on $Q \pmod 8$. We are therefore reduced to a small finite number of cases, which we leave to the reader to check. The next exercise gives a general procedure by which these last manoeuvres can be replaced.

Exercise 2: The Norm Residue Symbol (Hilbert, Hasse)

We assume the reciprocity law for Kummer extensions, and use Chapter VII, § 6. The symbols m, K, S, and $S(a_1, \ldots, a_r)$ have the same significance as in Exercise 1. For a and $b \in K^*$ and an arbitrary prime v of K we define $(a, b)_v$ by the equation

$$(\sqrt[m]{a})^{\psi_v(b)} = (a, b)_v \sqrt[m]{a},$$

where $\psi_v : K_v^* \to G^v$ is the local Artin map associated with the Kummer extension $K(\sqrt[m]{a})/K$.

EXERCISE 2.1. Show that $(a, b)_v$ is an mth root of 1 which is independent of the choice of $\sqrt[m]{a}$.

EXERCISE 2.2. Show $(a, b)_v(a, b')_v = (a, bb')_v$ and $(a, b)_v(a', b)_v = (aa', b)_v$. Thus, for each prime v of K, we have a bilinear map of $K^* \times K^*$ into the group μ_m of mth roots of unity.

EXERCISE 2.3. Show that $(a, b)_v = 1$ if either a or $b \in (K_v^*)^m$, and hence that there is a unique bilinear extension of $(a, b)_v$ to $K_v^* \times K_v^*$.

This extension is continuous in the v-adic topology, and can be described by a finite table of values, because $K_v^*/(K_v^*)^m$ is a finite group (of order $m^2/|m|_v$, where $|m|_v$ is the normed absolute value of m at v). Moreover, the extended function on $K_v^* \times K_v^*$ can be described purely locally, i.e. is independent of the field K of which K_v is the completion (because the same is true of ψ_v), and induces a *non-degenerate* pairing of $K_v^*/(K_v^*)^m$ with itself into μ_m; however we will not use these local class field theoretic facts in most of this exercise. For a general discussion of $(a, b)_v$, and also for some explicit formulas for it in special cases, see Hasse's "Bericht", Part II, pp. 53–123, Serre's "Corps Locaux", pp. 212–221, and the Artin–Tate notes, Ch. 12. The symbol $(a, b)_v$ defined here coincides with that of Hasse and Serre, but is the opposite of that defined in Artin–Tate. While we are on the subject, our local Artin maps ψ_v coincide with those in Serre and in Artin–Tate, but are the opposite of Hasse's.

EXERCISE 2.4. Show that $(a, b)_v = 1$ if b is a norm for the extension $K_v(\sqrt[m]{a})/K_v$. (See Chapter VII, § 6.2; the converse is true also, by local class field theory, but this does not follow directly from the global reciprocity law.)

EXERCISE 2.5. We have $(a, b)_v = 1$ if $a+b \in (K_v^*)^m$; in particular, $(a, -a)_v = 1 = (a, 1-a)_v$. (This follows from the purely algebraic lemma: *Let F be a field containing the group μ_m of mth roots of unity, and let $a \in F^*$. Then for every $x \in F$ the element $x^m - a$ is a norm from $F(\sqrt[m]{a})$.* Indeed, let $\alpha^m = a$. The map $\sigma \mapsto \alpha^\sigma/\alpha$ is an isomorphism of the Galois group onto a subgroup μ_d of μ_m and is independent of the choice of α. Hence if (ζ_i) is a system of representatives of the cosets of μ_d in μ_m, we have for each $x \in F$

$$x^m - a = \prod_{\zeta \in \mu_m} (x - \zeta\alpha) = N_{F(\alpha)/F}\left(\prod_{i=1}^{m/d} (x - \zeta_i \alpha)\right),$$

Q.E.D.)

EXERCISE 2.6. Show that $(a, b)_v (b, a)_v = 1$. (Just use bilinearity on $1 = (ab, -ab)_v$.)

EXERCISE 2.7. If v is archimedean, we have $(a, b)_v = 1$ unless K_v is real, both $a < 0$ and $b < 0$ in K_v, and $m = 2$. (In the latter case we do in fact have $(a, b)_v = -1$; see the remark in Exercise 2.4. Note that $m > 2$ implies that K_v is complex for every archimedean v.)

EXERCISE 2.8. (*Relation between norm-residue and power-residue symbols.*) If $v \notin S(a)$, then $(a, b)_v = \left(\frac{a}{v}\right)^{v(b)}$; in particular, $(a, b)_v = 1$ for $v \notin S(a, b)$.

(See the first lines of Exercise 1 for the definition of S and $S(a)$, etc. The result follows from the description of the local Artin map in terms of the Frobenius automorphism in the unramified case. More generally,

$$v \notin S \Rightarrow (a, b)_v = \left(\frac{c}{v}\right), \quad \text{where } c = (-1)^{v(a)v(b)} a^{v(b)} b^{-v(a)}$$

is a unit in K_v which depends bilinearly on a and b. To prove this, just write $a = \pi^{v(a)} a_0$ and $b = \pi^{v(b)} b_0$ where $v(\pi) = 1$, and work out $(a, b)_v$ by the previous rules; for the geometric analog discussed in remark 3.6 of Chapter VII, see Serre, loc. cit., Ch. III, Section 4.)

EXERCISE 2.9. (*Product Formula.*) For $a, b \in K^*$ we have $\prod (a, b)_v = 1$, the product being taken over all primes v of K.

EXERCISE 2.10. (*The general power-reciprocity law.*) For arbitrary a and b in K^* we define

$$\left(\frac{a}{b}\right) = \prod_{v \notin S(a)} \left(\frac{a}{v}\right)^{v(b)} = \left(\frac{a}{(b)^{S(a)}}\right),$$

where $(b)^s$ is defined in Chapter VII, § 3.2.

Warning: With $\left(\frac{a}{b}\right)$ defined in this generality the rule $\left(\frac{aa'}{b}\right) = \left(\frac{a}{b}\right)\left(\frac{a'}{b}\right)$ does not always hold, but it does hold if $S(b) \cap S(a, a') = S$, and especially if b is relatively prime to a and a'. The other rule, $\left(\frac{a}{bb'}\right) = \left(\frac{a}{b}\right)\left(\frac{a}{b'}\right)$ holds in general.

Using Exercises 2.6, 2.8 and 2.9, prove that

$$\left(\frac{a}{b}\right)\left(\frac{b}{a}\right)^{-1} = \prod_{v \in S(a) \cap S(b)} (b, a)_v.$$

In particular

(*) $$\left(\frac{a}{b}\right)\left(\frac{b}{a}\right)^{-1} = \prod_{v \in S} (b, a)_v, \quad \text{if } S(a) \cap S(b) = S,$$

and

(**) $$\left(\frac{\lambda}{b}\right) = \prod_{v \in S} (\lambda, b)_v, \quad \text{if } S(\lambda) = S.$$

EXERCISE 2.11. If $K = \mathbf{Q}$ and $m = 2$, then $S = \{2, \infty\}$, and for $P > 0$ as in Exercise 1.10, we have $(x, P)_\infty = 1$. Hence the results of Exercise 1.10 are equivalent with

$$(-1, P)_2 = (-1)^{\frac{P-1}{2}}, \quad (2, P)_2 = (-1)^{\frac{P^2-1}{8}}, \quad \text{and} \quad (P, Q)_2 = (-1)^{\frac{P-1}{2}\cdot\frac{Q-1}{2}},$$

for odd P and Q. On the other hand, these formulas are easily established working locally in $\mathbf{Q}_2$. In particular, the fact that $(1+4c, b)_2 = (-1)^{v_2(b)c}$, from which the value of $(a, b)_2$ is easily derived for all a, b using Exercises 2.2, 2.5 and 2.6, is a special case of the next exercise.

EXERCISE 2.12. An element $a \in K$ is called *v-primary* (for m) if $K(\sqrt[m]{a})/K$ is unramified at v. For $v \notin S$, there is no problem: an element a is v-primary if and only if $v(a) \equiv 0 \pmod{m}$. Suppose now v divides m and $m = p$ is a prime number. Let ζ be a generator of μ_p, and put $\lambda = 1-\zeta$. Check that λ^{p-1}/p is a unit at v, and more precisely, that $\lambda^{p-1} \equiv -p \pmod{p\lambda}$, so that $\lambda^{p-1}/p \equiv -1 \pmod{\mathfrak{p}_v}$. Let a be such that $a \equiv 1 \pmod{p\lambda\mathfrak{o}_v}$, so that we have $a = 1+\lambda^p c$, with $c \in \mathfrak{o}_v$. Prove that a is v-primary, and that for all b,

$$(a, b)_v = \zeta^{-S(\bar{c})v(b)},$$

where S denotes the trace from $k(v)$ to the prime field and $\bar{c}$ is the v-residue of c. Also, if $a \equiv 1 \pmod{p\lambda\mathfrak{p}_v}$, then a is *v-hyperprimary*, i.e. $a \in (K_v^*)^m$.

(Let $\alpha^p = a$, and write $\alpha = 1+\lambda x$. Check that x is a root of a polynomial $f(X) \in \mathfrak{o}_v[X]$ such that $f(X) \equiv X^p - X - c \pmod{\mathfrak{p}_v}$. Thus $f'(x) \equiv -1 \not\equiv 0 \pmod{\mathfrak{p}_v}$, so $K_v(x) = K_v(\sqrt[m]{a})$ is indeed unramified. And if $c \equiv 0 \pmod{\mathfrak{p}_v}$ then $f(X)$ splits by Hensel's lemma, so $K_v(\sqrt[m]{a}) = K_v$. Now $x^p \equiv x + c \pmod{\mathfrak{p}_v}$, so if $Nv = p^f$, then

$$x^F = x^{Nv} \equiv x + c + c^p + \ldots + c^{p^{f-1}} \equiv x + S(\bar{c}) \pmod{\mathfrak{p}_v}.$$

On the other hand, if $\alpha' = \zeta\alpha = 1+\lambda x'$, then $x' \equiv x - 1 \pmod{\mathfrak{p}_v}$. Combining these facts gives the formula for $(a, b)_v$.)

EXERCISE 2.13. Let p be an odd prime, ζ a primitive pth root of unity, $K = \mathbf{Q}(\zeta)$, and $m = p$. Then p is totally ramified in K, and $\lambda = 1-\zeta$ generates the prime ideal corresponding to the unique prime v of K lying over p. Let U_i denote the group of units $\equiv 1 \pmod{\lambda^i}$ in K_v^*, for $i = 1, 2, \ldots$. Then the image of $\eta_i = 1-\lambda^i$ generates U_i/U_{i+1}, which is cyclic of order p, and the image of λ generates $K_v^*/(K_v^*)^p U_1$. By the preceding exercise,

$U_{p+1} \subset (K_v^*)^p$. Hence the elements λ, $\zeta = \eta_1$, $1-\lambda^2 = \eta_2, \ldots, 1-\lambda^p = \eta_p$ generate $(K_v^*)/(K_v^*)^p$. But that group is of order $p^2/\|p\|_v = p^{1+p}$, so these generators are independent mod pth powers. Show that

(a) $(\eta_i, \eta_j)_v = (\eta_i, \eta_{i+j})_v(\eta_{i+j}, \eta_j)_v(\eta_{i+j}, \lambda)_v^{-j}$, for all $i, j \geqslant 1$.

(b) If $i+j \geq p+1$, then $(a, b)_v = 1$ for all $a \in U_i$ and $b \in U_j$.

(c) $(\eta_i, \lambda)_v = \begin{cases} 1, & \text{for } 1 \leqslant i \leqslant p-1 \\ \zeta, & \text{for } i = p. \end{cases}$

(d) $(a, b)_v$ is the unique skew-symmetric pairing $K_v^* \times K_v^* \to \mu_p$ satisfying (a) and (c).

(For (a), note $\eta_j + \lambda^j \eta_i = \eta_{i+j}$, divide through by η_{i+j}, and use Exercise 2.5 and bilinearity; the oddness of p, which implies $(a, b) = (a, -b)$ in general and $(a, a) = 1$ in particular, is used here. The rest all follows easily, except for (c) which is a consequence of the preceding exercise; but note that the first $(p-1)$ cases of (c) are trivialities, because

$$(\eta_i, \lambda)_v^i = (1-\lambda^i, \lambda^i)_v = 1 \Rightarrow (\eta_i, \lambda)_v = 1 \quad \text{for } 1 \leq i \leq p-1.)$$

EXERCISE 2.14. (*Cubic reciprocity law.*) Specialize to $p = 3$ in the preceding exercise. The ring of integers $R = \mathbf{Z}+\mathbf{Z}\zeta$ is a principal ideal domain, whose non-zero elements can be written in the form $\lambda^\nu \zeta^\mu a$, with $a \equiv \pm 1 \pmod{3R}$. Prove

(*) $\quad \left(\dfrac{a}{b}\right) = \left(\dfrac{b}{a}\right)$, for relatively prime a and b, each $\equiv \pm 1 \pmod{3R}$,

and also

(**) $\quad \left.\begin{cases} \left(\dfrac{\zeta}{a}\right) = \zeta^{-m-n} \\ \left(\dfrac{\lambda}{a}\right) = \zeta^{m} \end{cases}\right\}$, for $a = \pm(1+3(m+n\zeta))$.

As an application, prove: If q is a rational prime $\equiv 1 \pmod 3$, then 2 is a cubic residue $(\text{mod } q)$ if and only if q is of the form x^2+27y^2 with $x, y \in \mathbf{Z}$. (Write $q = \pi\bar{\pi}$ with $\pi \equiv \pm 1 \pmod{3R}$. Then $\mathbf{Z}/q\mathbf{Z} \xrightarrow{\sim} R/\pi R$, so 2 is a cubic residue $(\text{mod } q)$ if and only if $\left(\dfrac{2}{\pi}\right) = 1$. Now use (*), and translate $\left(\dfrac{\pi}{2}\right) = 1$ into a statement about q.)

EXERCISE 2.15. Let L be the splitting field over $\mathbf{Q}$ of the polynomial X^3-2. The Galois group of $L/\mathbf{Q}$ is the symmetric group on three letters. Using the preceding exercise, show that for $p \neq 2, 3$ the Frobenius automorphism is given by the rules:

$F_{L/\mathbf{Q}}(p) = (1)$, if $p \equiv 1 \pmod 3$ and p of the form x^2+27y^2,
$F_{L/\mathbf{Q}}(p) =$ 3-cycle, if $p \equiv 1 \pmod 3$ and p not of the form x^2+27y^2,
$F_{L/\mathbf{Q}}(p) =$ 2-cycle, if $p \equiv -1 \pmod 3$.

Hence, by Tchebotarov's theorem, the densities of these sets of primes are 1/6, 1/3 and 1/2, respectively.

EXERCISE 2.16. Consider again an arbitrary K and m. Let $a_1, \ldots, a_r$ be a finite family of elements of K^*, and let L be the Kummer extension generated by the mth roots of those elements. Let T be a finite set of primes of K containing $S(a_1, \ldots, a_r)$, and big enough so that both $J_K = K^* J_{K,T}$, and $J_L = L^* J_{L,T'}$, where T' is the set of primes of L lying over T. Suppose we are given elements $\zeta_{v,i} \in \mu_m$, for $v \in T$ and $1 \leq i \leq r$, such that

(i) For each i, we have $\prod_{v \in T} \zeta_{v,i} = 1$, and

(ii) For each $v \in T$, there exists an $x_v \in K_v^*$ such that $(x_v, a_i)_v = \zeta_{v,i}$ for all i.

Show then that there exists a T-unit $x \in K_T$ such that $(x, a_i)_v = \zeta_{v,i}$ for all $v \in T$ and all $1 \leq i \leq r$.

The additional condition on T, involving T', is necessary, as is shown by the example $K = \mathbf{Q}$, $m = 2$, $T = \{\infty, 2, 7\}$, $r = 1$, $a_1 = -14$, $\zeta_{\infty,1} = -1$, $\zeta_{2,1} = -1$, $\zeta_{7,1} = 1$. To prove the statement, consider the group $X = \prod_{v \in T} (K_v^*)/(K_v^*)^m$, the subgroup A generated by the image of K_T, and the smaller subgroup A_0 generated by the images of the elements a_i, $1 \leq i \leq r$. The form $\langle x, y \rangle = \prod_{v \in T} (x_v, y_v)_v$ gives a non-degenerate pairing of X with itself to μ_m, under which A is self orthogonal, and indeed exactly so, because $[X] = m^{2t}$ and $[A] = m^t$, where $t = [T]$. (See step 4 in the proof of the second inequality in Chapter VII, § 9, the notations S, n, and s there being replaced by T, m, and t here.) Thus $X/A \approx \operatorname{Hom}(A, \mu_m)$ (note by the way that both groups are isomorphic to $\operatorname{Gal}(K(\sqrt[m]{K_T})/K)$, by class field theory and Kummer theory, respectively), and, vice versa, $A \approx \operatorname{Hom}(X/A, \mu_m)$. So far, we have not used the condition that $J_L = L^* J_{L,T'}$. Use it to show that if $a \in A$ and $\pi_v(a) \in \pi_v(A_0)$ for all v, where π_v is the projection of X onto $K_v^*/(K_v^*)^m$, then $a \in A_0$, i.e. $\sqrt[m]{a} \in L$. Now show that, in view of the dualities and orthogonalities discussed above, this last fact is equivalent to the statement to be proved.

Exercise 3: The Hilbert Class Field

Let L/K be a global abelian extension, v a prime of K, and $i_v : K_v^* \to J_K$ the canonical injection. Show that v *splits completely* in L if and only if $i_v(K_v^*) \subset K^* N_{L/K} J_L$, and, for non-archimedean v, that v is *unramified* in L if and only if $i_v(U_v) \subset K^* N_{L/K} J_L$, where U_v is the group of units in K_v. (See Chapter VII, § 5.1, § 6.3.) Hence, the maximal abelian extension of K which is unramified at all non-archimedean primes and is split completely at all archimedean ones is the class field to the group $K^* J_{K,S}$, where S now denotes the set of archimedean primes. (Use the Main Theorem

(Chapter VII, § 5.1) and the fact that $K^*N_{L/K}J_L$ is closed.) This extension is called the Hilbert class field of K; we will denote it by K'. Show that the Frobenius homomorphism $F_{K'/K}$ induces an isomorphism of the ideal class group $H_K = I_K/P_K$ of K onto the Galois group $G(K'/K)$. (Use the Main Theorem and the isomorphism $J_K/J_{K,S} \xrightarrow{\sim} I_K$.) Thus the degree $[K':K]$ is equal to the class number $h_K = [H_K]$ of K. The prime ideals in K decompose in K' according to their ideal class, and, in particular, the ones which split completely are exactly the principal prime ideals. An arbitrary ideal $\mathfrak{a}$ of K is principal if and only if $F_{K'/K}(\mathfrak{a}) = 1$.

The "class field tower", $K \subset K' \subset K'' = (K')' \subset \ldots$ can be infinite (see Chapter IX). Using the first two steps of it, and the commutative diagram (see (11.3), diagram (13))

$$\begin{array}{ccc} I_K & \xrightarrow{F_{K'/K}} & G(K'/K) \\ {\scriptstyle \mathrm{con}}\downarrow & & \downarrow{\scriptstyle V} \\ I_{K'} & \xrightarrow{F_{K''/K'}} & G(K''/K'), \end{array}$$

Artin realized that Hilbert's conjecture, to the effect that every ideal in K becomes principal in K', was equivalent to the statement that the Verlagerung† V was the zero map in this situation. Now $G(K''/K')$ is the commutator subgroup of $G(K''/K)$ (Why?), and so Artin conjectured the "Principal ideal theorem" of group theory: *If G is a finite group and G^c its commutator subgroup, then the map $V\colon (G/G^c) \to G^c/(G^c)^c$ is the zero map.* This theorem, and therewith Hilbert's conjecture, was then proved by Furtwängler. For a simple proof, see Witt, *Proc. Intern. Conf. Math., Amsterdam*, 1954, Vol. 2, pp. 71–73.

The first five imaginary quadratic fields with class number $\neq 1$ are those with discriminants -15, -20, -23, -24, and -31, which have class numbers 2, 2, 3, 2, 3, respectively. Show that their Hilbert class fields are obtained by adjoining the roots of the equations X^2+3, X^2+1, X^3-X-1, X^2+3, and X^3+X-1, respectively. In general, if K is an imaginary quadratic field, its Hilbert class field K' is generated over K by the j-invariants of the elliptic curves which have the ring of integers of K as ring of endomorphisms; see Chapter XIII.

Let J_S^+ denote the group of idèles which are positive at the real primes of K and are units at the non-archimedean primes. The class field over K with norm group $K^*J_{K,S}^+$ is the maximal abelian extension which is unramified at all non-archimedean primes, but with no condition at the archimedean primes; let us denote it by K_1. Let P_K^+ denote the group of principal ideals of the form (a), where a is a totally positive element of K. Show that $F_{K_1/K}$ gives an isomorphism: $I_K/P_K^+ \approx G(K_1/K)$. Thus, $G(K_1/K')$ is an elementary

† Called the *transfer* in Chapter IV, § 6, *Note* after Prop. 7.

abelian 2-group, isomorphic to P_K/P_K^+. Show that $(P_K : P_K^+)(K_S : K_S^+) = 2^{r_1}$, where $K_S^+ = K^* \cap J_{K,S}^+$ is the group of totally positive units in K, and r_1 is the number of real primes of K.

We have $\mathbf{Q}_1 = \mathbf{Q}$, clearly, but this is a poor result in view of Minkowski's theorem, to the effect that $\mathbf{Q}$ has no non-trivial extension, *abelian or not*, which is unramified at all non-archimedean primes (Minkowski, "Geometrie der Zahlen", p. 130, or "Diophantische Approximationen" p. 127). Consider now the case in which K is real quadratic, $[K : \mathbf{Q}] = 2$, and $r_1 = 2$. Show that $[K_1 : K'] = 1$ or 2, according to whether $N\varepsilon = -1$ or $N\varepsilon = 1$, where ε is a fundamental unit in K, and $N = N_{K/\mathbf{Q}}$. For example, in case $K = \mathbf{Q}(\sqrt{2})$ or $\mathbf{Q}(\sqrt{5})$ we have $K' = K$, because the class number is 1, and consequently also $K_1 = K$, because the units $\varepsilon = 1+\sqrt{2}$ and $\varepsilon = \frac{1}{2}(1+\sqrt{5})$ have norm -1. On the other hand, if $K = \mathbf{Q}(\sqrt{3})$, then again $K' = K$, but $K_1 \neq K$, because $\varepsilon = 2+\sqrt{3}$ has norm 1; show that $K_1 = K(\sqrt{-1})$. In general, when -1 is not a local norm everywhere (as in the case $K = \mathbf{Q}(\sqrt{3})$ just considered), then $N\varepsilon = 1$, and $K_1 \neq K'$. However, when -1 is a local norm everywhere, and is therefore the norm of a number in K, there is still no general rule for predicting whether or not it is the norm of a *unit*.

Exercise 4. Numbers Represented by Quadratic Forms

Let K be a field of characteristic different from 2, and

$$f(X) = \sum a_{ij} X_i X_j$$

a non-degenerate quadratic form in n variables with coefficients in K. We say that *f represents an element c in K* if the equation $f(X) = c$ has a solution $X = x \in K^n$ such that not all x_i are zero. *If f represents 0 in K, then f represents all elements in K.* Indeed, we have

$$(tX+Y) = t^2 f(X) + tB(X, Y) + f(Y).$$

If $f(x) = 0$ but $x \neq (0, 0, \ldots, 0)$, then by the non-degeneracy there is a $y \in K^n$ such that $B(x, y) \neq 0$, so that $f(tx+y)$ is a non-constant linear function of t and takes all values in K as t runs through K.

A linear change of coordinates does not affect questions of representability, and by such a change we can always bring f to diagonal form: $f = \sum a_i X_i^2$ with all $a_i \neq 0$. If $f = cX_1^2 - g(X_2, \ldots, X_n)$ then f represents 0 if and only if g represents c, because if g represents 0 then it represents c. Hence, the question of representability of non-zero c's by forms g in $n-1$ variables is equivalent to that of the representability of 0 by forms f in n variables. The latter question is not affected by multiplication of f by a non-zero constant; hence we can suppose f in diagonal form with $a_1 = 1$ in treating it:

EXERCISE 4.1. The form $f = X^2$ does not represent 0.

EXERCISE 4.2. The form $f = X^2 - bY^2$ represents 0 if and only if $b \in (K^*)^2$.

EXERCISE 4.3. The form $f = X^2 - bY^2 - cZ^2$ represents 0 if and only if c is a norm from the extension field $K(\sqrt{b})$.

EXERCISE 4.4. The following statements are equivalent:

(i) The form $f = X^2 - bY^2 - cZ^2 + acT^2$ represents 0 in K.
(ii) c is a product of a norm from $K(\sqrt{a})$ and a norm from $K(\sqrt{b})$.
(iii) c, as element of $K(\sqrt{ab})$, is a norm from the field $L = K(\sqrt{a}, \sqrt{b})$.
(iv) The form $g = X^2 - bY^2 - cZ^2$ represents 0 in the field $K(\sqrt{ab})$.

(We may obviously assume neither a nor b is a square in K. Then the equivalence of (i) and (ii) is clear because the reciprocal of a norm is a norm, and the equivalence of (iii) and (iv) follows from Exercise 4.3 with K replaced therein by $K(\sqrt{ab})$. It remains to prove (ii) $\Leftrightarrow$ (iii), and we can assume $ab \notin (K^*)^2$, for otherwise the equivalence is obvious. Then Gal(L/K) is a four-group, consisting of elements $1, \rho, \sigma, \tau$ such that ρ, σ, and τ leave fixed, respectively, $\sqrt{ab}$, $\sqrt{a}$, and $\sqrt{b}$, say. Now (ii) $\Leftrightarrow$ (ii′): $\exists\, x, y \in L$ such that $x^\sigma = x$, $y^\tau = y$, and $x^{1+\rho}y^{1+\rho} = c$; and (iii) $\Leftrightarrow$ (iii′) $\exists\, z \in L$ such that $z^{1+\rho} = c$. Hence (ii) $\Rightarrow$ (iii) trivially. Therefore assume (iii′), put $u = c^{-1}z^{\sigma+1}$, and check that $u^\sigma = u$, i.e. $u \in K(\sqrt{a})$, and $u^{\rho+1} = 1$. Hence by Hilbert's theorem 90 (Chapter V, § 2.7) for the extension $K(\sqrt{a})/K$, there exists $x \neq 0$ such that $x^\sigma = x$ and $x^{\rho-1} = u$. Now put $y = z^\rho/x$, and check that (ii′) is satisfied.)

So far, we have done algebra, not arithmetic. From now on, we suppose K is a *global field* of characteristic $\neq 2$.

EXERCISE 4.5. The form f of Exercise 4.3 represents 0 in a local field K_v if and only if the quadratic norm residue symbol $(b, c)_v = 1$. Hence f represents 0 in K_v for all but a finite number of v, and the number of v's for which it does not is even. Moreover, these last two statements are invariant under multiplication of f by a scalar and consequently hold for an arbitrary non-degenerate form in three variables over K.

EXERCISE 4.6. Let f be as in Exercise 4.4. Show that if f does *not* represent 0 in a local field K_v, then $a \notin (K_v^*)^2$, and $b \notin (K_v^*)^2$, but $ab \in (K_v^*)^2$, and c is *not* a norm from the quadratic extension $K_v(\sqrt{a}) = K_v(\sqrt{b})$. (Just use the fact that the norm groups from the different quadratic extensions of K_v are subgroups of index 2 in K_v^*, no two of which coincide.) Now suppose conversely that those conditions are satisfied. Show that the set of elements in K_v which are represented by f is $N - cN$, where N is the group of non-zero norms from $K_v(\sqrt{a})$, and in particular, that f does not represent 0 in K_v. Show, furthermore, that if $N - cN \neq K_v^*$, then $-1 \notin N$, and $N + N \subset N$. Hence f represents every non-zero element of K_v *unless* $K_v \approx \mathbf{R}$ and f is positive definite.

EXERCISE 4.7. A form f in $n \geq 5$ variables over a local field K_v represents 0 unless K_v is real and f definite.

EXERCISE 4.8. *Theorem: Let K be a global field and f a non-degenerate quadratic form in n variables over K which represents* 0 *in K_v for each prime v of K. Then f represents* 0 *in K.* (For $n = 1$, trivial; $n = 2$, cf. Chapter VII, § 8.8; $n = 3$, cf. Chapter VII, § 9.6 and Exercise 4.3; $n = 4$, use Exercise 4.4 to reduce to the case $n = 3$; finally, for $n \geq 5$, proceed by induction: Let

$$f(X) = aX_1^2 + bX_2^2 - g(X_3, \ldots, X_n),$$

where g has $n-2 \geq 3$ variables. From Exercise 4.5 we know that g represents 0 and hence every number in K_v for all v outside a finite set S. Now $(K_v^*)^2$ is open in K_v^*. Hence, by the approximation theorem there exist elements x_1 and x_2 in K, such that the element $c = ax_1^2 + bx_2^2 \neq 0$ is represented by g in K_v for all v in S, and hence for all v. By induction, the form $cY^2 - g(X_3, \ldots, X_n)$ in $n-1$ variables represents 0 in K. Hence f does.)

EXERCISE 4.9. *Corollary:* If $n \geq 5$, then f represents 0 in K unless there is a real prime v at which f is definite.

EXERCISE 4.10. A rational number c is the sum of three rational squares if and only if $c = 4^n r$ where r is a rational number > 0 and $\not\equiv 7 \pmod 8$; every rational number is the sum of four rational squares.

EXERCISE 4.11. The statements in the preceding exercise are true if we replace "rational" by "rational integral" throughout. (The 4 squares one is an immediate consequence of the 3 squares one, so we will discuss only the latter, although there are more elementary proofs of the four square statement not involving the "deeper" three square one. Let c be a positive integer as in 4.10, so that the sphere $|X|^2 = X_1^2 + X_2^2 + X_3^2 = c$ has a point $x = (x_1, x_2, x_3)$ with rational coordinates. We must show it has a point with *integral* coordinates. Assuming x itself not integral, let z be an integral point in 3-space which is as close as possible to x, so that $x = z + a$, with $0 < |a|^2 \leq 3/4 < 1$. The line l joining x to z is not tangent to the sphere; if it were then we would have $|a|^2 = |z|^2 - |x|^2 = |z|^2 - c$, an integer, contradiction. Hence the line l meets the sphere in a rational point $x' \neq x$. Now show that if the coordinate of x can be written with the common denominator $d > 0$, then those of x' can be written with the common denominator $d' = |a|^2 d < d$, so that the sequence $x, x', (x')', \ldots$ must lead eventually to an integral point. Note that d' is in fact an integer, because

$$d' = |a|^2 d = |x - z|^2 d = (|x|^2 - 2(x, z) + |z|^2)d = cd - 2(dx, z) + |z|^2 d.)$$

EXERCISE 4.12. Let f be a form in three variables over K. Show that if f does not represent 0 locally in K_v, then the other numbers in K_v not represented by f constitute one coset of $(K_v^*)^2$ in K_v^*. (Clearly one can assume $f = X^2 - bY^2 - cZ^2$; now use Exercise 4.6.) Using this, show that if $K = \mathbf{Q}$ and f is positive definite, then f does not represent all positive integers. (Note the last sentence in Exercise 4.5.)

For further developments and related work see O. T. O'Meara: "Introduction to Quadratic Forms" (Springer, 1963) or Z. I. Borevič and I. R. Šafarevič, "Teorija Čisel" ("Nauka", Moskva, 1964). [English translation, Z. I. Borevich and I. R. Shafarevich, "Number Theory", Academic Press, New York: German translation, S. I. Borevicz and I. R. Šafarevič, "Zahlentheorie", Birkhäuser Verlag, Basel.]

Exercise 5: Local Norms Not Global Norms, etc.

Let L/K be Galois with group $G = (1, \rho, \sigma, \tau) \approx (\mathbf{Z}/2\mathbf{Z})^2$, and let K_1, K_2, and K_3 be the three quadratic intermediate fields left fixed by ρ, σ, and τ, respectively. Let $N_i = N_{K_i/K}(K_i^*)$ for $i = 1, 2, 3$, and let $N = N_{L/K}(L^*)$.

EXERCISE 5.1. Show that $N_1 N_2 N_3 = \{x \in K^* | x^2 \in N\}$. (This is pure algebra, not arithmetic; one inclusion is trivial, and the other can be proved by the methods used in Exercise 4.3.)

EXERCISE 5.2. Now assume K is a global field. Show that if the local degree of L over K is 4 for some prime, then $N_1 N_2 N_3 = K^*$ (cf. Chapter VII, § 11.4). Suppose now that all local degrees are 1 or 2. For simplicity, suppose K of characteristic $\neq 2$, and let $K_i = K(\sqrt{a_i})$ for $i = 1, 2, 3$. For each i, let S_i be the (infinite) set of primes of K which split in K_i, and for $x \in K^*$ put

$$\varphi(x) = \prod_{v \in S_1} (a_2, x)_v = \prod_{v \in S_1} (a_3, x)_v = \prod_{v \in S_2} (a_3, x)_v = \prod_{v \in S_2} (a_1, x)_v$$
$$= \prod_{v \in S_3} (a_1, x)_v = \prod_{v \in S_3} (a_2, x)_v = \pm 1,$$

where $(x, y)_v$ is the quadratic norm residue symbol. Show that $N_1 N_2 N_3 = \operatorname{Ker} \varphi$ and is a subgroup of index 2 in K^*. (The inclusion $N_1 N_2 N_3 \subset \operatorname{Ker} \varphi$ is trivial. From Exercise 5.1 above and Chapter VII, § 11.4 one sees that the index of $N_1 N_2 N_3$ in K^* is at most 2. But there exists an x with $\varphi(x) = -1$ by Exercise 2.16.)

EXERCISE 5.3. Let $K = \mathbf{Q}$ and $L = \mathbf{Q}(\sqrt{13}, \sqrt{17})$. Show that if x is a product of primes p such that $\left(\frac{p}{13}\right) = -1$ (e.g. $p = 2, 5, 7, 11, \ldots$), then $\varphi(x) = \left(\frac{x}{17}\right)$. Hence $5^2, 7^2, 10^2, 11^2, 14^2, \ldots$ are some examples of numbers which are local norms everywhere from $\mathbf{Q}(\sqrt{13}, \sqrt{17})$ but are not global norms. Of course, not every such number is a square; for example, -14^2 is the global norm of $\frac{1}{2}(7+2\sqrt{13}+\sqrt{17})$, and comparing with the above we see that -1 is a local norm everywhere but not a global norm.

EXERCISE 5.4. Suppose now that our global 4-group extension L/K has the property that there is *exactly one* prime v of K where the local degree is 4: Let w be the prime of L above v and prove that $\hat{H}^{-1}(G, L^*) = 0$, but

$\hat{H}^{-1}(G, L_w^*) \approx \mathbf{Z}/2\mathbf{Z}$. (Use the exact sequence near the beginning of paragraph 11.4. The map g is surjective, as always when the l.c.m. of the local degrees is the global degree. And the map $g: \hat{H}^{-1}(G, J_L) \to \hat{H}(G, C_L)$ is also injective, because of our assumption that the local degree is 4 for only one prime.)

Let A, resp. A_w, be the group of elements in L^*, resp L_w^*, whose norm to K (resp. to K_v) is 1, and let $\bar{A}$ be the closure of A in L_w^*. It follows from the above that

$$A = (L^*)^{\rho-1}(L^*)^{\sigma-1}(L^*)^{\tau-1},$$

and that

$$\bar{A} = (L_w^*)^{\rho-1}(L_w^*)^{\sigma-1}(L_w^*)^{\tau-1}$$

is of index 2 in A_w. Now, as is well known, there is an algebraic group T defined over K (the twisted torus of dimension 3 defined by the equation $N_{L/K}(X) = 1$) such that $T(K) = A$ and $T(K_v) = A_w$. Hence we get examples which show that *the group of rational points on a torus T is not necessarily dense in the group of v-adic points* (see last paragraph below). However, it is not hard to show that if T is a torus over K split by a Galois extension L/K, then $T(K)$ is dense in $T(K_v)$ for every prime v of K such that there exists a prime $v' \neq v$ with the same decomposition group as v; in particular, whenever the decomposition group of v is cyclic, and more particularly, whenever v is archimedean.

As a concrete illustration, take $K = \mathbf{Q}$ and $L = \mathbf{Q}(\sqrt{-1}, \sqrt{2}) = \mathbf{Q}(\zeta)$, where $\zeta^4 = -1$. Then L is unramified except at 2, but totally ramified at 2, and consequently there is just one prime, 2, with local degree 4. Let $M = \mathbf{Q}(i)$ where $i = \zeta^2 = \sqrt{-1}$, and let L_w and M_v denote the completions at the primes above 2. It is easy to give an ad-hoc proof without cohomology that the elements of L with norm 1 are not dense in those of L_w^*: just check that the element $z = (2+i)/(2-i) \in M_v$ is a norm from L_w to L_v, but that $z(M_v^*)^2$ contains no element $y \in M$ such that y is a global norm from L to M *and* such that $N_{M/\mathbf{Q}}(y) = 1$.

Exercise 6: On Decomposition of Primes

Let L/K be a finite global extension and let S be a finite set of primes of K. We will denote by $\mathrm{Spl}_S(L/K)$ the set of primes $v \notin S$ such that v splits completely in L (i.e. such that $L \otimes_K K_v \approx K^{[L:K]}$), and by $\mathrm{Spl}'_S(L/K)$ the set of primes $v \notin S$ which have a split factor in L (i.e. such that there exists a K-isomorphism $L \to K_v$). Thus $\mathrm{Spl}_S(L/K) \subset \mathrm{Spl}'_S(L/K)$ always, and equality holds if K is Galois, in which case $\mathrm{Spl}'_S(L/K)$ has density $[L:K]^{-1}$ by the Tchebotarov density theorem. (Enunciated near end of Chapter VIII, § 3.)

EXERCISE 6.1. Show that if L and M are Galois over K, then

$$L \subset M \Leftrightarrow \mathrm{Spl}_S(M) \subset \mathrm{Spl}_S(L),$$

(Indeed, we have

$$\mathrm{Spl}_S(LM/K) = \mathrm{Spl}_S(L/K) \cap \mathrm{Spl}_S(M/K),$$

so

$$L \subset M \Rightarrow \mathrm{Spl}_S(M) \subset \mathrm{Spl}_S(L) \Rightarrow \mathrm{Spl}_S(LM/K) = \mathrm{Spl}_S(M/K) \Rightarrow [LM:K] = [M:K] \Rightarrow L \subset M;$$

where was Galoisness used?) Hence

$$L = M \Leftrightarrow \mathrm{Spl}_S(L) = \mathrm{Spl}_S(M).$$

Application: *If a separable polynomial* $f(X) \in K[X]$ *splits into linear factors* mod $\mathfrak{p}$ *for all but a finite number of prime ideals* $\mathfrak{p}$ *of* K, *then* f *splits into linear factors in* K. (Take L = splitting field of $f(X)$, and $M = K$, and S large enough so that f has integral coefficients and unit discriminant outside S.) Finally, note that everything in this exercise goes through if we replace "all primes $v \notin S$" and "all but a finite number of primes v" by "all v in a set of density 1".

EXERCISE 6.2. Let L/K be Galois with group G, let H be a subgroup of G, and let E be the fixed field of H. For each prime v of K, let G^v denote a decomposition group of v. Show that v splits completely in E if and only if all of the conjugates of G^v are contained in H, whereas v has a split factor in E if and only if at least one conjugate of G^v is contained in H. Hence, show that the set of primes $\mathrm{Spl}'_S(E/K)$ has density $[\bigcup_{\rho \in G} \rho H \rho^{-1}]/[G]$. Now prove the lemma on finite groups which states that the union of the conjugates of a proper subgroup is not the whole group (because they overlap a bit at the identity!) and conclude that if $\mathrm{Spl}'_S(E/K)$ has density 1, then $E = K$. Application: *If an* irreducible *polynomial* $f(X) \in K[X]$ *has a root* (mod $\mathfrak{p}$) *for all but a finite number of primes* $\mathfrak{p}$, *or even for a set of primes* $\mathfrak{p}$ *of density* 1, *then it has a root in* K. This statement is false for reducible polynomials; consider for example $f(X) = (X^2-a)(X^2-b)(X^2-ab)$, where a, b, and ab are non-squares in K. Also, the set $\mathrm{Spl}'(E/K)$ does not in general determine E up to an isomorphism over K; cf. Exercise 6.4 below.

EXERCISE 6.3. Let H and H' be subgroups of a finite group G. Show that the permutation representations of G corresponding to H and H' are isomorphic, as linear representations, if and only if each conjugacy class of G meets H and H' in the same number of elements. Note that if H is a normal subgroup then this cannot happen unless $H' = H$. However, there are examples of subgroups H and H' satisfying the above condition which are not conjugate; check the following one, due to F. Gassmann (*Math. Zeit.*, **25**, 1926): Take for G the symmetric group on 6 letters (x_i) and put

$$H = \{1, \ (X_1 X_2)(X_3 X_4), \ (X_1 X_3)(X_2 X_4), \ (X_1 X_4)(X_2 X_3)\}$$
$$H' = \{1, \ (X_1 X_2)(X_3 X_4), \ (X_1 X_2)(X_5 X_6), \ (X_3 X_4)(X_5 X_6)\}$$

(H leaves X_5 and X_6 fixed, where H' leaves nothing fixed; but all elements $\neq 1$ of H and H' are conjugate in G.) Note that there exist Galois extensions of **Q** with the symmetric group on 6 letters as Galois group.

EXERCISE 6.4. Let L be a finite Galois extension of **Q**, let $G = G(L/\mathbf{Q})$, and let E and E' be subfields of L corresponding to the subgroups H and H' of G respectively. Show that the following conditions are equivalent:

(a) H and H' satisfy the equivalent conditions of Exercise 6.3.

(b) The same primes p are ramified in E as in E', and for the non-ramified p the decomposition of p in E and E' is the same, in the sense that the collection of degrees of the factors of p in E is identical with the collection of degrees of the factors of p in E', or equivalently, in the sense that $A/pA \approx A'/pA'$, where A and A' denote the rings of integers in E and E' respectively.

(c) The zeta-function of E and E' are the same (including the factors at the ramified primes and at ∞.)

Moreover, if these conditions hold, then E and E' have the same discriminant. If H and H' are not conjugate in G, then E and E' are not isomorphic. Hence, by Exercise 6.3, there exist non-isomorphic extensions of **Q** with the same decomposition laws and same zeta functions. However, such examples do not exist if one of the fields is Galois over **Q**.

Exercise 7: A Lemma on Admissible Maps

Let K be a global field, S a finite set of primes of K including the archimedean ones, H a finite abelian group, and $\varphi: I^S \to H$ a homomorphism which is *admissible* in the sense of paragraph 3.7 of the Notes. We will consider "pairs" (L, α) consisting of a finite abelian extension L of K and an *injective* homomorphism $\alpha: G(L/K) \to H$.

EXERCISE 7.1. Show that there exists a pair (L, α) such that L/K is unramified outside S and $\varphi(\mathfrak{a}) = \alpha(F_{L/K}(\mathfrak{a}))$ for all $\mathfrak{a} \in I^S$, where $F_{L/K}$ is as in Section 3 of the Notes. (Use Proposition 4.1 and Theorem 5.1.)

EXERCISE 7.2. Show that if $\varphi(v) = 1$ for all primes v in a set of density 1 (e.g. for all but a finite number of the primes of degree 1 over **Q**), then φ is identically 1. (Use the Tschebotarov density theorem and Exercise 7.1.) Consequently, if two admissible maps of ideal groups into the same finite group coincide on a set of primes of density 1, they coincide wherever they are both defined.

EXERCISE 7.3. Suppose we are given a pair (L', α') such that $\alpha'(F_{L'/K}(v)) = \varphi(v)$ for all v in a set of density 1. Show that (L', α') has the same properties as the pair (L, α) constructed in Exercise 7.1; in fact, show that if L' and L are contained in a common extension M, then $L' = L$ and $\alpha' = \alpha$. (Clearly we may suppose M/K finite abelian. Let θ, resp. θ', be the canonical projection of $G(M/K)$ onto $G(L/K)$, resp. $G(L'/K)$. By Exercise 7.2 and Chapter VII, § 3.2 we have $\alpha \circ \theta \circ F_{M/K} = \alpha' \circ \theta' \circ F_{M/K}$. Since α and α' are injective, and $F_{M/K}$ surjective, we conclude $\operatorname{Ker} \theta = \operatorname{Ker} \theta'$, hence $L = L'$, and finally $\alpha = \alpha'$.)

Exercise 8: Norms from Non-abelian Extensions

Let E/K be a global extension, not necessarily Galois, and let M be the maximal abelian subextension. Prove that $N_{E/K} C_E = N_{M/K} C_M$, and note that this result simplifies a bit the proof of the existence theorem, as remarked during the proof of the Lemma in Chapter VII, § 12. [Let L be a Galois extension of K containing E, with group G, let H be the subgroup corresponding to E, and consider the following commutative diagram (cf. Chapter VII, § 11.3):

$$\begin{array}{ccccccc}
\hat{H}^{-2}(H, \mathbf{Z}) & \approx & H^{ab} & \xrightarrow{\sim} & C_E/N_{L/E} C_L & \approx & \hat{H}^0(H, C_L) \\
\text{cor} \downarrow & & \theta \downarrow & & \downarrow N_{E/K} & & \downarrow \text{cor} \\
\hat{H}^{-2}(G, \mathbf{Z}) & \approx & G^{ab} & \xrightarrow{\sim} & C_K/N_{L/K} C_L & \approx & \hat{H}^0(G, C_L).
\end{array}$$

Since $G^{ab}/\theta(H^{ab}) \approx G(M/K)$ this gives the result.]

Author Index

Numbers in *italics* indicate the pages on which the references are listed.

M

N

O

R

S

T

V

W

Z